PROBLEM SOLVING IN PASCAL for Engineers and Scientists

The Benjamin / Cummings Series in Structured Programming

G. Booch
Software Components with Ada: Structures, Tools, and Subsystems (1987)

G. Booch
Software Engineering with Ada, Second Edition (1987)

J. Brink and R. Spillman
Computer Architecture and VAX Assembly Language Programming (1987)

F. Carrano
Assembly Language Programming for the IBM 370 (1988)

D. M. Etter
Structured FORTRAN 77 for Engineers and Scientists, Second Edition (1987)

P. Helman and R. Veroff
Intermediate Problem Solving and Data Structures: Walls and Mirrors [Pascal Edition] (1986)

P. Helman and R. Veroff
Walls and Mirrors: Intermediate Problem Solving and Data Structures — Modula II (1988)

A. Kelley and I. Pohl
A Book on C (1984)

A. Kelley and I. Pohl
C by Dissection (1987)

A. Kelley and I. Pohl
Turbo C: The Essentials of C Programming (1988)

N. Miller
File Structures Using Pascal (1987)

W. J. Savitch
Turbo Pascal: An Introduction to the Art and Science of Programming, Second Edition (1988)

W. J. Savitch
Pascal: An Introduction to the Art and Science of Programming, Second Edition (1987)

Titles of Related Interest:

M. Sobell
A Practical Guide to the UNIX System (1984)

M. Sobell
A Practical Guide to UNIX System V (1985)

PROBLEM SOLVING IN PASCAL

FOR ENGINEERS AND SCIENTISTS

D. M. ETTER

University of New Mexico, Albuquerque

The Benjamin/Cummings Publishing Company, Inc.
Menlo Park, California • Reading, Massachusetts • Fort Collins, Colorado •
Don Mills, Ontario • Wokingham, U.K. • Amsterdam • Sydney • Singapore •
Tokyo • Madrid • Bogota • Santiago • San Juan

Dedicated with love to my parents, Janice and Murvin Van Camp.

Sponsoring Editor: Alan Apt
Production Editor: Laura Kenney
Text Designer: Linda M. Robertson
Cover Designers: Victoria Philp and Laura Kenney
Compositor: Progressive Typographers

Cover image and Chapter 7 photo, titled "The Rockies, the High Plains, and the Intermountain West," produced with modelling and mapping software by Dynamic Graphics, Berkeley, California. Copyright 1986. Available from Raven Maps & Images, Medford, Oregon.

The programs presented in this book have been included for their instructional value. They have been tested with care but are not guaranteed for any particular purpose. The publisher does not offer any warranties or representations, nor does it accept any liabilities with respect to the programs.

Library of Congress Cataloging-in-Publication Data

Etter, D. M.
   Problem Solving in Pascal for engineers and scientists/D.M. Etter.
      p.   cm.
   Includes index.
   ISBN 0-8053-2533-6
   1. Pascal (Computer program language)   2. Problem solving—Data processing.   I. Title.
QA76.73.P2E86   1988
005. 13'3—dc19   88-4026
                     CIP

ISBN: 0-8053-2533-6

6 7 8 9 10 MA 959493

The Benjamin/Cummings Publishing Company, Inc.
2727 Sand Hill Road
Menlo Park, California 94025

PREFACE TO THE INSTRUCTOR

This introductory text in Pascal has been designed specifically for an audience of engineering and science students who will be using the computer as a tool in college courses, in activities outside of school, and in their careers. We therefore present the material framed in real-world applications so that students can immediately begin to see the usefulness of the computer. However, knowing a computer language is to no avail if students cannot break down a problem solution into the properly ordered steps that a computer can perform. We stress a top-down design approach to problem solving throughout the text. Our objectives in this text are the following:

1. To acquaint students with the capabilities of computers and the types of problems that computers can solve.
2. To teach the fundamentals of Pascal so that students can use the computer to solve problems they encounter in both academic and nonacademic environments.
3. To establish good problem-solving techniques that can be applied to any problem, whether computer related or not.
4. To use practical, real-world engineering and science problems while accomplishing the first three objectives.

FEATURES

Engineering and Science Applications More than 350 examples and problems represent a wide range of real-world applications, including such topics as rocket trajectories, cable car velocities, quality-control analysis, cryptography, and terrain navigation. Many of the solved problems contain sample data and corresponding output from actual computer runs.

Motivational Problems as Chapter Openers Each chapter begins with a specific problem that cannot reasonably be solved with the Pascal statements presented up to that point; hence, we establish motivation to develop new elements of the language in order to solve the described problem. The introductory problem is solved after the new topics are covered.

Early Programming This book assumes no prior experience with computers; it therefore begins with an introductory chapter that explains many terms associated with computing. This chapter also introduces a five-step process for developing problem solutions. Simple complete programs that read data, compute new information, and write information are presented in this first chapter so that students immediately begin writing and running complete Pascal programs.

Problem Solving Design Process Chapter 1 presents a five-phase design process, which is then covered in detail in Chapter 2. This design process is used consistently with all complete programs that are developed. In addition to many complete examples in the regular sections, the text contains special Problem Solving sections (small case studies) devoted to illustrating this problem-solving technique.

Top-Down Design Techniques The five-step design process that appears throughout the text stresses top-down design techniques. A problem solution is first decomposed into general steps shown in a block diagram. Then stepwise refinement is used to develop the details needed to translate the steps into a computer language. Pseudocode is used in the development of the stepwise refinements so that students become familiar with first defining an algorithm in pseudocode before converting the steps into Pascal.

Pascal Statement Summary Most chapters contain a summary of the new Pascal statements presented in that chapter. The summary contains the general form of the statement, specific examples of the statement, and a brief discussion of the rules for using the statement. The Pascal language presented in this text is based on ISO (International Standards Organization) Pascal; a discussion of Turbo Pascal is presented in Appendix D.

Self-Tests and Solutions All chapters contain self-tests that allow students to check their understanding of the new material. Solutions to all self-tests are included at the end of the text, so students can immediately determine whether they are ready to proceed to the next section.

Style/Technique Guidelines Each chapter contains style/technique guidelines to promote good programming habits that stress readability and simplicity. Although entire books are devoted to programming style and technique, this topic is included in each chapter with the premise that developing good style and technique is an integral part of learning the language. In addition to this special section at the end of each chapter, a number of examples in the text have multiple solutions, thereby exposing the student to different approaches for solving the same problem. If one of the solutions has better style or technique than the others, this is pointed out in the accompanying discussion.

Debugging Aids Each chapter also contains debugging aids, a section that outlines efficient methods for locating and correcting program errors relevant to the programming techniques described in the chapter. With guidance from this section, students learn consistent methods for spotting and avoiding the common errors associated with each new Pascal statement. In addition to this special section at the end of each chapter, a number of examples in the text include an incorrect solution to a problem along with the correct solution. The incorrect solution is used to highlight common errors, thus helping students avoid making the same mistakes.

Key Words and Glossary A list of key words appears at the end of each chapter. The definition of each of the key words is included in the glossary at the end of the text for easy reference.

Large Number of End-of-Chapter Problems More than 300 problems are included for end-of-chapter review and practice. These problems vary in degree of difficulty, from simple to more challenging. Solutions to many of the problems are included at the end of the text; these problems are identified by colored problem numbers. Many of the problems include data to use when testing the programs on the computer.

Emphasis on Interactive Processing Although both batch processing and time-sharing are discussed, emphasis is placed on time-sharing with interactive terminals. The use of simple data files is presented in Chapter 4 and then included in many examples in the remainder of the book. Conversational computing is also emphasized in many of the examples.

Presentation of Common Techniques Emphasis is placed on making the student comfortable with common techniques encountered when solving problems with the computer. Examples and problems throughout the text present and then reinforce the techniques of averaging, computing minimums and maximums, inserting and deleting in a list, searching both ordered and unordered lists, sorting lists, and merging lists. A variety of algorithms are presented — for example, both sequential and binary searches are covered, along with selection sorts, insertion sorts, bubble sorts, and quicksorts.

Use of Color Color is used throughout the text to emphasize important material. Pedagogically, the use of color in emphasizing certain statements within a computer program is especially significant. Without using arrows, lines, or distracting symbols, we can clearly show the use of a new statement or point out the differences in two similar program segments. All pseudocode is highlighted in color for easy reference.

Appendices Appendix A contains a summary of all the Pascal syntax diagrams. Appendix B contains a complete discussion of flowcharting and includes flowcharts to accompany many of the Problem Solving special problems from the text. Appendix C presents several Pascal statements that are not frequently used but are included here for completeness. Appendix D compares the statements accepted by the Turbo Pascal compiler with the standard Pascal discussed in the text.

ORGANIZATION

Chapter 1 introduces students to computers, languages, and the compilation-linkage-execution process of running computer programs, emphasizing time-sharing and interactive processing. We begin writing complete Pascal programs in the first chapter. Top-down design, although very simple at this point, is used in developing all complete programs. Some of the built-in functions that are useful to engineering and science students are also covered, with a more detailed coverage in Chapter 6.

Chapter 2 is devoted entirely to problem solving. The objective of this chapter is to present a problem-solving process that can be used for noncomputer problems as well as computer problems. We develop solutions using a five-phase design process:

1. State the problem clearly.
2. Describe the input and output.
3. Work the problem by hand for a specific set of data.
4. Develop an algorithm that is general in nature.
5. Test the algorithm with a variety of data sets.

Top-down design is used in the algorithm development. We decompose a problem solution into a series of general steps and then refine the steps into a detailed form using pseudocode to describe the sequential, selection, and repetition steps. Block diagrams show the initial decomposition of a solution, and a second color shows pseudocode for easy reference.

With control structures, the topic of Chapter 3, a wide range of new problems can be solved with Pascal. The chapter covers the statements for selection (*if* statements) and the statements for repetition (*while* loops and *for* loops). We decided to combine these topics so that we could present problems with simple loops very quickly. Most realistic problems that use selection processes also use loops, so we feel that the combination works well. As a result, this chapter should not be covered as fast as some of the other chapters because of the number of new statements introduced. The level of difficulty of the problems at the end of the chapter is graduated to match the order of the material presented; problems can therefore be assigned as soon as the chapter is begun.

In Chapter 4 we present one-dimensional arrays. This is an earlier presentation of arrays than in many texts, but we feel that handling large amounts of data is an important technique for engineering and science students to learn. We also introduce students to simple data files in this chapter to acquaint them with the ease of processing large amounts of data. Through examples and discussions we help students learn how to read and write the information in arrays, how to perform computations with arrays, and how to determine whether they really need to use an array to solve a problem. Searching and sorting techniques, in addition to insertion and deletion techniques, are introduced in this chapter and used frequently in the rest of the text.

Procedures are presented in Chapter 5. This topic is an important one in top-down design because many of the steps in the initial decomposition of a problem solution can be implemented as procedures. After presenting several simple examples, we discuss the details of parameter lists and scope of variables. One section is devoted to implementing with procedures the techniques for insertions, deletions, and sorting. A final optional section presents recursion with procedures and illustrates the concept with the quicksort algorithm. The concept of testing procedures with a driver program is presented, and driver programs are included in the solutions of both examples and Problem Solving sections in this chapter.

Chapter 6 covers functions. This allows us to emphasize the distinction between procedures and functions. We illustrate with examples the built-in functions of the language. We also discuss additional functions that the user might want to add to a program. One secton is devoted to implementing the techniques for averages, minimums, maximums, and searching with functions. The concept of a function is one that engineering and science students are comfortable using, and as a result functions can be valuable tools for them. A final optional section presents recursion with functions and illustrates the concept with a factorial algorithm.

We return to array handling in Chapter 7, where we present two-dimensional arrays. We cover the definition of two-dimensional arrays and give examples of reading, writing, and manipulating them; we also practice using two-dimensional arrays as parameters in procedures and functions. Discussion is included to guide students in deciding the best structure (at this point, a one-dimensional array or two-dimensional array) for storing data in different applications. Again, common techniques used with two-dimensional arrays are implemented with procedures and functions.

Character and text processing are developed in Chapter 8 with many examples. We develop a procedure to print a bar graph from an array of numerical data. A simple line-graphics software package is also developed that allows the student to define a two-dimensional object and then translate it on the terminal screen. Common techniques for text editing and pattern detection are included.

In Chapter 9, we present the concept of records, contrasted with arrays. Record structures are illustrated with hierarchical records and arrays of records. We develop techniques for merging and updating data files. Nontext files are also discussed.

Chapter 10 summarizes dynamic data structures and sets. Examples illustrate the power of these features in an engineering and science environment. A detailed discussion centers on linked lists. Another section introduces the student to stacks, queues, and trees.

Chapter 11 introduces numerical applications and techniques. We discuss some of the common numerical techniques (approximations, iterative solutions, and matrix operations) used in solving engineering and science problems, and we present some suggestions for avoiding or minimizing precision errors. Complete applications are solved using linear modeling, numerical integration, roots of polynomials, and solutions to simultaneous equations. Additional problems (including numerical differentiation) are included at the end of the chapter. No new Pascal statements are presented in this chapter, so the various topics can also be included at earlier points in the course.

We recommend that the material in this text be covered sequentially through Chapter 6, because these first six chapters contain material that provides students with a thorough knowledge of the language. Since the last five chapters cover a variety of topics, they have been written to be as independent of each other as possible. A suggested order for covering the material in this text is to cover the first six chapters sequentially and then select topics from the last five chapters based on the background and needs of the students. The text is intended for an audience of engineering and science students who have no prior computer background. Calculus is not required, but knowledge of college algebra and trigonometry is assumed.

SUPPLEMENTS

Instructor's Guide An instructor's guide is available on request to the publisher. This supplement contains suggested course syllabi for both semester and quarter courses, viewgraphs, new computer projects, and complete solutions to the end-of-chapter problems. The new computer projects (along with their data files and solutions) and the complete solutions to the text end-of-chapter problems are available in diskette form.

Quiz Bank A quiz bank is also available on request to the publisher. This supplement contains 150 new quizzes that are printed one per page to allow simple copying of the pages for use in the classroom. Midterm and final exams are also included for class distribution as actual exams or practice exams. Solutions to the quizzes and exams are included. This material is also available in diskette form.

Software A diskette that contains all the programs and corresponding data files from the Problem Solving sections is available to instructors. With these programs accessible to students, they can run the programs to be sure they understand how the programs work; the students can also easily make modifications and test them. This process emphasizes hands-on experience with the programs as they are being studied. Ideally, instructors should request the software supplement from the publisher and then load the files into a computer library that can be accessed directly from the student's terminal.

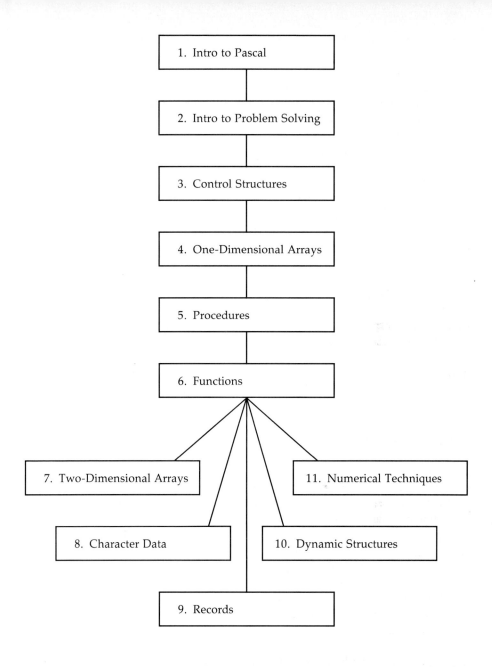

1. Intro to Pascal

2. Intro to Problem Solving

3. Control Structures

4. One-Dimensional Arrays

5. Procedures

6. Functions

7. Two-Dimensional Arrays

11. Numerical Techniques

8. Character Data

10. Dynamic Structures

9. Records

PREFACE TO
THE STUDENT

HOW TO USE THIS BOOK

The influence of computers on our lives grows with each new technological advance. Whether we use this influence to our advantage depends a great deal on our understanding of the computer's abilities and limitations. This text is designed to begin your computer education by introducing you to the process of problem solving with the computer language Pascal. The text does not assume any previous computer experience.

Chapter 1 introduces computers and the types of problems they can solve. A color section shows some of the many kinds of computers that are used as tools by engineers and scientists. If you have some prior computer experience, you will find that you can cover this chapter quickly. In this chapter we also begin writing simple but complete Pascal programs.

Chapters 2–6 should be covered sequentially. Each key section is followed by a short self-test. You should complete each self-test after you've read the corresponding section. Check your answers with the complete set of answers in the back of the text. If you have trouble completing a self-test, reread the section before continuing in the text.

Chapters 7–11 contain a number of topics that may be useful in special applications. These chapters were written to be as independent of each other as possible so that selected topics could be covered from them depending on your needs and interests

Color Color is used to identify pseudocode solutions throughout the text. In addition, key statements in Pascal programs are highlighted in color. All Pascal statements, output from programs, and data file contents are printed in a special typeface to distinguish them clearly from the other material.

Debugging and Style Each chapter contains a debugging section and a style/technique section. The debugging section points out errors commonly made with the Pascal statements presented in the chapter and gives suggestions for avoiding them. The style/technique section includes guidelines for developing a programming style that stresses readability and simplicity. It is a good idea to review these sections periodically as you progress through the text.

Key Words and Glossary A list of key words appears at the end of each chapter. The definition of each of these key words is included in the glossary at the end of the text for easy reference.

Pascal Statement Summary At the end of each chapter that presents new Pascal statements we have included a statement summary that gives the general form of each new statement, examples of the statement, and a discussion of the rules associated with the statement. Color is used at the bottom edge of these pages to help you locate them easily.

Problem Solving Programming, like most skills, becomes easier with practice. A large number of problems appears at the end of each chapter. Solutions to selected problems appear at the end of the text; those problems are identified by a colored problem number.

A special five-phase design process for solving problems is presented in Chapter 1 and illustrated throughout the text. This design process allows you to begin decomposing a problem solution into smaller and smaller pieces, thus simplifying the overall solution.

ACKNOWLEDGMENTS

After writing several textbooks, I appreciate more than ever the suggestions, guidance, and criticism provided by reviewers. The group of especially helpful reviewers that Alan Apt (Computer Science Editor) assembled for this text were Professors Gearold R. Johnson, Manoel Fernando Tenorio, Richard Haracz, Robert Pettus, George Stockman, Gordon Lee, Brian Johnson, Avery Catlin, Ray Hookway, Robert Franklin, Nonna Lehmkuhl, and Charles Gould. I also want to thank the following people at Benjamin/Cummings Publishing Company for their support and their willingness to involve me in all stages of the production of this text: Alan Apt (Computer Science Editor), Sally Elliott (Executive Editor), Laura Argento (Production Director), and Laura Kenney (Production Supervisor). Special thanks also go to my husband, who carefully read every word of both drafts of the manuscript, and to a group of students who assisted in testing the many programs in the text and its supplements: Leslie Brown, Vena Margo, Jae Kerr, Mike Otero, and Joe Bibbo.

D. M. Etter

BRIEF CONTENTS

DETAILED CONTENTS

Each chapter begins with an *opening problem* and an *introduction* and ends
with the following:

- *summary*
- *debugging aids*
- *style/technique guidelines*
- *key words*
- *problems*
- *Pascal statement summaries (most chapters)*

(*indicates sections that can be omitted without loss of continuity.)

Engineering And Science Applications

AERONAUTICAL ENGINEERING

Rocket Trajectory (Sec. 2-8; Probs. 2.15–2.19; Ex. 5-1; Ex. 6-2).
Retrorocket Performance (Prob. 3.24).

CIVIL ENGINEERING

Railroad Track Design (Probs. 1.28–1.33).
Beam Analysis (Probs. 3.27–3.28).
Traffic Flow (Sec. 6-4; Probs. 6.6–6.10).
Accident Survey (Sec. 10-5; Probs. 10.6–10.10).

COMPUTER ENGINEERING/COMPUTER SCIENCE

Computer Inventory (Ex. 3-14; Sec. 9-5; Probs. 9.11–9.15).
Searching (Sec. 4-5; Ex. 6-5).
Inserting and Deleting (Sec. 4-5; Ex. 5-3; Probs. 8.18–8.19; Ex. 10-3; Ex. 10-4).
Sorting (Sec. 4-5; Ex. 5-4; Sec. 5-7; Probs. 8.22–8.23).
Computer Security (Sec. 5-6; Probs. 5.11–5.15).
Computer Graphics (Ex. 7-8; Sec. 8-3; Probs. 8.6–8.10).
Character Editing (Ex. 8-1; Ex. 8-5; Ex. 8-6; Ex. 8-7; Sec. 8-5; Probs. 8.11–8.17;
  Prob. 8.21; Probs. 8.24–8.26; Probs. 8.28–8.29).
Cryptography (Ex. 8-2; Ex. 8-3; Ex. 8-4; Sec. 8-2; Probs. 8.1–8.5).
Printer Plotting (Prob. 8.27).
Software Sales Analysis (Probs. 10.19–10.26).
Education Training Program Analysis (Probs. 10.27–10.32).

ELECTRICAL ENGINEERING

Parallel Resistance (Prob. 1.22; Ex. 4-1; Ex. 4-2).
Circuit Board Quality Control (Sec. 4-1; Ex. 4-11; Sec. 4-4; Probs. 4.6 – 4.10).
Simulation Data (Sec. 5-4; Probs. 5.6 – 5.10).
Reliability (Sec. 6-3; Probs. 6.1 – 6.5).
Terrain Navigation (Sec. 7-3; Probs. 7.5 – 7.10).
Power in Frequency Bands (Sec. 11-3; Probs. 11.6 – 11.10).
Electrical Current Analysis (Sec. 11-7; Probs. 11.16 – 11.18).

MECHANICAL ENGINEERING

Cable Car Velocity (Ex. 3-1; Sec. 3-5; Ex. 3-14; Probs. 3.6 – 3.10).
Suture Packaging (Sec. 3-3; Probs. 3.1 – 3.5).
Power Plant Data Analysis (Sec. 7-2; Probs. 7.1 – 7.5).
Fuel Analysis (Prob. 8.20).
Coil Deflection Model (Sec. 11-2; Probs. 11.1 – 11.5).
Robot Arm Stability (Sec. 11.5; Probs. 11.11 – 11.15).

PETROLEUM ENGINEERING

Oil Well Production (Sec. 5-3; Probs. 5.1 – 5.5).
Seismic Drilling (Probs. 6.30 – 6.32).

ANTHROPOLOGY

Carbon Dating of Artifacts (Sec. 1-9; Probs. 1.11 – 1.15).

BIOLOGY

Bacteria Growth (Sec. 1-8; Probs. 1.6 – 1.10).
Nutrition Study (Prob. 1.21).
Germ Growth (Prob. 3.25).
Whooping Crane Migration (Sec. 10-2; Prob. 10.1 – 10.5).

ECONOMICS

Project Management (Sec. 6-6; Probs. 6.11 – 6.15).

FORESTRY

Timber Management (Sec. 3-6; Probs. 3.11 – 3.15).

GEOLOGY

Earthquake Measurements (Sec. 4-6; Probs. 4.11 – 4.15).

MATHEMATICS

Foreign Currency Exchange (Sec. 1-7; Probs. 1.1 – 1.5).
Rectangle Properties (Prob. 1.17).

METEOROLOGY

PHYSICS

SOCIOLOGY

STATISTICS

GENERAL

Inventory (Ex. 3-14; Sec. 9-5; Probs. 9.11–9.15).
Registration Systems (Probs. 3.22–3.23).
Sales Data (Prob. 4.26; Ex.7-6).
Gregorian-Julian Dates (Prob. 4.27–4.28).
Telephone Call Monitoring (Prob. 4.29).
Airline Reservations (Prob. 7–17).
Warehouse Shipping (Prob. 7–18; Prob. 10.11–10.18).
Instrument Log (Sec. 9-4; Probs. 9.6–9.10).
Library File (Probs. 9.16–9.36).

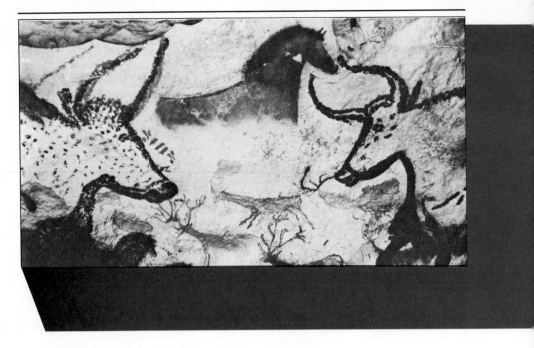

PROBLEM SOLVING — Carbon Dating

Carbon dating is a method for estimating the age of organic substances such as shells, seeds, and wooden artifacts. The technique compares the amount of a radioactive carbon, carbon 14, that is contained in the remains of the substance with the amount that would have been in the object's environment at the time it was alive. The age of the cave paintings at Lascaux, France, has been estimated at 15,500 years using this technique. Assume that you have been given the equation for carbon dating. Write a Pascal program to perform these calculations. (See Section 1-9 for the solution.)

1

AN INTRODUCTION TO PASCAL

INTRODUCTION

Problem solving is an activity in which we participate every day. Problems range from analyzing our chemistry lab data to finding the quickest route to work. Computers can solve many of our problems if we learn how to communicate with them in computer languages such as **Pascal.** Some people believe that if we describe a problem to a computer, it will solve the problem for us. Programming would be simpler if this were the case; unfortunately, it is not. Computers perform only the steps that we describe. You may wonder, then, why we go to the effort of writing computer programs to solve problems if we have to describe every step. The answer is that although computers can perform only simple tasks, they perform them extremely accurately and at fantastic speeds. In addition, computers never get bored. Imagine sitting at a desk analyzing laboratory data for eight hours a day, five days a week, year after year. This is a pretty dismal task, and yet thousands of laboratory results must be analyzed every year. Once the steps involved in performing a particular analysis (such as computing an average) have been carefully described to a computer, however, it can analyze data 24 hours a day, with more speed and accuracy than a group of technicians.

We must not forget that someone must first describe the steps to the computer using the proper computer language statements before problem solving can begin. We will spend much of this text teaching you the Pascal language, but any computer language is useless unless you can break a problem into steps that a computer can perform. Therefore, techniques for problem solving will also be presented in this chapter, expanded in the next chapter, and then illustrated in each of the rest of the chapters.

In this first chapter we discuss the different types of computers, from the supercomputer to the personal computer. We also compare different computer languages and discuss some of the reasons there are so many languages. We then present a design process for problem solving that we will use throughout the text. Finally, we present a simple set of Pascal statements and begin translating our problem solution steps into complete Pascal programs, thus using the computer to solve problems such as the carbon-dating problem presented at the beginning of this chapter.

1-1 COMPUTER ORGANIZATION

Computers come in all sizes, shapes, and forms, as illustrated in the color section in this chapter. All these computers have a common internal organization, which is shown in the block diagram in Figure 1-1. In a large computer system, each part is likely to be physically distinguishable from the others, whereas in a microcomputer or minicomputer, all the parts within the dotted line may be combined in a single integrated circuit chip.

The processing unit or **processor** (also called the control unit) is the part of the computer that controls all the other parts. The processor accepts input values and stores them in the memory. It also interprets the instructions in a computer program. If we want to add two values, the processor will retrieve them from the memory and send them to the **arithmetic logic unit** or **ALU.** The ALU performs

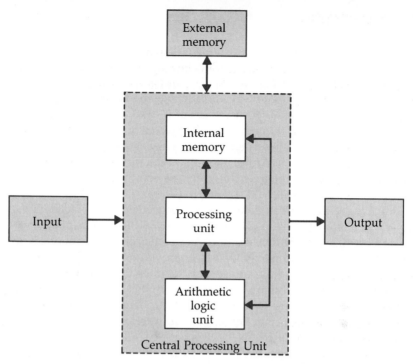

FIGURE 1-1 Block diagram of a computer.

the desired addition, and the processor then stores the result in the memory. If we desire, we may also direct the processor to print the result on paper. The processing unit and the ALU use a small amount of memory, the **internal memory,** in their processing; most data is stored in **external memory.** The processor, internal memory, and ALU are collectively called the **central processing unit** or **CPU.** Thus, a microprocessor is a CPU, but a microcomputer is a CPU with input and output capabilities.

The size of the computer system needed to solve a particular problem depends on the type and number of steps required to solve the problem. If the computer is to be part of a home security system, a microcomputer is sufficient; if the computer is to handle reservations for a major airline, then a large computer system may be required. Because the Pascal language is available on most computers, we will be able to use a variety of computers for our programs.

When working with computers, you will often hear the terms *software* and *hardware.* **Software** refers to the programs (problem solution steps written in a computer language) that direct computers to perform operations, compute new values, and manipulate data. **Hardware** refers to the physical components of the computer, such as the memory unit, the processor, and the ALU. A person who works with software might write computer programs, whereas a person who works with hardware might design new components or install devices. For example, a hardware engineer might design the interface equipment necessary to connect a microprocessor to an input terminal.

1-2 COMPUTER LANGUAGES

Computer hardware is based on two-state **(binary)** technology; that is, computers are built from components that have two values, such as open or closed, on or off, plus or minus, or high or low. These two values can be represented by the numbers 0 and 1. Computers are often defined as machines capable of interpreting and understanding sequences of 0's and 1's, called binary strings.

Since we have been trained to think in terms of English-like phrases and formulas, we use English-like languages such as Pascal to tell the computer the steps we want it to perform. A special program called a **compiler** then translates the Pascal program into binary strings that the computer can understand. This compilation procedure will be discussed in Section 1-3.

Pascal is a relatively new computer language, designed by Niklaus Wirth in 1968. It was named after Blaise Pascal (1623–1662), a French mathematician. Because Pascal is newer than many of the other common languages such as FORTRAN, COBOL, and BASIC, it has improved on many of the features in these other languages and has added new features that are unique to it. Most importantly, Pascal was designed to provide a simple yet very powerful language for solving problems. Some of the techniques used in designing such a language are the result of studying other languages that were designed for very different reasons. For example, FORTRAN (FORmula TRANslation), which was one of the first computer languages, was originally developed in the 1950s for technical applications. FORTRAN 77 is a specific version of FORTRAN based on a set of standards established in 1977. These standards greatly improved the language by adding new features that allow it to be considered a structured language. COBOL was designed to handle business-related problems and file manipulations. BASIC, a language similar to FORTRAN, is commonly used with minicomputers and personal computers. ALGOL, PL/I, and Modula-2 are other structured languages. Ada is a new language designed for the government to be used in technical applications. All these languages are considered to be **high-level languages** since their instructions are in English-like words as opposed to binary strings.

Learning a computer language is similar to learning a foreign language. Each step that you want the computer to perform must be translated into "computer language." Fortunately, computer languages have small vocabularies and no verb conjugations; however, computers do not forgive punctuation and spelling mistakes. A comma or letter in the wrong place will cause errors that keep your program from working properly. You will discover that you must pay close attention to many such details.

We have discussed high-level languages (such as Pascal) and **low-level languages** (binary or machine languages). At another level are assembly languages. **Assembly languages** are between high-level and low-level languages and do not require a compiler to translate them into binary code. A smaller program, called an **assembler,** translates the assembly language into machine language.

Most assembly languages do not have powerful statements, making them inconvenient to use. For example, you might have to do a series of additions to perform a single multiplication. You would also have to understand certain elements of your computer's design in order to use an assembly language. For these reasons, when given a choice, most people prefer to write programs in a high-level language. Assembly language is used primarily when it is necessary to minimize a program's memory and time requirements.

Some of the statements in various high-level languages are illustrated in Table 1-1. Each section of code represents the calculation of an employee's salary

TABLE 1-1 Examples of High-Level Languages

LANGUAGE	EXAMPLE STATEMENTS
| Pascal | ```
if hours <= 40.0 then
    salary := hours*payrate
else
    salary := 40.0*payrate +
              (hours - 40.0)*payrate*1.5;
``` |
| FORTRAN 77 | ```
if (hours.le.40.0) then
    salary = hours*payrte
else
    salary = 40.0*payrte +
             (hours - 40.0)*payrte*1.5
endif
``` |
| Ada | ```
if hours <= 40.0 then
    salary := hours*payrate;
else
    salary := 40.0*payrate +
              (hours - 40.0)*payrate*1.5;
``` |
| BASIC | ```
    if h > 40.0 then 200
    let s = h*p
    go to 250
200 let s = 40.0*p + (h - 40.0)*p*1.5
250
``` |
| COBOL | ```
if hours is less than 40.0 or
    hours is equal to 40.0,
        compute salary = hours*payrate
    else
        compute salary = 40.0*payrate +
                 (hours - 40.0)*payrate*1.5.
``` |
| PL/I | ```
if hours <= 40.0 then
    salary = hours*payrate;
else
    salary = 40.0*payrate +
             (hours - 40.0)*payrate*1.5;
``` |

based on the hours worked and the hourly pay rate. If the number of hours worked is less than or equal to 40, the salary to be paid is computed by multiplying the number of hours worked by the hourly pay rate. If the number of hours worked is greater than 40, time-and-a-half is paid for the hours over 40. The different names used to represent hours worked, pay rate, and salary reflect the various rules within the individual languages. Also note the differences in punctuation among the various languages.

1-3 RUNNING A COMPUTER PROGRAM

In the previous section we defined a compiler as a program that translates a high-level language to machine language. This **compilation** step is the first step in running a computer program. As the compiler translates statements, it also checks for **syntax errors,** also called compiler errors. These are errors in the statements themselves, such as misspellings and punctuation errors. If syntax errors (often referred to as **bugs**) are found, the compiler will print error messages or diagnostics for you. After correcting the errors (**debugging**), you can rerun your program, again starting with the compilation step. Once your program has been compiled without errors, a **linkage editor** program performs the final preparations so that it can be submitted to the execution step. It is in the execution step that the statements are actually performed. Errors can also arise in the **execution** step; these are called **logic errors,** run-time errors, or execution errors. These errors (also called bugs) are not in the statement syntax but are in the logic of the statements; they are detected only when the computer attempts to execute the statement. For example, the statement

$$x := a/b$$

is a valid Pascal statement that directs the computer to divide a by b and call the result x. The statement contains no syntax errors. Suppose, though, that the value of b is zero. Then, as we try to divide a by b, we are attempting to divide by zero, which is an invalid operation; we will get an execution error message. Logic errors do not always generate an error message. For instance, if we were supposed to divide by 0.10 and instead we multiplied by 0.10, the computer would not detect an error although our answer would be wrong.

A computer program is often called the **source program.** After it is converted into machine language by the compiler and prepared for execution by the linkage editor, it is in machine language and is now called the **object program.** A diagram of this compilation-linkage-execution process is shown in Figure 1-2.

It is uncommon for a program to compile, link, and execute correctly on the first run. Do not become discouraged if it takes several runs to get your answers. When you do get answers from your program, do not assume that they are correct. If possible, check your answer with a calculator or check to see if the answer makes sense. For example, if the answer represents the weight of an automobile, then 5 pounds is not reasonable and suggests that you have given the computer incorrect information or an incorrect program to execute.

COLOR OUTPUT DEVICES

Electrostatic printer/
plotters. (Courtesy of
Versatec.)

Pen plotters. (Courtesy
of Houston Instru-
ments.)

COMPUTER APPLICATIONS

Computer-aided tool design. (Courtesy of Control Data.)

Textile manufacturing. (Courtesy of IBM.)

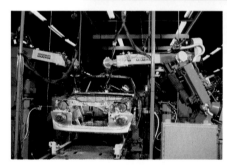

Robot used in auto assembly. (Courtesy of Cincinnati Milacron.)

Food-quality testing. (Courtesy of Perkin-Elmer Corp.)

Air-traffic controllers. (Courtesy of Sperry.)

Amino-acid research. (Courtesy of Perkin-Elmer Corp.)

Flight management system. (Courtesy of Lear Siegler, Inc.)

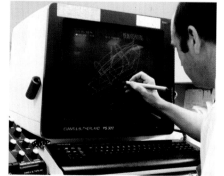

Aircraft design. (Courtesy of McDonnell Douglas.)

COMPUTER GRAPHICS

Weather forecasting. (Courtesy of the National Center for Atmospheric Research.)

Bone fracture. (Courtesy of Evans & Sutherland.)

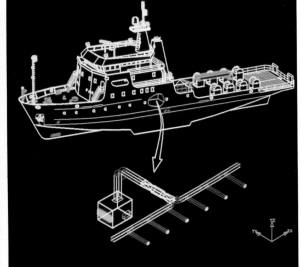

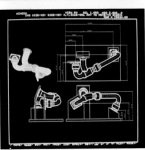

Plumbing design. (Courtesy of CADAM, Inc.)

Robot feasibility study. (Courtesy of Cincinnati Milacron.)

Transportation route designs. (Courtesy of CADAM, Inc.)

Aircraft design. (Courtesy of CADAM, Inc.)

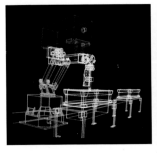

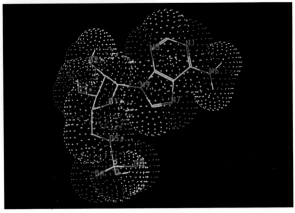

Molecular design. (Courtesy of Evans & Sutherland.)

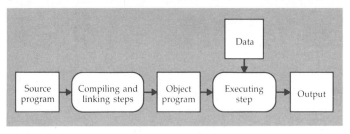

FIGURE 1-2 Compilation-linkage-execution process for running a computer program.

Two methods are used for running computer programs on large systems: **batch processing** and **time-sharing**. In batch-processing systems, the computer stores the program in its memory, compiles it, and completes its execution before beginning to compile and execute another program. In time-sharing systems, the program is typed into the terminal, followed by a command such as *run*, which immediately begins the processing. This technique is called time-sharing because the computer does a few steps of a program from one terminal, then a few steps of a program from another terminal, and so on until it returns to the first terminal. The computer then performs another cycle of steps in each program. We usually do not notice the time between cycles because the computer executes statements so quickly. We seem to have the computer's undivided attention, although we are actually sharing it with many other terminal users. Interaction with either type of system is generally done at a terminal. Hard-copy terminals use paper to record the input and output from the computer, and CRT (cathode ray tube) terminals use a video screen to display the input and output.

Most time-sharing systems allot each user a specified amount of memory to be used as a workspace in the computer. This workspace is usually divided into a temporary workspace and a permanent workspace. As you enter programs or data into the temporary workspace, you can edit the information, which means you can add to it, delete portions of it, or modify it with the use of an editing program (called an **editor**). When you have the program or data in the form that you want, you can save it in the permanent workspace. You can then clear the temporary workspace and begin entering new information, or you can "log off" the terminal. The next time you "log on," you can load any information that was previously saved in your permanent workspace into your temporary workspace and resume working with it.

A diagram of a computer system that supports both time-sharing and batch processing is shown in Figure 1-3. The additional memory is used by the time-sharing system.

Another term used to describe interaction with computers is *standalone*. When a computer is operated in a standalone mode of interaction, it is not connected to another computer, and thus it functions as a standalone piece of equipment. Personal computers are usually operated in a standalone mode, although they can also be used as a terminal to a larger system using a telephone line and a special piece of communication equipment called a modem. When a computer is used in a standalone mode, it can interact directly with the user or it

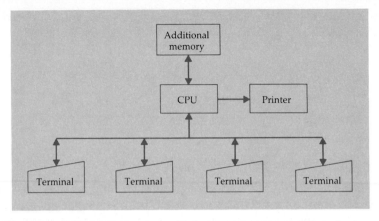

FIGURE 1-3 Computer system with batch processing and time sharing.

can operate in a batch-processing mode. Using a computer in a time-sharing mode or in standalone direct interaction is called **interactive computing** because we are interacting with the computer more than in a batch-processing system. This increased interaction generally results in more efficient use of our time.

1-4 COMPLETE PASCAL PROGRAMS

In this section we present Pascal statements to print and read information. With these two operations, we can construct simple but complete Pascal programs. However, before we discuss the specific statements, we will look at the **syntax diagrams** used to present new Pascal statements and discuss the general outline of a Pascal program.

SYNTAX DIAGRAMS

Each time we introduce a new Pascal element, we will show its corresponding syntax diagram enclosed in a box for quick reference. The syntax diagram is a graphical means of illustrating the rules needed to describe that Pascal element. You will soon find it easier to refer to these diagrams to refresh your memory than to read the narrative description of the rules.

To give you an example of a syntax diagram, let's define an **identifier.** An identifier is a name given to things that we want to reference in our Pascal program, such as the entire program, a specific value (called a constant), a variable (a memory location whose value may be changed), or a block of Pascal statements in the program. The rules for creating identifiers are simple. The names may contain alphabetic characters and numeric digits, but the first character of an identifier must be an alphabetic character. Pascal does not limit the total number of characters in an identifier, but most compilers recognize only the first eight characters as unique. Thus, *distance1* and *distance2* should not be used as identifiers in the same program because they may be treated as the same identifier by the compiler. The following list gives examples of both valid and invalid identifier names:

radius	valid identifier
tax-rate	invalid identifier—illegal character
2info	invalid identifier—begins with a digit
info2	valid identifier
volume	valid identifier
$f(x)$	invalid identifier—illegal characters

The corresponding syntax diagram for an identifier is shown in the following box. As the diagram indicates, the identifier must begin with an alphabetic letter. Any additional characters can then be alphabetic letters or numeric digits.

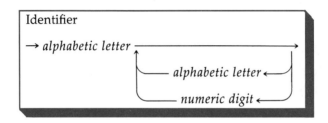

One group of words, called reserved words, cannot be used as identifiers because they have special meaning to the compiler. These reserved words are specific words that appear in Pascal statements and operations. When we introduce new Pascal statements, these reserved words will appear in computer type in the syntax diagrams. They are also listed on the inside back cover of the text for easy reference.

OUTLINE OF A PASCAL PROGRAM

The outline of a Pascal program can be broken into three sections. Each program will begin with a program header that assigns an identifier or name to the program and then defines the data files (input and output information) for the program. The next section defines the constants and variables in the program. (Constants and variables will be discussed in more detail in the next part of this section.) The last section of the program describes the steps in the problem solution (these steps are also called the **algorithm** for the solution), which begin with the word *begin*. After all the steps in the algorithm have been described in Pascal statements, the word *end*, followed by a period, terminates the program. Thus, the overall outline of a Pascal program is:

```
program   identifier (files);
     declaration of constants and variables
begin
     steps in the algorithm
end.
```

Pascal statements are format free, which means that they may appear anywhere on the line. Multiple statements may appear on the same line; however, blanks are used to separate symbols and semicolons are used both as terminators and to separate statements. The placement of semicolons is especially critical, since omitting a semicolon can cause a Pascal program to be interpreted very differently from what is intended. We recommend that you develop a consistent, readable format for your programs. Our example programs will use only one statement per line and will use indenting to show program structure.

Comments are enclosed by the brackets { and }. In case your terminal does not have these brackets, you can enclose comments with (* and *). Comments can appear anywhere in the program; the compiler ignores them. Because some Pascal compilers will accept only lowercase letters in Pascal statements, we will use lowercase letters in our programs.

Some program editors require that you number each line. These line numbers are used in editing, but cannot be referenced by a Pascal statement since they are not part of the statement itself.

Because we have already mentioned the program header, we now finish its definition. The following syntax diagram shows that the program heading must include the word *program* and an identifier. Typically, the identifier is followed by a left parenthesis, more identifiers separated by commas (these are the files, or sets of data, used in the program), a right parenthesis, and a semicolon.

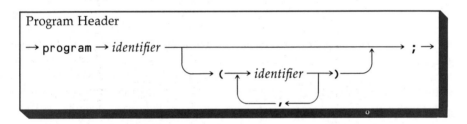

For now, we will use the terminal keyboard for our input device and the terminal screen for our output device. These are usually the standard input and output devices for a computer system, and are referenced as *input* and *output*. Thus, the header for a program called *compute* that uses the terminal for its input and output is:

```
program   compute (input,output);
```

In Chapter 4 we will learn how to read information that has been stored in the computer's memory (instead of reading from the keyboard) and how to write information into the computer's memory (instead of writing it on the terminal screen).

CONSTANTS AND VARIABLES

Data is introduced into a computer program either directly with the use of **constants** or indirectly with the use of **variables.** Constants are used directly in computations, such as -7, 3.141593, and 'ENGR'. Numeric constants may con-

---

tain plus or minus signs and decimal points, but they may not contain commas. Thus 3147.6 is a valid Pascal constant but 3,147.6 is not valid. If a numeric constant contains a decimal point, digits must be included on both sides of the decimal point, as in 0.2, 12.0, and 1.56. The value of character constants, such as 'ENGR', must be enclosed in apostrophes (single quotation marks). If a character constant contains an apostrophe, the apostrophe must be represented by two apostrophes, as in 'LET''S BEGIN'.

We may want to identify a constant with a name. For example, rather than use 3.141593 in a number of computations, we may prefer to use the identifier *pi* to improve the readability of our program. The Pascal statement to define *pi* as a constant is:

$$pi\ =\ 3.141593$$

This statement must appear in the declaration section of the program after the heading *const*. Thus a program using this constant might begin as follows:

```
program  compute (input,output);
    {This is an example program.}
const
    pi = 3.141593;
begin
    steps in the algorithm
end.
```

Note the use of semicolons to terminate the header and the constant section and the use of a period to specify the end of the program.

Following is a syntax diagram for the constant declaration section of a Pascal program.

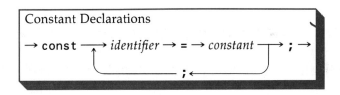

When multiple constants are defined, the word *const* appears only once and the individual definitions are separated by semicolons. For emphasis, we will put *const* on a line by itself and then indent the constant definitions that follow.

In addition to constants, we will also want to use variables in our Pascal programs. A memory location is assigned to the variable identifier. Then we can modify the contents of that memory location by referring to the identifier in our Pascal statements. It is helpful to visualize the storage of variables in the computer memory as shown below:

amount	36.84	volume	183.0
rate	0.065	total	586.5
temp	−17.5	info	2

A storage location is assigned by the compiler to a variable name; then the value in the storage location can be referenced by other Pascal statements using the variable identifier. It is helpful when the identifier chosen for a memory location reflects the information being stored in it. For example, if a storage location will hold a weight measurement, call it *weight* instead of a less meaningful name such as *x* or *a*.

Numerical values in Pascal can be one of two types: **integer** or **real.** (Pascal also allows two nonnumeric data types, character and Boolean, along with a special user-defined enumerated type, which are discussed in later chapters.) Integer-type values are those that represent whole numbers; that is, they have no fractional portion and no decimal point, such as 16, −7, 18633, and 0. Since these values have no fractional portion or decimal point, they are also called fixed-point values. Real-type values, on the other hand, contain a decimal point and must have at least one digit on each side of the decimal point, such as 13.86, 3.0, 0.0076, −14.2, 36.0, and −5.01. These real values are also called floating-point values.

A memory location can contain only one type of value. Therefore, the statement that assigns a memory location to an identifier must also specify its type. The variable definition contains the identifier followed by a colon, followed by the type of variable (integer or real). Semicolons are used to separate definitions of variables of different types. Thus the program segment that we used earlier might be expanded to the following:

```
program  compute (input,output);
    {This is an example program.}
const
    pi = 3.141593;
var
    radius, diameter, area, volume: real;
begin
    steps in the algorithm
end.
```

Following is a syntax diagram for the variable definition section of a Pascal program.

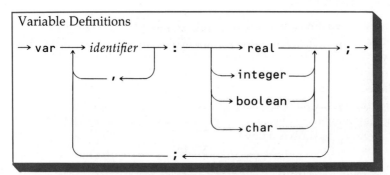

Note that *var* is included only once, even if there are identifiers defined with different types. Thus, a program with both integer and real variables might contain the following:

```
const
    pi = 3.141593;
var
    radius, diameter, area, volume: real;
    id, total: integer;
```

Note again that the words *const* and *var* are written on separate lines to clearly distinguish the definitions that follow them. We indent the definitions within the two sections for readability and use the semicolon to separate the definitions within the sections and to terminate the individual sections.

INPUT AND OUTPUT STATEMENTS

Nearly all programs will contain statements that direct the computer system to print data that has been computed or generated by the program. We will often want to enter data, such as a tax rate, when a program is run. Pascal has special statements for such types of operations. We will first look at output statements and then discuss input statements.

If we wish to write the value stored in a variable, we must tell the computer the variable's name or identifier. The computer can then access the storage location and write the contents. For now, we will assume that the value is to be written on the terminal screen. The *writeln* (read as "write line") statement can be used to skip lines, write character constants (also called character strings or literals), and write the values of variables and other constants. The following examples illustrate some of the different forms of this statement. Assume that values with decimal points represent real values and values with no decimal points represent integer values. The actual output that you would see on your terminal screen is outlined in a box with rounded corners, to model your terminal screen.

EXAMPLE 1-1   Income

Write the stored value of the variable *income*.

Solution

COMPUTER MEMORY

income   35000

PASCAL STATEMENT

writeln (income)

COMPUTER OUTPUT

35000

Although integer values are printed without any decimal positions, the number of decimal positions printed for real values will depend on the Pascal compiler that you are using. Some compilers will automatically print all values in scientific notation or **exponential notation** instead of decimal form. In these forms, a value is expressed as a number between 1.0 and 10.0 multiplied by a power of 10. For example, Avogadro's constant is 602,300,000,000,000,000,000,000, to four significant digits. In exponential form, Avogadro's constant becomes 6.023e+23, with the letter *e* separating the mantissa (6.023) and the exponent (23). Other examples of decimal values in exponential form are shown in the following list:

DECIMAL VALUE	EXPONENTIAL NOTATION
3,876,000,000.0	3.876e+09
0.0000010053	1.0053e−06
−8,030,000.0	−8.03e+06
−0.000157	−1.57e−04

EXAMPLE 1-2   Density

Print the stored value of the variable *density*.

Solution

COMPUTER MEMORY

density | 0.0000156 |

PASCAL STATEMENT

```
writeln (density)
```

COMPUTER OUTPUT

    1.560000e-04

As you saw in Example 1-2, it is not always easy to read values that are expressed in exponential notation. Pascal gives us the option of including the number of positions that we want to use for a variable, and the number of those positions that are fractional positions for a real variable. This information is included after the variable name in the *writeln* statement. The numbers are separated by colons, as shown in Example 1-3. (We can also specify the number of positions to be used for integer values, as will be shown in Example 1-7, and for character strings.) When we specify a form or format for a value, it will be right-justified in the allotted positions. The size of the format will automatically be extended if part of the value to the left of the decimal point does not fit. The number of positions in the format can even be specified by an integer variable.

EXAMPLE 1-3   Tax Rate

Print the variable *rate* along with character strings that identify this rate as the California sales tax rate.

Solution

Computer Memory

rate $\boxed{0.065}$

Pascal Statement

```
writeln ('SALES TAX RATE IS ',rate:5:3,' IN CALIFORNIA')
```

Computer Output

```
┌─────────────────────────────────────────────┐
│  SALES TAX RATE IS 0.065 IN CALIFORNIA        │
└─────────────────────────────────────────────┘
```

Each time the *writeln* statement is executed, a line of output will be printed. This property can be used to print values on different lines or to add blank lines between values.

EXAMPLE 1-4   Salary Information

Print the values of *hours* and *payrate* using a descriptive heading.

Solution

Computer Memory

hours $\boxed{37.5}$

payrate $\boxed{6.75}$

Pascal Statements

```
writeln ('HOURS WORKED AND PAY RATE');
writeln (hours:4:1,payrate:5:2)
```

Computer Output

```
┌─────────────────────────────────────────────┐
│  HOURS WORKED AND PAY RATE                    │
│  37.5 6.75                                    │
└─────────────────────────────────────────────┘
```

We can now write a very simple but complete program. Try running it on your computer system. Check with your instructor for details concerning the computer that you will use.

EXAMPLE 1-5   Complete Program To Print Your Name

Write a complete Pascal program to print your name.

Solution

The only step in this solution is to print your name. No variables or constants are needed. In all of our complete program examples we will use a comment line consisting of dashes to identify the beginning and end of the program.

PASCAL PROGRAM

```
{--------------------------------------------------------------}
program  first (output);
    {This is my first complete program.}
begin
    writeln ('MY NAME IS BILL R. ADAIR')
end.
{--------------------------------------------------------------}
```

COMPUTER OUTPUT

> MY NAME IS BILL R. ADAIR

Now that we have seen some examples of a simple *writeln* statement, we present its syntax diagram:

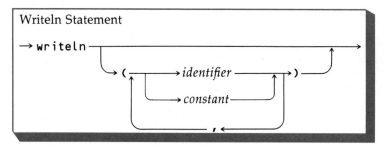

Pascal contains another output statement, the *write* statement, which is similar to the *writeln* statement but does not cause the information to appear automatically on an output line. Instead, the information to be written by a *write* statement is stored in memory until a *writeln* statement executes, which causes all the information to be printed. For example, if the value in memory for *distance* was 28.55 and the following three statements were executed,

```
write ('DISTANCE = ');
write (distance:5:2);
writeln (' FEET')
```

the output would be:

> DISTANCE = 28.55 FEET

The first two statements continue adding information to the data line being built in memory; the third statement causes that information to be printed after adding its information to it. Using these two output statement forms, we have the flexibility to make both our programs and our output clear and readable.

The syntax diagram for the *write* statement follows.

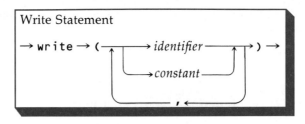

Write Statement

$\rightarrow$ **write** $\rightarrow$ ($\longrightarrow$ *identifier* $\longrightarrow$) $\rightarrow$
$\longrightarrow$ *constant* $\longrightarrow$
$\longleftarrow$, $\longleftarrow$

Extensions of the *writeln* and *write* statements that allow you to write information into data files in the computer's memory will be discussed later. These
extensions are included in the complete syntax diagram in Appendix A.

The *readln* (read as "read line") statement is used for reading information
from the terminal with our programs. A typical *readln* statement is:

readln (salary)

When the *readln* statement executes, a special character called a **prompt** may be
printed in a time-sharing mode of interaction to tell you that the computer is
ready for you to enter the data value you want to store in the variable *salary*
(although most systems will just wait for you to enter the data without prompting
you). If several identifiers are listed in the *readln* statement, the values should be
entered in the same order as they are listed in the *readln* statement with blanks
separating them. Data values can also be entered on different lines.

EXAMPLE 1-6   Account Balances

Read the beginning and ending balances for a checking account.

Solution 1

PASCAL STATEMENT

readln (startbal,endbal)

DATA LINE

186.93 386.21

COMPUTER MEMORY

startbal $\boxed{186.93}$

endbal $\boxed{386.21}$

Solution 2

PASCAL STATEMENTS

readln (startbal);
readln (endbal)

DATA LINES

186.93
386.21

startbal ⎡186.93⎤

endbal ⎡386.21⎤

The second solution would not have executed correctly if the two data values were entered on the same line because the first *readln* statement will "flush" or skip the rest of the information on its current input line. Therefore, the second input statement will begin with information from the second input line.

Because the input device and output device are often the same in time-sharing systems, **conversational computing** can be used in programs that are run on terminals. Before we enter the data, we can write a message that describes the data and the order of data values to be entered. After reading the data, we can write it for a validity check. This interaction between the program and the user who is entering the data resembles a conversation. Example 1-7 illustrates this interaction in a complete program.

EXAMPLE 1-7 Read and Print Birthday

Write a complete program to read the month, day, and last two digits of the year of your birthday. Print them in the form month-day-year. Use a number for the month. We will discuss the input of character information such as 'MAY' in a later chapter.

Solution

The solution to this problem is again very simple. As we write the steps in Pascal, we will print messages on the terminal screen to explain the information that needs to be entered. Recall that we are also beginning and ending each complete program with comment lines consisting of all dashes.

PASCAL PROGRAM

```
{----------------------------------------------------------}
program   birth (input,output);
    {This program prints a birthdate
    entered from the terminal.}
var
    month, day, year: integer;
begin
    writeln ('ENTER BIRTH MONTH');
    readln (month);
    writeln ('ENTER BIRTH DAY');
    readln (day);
    writeln ('ENTER LAST TWO DIGITS OF BIRTH YEAR');
    readln (year);
    writeln ('YOUR BIRTHDATE IS ',month:2,'-',
             day:2,'-',year:2)
end.
{----------------------------------------------------------}
```

```
ENTER BIRTH MONTH
11
ENTER BIRTH DAY
24
ENTER LAST TWO DIGITS OF BIRTH YEAR
65
YOUR BIRTHDATE IS 11-24-65
```

We used a colon and the integer 2 after the integer variables to specify the number of digits to be used in the output. Note that a semicolon is not used before the *end* statement.

The syntax diagram for this simplified *readln* statement follows.

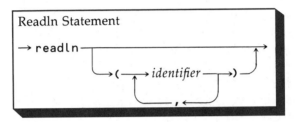

Note that it does not make sense to include a character string in the *readln* statement because we are reading information, not writing it.

Pascal contains another input statement, the *read* statement, which is similar to the *readln* statement but does not automatically flush the remaining information on a data line. For example, if the following statements were executed,

```
read (a);
read (b)
```

and the data line entered from the keyboard contained

$$57.2 \qquad 45.5$$

then the value 57.2 would be stored in *a* and the value 45.5 would be stored in *b*. Note that if the first *read* statement had been a *readln*, then the value 57.2 would be stored in *a*, and the 45.5 value would be flushed before the next statement was executed. Thus, a new value would need to be entered for the value of *b*, regardless of whether the second statement was a *read* or a *readln*. Having both types of input statements gives us more flexibility in writing clearer and easier-to-understand programs.

The syntax diagram for the *read* statement follows.

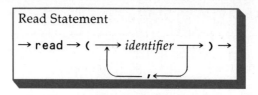

Read Statement

$\rightarrow$ **read** $\rightarrow$ ($\rightarrow$ *identifier* $\rightarrow$) $\rightarrow$

Extensions of the *readln* and *read* statements that allow you to read information from data files in the computer's memory will be discussed later. These extensions are included in the complete syntax diagrams in Appendix A.

SELF-TEST 1-1

This self-test allows you to check quickly to see if you have remembered some of the key points from Section 1-4. If you have any problems with the exercises, you should reread this section. The solutions are included at the end of the text.

Problems 1–10 contain both valid and invalid variable names. Explain why the invalid names are unacceptable.

1. area
2. perimeter
3. density
4. length
5. pay-rate
6. temp-a
7. $g(t)$
8. 2time
9. time2
10. amt$

In problems 11–16, tell whether or not the pair of real constants represents the same number. If not, explain.

11. 2300.0; 2.3e+04
12. 0.000007; 0.7e+04
13. 1.0; 1.00
14. 110.0; 11.01e+01
15. −34.7; −0.34e+02
16. −0.76; 7.60e − 01

1-5 ARITHMETIC COMPUTATIONS

Computations in Pascal may be specified with the assignment statement. Its syntax diagram follows.

> **Assignment Statement**
>
> → *identifier* → := → *expression* →

The simplest form of an **expression** is a constant. For example, if an interest rate of 10.5% is needed several times in a program, we could define a variable *rate* with the value 0.105. Then each time we need this value, we can refer to *rate*. The assignment statement that assigns a value to *rate* and thus initializes it is:

```
rate := 0.105
```

The name of the variable receiving the new value must always be on the left side of the statement. The symbol := can be read as "is assigned the value of" or "becomes." Thus, the statement above could be read "*rate* is assigned the value of 0.105." Because the variable *rate* could be assigned a different value in another Pascal statement, it is not considered to be a constant even though the value of *rate* might not change.

It is important to recognize that a variable can store only one value at a time. For example, suppose the following two statements were executed one after the other:

```
width := 36.7;
width := 105.2
```

The value 36.7 is stored in the variable *width* after the first statement is executed. The second statement, however, replaces that value with the new value 105.2, and the first value is lost. Notice that a semicolon was used to separate the two statements.

Consider these two statements:

```
temp1 := -52.6;
temp2 := temp1
```

The first statement stores the value −52.6 in *temp1*. The second statement stores in *temp2* the same value that is stored in *temp1*. Note that the value in *temp1* is not lost; both *temp1* and *temp2* now contain the value −52.6.

If *sum* is a real variable, the following is a valid statement:

```
sum := 3.25
```

However, if *sum* is an integer variable, the statement is invalid because an integer cannot store a real variable.

TABLE 1-2 Arithmetic Operations in Algebraic Form and Pascal

Operation	Algebraic Form	Pascal
Addition	$a + b$	a + b
Subtraction	$a - b$	a − b
Multiplication	$a \cdot b$	a*b
Division	$\dfrac{a}{b}$	Quotient: $\begin{cases} \text{a/b} & \text{(real values)} \\ \text{a div b} & \text{(integers)} \end{cases}$
		Remainder: a mod b (integers)

MATHEMATICAL OPERATIONS

Often we want to calculate a new value using mathematical operations with other variables and constants. For instance, assume that the variable *radius* has been assigned a value and we want to calculate the area of a circle having that radius. To do so, we need to square the radius and then multiply by the value of pi. Table 1-2 shows the Pascal expressions for the basic arithmetic operations. Note that an asterisk instead of an *x* is used to represent multiplication. This avoids confusion since *axb* (commonly used in algebra to indicate the product of *a* and *b*) represents a single variable name in Pascal. Division also has a new symbol since we do not have a method for raising or lowering characters on a terminal line. Also note that there are different symbols for real division and for integer division. We will assume real division in our examples here, and discuss integer division in another part of this section. Note that a syntax error will occur if two operators are adjacent; therefore we must use parentheses to keep this from occurring, as shown in the statement below:

$$\texttt{x := b*(-c)}$$

However, we could have interchanged the variables as shown in the following statement, eliminating the need for the parentheses:

$$\texttt{x := -c*b}$$

Both statements would give us the same value for the variable *x*.

Because several operations can be combined in one arithmetic expression, it is important to determine the priorities of the operations (the order in which they are performed). For instance, consider the following assignment statement that calculates the area of a trapezoid with a given *base, height1,* and *height2.*

$$\texttt{area := 0.5*base*height1 + height2}$$

If the addition is done first, we compute *0.5*base*(height1 + height2)*, but if the multiplications are done first, we compute *(0.5*base*height1) + height2*. Note that the two computations yield different results. The order of priorities for computations in Pascal is given in Table 1-3 and follows the standard algebraic priorities.

Note that operations in parentheses are performed first. When executing the previous Pascal statement, the multiplications would be performed first, giving

TABLE 1-3 Priorities of Arithmetic Operations

Priority	Operation
First	Parentheses, innermost first
Second	Multiplication and division, left to right
Third	Addition and subtraction, left to right

the wrong answer. Therefore, we must add parentheses to the expression to change the order in which the operations are performed. The correct statement for computing the area of a trapezoid is then:

```
area := 0.5*base*(height1 + height2)
```

The extra blanks around the plus sign are for readability and do not affect the execution of the statement.

The result of an arithmetic operation between two real values or between a real value and an integer is another real value. The result of an arithmetic operation between two integers is another integer, except for the division operator /, which always gives a real result.

There are limitations on the magnitude and precision of values that can be stored in a computer. For instance, pi is an irrational number and thus cannot be written exactly with a finite number of decimal positions. In a computer with seven digits of accuracy, pi could be stored as 3.141593. For real values, such as pi, we have limits on the number of significant positions in the mantissa and on the size of the exponent. These limitations on the values in a computer depend on the specific computer itself. Table 1-4 compares the approximate range of values that can be stored in several large computers. Check a reference manual to find the ranges of real and integer values for the computer you will be using for your classwork. The maximum integer value that can be represented by your computer can be referenced by using the standard identifier *maxint;* the minimum integer value is then −*maxint.* To determine the value of *maxint* for your computer, use the following statement:

```
writeln ('MAXIMUM INTEGER = ',maxint)
```

TABLE 1-4 Typical Ranges for Data Values

COMPUTER	REAL VALUE RANGES	MAXIMUM INTEGER
IBM 360/370	Mantissa: 6 significant digits Exponent: −77 to 75	2,147,483,647
VAX	Mantissa: 7 significant digits Exponent: −38 to 38	2,147,483,647
CRAY-1	Mantissa: 13 significant digits Exponent: −2465 to 2465	2.8×10^{14}
CDC 6000/7000	Mantissa: 14 significant digits Exponent: −293 to 322	9.2×10^{18}

MATHEMATICAL FUNCTIONS

Many simple operations are commonly needed in algorithms, such as computing the square root of a value, computing the absolute value of a number, or computing the sine of an angle. Because these operations are used so often, **built-in functions** are available in Pascal to handle them. Thus, when we want to compute the square root of x, we use the function *sqrt*. The following statement computes the square root of x and stores it in a variable called *root:*

```
root := sqrt(x)
```

Similarly, we can refer to the absolute value of b by *abs(b)*. A complete list of Pascal's mathematical functions is included in Table 1-5, and also on the inside of the back cover of the text for easy reference. Note that several of the functions will accept either real or integer inputs and return a real result. The argument, or input to the function, is enclosed in parentheses and follows the name of the function. This argument can be any arithmetic expression, but must be the proper type.

Suppose the real variable *angle* contains the value of an angle in degrees. We want to store the cosine of *angle* in the variable *cosine*. From Table 1-5, we see that the cosine function *cos* assumes that its argument is in radians. We can change the degrees to radians (1 degree = 3.141593/180 radians) and compute the cosine for the angle in the following statement:

```
cosine := cos(angle*(3.141593/180.0))
```

The inside set of parentheses is not required, but serves to emphasize the conversion factor.

It is also acceptable to use one function as the argument of another one. For example, we can compute e raised to the absolute value of a with the expression *exp(abs(a))*. When nesting functions, as done here, be sure to enclose the argument of each function in its own set of parentheses.

A function and its argument represent a value. This value can be used in other computations or stored in other memory locations. It does not in itself,

TABLE 1-5 Mathematical Functions in Pascal

FUNCTION NAME AND ARGUMENT	FUNCTION VALUE	INPUT	OUTPUT
`abs(x)`	$|x|$	real or integer	same as input
`exp(x)`	e^x	real or integer	real
`ln(x)`	$\log_e x \; (x > 0)$	real or integer	real
`sqr(x)`	x^2	real or integer	same as input
`sqrt(x)`	$\sqrt{x} \; (x > 0)$	real or integer	real
`round(x)`	closest integer to x	real	integer
`trunc(x)`	integer portion of x	real	integer
`arctan(x)`	arc tangent of x (x in radians)	real or integer	real
`cos(x)`	cosine of x (x in radians)	real or integer	real
`sin(x)`	sine of x (x in radians)	real or integer	real

however, represent a storage location; thus a function can never appear on the left of the assignment statement. For example, to compute the natural logarithm of x, we can use the statement:

```
nlogx := ln(x)
```

but we cannot reverse the order and begin the statement with $ln(x)$ because $ln(x)$ is not an identifier.

A more complex example is shown in the following expression for one of the real roots of a quadratic equation:

$$x1 = \frac{-b + \sqrt{b^2 - 4ac}}{2a}$$

where *a*, *b*, and *c* are coefficients of the quadratic equation. Since division by zero is not valid, we will assume *a* is not equal to zero. The value of *x1* can then be computed in Pascal with the following statement, assuming that the variables *a*, *b*, and *c* have been previously initialized:

```
x1 := (-b + sqrt(b*b - 4.0*a*c))/(2.0*a)
```

To check the order of operations in a long expression, it is best to start with the operations inside parentheses. That is, find the operation done first, then the one done second, and so on. The following diagram outlines this procedure, using underline braces to show the steps of operations. Beneath each brace is the value that has been calculated in that step.

$$x1 := (-b + \underbrace{sqrt(\underbrace{b*b - 4.0*a*c}_{\sqrt{b^2 - 4ac}}))}_{-b + \sqrt{b^2 - 4ac}} \underbrace{/(2.0*a)}_{2a}$$

$$\underbrace{\hspace{6cm}}_{\dfrac{-b + \sqrt{b^2 - 4ac}}{2a}}$$

As shown in the final brace, the expression computes the desired value. The placement of the parentheses is very important in this statement. If the outside set of parentheses on the numerator were omitted, our assignment statement becomes:

$$x1 := \underbrace{(-b)}_{-b} + \underbrace{sqrt(\underbrace{b*b - 4.0*a*c}_{\sqrt{b^2 - 4ac}})}_{} \underbrace{/(2.0*a)}_{2a}$$

$$\underbrace{\hspace{6cm}}_{-b + \dfrac{\sqrt{b^2 - 4ac}}{2a}}$$

As you can see, omission of the outside set of parentheses would cause the wrong value to be calculated as a root of the original equation.

As shown in the previous example, omitting necessary parentheses results in incorrect calculations. Using extra parentheses to emphasize the order of calculations is permissible. In fact, it is advisable to insert extra parentheses in a statement if it makes the statement more readable.

You may also want to break a long statement into several smaller statements. Recall that the expression $b^2 - 4ac$ in the quadratic equation is also called a discriminant. The solution could then be calculated with the following equations after initialization of *a*, *b*, and *c*:

```
discriminant := b*b - 4.0*a*c;
x1 := (-b + sqrt(discriminant))/(2.0*a);
x2 := (-b - sqrt(discriminant))/(2.0*a)
```

In the above statements, we assume that the discriminant is positive, thus enabling us to obtain the two real roots to the equation. If the discriminant were negative, an execution error would occur if we attempted to take the square root of the negative value. Also, if the value of *a* were zero, we would get an execution

---

error for attempting to divide by zero. In later chapters we will learn techniques for handling both these situations.

We often use variables as counters in Pascal programs. We first initialize the counter to a specific value and later, under certain conditions, change it to another value. An example of a statement to increment *counter* by 1 is given below:

```
counter := counter + 1
```

At first this statement may look invalid because, algebraically, *counter* cannot be equal to *counter + 1*. But remember, in Pascal this statement means "*counter* is assigned the value of *counter + 1*." Hence, if the old value of *counter* is 0, the new value of *counter* after executing this statement will be 1.

OPERATORS *div* AND *mod*

Integer division is handled differently from real division in Pascal. Consider the following statement:

```
x := y/z
```

The result of this operation is a real value, because the slash is the division operator that specifies a real result. In order to perform integer division, we must use *div* as the operator, as in the statement below:

```
a := b div c
```

Since this operator is only for integer division, an error will occur if any of the variables are real.

Integer division can sometimes surprise us with its results, so we must carefully consider its use in our programs. For example, the following statement will store the value 3 in the integer variable *quotient:*

```
quotient := 17 div 5
```

The *div* operator does not round the result to the nearest integer; instead, it **truncates** or drops any fractional part. Thus, the result of *29 div 10* is the integer 2.

In many applications we are interested in the remainder of integer division, instead of the quotient. In these cases we use the operator *mod*. The term *mod* comes from modulo arithmetic terminology, where it represents the remainder from integer division. For example, the value of *remainder* in the following statement is 2:

```
remainder := 17 mod 5
```

The remainder in an integer division is especially useful if we wish to determine whether a value is a multiple of another value. For example, suppose we want to determine if *sum* (an integer) is a multiple of 5. We can first compute the remainder of division by 5 with the following statement:

```
leftover := sum mod 5
```

If the value of *leftover* is zero, then *sum* is a multiple of 5; otherwise, *sum* is not a multiple of 5. This same technique can be very useful in determining if a value is odd or even because we can test the value to determine if it is a multiple of 2. (Chapter 6 presents another method for determining odd and even values.)

Sections 1-7, 1-8, and 1-9 solve problems involving arithmetic computations. You should try running these simple programs on your computer, but do not expect a program run on two different computers (or compilers) to yield exactly the same answers. Differences in computer architecture (or compiler programs) cause slight variations in the answers. Therefore, if you run a sample program for which we got an answer of 13.7100, don't be surprised if your computer gives an answer of 13.7099.

You may also have noticed that Pascal does not have an exponentiation operator that will allow us to perform operations such as 3.44 raised to the power of 2.4. Certainly these types of operations arise in engineering and science applications, so in Chapter 6 we will develop a user-written function to perform general exponentiation.

SELF-TEST 1-2

This self-test allows you to check quickly to see if you have remembered some of the key points from Section 1-5. If you have any problems with the exercises, you should reread this section. The solutions are included at the end of the text.

In problems 1-6, convert the equations into Pascal assignment statements. Assume that all variables represent real values.

1. Slope of straight line between two points:

$$\text{slope} = \frac{y2 - y1}{x2 - x1}$$

2. Correction factor in pressure calculation:

$$\text{factor} = 1 + \frac{b}{v} + \frac{c}{v^2}$$

3. Coefficient of friction between tires and pavement:

$$\text{friction} = \frac{v^2}{30 \cdot s}$$

4. Distance of center of gravity from reference plane in a hollow cylinder sector:

$$\text{center} = \frac{38.1972(r^3 - s^3)\sin a}{(r^2 - s^2)a} \quad \text{where } a \text{ is in radians}$$

5. Pressure loss from pipe friction:

$$\text{loss} = f \cdot p \cdot \frac{l}{d} \cdot \frac{v^2}{2}$$

---

6. Equivalent resistance of a parallel circuit:

$$req = \dfrac{1}{\dfrac{1}{x1} + \dfrac{1}{x2} + \dfrac{1}{x3} + \dfrac{1}{x4}}$$

In problems 7–12, convert the Pascal statements into algebraic form.

7. Uniformly accelerated motion:

```
motion := sqrt(vi*vi + 2.0*a*x)
```

8. Electrical oscillation frequency:

```
freq := 1.0/sqrt((2.0*3.141593)*(1.0/xl*c))
```

9. Range for a theoretical projectile:

```
range := 2.0*vi*vi*sin(b)*cos(b)/g
```

10. Length contraction:

```
length := li*sqrt(1.0 - (v/c)*(v/c))
```

11. Mass energy:

```
c := 2.99e10;
energy := 1.6747e-24*c*c
```

12. Volume of a fillet ring:

```
pi := 3.141593;
volume := 2.0*pi*x*x*
          ((1.0 - pi/4.0)*y - (0.8333 - pi/4.0)*x)
```

1-6 DEVELOPING A PROBLEM SOLUTION

We have discussed computer hardware and software, we have presented Pascal statements for writing simple but complete programs, and we are now ready to develop solutions to three problems. However, before we begin these examples, we will discuss the process that we will be using to develop a solution to a problem. Chapter 2 covers this in detail, but the three simple examples that we are about to consider give us an excellent opportunity to illustrate this design process.

Our design process for solving problems will be broken into five phases. The first phase of developing a problem solution is to state the problem clearly and concisely to avoid any misunderstandings.

The second phase is to describe carefully any information or data needed to solve the problem and then describe how the final answer is to be presented. These items represent the input and output for the problem.

The third phase is to work the problem by hand or with a calculator, using a simple set of data. If we aren't sure how to work a problem by hand, we aren't ready to try to work it with a computer.

The fourth phase is to describe in general terms the steps performed by hand. This sequence of steps that solves the problem is called an algorithm. Once the solution steps are determined, they are ready to be converted into Pascal.

The fifth phase of problem solving is to test the solution steps (or algorithm) that you have just described. The first set of data you might use is the data used in the hand example. Careful testing is necessary to be sure the problem solution is accurate.

As we develop the solutions to the problems presented in the next three sections, we will clearly show the five phases of the development of the problem solution. Then, in Chapter 2, we will discuss problem solving in more detail.

1-7 PROBLEM SOLVING — FOREIGN CURRENCY EXCHANGE

Assume that you have just been selected to participate in a student exchange program in which you will visit France during the summer after your freshman year in college. You want to be sure that you know how to perform foreign currency exchanges, so you are going to write a computer program for practice. Write the program to read a price in francs, convert it to dollars, and print it. Use the exchange rate of 5.9 francs to the dollar. Your program should convert one amount each time it executes.

All the information necessary to develop a Pascal solution to this problem has been presented. We now show the development of the solution using our five-phase process.

PROBLEM STATEMENT

Write a program to convert an amount in francs to dollars.

INPUT/OUTPUT DESCRIPTION

The input is a number that represents francs. The output will be the number read in francs and the computed value in dollars.

HAND EXAMPLE

In our hand example, we will convert 85 francs to dollars. Thus, we divide 85 by 5.9 to find that the equivalent amount in dollars is $14.41.

ALGORITHM DEVELOPMENT

We first determine the general steps involved in the solution. Since we just computed a specific solution by hand, we list these steps in the order in which we performed them:

GENERAL SOLUTION

Step 1. Read amount in francs.

Step 2. Convert amount to dollars.

Step 3. Write both amounts.

We now convert the steps in the general solution into Pascal. A special comment line of all dashes is used to clearly designate the beginning and end of our program. We will also include a brief comment describing the purpose of the program.

PASCAL PROGRAM

```
{-----------------------------------------------------------------}
program   convert (input,output);
   {This program converts francs to dollars.}
var
   francs, dollars: real;
begin
   writeln ('ENTER AMOUNT IN FRANCS');
   readln (francs);
   dollars := francs/5.9;
   writeln (francs:5:2,' FRANCS = ',dollars:5:2,' DOLLARS')
end.
{-----------------------------------------------------------------}
```

TESTING

Enter the program in your computer system and test it with the hand example. The output conversation should be similar to the following:

```
ENTER AMOUNT IN FRANCS
85.0
85.00 FRANCS = 14.41 DOLLARS
```

1-8 PROBLEM SOLVING—BACTERIA GROWTH

Your current biology laboratory experiment involves analysis of a strain of bacteria. Because the growth of bacteria in the colony can be modeled with an exponential equation, you have decided to write a computer program that will predict how many bacteria will be in the colony after a specified amount of time. Suppose that, for this type of bacteria, the equation to predict growth is:

$$y_{new} = y_{old}e^{1.386t}$$

where y_{new} is the new number of bacteria in the colony, y_{old} is the initial number of bacteria in the colony, and t is the elapsed time in hours. Thus, when $t = 0$, we have:

$$y_{new} = y_{old}e^{1.386*0} = y_{old}$$

PROBLEM STATEMENT

Using the equation

$$y_{new} = y_{old}e^{1.386t}$$

predict the number of bacteria (y_{new}) in a bacteria colony given the initial number in the colony (y_{old}) and the time that has elapsed (t) in hours.

INPUT/OUTPUT DESCRIPTION

The input will be two values, the initial number of bacteria and the time elapsed. The output will be the number of bacteria in the colony after the elapsed time.

HAND EXAMPLE

You will need your calculator or a logarithm table for these calculations. For $t = 1$ hour and $y_{old} = 1$ bacterium, the new colony contains:

$$y_{new} = 1 \cdot e^{1.386 \cdot 1} = 4.00$$

After 6 hours, the size of the colony is:

$$y_{new} = 1 \cdot e^{1.386 \cdot 6} = 4088.77$$

If we had started with 2 bacteria, after 6 hours the size of the colony is:

$$y_{new} = 2 \cdot e^{1.386 \cdot 6} = 8177.54$$

ALGORITHM DEVELOPMENT

The general solution can be described in the following steps:

GENERAL SOLUTION

Step 1. Read y_{old}, t.
Step 2. Compute y_{new}.
Step 3. Write y_{old}, t, y_{new}.

We now convert these steps into Pascal.

```
{-----------------------------------------------------------------}
program  growth (input,output);
   {This program predicts bacteria growth.}
var
   yold, ynew, time: real;
begin
   writeln ('ENTER INITIAL POPULATION');
   readln (yold);
   writeln ('ENTER TIME ELAPSED IN HOURS');
   readln (time);
   ynew := yold*exp(1.386*time);
   writeln ('INITIAL POPULATION = ',yold:9:2);
   writeln ('TIME ELAPSED (HOURS) = ',time:7:2);
   writeln ('PREDICTED POPULATION = ',ynew:7:2)
end.
{-----------------------------------------------------------------}
```

TESTING

The program output using data from one of our hand examples is the following:

```
ENTER INITIAL POPULATION
1.0
ENTER TIME ELAPSED IN HOURS
6.0
INITIAL POPULATION =      1.00
TIME ELAPSED (HOURS) =    6.00
PREDICTED POPULATION = 4088.77
```

You should try using some other values in the program to see if the results appear reasonable. Very large values of *time* may result in an execution error, because computers have limits. (See Table 1-4.) Negative values of *time* represent population decreases, but once the population goes below 1, the model is no longer applicable.

1-9 PROBLEM SOLVING — CARBON DATING

Carbon dating, a technique for estimating the age of organic substances, compares the amount of a radioactive carbon, carbon 14, that is contained in the remains of a substance with the amount that would have been in the object's environment at the time it was alive. The age of the cave paintings at Lascaux, France, has been estimated at 15,500 years using carbon dating.

Assume that you are working as an assistant to an archaeologist. Artifacts from a recent excavation have been sent to a laboratory for carbon analysis. The lab will determine the proportion of carbon that remains in the artifact. The archaeologist has shown you the following equation that gives the estimated age of the artifact in years:

$$age = \frac{-\log_e(\text{carbon proportion remaining})}{0.0001216}$$

Recall that $\log_e x$ is the natural logarithm of the value x.

The archaeologist would like you to write a Pascal program that will read the proportion of carbon remaining in an artifact from the terminal, then compute and print its estimated age.

PROBLEM STATEMENT

Write a program to read the proportion of carbon remaining in an artifact and then compute and print its estimated age.

INPUT/OUTPUT DESCRIPTION

The input will be a real number that represents the proportion of carbon left in the artifact. The output will be a number that estimates the age of the artifact in years.

HAND EXAMPLE

Suppose that no carbon has decayed. Then the carbon proportion is 1.0 and the estimated age is:

$$age = \frac{-\log_e(1.0)}{0.0001216} = \frac{0}{0.0001216} = 0$$

This age makes sense since the artifact must be relatively young if no carbon has decayed.

Let's assume that half of the carbon has decayed. We will use 0.5 as the proportion of carbon left and see what this formula gives for an age:

$$age = \frac{-\log_e(0.5)}{0.0001216} = 5700.2 \text{ years}$$

From a reference book we learn that the half-life of carbon 14 is 5700 years, so our equation works pretty well!

ALGORITHM DEVELOPMENT

The general steps in our problem solution are the following:

GENERAL SOLUTION

Step 1. Read proportion of carbon remaining.

Step 2. Compute estimated age.

Step 3. Write estimated age.

We now convert the general solution into Pascal. To compute the estimated age in Pascal, we need to compute a natural logarithm. Using Table 1-5, we find that the function *ln* performs this operation.

```
{------------------------------------------------------------}
program  age (input,output);
    {This program estimates the age of an artifact from
    the proportion of carbon remaining in the artifact.}
var
    carbon, age: real;
begin
    writeln ('ENTER PROPORTION REMAINING FOR CARBON DATING');
    readln (carbon);
    age := (-ln(carbon))/0.0001216;
    writeln ('ESTIMATED AGE OF ARTIFACT IS ',age:6:1,' YEARS')
end.
{------------------------------------------------------------}
```

TESTING

Test your program with the hand examples. A typical screen display should be:

```
ENTER PROPORTION REMAINING FOR CARBON DATING
0.5
ESTIMATED AGE OF ARTIFACT IS 5700.2 YEARS
```

SUMMARY

In this chapter we discussed some fundamental concepts about computers. We described the process of converting a computer program into a form that the computer can understand and execute. Most importantly, we introduced the basic Pascal statements for input, output, and computations. We wrote a number of complete programs and illustrated the five phases of problem solving that we will be studying in more detail in the next chapter.

DEBUGGING AIDS

If a program is not working correctly, you should **echo** the values that you read in the program. That is, immediately after reading them, print them out to be sure that the values you want to give the variables are being used. A common mistake is to enter data values in the wrong order. For example, instead of entering the initial number of bacteria followed by the elapsed time, you enter them in the reverse order.

If the input portion of your program works correctly, check your assignment statements next.

1. If the assignment statement is long, break it into several smaller statements.
2. Double-check your placement of parentheses. Add parentheses if you are not sure what order the computer will use to compute the operations involved. Be sure that you always have the same number of left parentheses as right parentheses.
3. Review each variable name used in an assignment statement to be sure you have spelled it properly. (Did you use *vel* when you should have used *velocity?*)
4. Make sure all variables on the right side of the assignment statement have been initialized.
5. Be sure that arguments to functions are in the correct units (e.g., trigonometric functions use angles in radians instead of degrees).

If you still are not getting correct answers, check the variable names in your *writeln* and *write* statements. Have you listed the correct names?

If these steps do not help you isolate your error, ask your instructor or a classsmate to check the program. If no one is available to check your program and you cannot find the error, start over on a clean sheet of paper. Sometimes it is very hard to spot your own errors because you know what you want the statements to do, and you read that into the statements when searching for errors.

STYLE/TECHNIQUE GUIDELINES

A program should be written so that another person competent in Pascal can readily understand the statements and interpret the procedures. This is especially important because the person updating a program is not always the one who originally wrote it. Building good habits while you are learning a language will enable you to write clearly understood programs. The following guidelines will help you develop a style and technique to do this.

1. Use variable names that indicate something about the values being stored in the variable. For instance, represent velocity by *velocity* instead of *v, x,* or something similarly obscure.
2. Use a consistent number of significant digits in constants. Do not use 3.14 as the value for pi in the beginning of your program and 3.141593 as the value at the end. Accomplish this by using the constant section of the Pascal program to define and initialize your constants. Then use the constant name instead of the constant value in your statements.
3. Break long expressions into smaller expressions and recombine them in another statement. A complicated fraction can be computed by first calculating a numerator, then calculating a denominator, and finally dividing in a separate statement.
4. Insert extra parentheses for readability. It is never wrong to insert extra pairs of parentheses as long as they are properly located. Extra parentheses often make arithmetic expressions much more readable.

5. Use the Pascal built-in functions where possible.
6. Develop the habit of echo-printing values that you have read.
7. Print the physical units that correspond to the numerical values being printed. This information is vital for proper interpretation of results.

KEY WORDS

algorithm

arithmetic logic unit (ALU)

assembly language

batch processing

binary

bug

built-in function

central processing unit (CPU)

compilation

compiler

constant

conversational computing

debugging

editor

execution

exponential notation

hardware

high-level language

identifier

integer value

interactive computing

linkage editor

logic error

memory

object program

Pascal

processor

real value

software

source program

syntax diagram

syntax error

time-sharing

truncation

variable

PROBLEMS

We begin our problem set with modifications to programs given earlier in this chapter. Give the general solution and Pascal program for each problem. Color is used on problem numbers to indicate that solutions to these problems are included at the end of the text.

Problems 1–5 modify the foreign currency program *convert*, given on page 31.

1. Modify the foreign currency program so that it converts dollars to francs.
2. Modify the foreign currency program so that it converts pounds sterling to dollars. (Use the exchange rate of 1 pound sterling to $1.68.)
3. Modify the foreign currency program so that it converts deutsche marks to dollars. (Use the exchange rate of 1.8 deutsche marks to $1.00.)

4. Modify the foreign currency program so that it converts dollars to pounds sterling and deutsche marks.
5. Modify the foreign currency program so that it converts francs to deutsche marks.

Problems 6 – 10 modify the bacteria growth program *growth*, given on page 33.

6. Modify the bacteria growth program so that the time elapsed is entered in minutes even though the equation still requires a time in hours.
7. Modify the bacteria growth program so that the time elapsed is entered in days even though the equation still requires a time in hours.
8. Modify the bacteria growth program so that an initial population is read from the terminal. The program should then compute and print the percent increase in population as time increases from 2 hours to 3 hours.
9. Modify the bacteria growth program so that the program reads two time values from the terminal, where the first time is less than the second time. Compute and print the amount of growth between the two times, assuming an initial population value of 1.
10. Modify the bacteria growth program so that the program reads two time values from the terminal, with no restrictions on which time is larger. Compute and print the amount of growth between the two times, assuming an initial population value of 1. (*Hint:* Review the absolute value function.)

Problems 11 – 15 modify the carbon-dating program *age*, given on page 35.

11. Modify the carbon-dating program so that it truncates the age to the nearest year.
12. Modify the carbon-dating program so that it rounds the age to the nearest year.
13. Modify the carbon-dating program so that it gives the age in centuries instead of years. Use two decimal places in the output age.
14. Modify the carbon-dating program so that it gives the age in centuries instead of years. Truncate the resulting age to the nearest century.
15. Modify the carbon-dating program so that it gives the age in centuries instead of years. Round the resulting age to the nearest century.

Here are some new programs to develop. Use the five-phase design process.

16. Write a program to read the number of hours worked and the hourly pay rate for a student laboratory assistant. Compute and print the amount of money earned. Do not assume special rates for hours over 40.
17. Write a program to read the length and width of a rectangle and then compute and print its perimeter and area.
18. Write a program to read the coordinates of two points, $(x1,y1)$, $(x2,y2)$. Compute the slope of the straight line between these two points where:

$$\text{slope} = \frac{y2 - y1}{x2 - x1}$$

Print the points and the slope of the line between them.

19. Write a program to read the diameter of a circle. Compute the radius, circumference, and area of the circle. Print these new values in the following form:

```
PROPERTIES OF A CIRCLE WITH DIAMETER XXXX.XXX
(1) RADIUS = XXXX.XXX
(2) CIRCUMFERENCE = XXXX.XXX
(3) AREA = XXXX.XXX
```

20. Write a program to read a measurement in meters. Print the value read followed by the units, meters. Convert the measurement to kilometers and print on the next line, again with the correct units. Convert the measurement to miles and print on the third line, with correct units. (Use 1 mile = 1.6 kilometers.)

21. A research scientist performed nutrition tests using three animals. Data on each animal includes an identification number, the animal's weight at the beginning of the experiment, and the animal's weight at the end of the experiment. Write a program to read this data and print a report. The report is to include the original information plus the percentage increase in weight for each test animal.

22. Write a program to read three resistance values ($r1$, $r2$, $r3$) and compute their combined resistance rc for the parallel arrangement shown below. Print the values of $r1$, $r2$, $r3$, and rc.

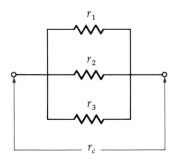

$$rc = \frac{1}{\dfrac{1}{r1} + \dfrac{1}{r2} + \dfrac{1}{r3}}$$

23. The distance between points (xa, ya) and (xb, yb) is given by:

$$\text{distance} = \sqrt{(xa - xb)^2 + (ya - yb)^2}$$

You are given the coordinates of three points:

point 1: $(x1, y1)$
point 2: $(x2, y2)$
point 3: $(x3, y3)$

Write a program to read the coordinates. Next calculate and print the distance $dist12$ between points 1 and 2, the distance $dist13$ between points 1 and 3, and the distance $dist23$ between points 2 and 3, as shown in the following diagram:

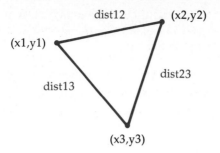

dist12   (x2,y2)

(x1,y1)

dist23

dist13

(x3,y3)

24. Write a program to read the following information from the terminal:

>Year
>Number of people in the civilian labor force
>Number of people in the military labor force

Compute the percentage of the labor force that is civilian and the percentage that is military. Print the following information:

```
LABOR FORCE-YEAR XXXX
NUMBER OF WORKERS (MILLIONS) AND PERCENTAGE OF WORKERS
CIVILIAN          XXX.XXX                    XXX.XXX
MILITARY          XXX.XXX                    XXX.XXX
TOTAL             XXX.XXX                    XXX.XXX
```

25. The approximate time for electrons to travel from the cathode to the anode of a rectifier tube is given by:

$$\text{time} = \sqrt{\frac{2 \cdot m}{q \cdot v}} \cdot r1 \cdot z \cdot \left(1 + \frac{z}{3} + \frac{z^2}{10} + \frac{z^3}{42} + \frac{z^4}{216}\right)$$

where q = charge of the electron (1.60206e − 19 coulombs)
m = mass of the electron (9.1083e − 31 kilograms)
v = accelerating voltage in volts
$r1$ = radius of the inner tube (cathode)
$r2$ = radius of the outer tube (anode)
z = natural logarithm of $r2/r1$

Define the values of q and m in the constant section of your program. Read values for v, $r1$, and $r2$. Then calculate z and *time*. Print the values of v, $r1$, $r2$, and *time*.

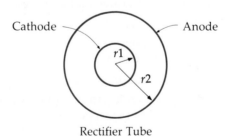

Cathode   Anode

r1

r2

Rectifier Tube

26. Write a program to compute the volume of a hollow ball. Assume that the values for the ball's radius and thickness are to be read. The volume of a sphere is related to the radius r by:

$$\text{volume} = (4/3) \cdot \text{pi} \cdot r^3$$

27. A standard Gaussian density function is commonly used in engineering statistics. This function is defined in the equation below:

$$y = \frac{1}{\sqrt{2 \cdot \text{pi}}} \cdot e^{-0.5 \cdot x^2}$$

Write a program to read a value of x and compute the corresponding value of y. Print the values in the following form:

```
THE STANDARD NORMAL DENSITY FUNCTION EVALUATED
AT XXX.XX GIVES A VALUE OF XX.XXXXX
```

28. When a train travels over a straight section of track, it exerts a downward force on the rails; but when it rounds a level curve, it also exerts a horizontal force outward on the rails. Both of these forces must be considered when designing the track. The downward force is equivalent to the weight of the train. The horizontal force, called centrifugal force, is a function of the weight of the train, its speed as it rounds the curve, and the radius of the curve. The equation to compute the horizontal force in pounds is:

$$\text{force} = \frac{\text{weight} \cdot 2000}{32} \cdot \frac{(\text{mph} \cdot 1.4667)^2}{\text{radius}}$$

where *weight* is the weight of the train in tons, *mph* is the speed of the train in miles per hour, and *radius* is the radius of the curve in feet. Write a program to read values for *weight*, *mph*, and *radius*. Compute and print the corresponding horizontal force generated.

29. Modify the railroad track analysis program in problem 28 so that the weight of the train is entered in pounds instead of tons.

30. Modify the railroad track analysis program in problem 28 so that the radius of the curve is entered in yards instead of feet.

31. Modify the railroad track analysis program in problem 28 so that the horizontal force printed is truncated to the nearest pound.

32. Modify the railroad track analysis program in problem 28 so that the horizontal force printed is rounded to the nearest pound.

33. Modify the railroad track analysis program in problem 28 so that the speed is entered in kilometers per hour instead of miles per hour. (Recall that 1 mile is equal to 1.609 kilometers.)

PASCAL STATEMENT SUMMARY

Assignment Statement:

$$variable := expression$$

Examples:

```
total := 0.0
area := side*side
root := sqrt(x)
```

Discussion:

The left-hand side of the assignment statement must be a variable name. The right-hand side can be any form of an expression, from a simple constant to a complicated arithmetic expression involving other variables, constants, and built-in functions.

Read Statement:

read (*variable list*)

Examples:

```
read (time,distance)
read (a)
```

Discussion:

The *read* statement is an input statement that reads values for the variables in its list. The values are read and stored in the order in which the variables are listed. Data values must be separated by blanks; as many lines as are needed will be read. The *read* statement begins reading information from the point in the input information where the previous input statement finished.

Readln Statement:

readln (*variable list*)

Examples:

```
readln (time,distance)
readln (a)
readln
```

Discussion:

The *readln* statement is an input statement that reads values for the variables in its list. The values are read and stored in the order in which the variables are listed. Data values must be separated by blanks; as many lines as are needed will be read. The *readln* statement begins reading information from the point in the input information where the previous input statement finished. When the *readln* statement has read values for the variables in its list, it skips or flushes any remaining input on the current input line. If the *readln* statement does not have any variables listed, it skips or flushes any remaining input on the current input line.

Write Statement:

write (*expression list*)

Examples:

```
write ('FINAL GRADE SUMMARY')
write ('AIRCRAFT WEIGHT = ',weight:5:2,' TONS')
write (x,y)
```

Discussion:
The *write* statement is an output statement that writes the value of the constants, variables, or expressions in its expression list, in the order in which they are listed. The actual output line is stored in memory until a *writeln* statement is executed that may or may not add more information to the line, and then causes it to be printed.

Writeln Statement:

writeln (*expression list*)

Examples:

```
writeln ('FINAL GRADE SUMMARY')
writeln ('AIRCRAFT WEIGHT = ',weight:5:2,' TONS')
writeln (x,y)
writeln
```

Discussion:
The *writeln* statement is an output statement that writes the value of the constants, variables, or expressions in its expression list, in the order in which they are listed. This information is added to any previous output stored by a *write* statement, and then the combined output is printed. If a *writeln* statement is executed without any expressions, it causes any previous output stored by a *write* statement to be printed, and if there is no previous output stored, a blank line will be printed.

PROBLEM SOLVING — Rocket Trajectory

During rocket design, equations are developed to predict important characteristics of the rocket, such as its trajectory. Computer programs use these equations to analyze the rocket and its trajectory before it is built. If the computer results indicate that the rocket's performance meets specifications, then actual development can begin. If the computer results indicate design problems, the engineers return to the design stage and modify their initial designs. They test the modified design equations and repeat the process until they are satisfied that their design meets all specifications. After the rocket is built, the engineers compare actual test data to computer test data to evaluate the equations used to model the rocket.

Develop a computer algorithm to predict the height of a test rocket during a maximum flight of 100 seconds. The height should be computed in increments of 2 seconds from launch through the ascending and descending portions of the trajectory until the rocket descends to within 50 feet of ground level. Below 50 feet, the time increments are to be 0.05 seconds. (See Section 2-8 for the solution.)

Photo courtesy of Rockwell International—Rocketdyne Division.

2

AN INTRODUCTION TO PROBLEM SOLVING

INTRODUCTION

Many similarities exist between the process of learning to play chess and that of learning to use a computer to solve problems. To play chess you must first learn the moves that each piece can make; to program, you must learn the small set of instructions in a computer language. The next step in chess is to learn techniques and game plans for winning. In programming, you learn techniques and methods for solving commonly encountered problems. To improve in either chess or programming, you must practice and learn from your mistakes. Fortunately, the analogy ends here, because problem solving with the computer does not pit programmer against computer, with only one winner. Rather, the computer becomes a valuable tool to solve problems using the methods and techniques that you describe in your programs. In this chapter, we present a design process that can be used to develop computer solutions to problems. We illustrate this design process with a number of examples, and we stress the importance of building good habits and good style in the development of computer programs.

2-1   A TOP-DOWN DESIGN PROCESS

The procedure for designing solutions to problems has five phases, which we will use each time we present a complete problem solution. We briefly mentioned these phases in Chapter 1, but to understand them clearly we will now go through them with the familiar problem of computing an average. We may need to compute a test average in one of our courses, or to summarize experimental data from a lab experiment. This example illustrates our problem-solving steps. After you complete Chapter 3, you can convert these steps into a computer program to solve this task for you the next time you need an average.

The first phase of the design process is to state the problem clearly and concisely. It is important to avoid any misunderstandings. Our problem statement is:

Compute the average of a set of experimental data values.

The second phase is to describe carefully any information or data needed to solve the problem and then describe the way the final answer is to be presented. These items represent the input and the output for the problem. Collectively, they are referred to as **input/output,** or **I/O.** Our input information is the list of experimental data values. The output is the average of these data values.

The third phase is to work the problem by hand, using a simple set of data. A set of data values and the computed average are shown on the next page.

TIME OF DAY	TEMPERATURE VALUE (DEGREES FAHRENHEIT)
1 PM	23.43
2 PM	37.43
3 PM	34.91
4 PM	28.37
5 PM	30.62
Total	154.76

Average Temperature = Total/5 = 30.95

The fourth phase is to describe, in general terms, the steps that you performed by hand. This sequence of steps that solve the problem is called an algorithm. The procedure that we use in algorithm development is called **top-down design.** It is composed of two techniques: **decomposition** and **stepwise refinement.** We break the problem into a series of smaller problems (decomposition) and address each smaller problem separately (stepwise refinement). Decomposition is a form of "dividing and conquering" in which each part of the overall problem is described in general terms. Stepwise refinement begins with this general description and successively refines and describes each step in greater detail. The refining continues until the solution is specific enough to convert into computer instructions.

The advantage of decomposition is that we can initially think of the overall steps required without getting lost in the details. Details are introduced only as we begin the refinement of the algorithm. We will show the decomposition in block diagrams to emphasize that we are breaking the solution into a series of sequentially executed steps. Two tools assist us in refining the general steps of the decomposition: **pseudocode** and **flowcharts.** Pseudocode presents algorithm steps in a series of English-like statements, and a flowchart shows the steps in graphic form. Both these tools will be discussed in the next section. We will use a longhand form similar to pseudocode for the example in this section.

Applying the concept of "divide and conquer," or decomposition, to the problem of computing an average, we first break the problem into a series of smaller problems.

DECOMPOSITION

Read, sum, and count the data values.
Divide the sum by the number of data values.
Write the average.

The second part of top-down design is to refine each step in the decomposition into more detailed steps. The first step in the decomposition is "Read, sum, and count the data values." As we define this step in more detail, we need to specify how we will know when we have read all the data values. A common way to indicate the end of the data is to use a special value in the data. In this example, we will assume that a data value equal to zero will tell us when we have read all the data values. As you read the following algorithm, remember the steps you just performed in the hand example; they should be similar to these steps.

ALGORITHM FOR COMPUTING AN AVERAGE

Step 1. Set the sum of the values to zero.
Set a count of the values to zero.

Step 2. Read the first data value.

Step 3. As long as the data value is not zero, repeat the following:
Add the data value to the sum.
Add 1 to the count.
Read the next data value.
When the data value is zero, go to the next step.

Step 4. Divide the sum by the count to get the average.

Step 5. Write the average.

Step 6. Stop.

Once the solution steps are detailed, they are ready to be converted into Pascal. The statements for solving this particular problem will not all be presented until Chapter 3, so there are items in the solution that you probably won't understand at this time. We present the solution here so you can see how similar it is to the refined steps previously described.

PASCAL PROGRAM

```
{------------------------------------------------------------}
program  compute (input,output);
   {This program computes the average of
   a set of experimental data values.}
var
   x, sum, average: real;
   count: integer;
begin
   sum := 0.0;
   count := 0;
   readln (x);
   while  x <> 0.0  do
      begin
         sum := sum + x;
         count := count + 1;
         readln (x)
      end;
   average := sum/count;
   writeln ('THE AVERAGE TEMPERATURE IS ',average:6:2,
            ' DEGREES FAHRENHEIT')
end.
{------------------------------------------------------------}
```

The fifth phase of problem solving is to test the algorithm that you have just described. Testing an algorithm is not an easy task. We can usually find data for which our algorithm works correctly, but it's just as important to search for sequences of data that cause our algorithm to fail, so that we can correct the steps in the program. A correct algorithm to average data should work properly for any set of data. If the data from our hand example were used in the Pascal program presented here, the output on our terminal screen would be:

THE AVERAGE TEMPERATURE IS 30.95 DEGREES FAHRENHEIT

Before we go to the next section, which discusses the structure and development of algorithms, we list the **five design phases** for solving problems:

1. State the problem clearly.
2. Describe the input and output.
3. Work the problem by hand for a specific set of data.
4. Develop an algorithm that is general in nature.
5. Test the algorithm with a variety of data sets.

We use these five phases to develop algorithms in the problem-solving sections throughout the rest of the text.

2-2 ALGORITHM STRUCTURE AND DEVELOPMENT

In order to be consistent in the way we describe algorithms, we will use a set of standard forms or structures. When an algorithm is described in these standard structures, it is a **structured algorithm.** When the algorithm is converted into computer instructions, the corresponding program is a **structured program.**

Each structure for building algorithms can be described in an English-like notation called **pseudocode,** which we will soon discuss in detail. Pseudocode is not really computer code; it is computer-language independent. Pseudocode depends only on the steps needed to solve a problem, not on the particular computer language that will be used. **Flowcharts** are another way of describing the steps in an algorithm, but flowcharts use a graphical or diagram form. Since flowcharts are not used as much as pseudocode, we have included the discussion of flowcharts, along with a number of examples, in Appendix B. Neither pseudocode nor flowcharts are intended to be a formal way of describing the algorithm; they are informal ways of easily describing the steps in the algorithm without worrying about the syntax of a specific computer language. After we present the structures that we will be using and some examples of their corresponding pseudocode, we develop complete problem solutions using pseudocode. We use color to highlight pseudocode so that it can be referenced easily.

The steps to solve problems can be divided into three major structures:

1. Sequence: Contains steps that are performed one after another, or sequentially. All of the steps in the programs in Chapter 1 were sequential.

2. Selection: Asks a question or tests a **condition** to determine which steps are to be performed next. For example, a step of this structure might be "if the data value is not zero, add it to the sum; otherwise, compute the average."

3. Repetition: Allows us to use **loops,** which are steps in an algorithm that are repeated. One type of loop, the **while loop,** repeats the steps as long as a certain condition is true. Another type of loop, the **counting loop,** repeats the steps a specified number of times.

Other special structures are sometimes included in a list of algorithm structures. Generally, these other structures are special forms of the three structures presented here, so we do not include them as separate structures. In the detailed discussion of these three structures, we will describe the **repeat until loop** and the **case structure.**

SEQUENCE

The sequence structure does not need a special pseudocode notation. If we list a series of steps one after another, it is clear that they are to be performed sequentially. However, the individual steps should be described with pseudocode. These individual steps are primarily computations, input, and output. We now present the pseudocode for these three operations.

Computations In pseudocode, computations are indicated with an arrow, as in

$$average \leftarrow total/count$$

We read this pseudocode statement as "average is replaced by total divided by count" or "total is divided by count, giving average."

Another example of a computation statement in pseudocode is

$$count \leftarrow count + 1$$

We read this statement as "count is incremented by 1, giving the new count" or "count is replaced by the sum of the old count plus 1."

Input Input statements in pseudocode are specified by the word *read* followed by the variables that are to be read. For example, to read a temperature value and a humidity value, we use the following pseudocode:

$$read\ temperature,\ humidity$$

The words *temperature* and *humidity* are chosen as you develop the pseudocode. We could also have used the statement:

$$read\ temperature\ value,\ humidity\ value$$

Output Output statements are specified in pseudocode by the word *write* followed by a list of variable names and constants. The following pseudocode statement prints a character constant and the value of an average:

$$write\ 'THE\ AVERAGE\ IS\ ',\ average$$

SELECTION

The selection structure is used to choose between sets of steps. It is most commonly described in terms of an *if* structure that may itself have several forms. We use three forms of the *if* structure for selection. The simple *if* form tests a condition; if the condition is true, then a certain step or series of steps is performed. For example, suppose the algorithm that we are developing must count the number of students who are on the honor roll and write their student ID (identification) numbers. One step in our algorithm might be "if the grade point average (GPA) is greater than 3.0, then write the ID and add 1 to the number of students on the honor roll." Note the use of indenting in the pseudocode.

```
if gpa > 3.0 then
    write id
    honor roll ← honor roll + 1
```

Another form of the *if* structure is the *if-else* form. This form specifies one series of steps to be executed if a condition is true and an alternative series if the condition is false. For example, suppose we want to modify the honor roll example to print the ID of each student; however, if the student is on the honor roll, we want to increment our honor roll count and also write the GPA beside the student's ID. We could describe this step with the following pseudocode:

```
if gpa > 3.0 then
    write id, gpa
    honor roll ← honor roll + 1
else
    write id
```

The last form of the *if* structure is the *if-else-if* form, which allows us to test for multiple conditions. It is sometimes called a *case* structure because it examines multiple cases or conditions. This *if-else-if* form can be illustrated by extending the honor roll example. Assume that the president's honor roll requires a GPA of greater than 3.5 and that the dean's honor roll requires a GPA of greater than 3.0. We want to count the number of students on each honor roll. Students on the president's honor roll are not to be included on the dean's honor roll. Write each student's ID and GPA if above 3.0; include an asterisk beside the GPA if it is above 3.5. The following pseudocode describes this set of steps.

```
if gpa > 3.5 then
    write id, gpa, '*'
    president's count ← president's count + 1
else if gpa > 3.0 then
    write id, gpa
    dean's count ← dean's count + 1
else
    write id
```

REPETITION

A *while* loop identifies a series of steps that are to be repeated if a certain condition is true. This series of steps is composed of sequential, selection, or other repetition steps. Suppose we wish to continue reading data values and adding them to a sum as long as that sum is less than 1000. These steps are described in the following pseudocode:

> while sum < 1000 do
>   read data value
>   sum ← sum + data value

Again, note that the indenting in the pseudocode specifies the steps that are included in the *while* loop. If we wish to write the value of the sum after exiting the *while* loop, we can use the following pseudocode:

> while sum < 1000 do
>   read data value
>   sum ← sum + data value
> write sum

Counting loops repeat steps a specific number of times. For example, suppose we are going to read ten values from the terminal and perform some calculations with each value. We can describe the steps in a counting loop that is repeated ten times. However, a counting loop can be considered a special form of a *while* loop in which a counter has been introduced. The counter represents the number of times to execute the loop. The counter is usually initialized to zero before the loop executes. Inside the loop, the counter is incremented by one. The loop then executes "while the value of the counter is less than ten." The pseudocode for this counting loop example is:

> count ← 0
> while count < 10 do
>   read data
>   perform calculations
>   count ← count + 1

Another special form of the *while* loop structure that is sometimes presented separately is the *repeat until* loop. In this loop, a set of statements executes until a condition is true. An example of this loop is:

> repeat
>   set of steps
> until a ≤ b

Using the *while* loop structure, we can rewrite this as:

> while a > b do
>   set of steps

These two forms seem equivalent, but there is one difference. In the *repeat* structure, the set of steps executes before the condition is tested; in the *while* loop, the condition test is made first. Thus, if $a = 3$ and $b = 5$, the set of steps will be executed once in the *repeat* loop but not at all in the *while* loop. When converting one form to the other, you must be careful to add the steps necessary to make them exactly equivalent.

Now that we have presented the pseudocode for the three main structures and for the steps included in them, we can write pseudocode for complete algorithms. To keep the style consistent, we will begin the pseudocode for a complete algorithm with an identifying name of our choosing followed by the steps in the algorithm. Indenting will be used to show when steps are part of another structure, such as a selection structure or a repetition structure. This indenting is not only necessary in order to understand the pseudocode, but it also greatly improves the readability of our algorithms.

We now illustrate the process of developing algorithms with examples. The best way to become proficient at developing algorithms is to study examples of algorithm development in pseudocode and then apply the ideas to similar problems.

EXAMPLE 2-1   Average of a Set of Data Values

In the previous section we illustrated top-down design in algorithm development with an algorithm and a program to compute the average of a set of data values. In developing the algorithm, we wrote a set of English-like steps to describe the problem solution. Let's look at that problem again and develop an algorithm using the pseudocode notation that we have presented in this section. Recall that we are reading data values from the terminal, and we want to compute the average of the values. A value of zero indicates that we have reached the end of the data values.

Solution

The first step in top-down algorithm development is to decompose the problem into a series of sequential steps. We did that when we first considered this problem, so we show again the decomposition steps:

DECOMPOSITION

| Read, sum, and count the data values. |
| Divide the sum by the number of data values. |
| Write the average. |

The decomposition provides a top-level picture of the solution in general terms. We now take each of the sequential steps in the decomposition and refine it using the structures that we have just discussed: sequential steps, selection steps, and repetition steps. The first step in the decomposition is "read, sum, and count the data values." This step can be refined by recognizing that it is composed of setting a count and a sum to zero (sequential steps) followed by a loop to read the values and update the count and sum (repetition step). The loop should be structured as a *while* loop, so we must determine the condition necessary to keep us in the loop. The problem statement tells us to assume that the data values have all been read when a zero is entered; thus, we want to stay in the loop "while the data value is not a zero." We need to read a data value at the beginning of the *while* loop so that we can test that value for zero as we enter the *while* loop. If we have not just read a data value of zero, we add the data value to our sum, add one to our count, and then read another data value. We return to the condition at the beginning of the loop to see if we have read a zero data value or not. This cycle of steps is repeated until we read a data value of zero that will cause us to exit the *while* loop. We then need sequential steps to compute the average and print it. We can now put this refinement into pseudocode.

PSEUDOCODE FOR THE ALGORITHM FOR COMPUTING AN AVERAGE

```
compute: sum ← 0
         count ← 0
         read a data value
         while the data value is not zero do
             sum ← sum + data value
             count ← count + 1
             read the next data value
         average ← sum/count
         write 'AVERAGE =', average
```

If you compare the pseudocode with the longhand form of these steps from the previous section, you should see several advantages to using pseudocode. Most importantly, the organization of the pseudocode shows the structure of the algorithm immediately. The indenting and the words such as *while* and *read* indicate that the overall structure is a *while* loop with a *read* step inside. To determine this structure from the earlier version of the algorithm, we have to read the entire algorithm.

EXAMPLE 2-2   Experimental Data Analysis

We return to our example of analyzing laboratory data. Since we have already looked at the steps necessary to compute an average, let's now suppose that we want to find the maximum data value and the minimum data value so that we can compute the range of data values. If the measurements were taken after the experiment was in a stable configuration, we might expect this range to be small. If there were still dynamic or changing elements in the experiment, the range could be quite large. Assume that a data value of zero will indicate the end of the data.

Solution

Even when a problem seems simple, such as this one, we recommend using the five-phase process. Before we begin to write pseudocode, we must thoroughly understand the problem statement and should have done an example by hand. This preparation sometimes makes the solution so obvious that we can define the necessary steps right away. However, developing most solutions requires more effort.

PROBLEM STATEMENT

Find the maximum and minimum data values, and then compute the range of the data values.

INPUT/OUTPUT DESCRIPTION

The input is a list of experimental data values and the output is the maximum data value, minimum data value, and computed range of values.

HAND EXAMPLE

Assume that the lab worksheet below contains data from a laboratory experiment that we recently ran in the chemistry lab.

LAB MEASUREMENTS, 9/30/88

Experiment 1	40.56
Experiment 2	55.92
Experiment 3	66.31
Experiment 4	58.35
Experiment 5	62.88
Experiment 6	41.99
Experiment 7	49.70
Experiment 8	53.21

Let's begin with the steps to find the maximum value. We look at the first value, compare it to the second value, and denote the larger of the two as the "maximum so far." Now we look at the third value and compare it to our "maximum so far." If the "maximum so far" is larger, we go to the fourth value; but if the third value is larger than our "maximum so far," we update the value in our "maximum so far." Continuing this process with the entire list of data results in the maximum value being stored in the "maximum so far." A similar process finds the minimum value. For the preceding data, our results are:

maximum value = 66.31
minimum value = 40.56

Now we can compute the range of values by subtracting the minimum value from the maximum value:

$$\text{range of values} = 66.31 - 40.56 = 25.75$$

ALGORITHM DEVELOPMENT

Having worked out a simple problem by hand, we are ready to begin our algorithm development. We start with decomposition of the problem; this is a good example of the "divide and conquer" concept discussed in the first section of this chapter.

DECOMPOSITION

Read data values and determine maximum and minimum values.
Subtract minimum value from maximum value to get range.
Write maximum, minimum, range.

We now refine the solution using pseudocode. We take each step of the decomposition and decide which structures (sequential, selection, and repetition) define the step in greater detail. Clearly, our first decomposition step requires the greatest refinement because it includes sequential steps (initializing our maximum and minimum values) plus the repetition step (the loop to read values and update our maximum and minimum values if necessary). The maximum and minimum values are commonly initialized to the first data value so we need to read the first data value to initialize them. We then enter the *while* loop. "While the data value is not zero," we update the maximum and minimum values as necessary. Note that we do not need a count of the data values or a sum for this problem. Let's write these refined steps in pseudocode.

REFINEMENT IN PSEUDOCODE

```
range1: read data value
        maximum ← data value
        minimum ← data value
        while data value is not zero do
           if data value > maximum then
              maximum ← data value
           if data value < minimum then
              minimum ← data value
           read a data value
        range ← maximum − minimum
        write 'MAXIMUM DATA VALUE = ', maximum
        write 'MINIMUM DATA VALUE = ', minimum
        write 'RANGE OF VALUES = ', range
```

This was a simple algorithm; only one refinement was needed. Additional refinements are often necessary for more complex problems.

TESTING

If we use our example data in the refined algorithm, the output is:

```
MAXIMUM DATA VALUE = 66.31
MINIMUM DATA VALUE = 40.56
RANGE OF VALUES = 25.75
```

Similar results are obtained with different sets of data. Note that the *while* loop will not be executed if the first data value is zero. In this case, the maximum value, minimum value, and range of values will all be computed as zero.

SELF-TEST 2-1

This self-test allows you to check quickly to see if you have remembered some of the key points from Section 2-2. If you have any problem with the execise, you should reread this section. The solution is included at the end of the text.

Modify the data range computation algorithm *range1*, which is on page 56, to count the number of data values. Print this count at the end of the algorithm.

2-3 EVALUATION OF ALTERNATIVE SOLUTIONS

There are always many ways to solve the same problem. We emphasize this now because you may be concerned when you find that your algorithms contain steps different from those of other students. In most cases, there is no best solution to a problem; however, some solutions are definitely better than others. Don't assume that the best solution is also the shortest solution; experience shows that this is not always the case. A good solution is one that is simple to understand and clearly written. Subtle or clever steps may shorten the algorithm but should be used only if they improve the overall clarity of the algorithm.

Try to think of several ways to solve a problem when you begin developing the general solution. As you refine the solution, choose the one that is the simplest and most straightforward. Sometimes you will need to write the refined pseudocode for several solution methods before you can choose the simplest approach.

As an example, another way to solve the experimental data range problem is to sort the data values into ascending numerical order. Then the first value is the minimum value, and the last value is the maximum value. This is a reasonable solution but not as simple as the solution presented in the last section, because this solution requires that we sort the data first. The following is the first refinement of this alternative solution.

ALTERNATIVE PSEUDOCODE FOR COMPUTATION OF DATA RANGE

range2: read and save the data values
      sort the data values
      minimum ← first data value in sorted list
      maximum ← last data value in sorted list
      range ← maximum − minimum
      write 'MINIMUM DATA VALUE =', minimum
      write 'MAXIMUM DATA VALUE =', maximum
      write 'RANGE OF DATA VALUES =', range

Additional refinements would be necessary to define in detail the steps necessary to perform the sort. Techniques for sorting data will be presented in subsequent chapters.

Can you think of a problem that would require that we sort the data values? If we wanted to know the median data value, we would need to sort the data values first, and then determine which value was the middle value. We would also need to count the number of data values. If the number of data values is odd, then the median value would be the middle value. For example, if we had 21 data values, then the eleventh value in the sorted list is the median. If we had 20 values, there would be no exact middle point in the list. Generally, the median is then defined to be the average of the tenth and eleventh values. Let's put these steps into the decomposition block diagram and an initial refinement in pseudocode for practice. We will assume that a value of zero indicates the end of the data and furthermore that the zero value is not part of the data values to be used in determining the median.

DECOMPOSITION

Read and save the data values.
Determine median value.
Write median value.

median: count ← 0
    read and save data value
    while the data value is not zero do
        count ← count + 1
        read and save data value
    sort the data values
    if count is odd then
        median value ← middle value in sorted list
    else
        median value ← (sum of two middle values)/2
    write 'TOTAL NUMBER OF DATA VALUES =', count
    write 'MEDIAN VALUE =', median value

The important message of this section is that there are usually several ways to solve a problem, and you should consider alternative solutions when you begin solving a problem. Generally, the best solution is the simplest solution. Occasionally, other aspects of a solution such as memory requirements and execution speed must also be considered.

SELF-TEST 2-2

This self-test allows you to check quickly to see if you have remembered some of the key points from Section 2-3. If you have any problem with the exercise, you should reread this section. The solution is included at the end of the text.

Modify the median computation algorithm, *median*, which is shown above, to determine and print a count of negative values and positive values.

2-4 ERROR CONDITIONS

When we write an algorithm to solve a problem, we begin with the assumption that the input data will be correct. As we refine the algorithm, we usually find logical places to test the data for error conditions. It is important to distinguish between an error in the algorithm and an error condition in the data. Any error discovered in the algorithm must be corrected so that the modified algorithm correctly performs the requirements in the problem statement. **Error conditions** in the data are data values that are not valid or desirable, but may still occur. Thus, a correct algorithm must include steps to handle certain error conditions in the data. For example, the algorithm described on page 54 is a correct algorithm for computing the average of a set of data values. However, we might want to assume that a negative data value indicated an error in the instrument that we were using to measure the data value, and thus we would want to ignore any negative data values. We would also want to skip the statement that incremented the data count when the value was negative; otherwise our average would not be correct.

When you are developing an algorithm, how do you know which error conditions in the data could occur? Sometimes the problem statement will include a list of error conditions that might occur and indications of how to handle them, but it is more likely that the problem statement will not mention error conditions at all. When you have no information on error conditions, our advice is to include error checks that fit easily into the structure of your algorithm. For example, in the modified average computation algorithm discussed in the previous paragraph, it is easy to add an *if* structure to test for negative data values. If the data value is positive, then add it to the sum and increment the count; otherwise, skip these two steps. As we develop algorithms throughout this text, you will learn more about typical error conditions that can occur. Unless you decide which error conditions to include, your program can become primarily statements that perform error checks, and you generally do not want that to happen.

Once you have decided that an error condition will be handled in your algorithm, you still have to decide what to do if it occurs. Usually, you have two choices: either print an error message and exit the algorithm, or print an error message but continue executing the steps in the algorithm. Note that in either case an error message is printed. Be sure that the error message is specific. Do not use messages such as 'ERROR,' 'ERROR CODE 3,' 'YOU BLEW IT!' or 'SOMETHING IS WRONG.' Since you made a specific test to determine that the error occurred, use that information in your message. Examples of more descriptive messages are 'ERROR IN DATA MEASUREMENT' and 'PRESSURE VALUE EXCEEDS SAFETY LIMIT.'

If the error condition occurred in the input data, we recommend that you continue performing steps in the algorithm so that you can check the rest of the data for errors. The final result will be wrong, but hopefully you will locate all the errors in the data and will get valid results after the input data is corrected. If the error is not in the input data, then it is advisable to exit the algorithm immediately after writing an appropriate error message.

Check all loops to see if they could become infinite loops under certain conditions. An **infinite loop** is one in which the loop condition is always true. Consider the following *while* loop:

$$\text{count} \leftarrow 0$$
$$\text{while count} < 12 \text{ do}$$
$$\text{steps in the loop}$$

In this algorithm, assume that the steps in the loop do not modify *count*. The count is always zero, which is always less than 12, and thus we have an infinite loop. This example is a case of an algorithm error and requires a modification in the algorithm itself. Infinite loops cannot always be detected before the steps of an algorithm are performed because the loop may depend on values related to the input data. For example, consider the following steps:

```
read n
count ← 0
while count < n do
    steps in the loop
    count ← count + 1
```

If *n* is less than zero, this becomes an infinite loop because *count* increases in value and thus will never be equal to *n*. Since it is not always possible to avoid an infinite loop, you may be worried about the effect that this will have on the computer. In Chapter 3 we will explain more about the program execution process, but for now, if you are using a large time-sharing computer system, you can probably safely assume that your computer system has set certain limits to keep it from staying in an infinite loop. For example, most computer systems will only allow your program to run for a few seconds before they assume that you have exceeded your time limit. This time limit is set to give you plenty of time for small programs, but also to stop automatically if you get in an infinite loop. If you exceed the time limit, the computer system will usually give you an error message stating that you have exceeded your time limit, and if you need more time for your program, you need to see the system manager. If you are using a personal computer, you will need a special command to terminate the program if it gets in an infinite loop. This command is often called a "break" command and will be discussed in the operating systems manual for your system.

2-5 GENERATION OF TEST DATA

Generating **test data** is an important part of testing an algorithm. As we have already mentioned, it is usually not difficult to create test data that works correctly with an algorithm. It is more difficult, though, to generate data that will test each step in an algorithm. For each condition tested in the algorithm (in *while* loops and *if* structures), data should be included that yields true conditions and other data should be included that yields false conditions. By using test data that represents both values, we are testing different paths or sets of steps that are executed together. As you begin putting test data together and trying it in the algorithm, you will find that it is usually easier to test an algorithm with a number of small sets of data rather than one large set. To test the average computation algorithm, here are test sets that we could use:

Set 1. Use the data from the hand problem. If this doesn't work in the algorithm, we aren't off to a good start!

Set 2. Use a data set in which every data value is the same value. The average should also be this value.

Set 3. Use a data set that has only one data value. The average should also be this one value.

Since this algorithm is not complicated, neither is generating test data for it. As we develop more complicated algorithms throughout the text, we will suggest types of data that should be used to test them.

What do you do if you find an error in the algorithm while testing it? If the error is a major one, you may need to go back to the algorithm development phase and begin again. For smaller errors, you will find that you have a natural tendency to patch the old algorithm and retest it on the data set that did not work correctly initially. If the algorithm now works, don't immediately assume that it is correct. How do we know that the new algorithm will still work for the data that has already been tested on the initial algorithm? Clearly we do not know, so we must start the test procedure over whenever we modify an algorithm.

An algorithm should correctly handle all the test data sets before we assume it is correct, but actually all we know for sure is that it works on our test data. If we did a careful job developing the algorithm and generating test data, then we can have confidence in our algorithm. Computer science curricula usually include a course in proving the correctness of algorithms. Since this subject is beyond the scope of this book, we again stress the importance of careful algorithm development and thorough generation of test data so that we can be confident of the correctness of our algorithms.

As a final note on the generation of test data, we want to mention a technique that is commonly used in industry and business. In projects that include the development of long or complex algorithms, it is very common for one group of people to develop an algorithm and for another group of people to generate test data and do the actual testing. You could use this technique with long or complex algorithms that you develop. Ask a friend (preferably someone else in your class) to help you generate test data—but do your own testing. By doing your own testing, you find any errors in the program, and you should correct them yourself since you are still learning the computer language and you benefit from making your own corrections.

We now develop pseudocode for three new problems. In later chapters, we present the Pascal statements needed to convert these algorithms into Pascal. At that time, we will review the pseudocode solutions and then convert them into complete Pascal programs.

2-6 PROBLEM SOLVING—DEGREE TO RADIAN CONVERSION

One of the simplest types of programs that uses a repetition structure or a loop is a program to compute and print a table of data. This table could be a conversion table that converts a given value in one set of units to the corresponding value in another set of units. Another type of useful table computes the interest on an initial amount deposited and prints the simple interest, compound interest, and new principal after each year. In these examples, the condition used to determine when to exit the loop could be when the value to be converted exceeds a specified value or when the interest has been computed for a specified number of years.

In this section we develop an algorithm to generate a table that converts degrees to radians. The algorithm development is again presented in five phases.

PROBLEM STATEMENT

Generate a table that converts degrees to radians. Begin with 0 degrees and increment by 10 degrees through the final value of 360 degrees.

INPUT/OUTPUT DESCRIPTION

No input is needed for this algorithm. The output is a table with columns for degrees and corresponding radians.

HAND EXAMPLE

The formula for conversion of degrees to radians is:

$$\text{radians} \leftarrow \text{degrees} \cdot (3.1416/180.0)$$

We can use the multiplying constant in the form above to show that it is the value of pi divided by 180.0, or we can use the result of the division, which is 0.01745. The first few entries in the table can then be determined with a calculator.

DEGREES	RADIANS
0.00	0.0000
10.00	0.1745
20.00	0.3490

The rest of the computations seem to be straightforward, so we now go to the next phase.

ALGORITHM DEVELOPMENT

The algorithm for this problem solution contains a loop that prints a line in the table each time the loop executes. This loop could be described as a *while* loop that is executed while the number of degrees is less than or equal to 360. It could also be described as a counting loop since it is executed a specific number of times. (How many times is it executed? The answer is 37 times. If you did not get 37, go back to the problem description and read it again. Are you counting the first line?) We will choose a counting loop for this algorithm. The top-down design is shown with the decomposition into general steps and the refinement into detailed steps in pseudocode.

DECOMPOSITION

Write report heading.
Write conversion table.

```
table: write report heading
        degrees ← 0.0
        count ← 0
        while count < 37 do
                radians ← degrees * 0.01745
                write degrees, radians
                degrees ← degrees + 10.0
                count ← count + 1
```

Can you think of some other ways of computing the conversion table? Instead of computing the number of radians from the number of degrees, we could add the number of radians in 10 degrees to the previous number of radians to get the new number of radians.

In Chapter 3, we present all the control structures necessary to convert this algorithm into Pascal, so we will perform the conversion in Example 3-5.

TESTING

To test this algorithm, we should print the entire table and then use a calculator to check the first few entries, the last few entries, and a few entries in the middle. We should also check the number of times that the loop executes. It is easy to make the mistake of writing an algorithm that executes a counting loop one time more or one time less than intended.

2-7 PROBLEM SOLVING—GRADE POINT AVERAGE

In this section we develop an algorithm to compute a grade point average. Since the problem is more complicated than the average computation problem, we will use two refinements to derive our final algorithm. The five design phases presented earlier in the chapter will again be used as the framework for solving this problem.

PROBLEM STATEMENT

You have just received grades for your college courses. Compute your grade point average, using a 4.0 system.

INPUT/OUTPUT DESCRIPTION

The input information is contained on the final grade form, which gives each course number, the number of credit hours for the course, and its letter grade.

The output should be the words GRADE POINT AVERAGE followed by the computed grade point average.

HAND EXAMPLE

We use the grades from the following form for our hand example:

Gold Trail University Alma, NJ		
JANE DOE FRESHMAN		SPRING SEMESTER 1989
Course	Credit Hours	Final Grade
INTRO. TO COMPUTING	3	A
ENGLISH I	3	B
CHEMISTRY	4	B
AMERICAN HISTORY	3	C
CALCULUS I	3	B

Each letter grade should be converted to a number grade using the following table:

LETTER GRADE	NUMBER GRADE
A	4.0
B	3.0
C	2.0
D	1.0
F	0.0

Multiply the number grade by the number of credit hours to get the number of points for a specific class. Since the grade point average is the total number of points divided by the total number of credit hours, compute the number of points for each class and then total the hours and the points.

COURSE	CREDIT HOURS	LETTER GRADE	NUMBER GRADE	POINTS
Intro. to Computing	3	A	4.0	12.0
English I	3	B	3.0	9.0
Chemistry	4	B	3.0	12.0
American History	3	C	2.0	6.0
Calculus I	3	B	3.0	9.0
Totals	16			48.0

The grade point average is then 48.0 divided by 16, or 3.00.

ALGORITHM DEVELOPMENT

After working the hand example, we are ready to develop the algorithm. The top-down design with its decomposition into general steps and the first refinement into pseudocode are given below:

DECOMPOSITION

Read grades and compute total hours and total points.
Compute grade point average.
Write grade point average.

As we begin to add details to the decomposition in order to refine the solution, we need to decide what type of input we need from the terminal in order to solve the problem. Certainly, we will need to enter the grade and the number of hours for each course. But how will we know when we have all the data? We could have the user enter a course with zero hours when all the data has already been entered, or we could have the user tell us at the beginning how many courses were taken. We will choose the latter approach and ask the user to tell us the number of courses taken. Then, in our refinement, we can use that number to specify the number of times to execute the repetition structure.

INITIAL REFINEMENT IN PSEUDOCODE

gpa: total points $\leftarrow$ 0
      total hours $\leftarrow$ 0
      count $\leftarrow$ 0
      read number of courses
      while count < number of courses do
          write message to user to enter course data
          read course hours, letter grade
          total hours $\leftarrow$ total hours + course hours
          convert letter grade to number grade
          points $\leftarrow$ number grade * course hours
          total points $\leftarrow$ total points + points
      grade point average $\leftarrow$ total points/total hours
      write 'GRADE POINT AVERAGE', grade point average

We now need to refine the steps that are still not specific. In particular, we must be more specific about the conversion of a letter grade to a number grade. The conversion is done with a sequence of tests. If the letter grade is A, then the number grade is 4.0. If the letter grade is B, then the number grade is 3.0, and so on. These tests translate easily to an *if-then-else* structure. In the final *else* clause we print an error message if the letter grade is invalid, and we ask the user to reenter the information. We then change the number of hours to zero so that we will know that the letter grade was invalid, and we then do not update the totals and course count. If the letter grade is valid, we update the totals and the course count.

FINAL REFINEMENT IN PSEUDOCODE

gpa: total points ← 0
    total hours ← 0
    count ← 0
    read number of courses
    while count < number of courses do
        write message to user to enter course data
        read course hours, letter grade
        if letter grade = A then
          number grade ← 4.0
        else if letter grade = B then
          number grade ← 3.0
        else if letter grade = C then
          number grade ← 2.0
        else if letter grade = D then
          number grade ← 1.0
        else if letter grade = F then
          number grade ← 0.0
        else
          write 'ERROR IN LETTER GRADE, ENTER AGAIN'
          number grade ← 0.0
          course hours ← 0
        if course hours > 0 then
          total hours ← total hours + course hours
          points ← number grade * course hours
          total points ← total points + points
          count ← count + 1
    grade point average ← total points/total hours
    write 'GRADE POINT AVERAGE', grade point average

The Pascal statements for the control structures in this algorithm are presented in the next chapter, but character data is not presented until Chapter 8. Therefore, in Example 8-5 we will convert this algorithm to Pascal.

TESTING

Test the algorithm first with the hand example. Then try a couple of your previous grade reports or some from your friends. Is there a problem if the total points are zero but the total hours are greater than zero? No, since the grade point average in this case is computed to be 0.00, and could occur if a student received an F in all courses. As we continue to look for limitations in our algorithm, we find that it does not work correctly if the total hours are zero because dividing by zero is undefined. However, our algorithm assumes that if the course hours are zero, then the letter grade was invalid, and the algorithm asks the user to reenter the course data. Thus, we cannot get to the division step with a total number of hours of zero, so we do not have to worry about division by zero.

2-8 PROBLEM SOLVING—ROCKET TRAJECTORY

A retrorocket is being designed to permit softer landings. Before actual development begins, the designers work on a rocket to test their theories. They have derived the following equation that they believe will predict the performance of their test rocket, where t is the elapsed time in seconds:

$$\text{height} = 60 + 2.13t^2 - 0.0013t^4 + 0.000034t^{4.751}$$

The equation gives the height above ground level at time t. The first term (60) is the height in feet above ground level of the nose of the rocket. To check the predicted performance, the designers "fly" the rocket on a computer using the preceding equation.

Develop an algorithm and use it to write a complete program to cover a maximum flight of 100 seconds. Increments in time are to be 2.0 seconds from launch through the ascending and descending portions of the trajectory until the rocket descends to within 50 feet of ground level. Below 50 feet the time increments are to be 0.05 seconds. If the rocket hits the ground prior to 100 seconds, the program is to stop immediately after impact. The output is to be in the following form:

```
TIME (SEC.)     HEIGHT (FT.)
  0.0000        XXXX.XXXX
  2.0000        XXXX.XXXX
    .
    .
    .
```

As shown in the following diagram, several possible events could occur as we simulate the flight. The height above the ground should increase for a period and then decrease until the rocket reaches the ground. We can test for impact by testing the height for a value equal to or less than zero. It is also possible that the rocket will still be airborne after 100 seconds of flight time. Therefore, we must also test for this condition and stop the program if the value of time becomes greater than 100. In addition, we need to observe the height above ground. As the rocket approaches the ground, we want to monitor its progress more frequently; we will need to reduce our time increment from 2.0 seconds to 0.05 seconds.

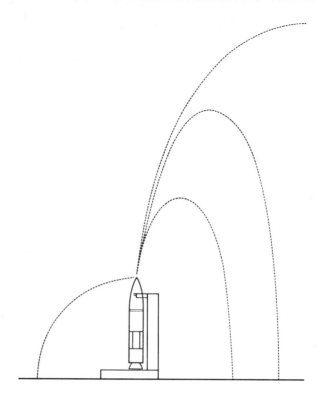

PROBLEM STATEMENT

Using the equation below, compute height values and write them along with their corresponding time values. Start time at zero and increment it by 2.0 seconds until the height is less than 50 feet, then increment time by 0.05 seconds. Stop the program if the rocket reaches the ground or if the total time exceeds 100 seconds.

$$\text{height} = 60 + 2.13t^2 - 0.0013t^4 + 0.000034t^{4.751}$$

INPUT/OUTPUT DESCRIPTION

There is no input to the program. The output is a table of time and height values in the following form:

```
TIME (SEC.)      HEIGHT (FT.)
  0.0000         XXXX.XXXX
  2.0000         XXXX.XXXX
   .
   .
   .
```

HAND EXAMPLE

Using a calculator, compute the first three entries in the table as shown:

TIME (SEC.)	HEIGHT (FT.)
0.0000	60.0000
2.0000	68.5001
4.0000	93.7719

We are now ready to develop the algorithm so that the computer can compute the rest of the table for us.

ALGORITHM DEVELOPMENT

The initial decomposition comprises two sequential steps, as shown:

DECOMPOSITION

Set time to zero.
Write report.

As we begin the refinement, we find that it is easiest to do it in two steps. Our initial refinement yields:

INITIAL REFINEMENT IN PSEUDOCODE

rocket: time ← 0
        while above ground and time ≤ 100 do
          compute height using equation
          write time, height
          increment time

In our final refinement, we replace "increment time" with the steps that take into account our height above ground. We also replace the condition "above ground" with a specific condition based on our height above ground.

FINAL REFINEMENT IN PSEUDOCODE

rocket: time ← 0
      height ← 60
      while height > 0 and time ≤ 100 do
        compute height using equation
        write time, height
        if height < 50 then
          time ← time + 0.05
        else
          time ← time + 2.0

Notice that the height variable was initialized to 60.0 (the value given by the equation when time is zero) before entering the *while* loop. Why? Could it have been initialized to any value? Because the condition in the *while* loop used the height variable, it had to be initialized before the condition was tested. The height must also be set to a value greater than zero or the *while* loop would never be executed.

The function for exponentiation will be developed in Chapter 6, and the Pascal solution to this problem is developed in Example 6-2.

TESTING

The first few lines and the last few lines of output are shown. The values are in agreement with the hand-worked example.

```
TIME (SEC.)      HEIGHT (FT.)

    0.0000         60.0000
    2.0000         68.5001
    4.0000         93.7719
    6.0000        135.1644
    8.0000        191.6590
      .
      .
      .
   54.0000        999.1558
   56.0000        827.4219
   58.0000        633.3003
   60.0000        418.3994
   62.0000        184.8125
   64.0000         -6.8574
```

Can you think of ways to test different parts of the algorithm? We now know that the rocket reaches the ground before 100 seconds of flight time; we could change the cutoff time to 50 seconds to see if this exit from the *while* loop works correctly. How could you modify the program to check the change in the increment of the time variable from 2.0 seconds to 0.05 seconds?

SUMMARY

We have presented a five-phase procedure for developing problem solutions (algorithms). The procedure begins with a clear statement of the problem and continues with a description of the input or information available. The form of the output is also described; for instance, the output might be an average of a set of laboratory measurements or a grade point average.

The algorithm to solve the specified problem is developed using top-down design. Decomposition assists in describing the general steps that have to be performed to solve the problem, and then stepwise refinement guides us in refining the steps and adding the detail necessary to perform them. Pseudocode describes these steps using structures that will be easy to convert into computer languages. There are usually many ways to solve a problem, but we want to choose simple, easy-to-understand solutions. These solutions will then be easier to test for correctness and easier to modify if we should need to modify them to fit new problem statements.

DEBUGGING AIDS

Throughout this chapter we have given advice on testing algorithms and developing test data. We now summarize those debugging aids:

1. Spend the time necessary to generate test data that adequately tests all paths through your algorithm.
2. Use several small sets of test data instead of one large set.
3. Be sure that you perform each step in the algorithm as specified. You know what you want the steps to do, but do they really specify what you want?
4. If you find a major error, go back to the algorithm development phase and begin again.
5. If you find a small error, modify the algorithm and begin the testing phase at the beginning.
6. If the algorithm is long or complex, ask someone else to help you generate test data.
7. Perform error checks on input data to verify that the data is valid. (Note that there is a difference between an algorithm error and a data error.)

STYLE/TECHNIQUE GUIDELINES

The guidelines presented in this section of each chapter will reinforce good habits in the construction and presentation of algorithms and computer programs. It is much easier to learn good habits from the beginning than to change bad habits later. Using poor style in algorithms and programs is much like using poor grammar when you speak: It makes a bad impression initially and will make it harder for you to get your point across and to develop credibility. The style that we recommend for describing algorithms has been used in the examples already developed.

1. Use pseudocode or flowcharts to describe your algorithm. This gives a uniform appearance to all your algorithms and allows other people to read them more easily.
2. Use only a small number of structures in constructing the algorithm. We prefer using the sequence structure, the selection structure and its three forms, and the repetition structure in the form of *while* loops.
3. Indent the internal steps of loops and selection structures.
4. Do the decomposition step for every algorithm. Even very simple problem solutions break down into a series of general steps.
5. Do not try to develop every algorithm with one refinement. Use as many refinements as are needed to get to the level of detail that you want.

6. Model your algorithms in structure and appearance after those presented in the text.
7. Pseudocode and flowcharts are flexible tools for describing algorithms. Do not be afraid to modify them to fit your own style, as long as the overall structures remain consistent.

KEY WORDS

condition	*repeat until* loop
counting loop	repetition structure
decomposition	selection structure
design phases	sequence structure
error condition	stepwise refinement
flowchart	structured algorithm
infinite loop	structured program
input/output (I/O)	test data
loop	top-down design
pseudocode	*while* loop

PROBLEMS

A good way to learn new techniques is to practice making small changes in an algorithm that is already written. The first set of problems requires modifications to the average computation algorithm, *compute*, which is on page 54. Start with the original algorithm each time you begin a new problem.

1. Modify the average computation algorithm to print the count that it uses in the average formula.
2. Modify the average computation algorithm to print all the data values in a table with an appropriate heading.
3. Modify the average computation algorithm to skip any negative data values. Be sure that the count is not incremented when a negative data value is found.
4. Modify the average computation algorithm to use an iterative loop to read 100 values, and compute the corresponding average.

5. Modify the average computation algorithm to read a value *n* that specifies the number of data values that follow. Read the *n* data values and compute the corresponding average.

This set of problems requires modifications to the degree to radian conversion algorithm, *table*, which is on page 64. Start with the original algorithm each time you begin a new problem.

6. Modify the conversion algorithm so that the increment between lines in the table is 5 degrees.
7. Modify the conversion algorithm so that the increment between lines in the table is read as a data value.
8. Modify the conversion algorithm so that the starting degree value, the increment, and the number of lines to print in the table are all read as data values.
9. Modify the conversion algorithm so that it converts radians to degrees, starting at 0.0 radians and incrementing by 0.01 radians, until the number of radians is greater than 6.28.

This set of problems requires modifications to the grade point average algorithm, *gpa*, which is on page 67. Start with the original algorithm each time you begin a new problem.

10. Modify the grade point average algorithm to print the hours and letter grade for an invalid grade.
11. Modify the grade point average algorithm to print HONOR ROLL after the grade point average if it is 3.0 or above.
12. Modify the grade point average algorithm so that a grade of incomplete (I) is not used in the grade calculation and also is not printed as an error.
13. Modify the grade point average algorithm so that a grade of credit (CR) or no credit (NC) does not affect the calculation of the grade point average.
14. Modify the grade point average algorithm so that a count of the number of classes is printed in addition to the grade point average.

This set of problems requires modifications to the degree to rocket trajectory algorithm, *rocket*, which is on page 70. Start with the original algorithm each time you begin a new problem.

15. Modify the rocket trajectory program so that it stops if the rocket reaches the ground or if the total time exceeds 50 seconds.
16. Modify the rocket trajectory program so that it starts time at zero seconds and increments it by 0.5 seconds until the height is less than 50 feet; then have it increment time by 0.25 seconds.
17. Modify the rocket trajectory program so that it starts time at zero seconds and increments it by 0.5 seconds until the height is less than 80 feet; then have it increment time by 0.25 seconds.

18. Modify the rocket trajectory program so that it reads two values, *incr1* and *incr2*. Start time at zero seconds and increment it by *incr1* seconds until the height is less than 50 feet; then increment time by *incr2* seconds.

19. Modify the rocket trajectory program so that it does not print a table but instead prints two values. The first value is the time at which the rocket begins falling back to the ground and the second value is the time at which the rocket reaches the ground. Start time at zero and increment it by 0.01 seconds.

Now that you are comfortable making changes to an existing algorithm, here are some new algorithms to develop. Remember to use the five-phase design process.

20. Given three packages of graph paper, each with a different number of sheets, develop an algorithm to determine the best buy for your money.

21. Develop an algorithm to compute the tuition at your school.

22. Develop an algorithm to compute the amount of interest that you will earn at the end of each month over a 2-year period on an initial deposit of $1000. Use a compound interest calculation. The interest rate will be used as an input value.

23. Assume that you have just bought a car. Develop an algorithm to print a table giving the amount that you still owe at the end of each month, over the period of the payments. The initial cost of the car and the monthly payment should be input values to the algorithm.

24. Assume that you have just bought a car with a loan from your father. Develop an algorithm to compute the number of months necessary to repay the loan, assuming you pay $250 per month. Print the number of months necessary and the amount of the last payment. The cost of the car represents the input to the algorithm.

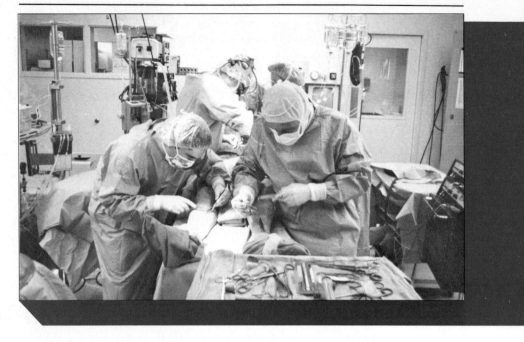

PROBLEM SOLVING — Suture Packaging

Sutures are strands or fibers used to sew living tissue together after
an injury or an operation. Packages of sutures must be sealed
carefully before they are shipped to hospitals so that contaminants
cannot enter the packages. The object that seals the package is
referred to as a sealing die. Generally, sealing dies are heated with
an electric heater. For the sealing process to be a success, the
sealing die is maintained at an established temperature and must
contact the package with a predetermined pressure for an
established time period. The time period in which the sealing die
contacts the package is called dwell. An engineering assistant in a
packaging company might be asked to write a program to analyze
the data collected during the sealing of several batches of sutures.
The information available would be the temperature, pressure, and
dwell time for each batch, along with the acceptable range of these
parameters. Write a program to generate a report analyzing the
data for batches that were rejected because the packages were not
sealed properly. (See Section 3-3 for the solution.)

Photo courtesy of Northridge Hospital Medical Center.

3

CONTROL STRUCTURES

INTRODUCTION

In Chapter 1 we wrote complete Pascal programs in which the steps were executed sequentially, one after the other. The programs read data, computed new data, and printed results. In Chapter 2 we discussed sequence, selection, and repetition structures, and we described them in pseudocode. We now want to introduce Pascal statements that will allow us to write programs with the selection and repetition structures that control the sequence of the steps that are executed. This control is achieved through *if* structures and loops. In addition to presenting the Pascal statements for these **control structures,** we also introduce a new data type, Boolean data. Boolean data is used to write conditions that can be evaluated as true or false. These conditions are then used in the *if* structures to determine which statements to execute next in the program.

Starting with this chapter, color is used in Pascal programs to highlight the new statements and new programming techniques.

3-1 *IF* STRUCTURES

In Chapter 2 we presented the pseudocode for three forms of the *if* **structure.** In this section we present the corresponding Pascal statements. All forms of the *if* structure use a condition to determine which statements to execute in the structure. Therefore, before we discuss the forms of these statements, we will discuss Boolean expressions, which are used as the conditions to be tested.

BOOLEAN EXPRESSIONS

A **Boolean expression** is analogous to an arithmetic expression in many ways, but it is always evaluated as either true or false, instead of as a number. Boolean expressions can be formed using the **relational operators** listed below:

RELATIONAL OPERATOR	INTERPRETATION
=	is equal to
<	is less than
>	is greater than
<=	is less than or equal to
>=	is greater than or equal to
<>	is less than or greater than (or not equal to)

Numeric variables can be used on both sides of the relational operators to yield a Boolean expression whose value is either true or false. For example, consider the Boolean expression in the following *if* statement (we center our interest on the Boolean expression for the moment, and then we will discuss the *if* statement in detail):

```
if   a = b   then
     count := count + 1
```

where *a* and *b* are real values. If the value of *a* is equal to the value of *b*, then the Boolean expression "a = b" is true and *count* is incremented by one. Otherwise the expression "a = b" is false and the value of *count* does not change. Similarly, if the Boolean expression "x > 3.0" in the next statement is true, then the values of *x* and *y* will be printed:

```
if   x > 3.0   then
     writeln (x,y)
```

We can also combine two Boolean expressions into a **compound Boolean expression** with the **connectors** *or* and *and*. When two Boolean expressions are joined by *or*, the entire expression is true if either or both expressions are true. It is false only when both expressions are false. When two Boolean expressions are joined by *and*, the entire expression is true only if both expressions are true. These connectors (or **Boolean operators**) can be used only with complete Boolean expressions on both sides of the connector. For example, $(a < b)$ *or* $(a < c)$ is a valid compound Boolean expression because *or* joins $a < b$ and $a < c$. However, $(a < b)$ *or c* is an invalid compound expression because *c* is a numeric variable, not a complete Boolean expression.

Boolean expressions can also be preceded by the connector *not*. This connector changes the value of the expression to the opposite value. Hence if $a > b$ is true, then *not*$(a > b)$ is false. The expression *not*$(a < b)$ is equivalent to $a >= b$.

When an expression contains Boolean operators, relational operators, and arithmetic operators, you must be very careful to ensure that the evaluation of the expression will proceed as you intend. Precedence follows this order:

1. Boolean not
2. *, /, div, mod, Boolean and
3. +, −, Boolean or
4. Relational operators

Operations on the same level are evaluated from left to right.

Because the precedence order for these combined expressions can sometimes be complicated to determine, the best solution is to use parentheses in the expression to indicate exactly how you want it evaluated. Remember that parentheses always have highest priority. Here is a group of incorrect and corrected expressions:

Incorrect Expression	Corrected Expression
$a > b$ or $c = 4.0$	$(a > b)$ or $(c = 4.0)$
not $a <= b$	not $(a <= b)$
$a + b > d + e$ or $x = y$	$(a + b > d + e)$ or $(x = y)$

We have been using relational operators in our Boolean expressions, but an even simpler form exists in Boolean variables and constants. Pascal allows us to define a **Boolean data type** in much the same way that we define integer or real data types. A Boolean constant can be defined to be either true or false. A Boolean variable can be defined in the variable section of a Pascal program and its value can be changed with the assignment statement, but it cannot be changed with an input statement.

The following statements illustrate the definition of a Boolean variable, a statement to initialize it, and a statement that uses it:

```
var
    error: boolean;
    .
    .
    .
if   temp < 85.0   then
     error := true
else
     error := false
    .
    .
    .
if   error   then
     writeln ('TEMPERATURE OUT OF BOUNDS')
```

Many of the examples in the remainder of the text will use Boolean variables because they improve the readability of programs. The syntax diagram for the variable declarations in Chapter 1 included the Boolean data type and can be referred to for the complete variable definition diagram.

IF STATEMENT

The simplest form of the *if* structure tests a condition and then performs a statement if the condition is true. The syntax diagram for this form of the *if* structure is given below:

> If Statement
>
> → if → *Boolean expression* → **then** → *statement* →

An example of this structure is:

```
if   a < b   then
     sum := sum + 1
```

If the value of *a* is less than the value of *b*, then the value of *sum* is incremented by one. If the value of *a* is greater than or equal to *b*, then control passes to whatever statement follows the *then* section of the statement in the program. The statement could be written all on one line, but to improve readability, we split the *if* statement after the Boolean condition and the word *then* and indent the remainder of the statement on the next line to clearly show that it is part of the previous line. Some other examples of *if* statements written in this manner are:

```
if   time > 1.5   then
     readln (dist)

if   den <= 0.0   then
     writeln ('DENOMINATOR = ',den)

if   -4 <> num   then
     num := num - 1
```

In many instances we would like to perform more than one statement if a Boolean expression is true. This can be done by defining a **compound statement.** A compound statement can contain any number of Pascal statements. It starts with *begin* and ends with *end.* The syntax diagram for a compound statement follows.

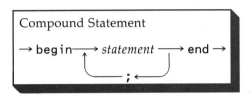

The following example contains a compound statement:

```
if   gpa >= 3.0   then
     begin
        total := total + gpa;
        honors := honors + 1
     end
```

Note that statements within the compound statement are separated from each other by a semicolon, but the last statement in the compound statement is not followed by a semicolon since it is followed by the word *end.*

We can also include an *if* statement within an *if* statement. Consider the following statements:

```
if   gpa >= 3.0   then
     begin
        writeln ('HONOR ROLL');
        if   gpa > 3.5   then
           writeln ('PRESIDENT''S LIST')
     end
```

If the GPA is less than 3.0, the entire construction is skipped. If the GPA is between 3.0 and 3.5, only HONOR ROLL is printed. If the GPA is greater than 3.5, then HONOR ROLL is printed, followed on the next line by PRESIDENT'S LIST. Note the two consecutive single quote marks in the constant in the last *writeln* statement. If we want to include a single quote mark in a character constant, we must include two single quote marks (not a double quote mark) in the constant. The compiler will interpret them as a single quote mark in the constant.

IF-ELSE STATEMENT

The *if-else* statement implements another form of the *if* structure. It allows us to execute one statement if the condition is true and a different statement if the condition is false. Remember that any time a statement is included as part of the instruction, it could also be a compound statement. The following syntax diagram shows the general structure of this statement.

> If-Else Statement
>
> → if → *Boolean expression* → then → *statement* → else → *statement* →

For readability, we will split the statement so that the statement executed when the Boolean expression is true is indented and listed on a separate line, and the statement executed when the Boolean expression is not true is also indented and listed on a separate line.

EXAMPLE 3-1   Velocity Computation

Give the statements for calculating the velocity of a cable car. The variable d in the equations below represents the distance of the cable car from the nearest tower. If the cable car is within 30 feet of the tower (including exactly 30 feet from the tower), use this equation:

$$velocity = 2.425 + 0.00175 \cdot d^2 \text{ ft/sec}$$

If the cable car is more than 30 feet from the tower, use this equation:

$$velocity = 0.625 + 0.12 \cdot d - 0.00025 \cdot d^2 \text{ ft/sec}$$

Correct Solution

```
if  distance <= 30.0   then
    velocity := 2.425 + 0.00175*distance*distance
else
    velocity := 0.625 + 0.12*distance -
                0.00025*distance*distance
```

Incorrect Solution

```
if  distance <= 30.0   then
    velocity := 2.425 + 0.00175*distance*distance;
velocity := 0.625 + 0.12*distance -
            0.00025*distance*distance
```

This incorrect solution points out a very common error. Let us follow the execution of the statements to find the error. Suppose *distance* is greater than 30. Then the first logical expression is false, and we therefore proceed to the next statement to calculate *velocity*. This part works fine. But now suppose the logical expression is true; that is, *distance* is less than or equal to 30. We execute the assignment statement in the *if* statement, correctly calculating *velocity* when *distance* is less than or equal to 30. But the next statement that is executed is the other assignment statement, which replaces the correct value of *velocity* with an incorrect value.

When we **nest** several levels of *if-else* statements, it may be difficult to determine which conditions must be true (or false) to execute a specific statement. In these cases, we can implement the *if-else-if* structure with nested *if-else* statements. Thus we are not adding another Pascal statement, but use statements already presented in order to develop the *if-else-if* structure. To match the pseudocode forms that we used in Chapter 2, we also modify the indenting scheme used in the *if-else* statement, as shown in the next example.

EXAMPLE 3-2   Weight Category

An analysis of a group of weight measurements involves converting a weight value into an integer category number that is determined as follows:

CATEGORY	WEIGHT (POUNDS)
1	weight $\leq$ 50.0
2	50.0 $<$ weight $\leq$ 125.0
3	125.0 $<$ weight $\leq$ 200.0
4	200.0 $<$ weight

Write Pascal statements that put the correct value (1, 2, 3, or 4) into *category* based on the value of *weight*. Assume that *category* is an integer variable.

Solution 1

```
if  weight <= 50.0   then
    category := 1
else
    if  weight <= 125.0   then
       category = 2
    else
       if  weight <= 200.0   then
          category := 3
       else
          category := 4
```

This solution uses nested *if-else* statements. In the next solution, we modify the indenting in these nested statements to implement the *if-else-if* structure.

Solution 2

```
if  weight <= 50.0   then
    category := 1
else if  weight <= 125.0   then
    category := 2
else if  weight <= 200.0   then
    category := 3
else
    category := 4
```

In general, solutions in the form of Solution 2 are easier to read and thus are preferable.

The order of the conditions is important in both solutions because the evaluation will stop as soon as a true condition has been encountered. Changing the order of the conditions and the category assignments can cause the category to be set incorrectly.

SELF-TEST 3-1

This self-test allows you to check quickly to see if you have remembered some of the key points from Section 3-1. If you have any problems with the exercises, you should reread this section. The solutions are included at the end of the text.

For problems 1–8, use the values given below to determine whether the following Boolean expressions are true or false.

$$a = 5.5 \qquad b = 1.5 \qquad i = -3 \qquad done = false$$

1. $a < 10.0$
2. $a + b >= 6.5$
3. $i <> 0$
4. $b - 1.0 > a$
5. not $(a < 3.0*b)$
6. $-i <= i + 6$
7. $(a < 10.0)$ and $(a > 5.0)$
8. $(abs(i) > 3)$ or done

For problems 9–14, give Pascal statements that perform the steps indicated.

9. If *time* is greater than 15.0, increment *time* by 1.0.
10. When the square root of *poly* is less than 0.5, print the value of *poly*.
11. If the difference between *volt1* and *volt2* is larger than 10.0, print the values of *volt1* and *volt2*.
12. If the value of *den* is less than 0.005, print the message DENOMINATOR IS TOO SMALL.
13. If the logarithm of *x* is greater than or equal to 3, set *time* equal to zero and increment *count* by 1.
14. If *distance* is less than 50.0 and *time* is greater than 10.0, increment *time* by 0.05; otherwise increment *time* by 2.0.

3-2 *WHILE* LOOPS

The *while* loop is an important structure for repeating a set of statements as long as a certain condition is true. The syntax diagram for a *while* loop, or a *while* statement, follows.

> While Statement
> → **while** → *Boolean expression* → **do** → *statement* →

If the condition is true, the statement (which may be a compound statement and thus could contain several instructions) is executed. After executing the statement, the Boolean expression or condition is retested. If the condition is still true, the statement is reexecuted. When the condition is false, execution continues with the statement following the *while* loop. The variables modified in the group of statements in the *while* loop must involve the variables tested in the loop's condition, or the value of the condition will never change.

We are now ready to write programs for some of the algorithms we developed in Chapter 2.

EXAMPLE 3-3   Average of a Set of Data Values

In Example 2-1 we developed the decomposition and pseudocode for an algorithm to compute the average of a set of data values. The decomposition and pseudocode are presented again below:

DECOMPOSITION

| Read, sum, and count the data values. |
| Divide the sum by the number of data values. |
| Write the average. |

Recall that a data value of zero is used to tell us when all the data values have been read.

PSEUDOCODE FOR THE ALGORITHM FOR COMPUTING AN AVERAGE

```
compute: sum ← 0
         count ← 0
         read a data value
         while the data value is not zero do
             sum ← sum + data value
             count ← count + 1
             read the next data value
         average ← sum/count
         write 'AVERAGE =', average
```

Convert this pseudocode into a Pascal program.

Solution 1

We have covered the Pascal statements for the *if* structures and for the *while* loop. Using these statements, we can translate each step in the pseudocode into Pascal. This Pascal program was presented in Section 2-1 as an example of a complete program, even though we had not discussed all the pieces at that time.

PASCAL PROGRAM

```
{- - - - - - - - - - - - - - - - - - - - - - - - - - - - - - - - - - - - - - - - - - - - - -}
program  compute (input,output);
    {This program computes the average of
    a set of experimental data values.}
var
    x, sum, average: real;
    count: integer;
begin
    sum := 0.0;
    count := 0;
    readln (x);
    while  x <> 0.0   do
        begin
            sum := sum + x;
            count := count + 1;
            readln (x)
        end;
    average := sum/count;
    writeln ('THE AVERAGE TEMPERATURE IS ',average:6:2,
             ' DEGREES FAHRENHEIT')
end.
{- - - - - - - - - - - - - - - - - - - - - - - - - - - - - - - - - - - - - - - - - - - - - -}
```

Solution 2

Another Pascal solution is included here to show the use of a Boolean variable to control the *while* loop. The Boolean variable is named *done*. We determine the value of *done* after reading a data value. If the data value is zero, then the variable is given a value of true; if the data value is not zero, then the variable is given a value of false. The condition used in the *while* loop is the Boolean expression *not done*. When the condition is true (*done* is false), we stay in the loop; when the condition is false (*done* is true), we exit the loop.

PASCAL PROGRAM

```
{--------------------------------------------------------}
program   compute (input,output);
    {This program computes the average of
    a set of experimental data values.}
var
    x, sum, average: real;
    count: integer;
    done: boolean;
begin
    sum := 0.0;
    count := 0;
    readln (x);
    if   x <> 0.0   then
        done := false
    else
        done := true;
    while   not done   do
        begin
            sum := sum + x;
            count := count + 1;
            readln (x);
            if   x <> 0.0   then
                done := false
            else
                done := true
        end;
    average := sum/count;
    writeln ('THE AVERAGE TEMPERATURE IS ',average:6:2,
             ' DEGREES FAHRENHEIT')
end.
{--------------------------------------------------------}
```

EXAMPLE 3-4   Experimental Data Analysis

In Example 2-2 we developed the decomposition and pseudocode for the
algorithm to analyze a set of experimental data values, determine the
minimum and maximum values, and compute the range of data values.
This decomposition and pseudocode is repeated again:

DECOMPOSITION

| Read data values and determine maximum and minimum values. |
| Subtract minimum value from maximum value to get range. |
| Write maximum, minimum, range. |

    range1: read data value
            maximum ← data value
            minimum ← data value
            while data value is not zero do
                if data value > maximum then
                    maximum ← data value
                if data value < minimum then
                    minimum ← data value
                read a data value
            range ← maximum − minimum
            write 'MAXIMUM DATA VALUE = ', maximum
            write 'MINIMUM DATA VALUE = ', minimum
            write 'RANGE OF VALUES = ', range

Convert this pseudocode into a Pascal program.

Solution

Again, using the statements presented in this chapter for the *if* structure and the *while* loop, we can convert each step of the pseudocode into Pascal.

Pascal Program

```
{-----------------------------------------------------------}
program  range1 (input,output);
    {This program determines the maximum, minimum, and
    range for a set of experimental data values.}
var
    x, max, min, range: real;
begin
    readln (x);
    max := x;
    min := x;
    while  x <> 0.0  do
        begin
            if  x > max  then
                max := x;
            if  x < min  then
                min := x;
            readln (x)
        end;
    range := max - min;
    writeln ('MAXIMUM DATA VALUE = ',max:8:2);
    writeln ('MINIMUM DATA VALUE = ',min:8:2);
    writeln ('RANGE OF VALUES = ',range:8:2)
end.
{-----------------------------------------------------------}
```

If we use the sample data from Example 2-2, the output is

```
MAXIMUM DATA VALUE =     66.31
MINIMUM DATA VALUE =     40.56
RANGE OF VALUES =    25.75
```

EXAMPLE 3-5   Degree To Radian Conversion

In Section 2-6 we developed the decomposition and pseudocode for the algorithm to convert degrees to radians and print the conversion information in a table. This decomposition and pseudocode are repeated again:

DECOMPOSITION

Write report heading.
Write conversion table.

REFINEMENT IN PSEUDOCODE

```
table: write report heading
        degrees ← 0.0
        count ← 0
        while count < 37 do
            radians ← degrees * 0.01745
            write degrees, radians
            degrees ← degrees + 10.0
            count ← count + 1
```

Convert this pseudocode into a Pascal program.

Solution

Using the *while* loop presented in this chapter, we can convert each step of the pseudocode into Pascal.

PASCAL PROGRAM

```
{----------------------------------------------------------}
program   table (output);
   {This program generates table that converts degrees
   to radians, ranging from 0 degrees to 360 degrees.}
const
   scale = 0.01745;
var
   degrees, radians: real;
   count: integer;
begin
   writeln ('   CONVERSION TABLE');
   writeln ('DEGREES          RADIANS');
   degrees := 0.0;
   count := 0;
   while  count < 37   do
      begin
         radians := degrees*scale;
         writeln (degrees:7:2,' ':8,radians:7:4);
         degrees := degrees + 10.0;
         count := count + 1
      end
end.
{----------------------------------------------------------}
```

There are several things to note in this solution. First, since there was no input, the program statement did not list the file *input*. Second, the scaling factor to convert degrees to radians was defined as a constant. Finally, we used a character constant of blanks to separate the two values in the output line. Using blanks within a line or using blank lines in the output is a simple way to help make our output more readable. The output is as shown:

```
           CONVERSION TABLE
           DEGREES          RADIANS
              0.00           0.0000
             10.00           0.1745
             20.00           0.3490
                .
                .
                .
            340.00           5.9330
            350.00           6.1075
            360.00           6.2820
```

3-3 PROBLEM SOLVING—SUTURE PACKAGING

As we mentioned in the introductory problem for this chapter, sutures are strands or fibers used to sew living tissue together after an injury or an operation. Packages of sutures must be sealed carefully before they are shipped to hospitals so that contaminants cannot enter the packages. The object that seals the package is referred to as a sealing die. Generally, sealing dies are heated with an electric heater. For the sealing process to be a success, the sealing die is maintained at an established temperature and must contact the package with a predetermined pressure for an established time period. The time period in which the sealing die contacts the package is called dwell. We want to develop an algorithm and a Pascal program to analyze the data collected on batches of sutures that have been rejected. We assume that we will be given the temperature, pressure, and dwell time for each batch. For the sutures that have been sealed, the following acceptable range of parameters has been established:

Temperature: 150.0 – 170.0 degrees centigrade
Pressure: 60 – 70 psi (lb/sq in)
Dwell: 2.0 – 2.5 seconds

All sutures in a batch will be rejected if all these conditions are not met.

Our program will ask the user to enter the batch code, temperature, pressure, and dwell time for each batch that has been rejected during some time period. We want to collect data on the reasons why the batches were rejected to attempt to find the underlying problem. For example, if most of the rejections were due to temperature problems, then we need to check the electric heater in the sealing die. If most of the rejections were due to pressure problems, then we need to check the pressure in the air cylinder that lowers the die to the package. Or, if most of the rejections were due to dwell time, then the control information in the sealing die may be in error. Clearly, the first step in locating the source of the problem must be to get a good analysis of the data from rejected batches of sutures. The data we will compute in this program will be the percentage of rejections due to temperature, the percentage of rejections due to pressure, and the percentage of rejections due to dwell time. If a batch was rejected for more than one reason, it should be counted in the total for each rejection category.

We now use our five-phase design process to develop an algorithm and a Pascal solution to this problem.

PROBLEM STATEMENT

Write a program to print a report analyzing the information for all batches of sutures that were not properly sealed, where a proper seal requires the following range of parameters in the sealing process:

Temperature: 150.0–170.0 degrees centigrade
Pressure: 60–70 psi (lb/sq in)
Dwell: 2.0–2.5 seconds

INPUT/OUTPUT DESCRIPTION

The input to the program will be four values for each batch that was rejected: the batch number, the temperature, the pressure, and the dwell time. A negative batch number indicates the end of the data. The output from the program will be a report giving the percentages of the batches rejected because of temperature problems, pressure problems, and dwell time problems.

HAND EXAMPLE

Assume the following data represents the information on the batches rejected during one day:

BATCH NUMBER	TEMPERATURE	PRESSURE	DWELL TIME
24551	145.5	62.3	2.13
24582	153.7	63.0	2.52
26553	160.3	58.9	2.51
26623	159.5	58.9	2.01
26624	160.5	61.3	1.98

In this data, batch 24551 was rejected because of temperature, batch 24582 was rejected because of dwell time, batch 26553 was rejected because of pressure and dwell time, batch 26623 was rejected due to pressure, and batch 26624 was rejected due to dwell time. The report summarizing this information is the following:

```
        SUMMARY OF BATCH REJECT INFORMATION

        20.00 % REJECTED DUE TO TEMPERATURE
        40.00 % REJECTED DUE TO PRESSURE
        60.00 % REJECTED DUE TO DWELL TIME
```

ALGORITHM DEVELOPMENT

The decomposition contains the following sequential steps:

DECOMPOSITION

Read data and collect information.
Write report.

Using the hand-worked example solution as a guide, we can develop the initial pseudocode for this problem.

INITIAL REFINEMENT IN PSEUDOCODE

seals: count ← 0
       read batch, temperature, pressure, dwell
       while batch ≥ 0 do
           determine reject reason and add to totals
           count ← count + 1
           read batch, temperature, pressure, dwell
       convert totals to percentages
       write report

We still need to refine the step further to determine which parameters were not within the specified values, and then add to the corresponding totals. This involves three different tests: one for the temperature, one for the pressure, and one for the dwell time. We will call the rejection totals *rejectt* (for rejections due to temperature), *rejectp* (for rejections due to pressure), and *rejectd* (for rejections due to dwell time). The final refinement in pseudocode is:

FINAL REFINEMENT IN PSEUDOCODE

seals: count ← 0
       rejectt ← 0
       rejectp ← 0
       rejectd ← 0
       read batch, temperature, pressure, dwell
       while batch ≥ 0 do
          if temperature out of bounds then
            rejectt ← rejectt + 1
          if pressure out of bounds then
            rejectp ← rejectp + 1
          if dwell out of bounds then
            rejectd ← rejectd + 1
          count ← count + 1
          read batch, temperature, pressure, dwell
       convert reject totals to percentages
       write report

We now convert the pseudocode steps to Pascal.

```
{-------------------------------------------------------------}
program  seals (input,output);
    {This program analyzes data on batches of sutures that have
    not been properly sealed, and then writes a report.}
var
    temperature, pressure, dwell, perct, percp, percd: real;
    batch, count, rejectt, rejectp, rejectd: integer;
begin
    count := 0;
    rejectt := 0;
    rejectp := 0;
    rejectd := 0;

    writeln ('ENTER BATCH NUMBER, TEMPERATURE, PRESSURE, DWELL');
    writeln ('FOR BATCHES THAT HAVE BEEN REJECTED');
    writeln ('(NEGATIVE BATCH NUMBER TO STOP)');
    readln (batch,temperature,pressure,dwell);

    while  batch >= 0   do
       begin
          if  (temperature < 150.0) or (temperature > 170.0)   then
             rejectt := rejectt + 1;
          if (pressure < 60.0) or (pressure > 70.0)   then
             rejectp := rejectp + 1;
          if (dwell < 2.0) or (dwell > 2.5)   then
             rejectd := rejectd + 1;
          count := count + 1;
          writeln ('ENTER NEXT SET OF DATA');
          readln (batch,temperature,pressure,dwell)
       end;
    percp := rejectp/count*100.0;
    perct := rejectt/count*100.0;
    percd := rejectd/count*100.0;

    writeln;
    writeln ('SUMMARY OF BATCH REJECT INFORMATION');
    writeln;
    writeln (perct:6:2,' % REJECTED DUE TO TEMPERATURE');
    writeln (percp:6:2,' % REJECTED DUE TO PRESSURE');
    writeln (percd:6:2,' % REJECTED DUE TO DWELL TIME')
end.
{-------------------------------------------------------------}
```

TESTING

The output of this program from the data used in the hand example is:

```
SUMMARY OF BATCH REJECT INFORMATION

20.00 % REJECTED DUE TO TEMPERATURE
40.00 % REJECTED DUE TO PRESSURE
60.00 % REJECTED DUE TO DWELL TIME
```

3-4 *FOR* LOOPS

A special case of the *while* loop is the counting loop. Implementing a counting loop generally involves initializing a counter before entering the loop, modifying the counter within the loop, and exiting the loop when the counter reaches a specified value. Thus, counting loops are executed a specified number of times. The three steps (initialize, modify, and test) can be incorporated with a *while* loop as we have already seen, but they still require three different statements. A special statement, the *for* statement, combines all three steps into one. Using the *for* statement to construct a loop results in a structure called a *for* **loop.**

FOR STATEMENT

The syntax diagram of the *for* statement is:

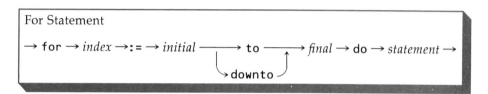

For Statement

$$\rightarrow \texttt{for} \rightarrow index \rightarrow \texttt{:=} \rightarrow initial \longrightarrow \texttt{to} \longrightarrow final \rightarrow \texttt{do} \rightarrow statement \rightarrow$$
$$\hookrightarrow \texttt{downto} \hookrightarrow$$

The index is a variable used as the loop counter. *Initial* represents the initial value given to the loop counter. *Final* represents the value used to determine when the *for* loop has been completed. The loop counter is incremented by 1 after executing the loop if *to* is selected, or decremented by 1 after executing the loop if *downto* is selected. The *for* loop will not be executed at all if the initial value is greater than the final value when the loop increment is 1, or if the initial value is less than the final value when the loop decrement is 1. Before we list all the rules that must be followed when using a *for* loop, we will look at a simple example.

EXAMPLE 3-6   Integer Sum

The sum of the integers 1 through 50 is represented mathematically as

$$\sum_{i=1}^{50} i = 1 + 2 + \ldots + 49 + 50$$

Obviously we do not want to write one long assignment statement of the form:

```
sum := 1 + 2 + 3 + 4 + 5 + ... + 50
```

A better solution is to build a loop that executes 50 times and adds a number to the sum each time through the loop.

While **Loop Solution**

```
var
    sum, number: integer;
    .
    .
    .
    sum := 0;
    number := 1;
    while  number <= 50   do
        begin
            sum := sum + number;
            number := number + 1
        end
```

For **Loop Solution**

```
var
    sum, number: integer;
    .
    .
    .
    sum := 0;
    for number := 1 to 50 do
        sum := sum + number
```

The *for* statement initializes the variable *number* to 1. After executing the loop (which consists of adding *number* to *sum*), *number* is automatically incremented by 1, and the process repeats until *number* exceeds 50. Comparing the *for* loop solution with the *while* loop solution, we see that the *for* loop is shorter, but that both compute the same value for *sum*.

Now that you have seen a *for* loop in a simple example, we will summarize the general rules to be followed when building a *for* loop:

1. The index or loop control variable may not be changed within the loop. However, you may use its value to calculate another value. You may also want to print its value.
2. The index can be incremented by one or decremented by one, each time through the loop. If a different increment is desired, you can use an additional variable and modify it within the loop, or you may want to use a *while* loop.
3. The index cannot be a real variable. For now, we will use only integer variables, but later in the text we will define ordinal variables. The index can be any ordinal type; integers are one example of this type.
4. The index is undefined after the loop is executed. If you need a variable set to the last value of the index, you will have to assign it in a separate statement within the loop.
5. Under certain conditions, a *for* loop may not be executed at all. For example, consider this loop:

```
for i := 5 downto 10 do
    x := x + 1
```

The *downto* selection causes the index i to decrement by 1. However, if we decrement the value of i starting with 5, we never reach the value 10. Therefore, this loop is not executed. If the initial and the final values are the same, the loop will be executed once.

6. The number of times a *for* loop will be executed, assuming that it will be executed at least once, can be computed as follows:

$$|\text{final} - \text{initial}| + 1$$

Thus, if we had a *for* loop such as:

```
for num := 5 to 83 do
     writeln (num)
```

it would be executed $|83 - 5| + 1$, or 79, times. This same equation is valid for incrementing loops and decrementing loops.

Now that we have summarized the rules for building and executing *for* loops, we will look at a number of examples illustrating these rules.

EXAMPLE 3-7   Polynomial Model with Integer Time

Polynomials are often used to model data and experimental results. Assume that the polynomial

$$3t^2 + 4.5$$

models the results of an experiment where t represents time in seconds. Write a complete program to evaluate this polynomial for the period of time from 1 second to 10 seconds in increments of 1 second (i.e., let time $= 1, 2, 3, 4, 5, 6, 7, 8, 9,$ and 10). For each value of time, print the time and the polynomial value.

Solution

The solution to this problem requires printing the headings of the report and a counting loop to evaluate the polynomial.

DECOMPOSITION

Write headings.
Write report.

Refining the "Write report" step into a counting loop yields the following pseudocode.

REFINEMENT IN PSEUDOCODE

```
poly1: write headings
       for time = 1 to 10 do
           poly ← 3*time*time + 4.5
           write time, poly
```

We now convert the pseudocode into a Pascal program.

PASCAL PROGRAM

```
{----------------------------------------------------------}
program  poly1 (output);
   {This program prints values for a polynomial.}
var
   poly: real;
   time: integer;
begin
   writeln ('POLYNOMIAL MODEL');
   writeln ('TIME     POLYNOMIAL');
   writeln ('(SEC)');
   for time := 1 to 10 do
      begin
         poly := 3.0*time*time + 4.5;
         writeln (time:4,poly:12:2)
      end
end.
{----------------------------------------------------------}
```

The output from this program is:

```
POLYNOMIAL MODEL
TIME      POLYNOMIAL
(SEC)
   1          7.50
   2         16.50
   3         31.50
   4         52.50
   5         79.50
   6        112.50
   7        151.50
   8        196.50
   9        247.50
  10        304.50
```

EXAMPLE 3-8   Polynomial Model with Real Time

We again assume that the polynomial

$$3t^2 + 4.5$$

models an experiment where t represents time in seconds. Write a program to evaluate this polynomial for time beginning at zero seconds and ending at 5 seconds in increments of 0.5 seconds.

Solution

The solution to this problem requires printing the headings of the report and a loop to evaluate the polynomial and print the report. Thus, the decomposition is the same as in the previous problem.

Write headings.
Write report.

Since the time variable needs to increment by 0.5 in this example, we could return to the *while* loop to implement it. However, we can also use the index in the *for* loop as a counter for the number of times to execute the loop, and then compute the correct time value inside the loop. This means that we have to determine the total number of times to execute the loop, and also increment the time variable within the loop. In our specific example, the time variable is to begin at zero seconds, increment by 0.5 seconds, and end at 5 seconds. The total number of values of time that we are interested in is 11 (don't forget to count time equal to zero). Thus, our refinement of the decomposition is the following:

REFINEMENT IN PSEUDOCODE

```
poly2: write headings
       time ← 0.0
       for count = 1 to 11 do
           poly ← 3*time*time + 4.5
           write time, poly
           time ← time + 0.5
```

Converting the pseudocode into Pascal gives the following program:

PASCAL PROGRAM

```
{----------------------------------------------------------}
program  poly2 (output);
   {This program prints values for a polynomial.}
var
   time, poly: real;
   count: integer;
begin
   writeln ('POLYNOMIAL MODEL');
   writeln ('TIME     POLYNOMIAL');
   writeln ('(SEC)');
   time := 0.0;
   for count := 1 to 11 do
      begin
         poly := 3.0*time*time + 4.5;
         writeln (time:3:1,poly:12:2);
         time := time + 0.5
      end
end.
{----------------------------------------------------------}
```

The output from this program is:

```
POLYNOMIAL MODEL
TIME      POLYNOMIAL
(SEC)
0.0          4.50
0.5          5.25
1.0          7.50
1.5         11.25
2.0         16.50
2.5         23.25
3.0         31.50
3.5         41.25
4.0         52.50
4.5         65.25
5.0         79.50
```

EXAMPLE 3-9   Polynomial Model with Variable Time

Assume that we want to evaluate the same polynomial

$$3t^2 + 4.5$$

beginning at t equal to zero, in increments of 0.25 seconds, for a variable number of seconds. Write a program to read an integer that represents the number of seconds to be used for evaluating the polynomial. Then print the corresponding table.

Solution 1

The solution to this problem requires reading the number of seconds that the report is supposed to cover, writing the headings of the report, and writing a loop to evaluate the polynomial and write the report. Thus, the decomposition is similar to the one in the previous problems.

DECOMPOSITION

Read number of seconds.
Write headings.
Write report.

As we refine the steps for writing the report, we need a loop. The number of times that the loop should execute depends on the number of seconds read from the terminal. Once we have read the number of seconds, we can compute the number of times to execute the loop using the following equation:

loop count ← number of seconds · 4 + 1

We multiplied the number of seconds by 4 since the increment is 0.25 seconds (one-fourth second) and added 1 since we start the report at zero seconds. The pseudocode for this problem solution is:

REFINEMENT IN PSEUDOCODE

> poly3: read seconds
>   write headings
>   maxcount ← seconds*4 + 1
>   time ← 0.0
>   for count = 1 to maxcount do
>   poly ← 3*time*time + 4.5
>   write time, poly
>   time ← time + 0.5

Converting the pseudocode into Pascal gives the following program:

PASCAL PROGRAM

```
{----------------------------------------------------------}
program  poly3 (input,output);
   {This program prints values for a polynomial.}
var
   time, poly: real;
   count, seconds, maxcount: integer;
begin
   writeln ('ENTER NUMBER OF SECONDS');
   readln (seconds);
   writeln;
   writeln ('POLYNOMIAL MODEL');
   writeln ('TIME     POLYNOMIAL');
   writeln ('(SEC)');
   maxcount := 4*seconds + 1;
   time := 0.0;
   for count := 1 to maxcount do
      begin
         poly := 3.0*time*time + 4.5;
         writeln (time:4:2,poly:12:4);
         time := time + 0.25
      end
end.
{----------------------------------------------------------}
```

If we enter the value 3 for the number of seconds, the output from this program is:

```
ENTER NUMBER OF SECONDS
3

POLYNOMIAL MODEL
TIME      POLYNOMIAL
(SEC)
0.00       4.5000
0.25       4.6875
0.50       5.2500
0.75       6.1875
1.00       7.5000
1.25       9.1875
1.50      11.2500
1.75      13.6875
2.00      16.5000
2.25      19.6875
2.50      23.2500
2.75      27.1875
3.00      31.5000
```

There are several things to note about the program and its output. For example, we asked the user to enter the number of seconds before we wrote the heading. Otherwise, the heading would be separated from the rest of the report by the interaction with the user to get the number of seconds for the table. Also, notice that a single *writeln* statement produced a blank line in the output in order to separate the heading from the number of seconds entered by the user.

Solution 2

We now solve this example with a *while* loop so that we can compare the two solutions. Once a solution begins to deviate from the standard *for* loop form, you may find that the *while* loop is more readable.

```
{--------------------------------------------------------}
program  poly4 (input,output);
   {This program prints values for a polynomial.}
var
   time, poly: real;
   seconds: integer;
begin
   writeln ('ENTER NUMBER OF SECONDS');
   readln (seconds);
   writeln;
   writeln ('POLYNOMIAL MODEL');
   writeln ('TIME     POLYNOMIAL');
   writeln ('SEC');
   time := 0.0;
   while  time <= seconds  do
      begin
         poly := 3.0*time*time + 4.5;
         writeln (time:4:2,poly:12:4);
         time := time + 0.25
      end
end.
{--------------------------------------------------------}
```

This program generates the same output as Solution 1; thus it is an equivalent solution.

One caution needs to be considered when you use *while* loops and *if* statements. In the previous example, we add 0.25 to the variable *time* each time through the loop. When we use fractional values in the computer, the values may often differ slightly from what we expect because of the limits imposed by the computer hardware itself. Thus, instead of adding 0.25, we may be adding 0.2499999. This slight difference can cause errors in the programs if we look for a value of time equal to 3.000000, because the value may go from 2.999999 to 3.249998, never exactly equaling 3.000000. The solution is simple, and illustrated in this Pascal program: use a condition in the *while* statement that checks for *time* <= *seconds*, instead of a condition that checks for *time* <> *seconds*. In general, if you are looking for a specific real value, you may want to write the condition test to look for a small interval around the value, as illustrated in the following *if* statement:

```
if  abs(sum - 50.0) < 0.01  then ...
```

In this statement, if *sum* is between 49.99 and 50.01, the condition will be true and the rest of the *if* statement will execute.

NESTED *FOR* LOOPS

For loops may be independent of each other, or they may be nested within other *for* loops. If loops are nested, they must use different indices or loop counters. When one loop is nested within another, the inside loop executes each pass through the outer loop. To see this, consider the following program:

```
{-----------------------------------------------------------------}
program  nest (output);
   {This program prints the indices in nested for loops.}
var
   i, j: integer;
begin
   writeln ('I    J');
   writeln;
   for i := 1 to 5 do
      begin
         for j := 3 downto 1 do
            writeln (i:1,j:4);
         writeln ('END OF PASS')
      end
end.
{-----------------------------------------------------------------}
```

The output from this program is:

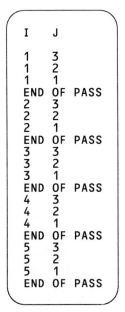

```
I    J

1    3
1    2
1    1
END OF PASS
2    3
2    2
2    1
END OF PASS
3    3
3    2
3    1
END OF PASS
4    3
4    2
4    1
END OF PASS
5    3
5    2
5    1
END OF PASS
```

The first time through the outer loop, i is initialized to the value 1. We thus begin executing the inner loop, and the variable j is initialized to the value 3. After executing the *writeln* statement with i and j listed as variables, we reach the end of the inner loop and j is decremented by 1 to the value 2. Because 2 is still larger than the final value of 1, we repeat the inner loop. Again j is decremented by 1 to the value 1, and the inner loop is repeated again. When j is decremented again, it is less than the final value of 1, so we have completed the inner loop and the message 'END OF PASS' is written. Now i is incremented to 2, and we begin the inner loop again. This process is repeated until i is greater than 5.

EXAMPLE 3-10   Experimental Sums

Write a program to read 20 data values. Compute the sum of the first 5 values, the next 5 values, and so on. Print the four sums. Assume that the values are real.

Solution

Although we will read a total of 20 data values, we need only 5 at a time; thus, an outer loop is needed to read 4 sets of data. Each set of data is 5 values; thus, the inner loop reads the 5 values. It is important to initialize to zero the variable being used to store the sum before the inner loop begins. We add 5 values, write the sum, and then set the sum back to zero before we read the next 5 values.

The decomposition is a single step in this problem; all the other steps are performed inside the overall loop.

DECOMPOSITION

Write report.

The refinement in pseudocode illustrates the structure of this algorithm, which is a loop within a loop.

REFINEMENT IN PSEUDOCODE

> sums: for i = 1 to 4 do
>   sum ← 0
>   for j = 1 to 5 do
>   read data value
>   sum ← sum + data value
>   write sum

We can now translate the pseudocode into Pascal.

PASCAL PROGRAM

```
{- - - - - - - - - - - - - - - - - - - - - - - - - - - - - - - - - - - - - - - - - - - - - -}
program  sums (input,output);
    {This program reads 20 values and prints
    the sum of each group of 5 values.}
var
    value, sum: real;
    i, j: integer;
begin
    for i := 1 to 4 do
        begin
            sum := 0.0;
            for j := 1 to 5 do
                begin
                    readln (value);
                    sum := sum + value
                end;
            writeln ('SUM ',i:1,' = ',sum:6:2)
        end
end.
{- - - - - - - - - - - - - - - - - - - - - - - - - - - - - - - - - - - - - - - - - - - - - -}
```

Here is a sample of the type of output that would be printed from this program:

```
SUM 1 =  23.44
SUM 2 =  10.23
SUM 3 =  -5.69
SUM 4 =   1.01
```

EXAMPLE 3-11   Factorial Computation

Write a program to compute the factorial of an integer. A few factorials and their corresponding values are shown below (an exclamation point after a number symbolizes a factorial):

$$0! = 1 \qquad\qquad = \quad 1$$
$$1! = 1 \qquad\qquad = \quad 1$$
$$2! = 2 \cdot 1 \qquad\qquad = \quad 2$$
$$3! = 3 \cdot 2 \cdot 1 \qquad\quad = \quad 6$$
$$4! = 4 \cdot 3 \cdot 2 \cdot 1 \quad = \quad 24$$
$$5! = 5 \cdot 4 \cdot 3 \cdot 2 \cdot 1 = 120$$

Compute and print the factorial for four different values that are read from the terminal. (We will see this problem again in Chapter 6 when we discuss recursion.)

Solution

Because the factorial of a negative number is not defined, we should include an error check for this condition in the algorithm. In computing a factorial, we use a *for* loop to perform the successive multiplications. Because the overall structure of this problem solution is a loop, the decomposition is again a single step.

DECOMPOSITION

Write report.

As you read the pseudocode refinement, notice that the overall structure of the algorithm is a counting loop. Within the counting loop is an input statement and an *if-else* structure. Within the *else* portion is another counting loop.

REFINEMENT IN PSEUDOCODE

```
factorial: for i = 1 to 4 do
              read n
              if n < 0 then
                 write error message
              else
                 nfactorial ← 1
                 for k = 2 to n do
                    nfactorial ← nfactorial*k
                 write n, nfactorial
```

Note that we first set *nfactorial* equal to one. Then, when *n* is equal to zero or 1, the *for* loop has an initial value of 2, which is greater than *n*, and the *for* loop will be skipped in this situation.

Converting the refined pseudocode into Pascal gives the following program:

PASCAL PROGRAM

```
{------------------------------------------------------------}
program  factorial (input,output);
    {This program computes the factorial
    of four values read from the terminal.}
var
    n, nfactorial, i, k: integer;
begin
    for i := 1 to 4 do
        begin
            writeln ('ENTER N');
            readln (n);
            if  n < 0  then
                writeln ('INVALID N = ',n:4)
            else
                begin
                    nfactorial := 1;
                    for k := 2 to n do
                        nfactorial := nfactorial*k;
                    writeln (n:4,'! = ',nfactorial:6)
                end
        end
end.
{------------------------------------------------------------}
```

The output from a sample run of this program is:

```
ENTER N
3
    3! =          6
ENTER N
-2
INVALID N =    -2
ENTER N
11
   11! = 39916800
ENTER N
0
    0! =          1
```

Note that a large value for *n* will cause an execution error because the value for *n*! will exceed the range for integers.

This self-test allows you to check quickly to see if you have remembered some of the key points from Section 3-4. If you have any problems with the exercises, you should reread this section. The solutions are included at the end of the text.

In problems 1–6, determine the number of times that the statement in the *for* loop will be executed.

1. for num := 3 to 20 do
       statement
2. for count := -2 to 14 do
       statement
3. for k := -2 downto -10 do
       statement
4. for time := 10 downto 0 do
       statement
5. for time := 10 to 5 do
       statement
6. for index := 314 downto -52 do
       statement

For problems 7–14, give the value in *count* after each of the following loops is executed. Assume that *count* is initialized to zero before starting each problem.

7. for i := 1 to 10 do
       count := count + 1
8. for k := 1 to 10 do
       count := count + k
9. for index := -2 to 2 do
       count := count + index
10. for num := 5 downto 0 do
       count := count - num
11. for m := 5 to 5 do
       count := count*m
12. for i := 1 to 5 do
       for k := 2 downto 0 do
           count := 100
13. for i := 5 to 8 do
       for k := -2 to 1 do
           count := count + 1
14. for i := 2 downto 0 do
       for k := 2 downto 0 do
           count := 130

3-5 PROBLEM SOLVING—CABLE CAR VELOCITY

This problem involves a thousand-foot cable that is stretched between two towers, with a supporting tower midway between the two end towers. The velocity of the cable car depends on its position on the cable. When the cable car is within 30 feet of a tower, its velocity is

$$\text{velocity} = 2.425 + 0.00175d^2 \text{ ft/sec}$$

where d is the distance in feet from the cable car to the nearest tower. If the cable car is not within 30 feet of a tower, its velocity is

$$\text{velocity} = 0.625 + 0.12d - 0.00025d^2 \text{ ft/sec}$$

Print a table starting with the cable car at the first tower and moving to the last tower in increments of 10 feet. At each increment of 10 feet, print the number of the nearest tower (1 = first, 2 = middle, 3 = end), the distance from the first tower, and the velocity of the cable car.

PROBLEM STATEMENT

Write a program to print a table containing distances and velocities of a cable car as it moves from the first tower to the last tower in increments of 10 feet.

INPUT/OUTPUT DESCRIPTION

There is no input to the program. The output is a table containing distances and velocities.

HAND EXAMPLE

As we begin thinking about this problem, we may find it helpful to draw a rough picture of the tower configuration.

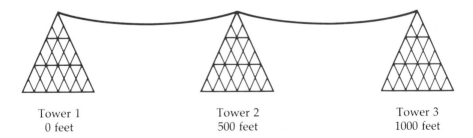

Tower 1
0 feet

Tower 2
500 feet

Tower 3
1000 feet

The cable car will be closest to Tower 1 if the total distance of the cable car from Tower 1 is 0 to 250 feet. When the total distance is greater than 250 feet but less than 750 feet, the cable car is closest to Tower 2. When the total distance is greater than or equal to 750 feet, the cable car is closest to Tower

3. (Note that when the total distance is 250, we could choose Tower 1 or Tower 2. A similar situation occurs with Tower 2 and Tower 3 when the total distance is 750 feet.)

Furthermore, the distance to the nearest tower is the total distance if the total distance is less than or equal to 250. When the total distance is between 250 and 750, the distance to the nearest tower is the absolute value of the total distance minus 500. We use the absolute value here so that the distance is always positive. Finally, the distance to the nearest tower is 1000 minus the total distance when the total distance is greater than 750. Pick a few values of the total distance and use these formulas to convince yourself that they are correct.

TOTAL DISTANCE	DISTANCE TO NEAREST TOWER
200	200
300	$\lvert 300 - 500 \rvert = 200$
650	$\lvert 650 - 500 \rvert = 150$
850	$1000 - 850 = 150$

ALGORITHM DEVELOPMENT

Because there is no input from the user, the decomposition is

DECOMPOSITION

Write headings.
Write report.

Using the hand-worked example solution as a guide, we can develop an initial pseudocode for this problem.

INITIAL REFINEMENT IN PSEUDOCODE

cable: write headings
     for i = 0 to 100 do
          distance ← i * 10
          determine nearest tower
          compute velocity
          write distance, nearest tower, velocity

We still need to further refine two steps in the pseudocode: "determine nearest tower" and "compute velocity." Relying on the steps developed in our hand-worked example, we develop this refined pseudocode:

FINAL REFINEMENT IN PSEUDOCODE

```
cable: write headings
        for i = 0 to 100 do
            distance ← i * 10
            if distance ≤ 250 then
                tower ← 1
                nearest ← distance
            else if distance ≤ 750 then
                tower ← 2
                nearest ← |distance − 500|
            else
                tower ← 3
                nearest ← 1000 − distance
            if nearest ≤ 30 then
                velocity ← 2.425 + 0.00175*nearest*nearest
            else
                velocity ← 0.625 + 0.12*nearest −
                            0.00025*nearest*nearest
            write distance, tower, velocity
```

Once the pseudocode has been refined into final form, we convert the steps into Pascal. Note the use of blank lines to separate sets of steps in the Pascal solution.

```
{- - - - - - - - - - - - - - - - - - - - - - - - - - - - - - - - - - - - - - - - - - -}
program  cable (output);
   {This program computes the velocity of a cable car
   on a thousand-foot cable with three towers.}
var
   velocity: real;
   tower, distance, nearest, i: integer;
begin
   writeln ('          CABLE CAR REPORT');
   writeln;
   writeln ('DISTANCE  NEAREST TOWER  VELOCITY');
   writeln ('  (FT)                   (FT/SEC)');
   for i := 0 to 100 do
      begin
         distance := i*10;
         if distance <= 250  then
            begin
               tower := 1;
               nearest := distance
            end
         else if  distance <= 750  then
            begin
               tower := 2;
               nearest := abs(distance-500)
            end
         else
            begin
               tower := 3;
               nearest := 1000 - distance
            end;
         if  nearest <= 30  then
            velocity := 2.425 + 0.00175*nearest*nearest
         else
            velocity := 0.625 + 0.12*nearest -
                        0.00025*nearest*nearest;
         writeln (distance:5,tower:10,velocity:16:2);
      end
end.
{- - - - - - - - - - - - - - - - - - - - - - - - - - - - - - - - - - - - - - - - - - -}
```

TESTING

A portion of the output from this program is:

```
              CABLE CAR REPORT
     DISTANCE   NEAREST TOWER   VELOCITY
       (FT)                     (FT/SEC)
         0         1              2.42
        10         1              2.60
        20         1              3.13
         .         .               .
         .         .               .
         .         .               .
       980         3              3.13
       990         3              2.60
      1000         3              2.42
```

One problem in timber management is to determine how much of an area to leave uncut so that the harvested area will be reforested in a certain period of time. It is assumed that reforestation takes place at a known rate per year, depending on climate and soil conditions. A reforestation equation expresses this growth as a function of the amount of timber standing and the reforestation rate. For example, if 100 acres are left standing and the reforestation rate is 0.05, then $100 + 0.05*100$, or 105 acres, are forested at the end of the first year. At the end of the second year, the number of acres forested is $105 + 0.05*105$ or 110.25 acres.

Write a program to read the identification number of an area, the total number of acres in the area, the number of acres of uncut area, and the reforestation rate. Print a report that tabulates for 20 years the number of acres reforested and the total number of acres forested at the end of each year.

PROBLEM STATEMENT

Compute the number of acres forested at the end of each year for 20 years for a given area.

INPUT/OUTPUT DESCRIPTION

The input information consists of an identification number for the area of land, the total acres, the number of acres with trees, and the reforestation rate. The identification number is an integer, and the rest of the numbers are real numbers. The output is a table with a row of data for each of 20 years. Each row of information contains the number of acres reforested during that year and the total number of acres forested at the end of the year.

HAND EXAMPLE

Assume that there are 14,000 acres total with 2500 acres uncut. If the reforestation rate is 0.02, then we can compute a few entries as shown:

Year 1 $2500 \cdot 0.02 = 50$ acres of new growth,
original 2500 acres $+ 50$ new acres $= 2550$ acres
Year 2 $2550 \cdot 0.02 = 51$ acres of new growth,
original 2550 acres $+ 51$ new acres $= 2601$ acres
Year 3 $2601 \cdot 0.02 = 52.02$ acres of new growth,
original 2601 acres $+ 52.02$ new acres $= 2653.02$ acres

ALGORITHM DEVELOPMENT

The overall structure is a counting loop which is executed 20 times, once for each year. Inside the loop we need to compute the number of acres reforested during that year and add that number to the acres forested at the beginning of the year; this will compute the total number of acres forested at the end of the year. The output statement should be inside the loop since we want to print the number of acres forested at the end of each year.

DECOMPOSITION

Read initial information.
Print headings.
Print report.

INITIAL REFINEMENT IN PSEUDOCODE

timber: read initial information
        write headings
        for year = 1 to 20 do
            compute reforested amount
            add reforested amount to uncut amount
            write reforested amount, uncut amount

Clearly an error condition exists if the uncut area exceeds the total area. We test for this error condition and exit after printing an error message if it occurs. Since it may be possible to have soil conditions that would produce a zero or negative reforestation rate, we do not perform any error checking on the rate. However, all the values read are written, or **echoed,** so that the user should recognize an error in an input value. We now add these refinements to our initial pseudocode.

FINAL REFINEMENT IN PSEUDOCODE

timber: read identification, total, uncut, rate
        write identification, total, uncut, rate
        if uncut > total then
            write error message
        else
            write headings
            for year = 1 to 20 do
                reforested ← uncut*rate
                uncut ← uncut + reforested
                write year, reforested, uncut

From the pseudocode, the overall structure of the program becomes evident. The outer structure is an *if-else* structure, with a *for* loop in the *else* portion. We can now convert the pseudocode into Pascal.

```
{-------------------------------------------------------------}
program   timber (input,output);
   {This program computes a reforestation summary
   for an area which has not been completely harvested.}
var
   total, uncut, rate, reforested: real;
   id, year: integer;
begin
   writeln ('ENTER LAND IDENTIFICATION (5 DIGITS)');
   readln (id);
   writeln ('ENTER TOTAL NUMBER OF ACRES');
   readln (total);
   writeln ('ENTER NUMBER OF ACRES UNCUT');
   readln (uncut);
   writeln ('ENTER REFORESTATION RATE');
   readln (rate);

   if uncut > total then
      writeln ('UNCUT AREA LARGER THAN ENTIRE AREA')
   else
      begin
         writeln;
         writeln ('REFORESTATION SUMMARY');
         writeln;
         writeln ('IDENTIFICATION NUMBER ',id:5);
         writeln ('TOTAL ACRES = ',total:10:2);
         writeln ('UNCUT ACRES = ',uncut:10:2);
         writeln ('REFORESTATION RATE = ',rate:5:3);
         writeln;
         writeln ('YEAR  REFORESTED   TOTAL REFORESTED');

         for year := 1 to 20 do
            begin
               reforested := uncut*rate;
               uncut := uncut + reforested;
               writeln (year:3,reforested:11:3,uncut:17:3)
            end
      end
end.
{-------------------------------------------------------------}
```

TESTING

Using the test data from the hand example, a typical interaction is:

```
ENTER LAND IDENTIFICATION (5 DIGITS)
25599
ENTER TOTAL NUMBER OF ACRES
14000.0
ENTER NUMBER OF ACRES UNCUT
2500.0
ENTER REFORESTATION RATE
0.02

REFORESTATION SUMMARY

IDENTIFICATION NUMBER 25599
TOTAL ACRES  =    14000.00
UNCUT ACRES  =     2500.00
REFORESTATION RATE = 0.020

YEAR   REFORESTED   TOTAL REFORESTED
  1      50.000          2550.000
  2      51.000          2601.000
  3      52.020          2653.020
  4      53.060          2706.080
  5      54.122          2760.202
  6      55.204          2815.406
  7      56.308          2871.714
  8      57.434          2929.148
  9      58.583          2987.731
 10      59.755          3047.486
 11      60.950          3108.436
 12      62.169          3170.604
 13      63.412          3234.017
 14      64.680          3298.697
 15      65.974          3364.671
 16      67.293          3431.964
 17      68.639          3500.604
 18      70.012          3570.616
 19      71.412          3642.028
 20      72.841          3714.868
```

The numbers match the ones we computed by hand. Try an example to test the error condition by using an uncut area larger than the total area. What happens if the reforestation rate is 0.00, or −0.02? Should there be an upper limit on the reforestation rate? This information is not given in the original problem so we probably should not set one arbitrarily. What happens if you enter 14,000.0 instead of 14000.0? It might be a good idea to remind the program user not to use commas in numbers. How would you do this?

3-7 OTHER CONTROL STATEMENTS

The *if* structures and the *while* and *for* loops are sufficient to implement structured algorithms. While these are the only control statements that we will use in our examples and problem-solving sections, Pascal contains several other control statements. Therefore, you should be aware of how these other statements execute. You may occasionally find that an algorithm you are implementing seems to fit one of these structures especially well. We cover the *repeat until* and *case* structures in this section, and the *go to* statement in Appendix C.

REPEAT UNTIL LOOP

The *repeat until* loop is similar to the *while* loop, but the condition test is performed at the end of the loop instead of the beginning. Thus, a *repeat until* loop always executes at least once. At the end of the first pass through the loop, the Boolean expression is evaluated. If the expression is true, the loop is exited; if the expression is false, the loop repeats. The syntax diagram of the *repeat until* loop follows.

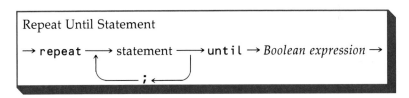

Repeat Until Statement

→ **repeat** ——→ statement ——→ **until** → *Boolean expression* →

To compare the *while* loop with the *repeat until* loop, we review two previous problems solved with the *while* loop. Now we solve them with the *repeat until* loop.

EXAMPLE 3-12   Average of a Set of Data Values

In Example 3-3, we developed an algorithm and a Pascal program to compute the average of a set of data values. The refined pseudocode used a *while* loop. It is shown below:

REFINED PSEUDOCODE

compute: sum ← 0
count ← 0
read a data value
while the data value is not zero do
   sum ← sum + data value
   count ← count + 1
   read the next data value
average ← sum/count
write 'AVERAGE =', average

Convert the pseudocode solution into one that uses the *repeat until* loop, and then write the corresponding Pascal program.

Solution

We first modify the pseudocode to include the *repeat until* loop. This requires that the loop be restructured so that the Boolean expression is tested at the end of the loop instead of the beginning. By putting the test at the end of the loop, we will have incremented our count and sum after reading the final data value of zero. Adding a zero to the sum will not affect the answer, but we must modify the average computation so that we divide the sum by *count* minus one.

REFINED PSEUDOCODE

```
compute: sum ← 0
         count ← 0
         repeat
            read a data value
            sum ← sum + data value
            count ← count + 1
         until the data value = zero
         average ← sum/(count − 1)
         write 'AVERAGE =', average
```

We now convert the pseudocode to Pascal.

PASCAL PROGRAM

```
{--------------------------------------------------------}
program  compute (input,output);
   {This program computes the average of
   a set of experimental data values.}
var
   x, sum, average: real;
   count: integer;
begin
   sum := 0.0;
   count := 0;
   repeat
      readln (x);
      sum := sum + x;
      count := count + 1
   until x = 0.0;
   average := sum/(count - 1);
   writeln ('THE AVERAGE TEMPERATURE IS ',average:6:2,
            ' DEGREES FAHRENHEIT')
end.
{--------------------------------------------------------}
```

EXAMPLE 3-13 Cable Car Velocity

In Section 3-5, we developed a solution to the cable car velocity problem that used a *while* loop. The initial pseudocode is shown following:

INITIAL REFINEMENT IN PSEUDOCODE

```
cable: write headings
       distance ← 0
       while distance <= 1000 do
           determine nearest tower
           compute velocity
           write distance, nearest tower, velocity
           distance ← distance + 10
```

Convert this solution to one with a *repeat until* loop.

Solution

To convert the *while* loop to a *repeat until* loop, we must move the Boolean expression that determines whether we stay in the loop or exit the loop. This expression now goes at the bottom of the loop, as shown in the modified pseudocode.

INITIAL REFINEMENT IN PSEUDOCODE

```
cable: write headings
       distance ← 0
       repeat
           determine nearest tower
           compute velocity
           write distance, nearest tower, velocity
           distance ← distance + 10
       until distance > 1000
```

We now refine the pseudocode again to add the details needed before we convert to Pascal. If necessary, refer to Section 3-5 for the details of this problem.

```
cable: write headings
        distance ← 0
        repeat
          if distance ≤ 250 then
              tower ← 1
              nearest ← distance
          else if distance ≤ 750 then
              tower ← 2
              nearest ← |distance − 500|
          else
              tower ← 3
              nearest ← 1000 − distance
          if nearest ≤ 30 then
              velocity ← 2.425 + 0.00175*nearest*nearest
          else
              velocity ← 0.625 + 0.12*nearest -
                          0.00025*nearest*nearest
          write distance, tower, velocity
          distance ← distance + 10
        until distance > 1000
```

We now convert the refined pseudocode to Pascal.

```
{----------------------------------------------------------}
program  cable (output);
    {This program computes the velocity of a cable car
    on a thousand-foot cable with three towers.}
var
    velocity: real;
    tower, distance, nearest: integer;
begin
    writeln ('CABLE CAR REPORT');
    writeln;
    writeln ('DISTANCE  NEAREST TOWER   VELOCITY');
    writeln ('  (FT)                      (FT/SEC)');
    distance := 0;
    repeat
        if  distance <= 250   then
            begin
                tower := 1;
                nearest := distance
            end
        else if  distance <= 750   then
            begin
                tower := 2;
                nearest := abs(distance - 500)
            end
        else
            begin
                tower := 3;
                nearest := 1000 - distance
            end;
        if  nearest <= 30   then
            velocity := 2.425 + 0.00175*nearest*nearest
        else
            velocity := 0.625 + 0.12*nearest -
                        0.00025*nearest*nearest;
        writeln (distance:5,tower:10,velocity:16:2);
        distance := distance + 10
    until distance > 1000
end.
{----------------------------------------------------------}
```

This solution yields the same computer output as the program with the *while* statement in Section 3-3. Note that the Boolean expression was changed in the conversion from the *while* loop to the *repeat until* loop. In the *while* loop we remain in the loop as long as the specified condition is true, but in the *repeat until* loop we exit the loop when the specified condition is true.

CASE STATEMENT

The *case* statement provides a specific structure for selecting different statements to perform based on the value of a variable or expression. Before we look at the general form of this statement, let's look at a specific example and compare it to an equivalent form that uses the nested *if-else* statement.

EXAMPLE 3-14 Item Identification

Assume that an item identification called *id* has been read from a data line. We now wish to print the type of item represented by that identification. The table below contains the valid identifications:

IDENTIFICATION NUMBER	DESCRIPTION
1	Computer Modem
2	Computer Printer
3	Computer Monitor
4, 5	Miscellaneous Supplies

Solution 1

We first solve this problem using the familiar *if-else* structure.

```
if  id = 1  then
    writeln ('ITEM IS A COMPUTER MODEM')
else if  id = 2  then
    writeln ('ITEM IS A COMPUTER PRINTER')
else if  id = 3  then
    writeln ('ITEM IS A COMPUTER MONITOR')
else if  (id = 4) or (id = 5)  then
    writeln ('ITEM IS MISCELLANEOUS SUPPLIES')
```

Solution 2

This solution uses the new *case* statement. We show the solution first and look at the general form after discussing this specific example.

```
case  id  of
    1:  writeln ('ITEM IS A COMPUTER MODEM');
    2:  writeln ('ITEM IS A COMPUTER PRINTER');
    3:  writeln ('ITEM IS A COMPUTER MONITOR');
  4,5:  writeln ('ITEM IS MISCELLANEOUS SUPPLIES')
end
```

Now that you have seen an example of the *case* statement, let's look at the syntax diagram.

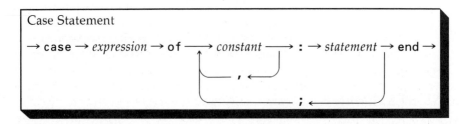

When the *case* statement executes, the expression (also called a case selector) is evaluated first. This expression can be any type that we have discussed except real; it can be integer, Boolean, or character. (Later in the text we will discuss other data types—called scalar data types—that can also be used in the case selector.) Each list of constants is then examined to find the one that contains the value equivalent to the expression (or case selector). The corresponding statement then executes, and control transfers to the statement following the *end* statement. When using this statement, you must be sure that the value of the case selector expression matches one of the constants. Otherwise, the results are unpredictable. Thus, in the example solution with the *if-else* structure, a value of 6 for *id* results in no output, and control passes to the next statement. But if *id* contains a value of 6 in the second solution, the results of executing the *case* statement are unpredictable. A safer way of using the *case* statement in Example 3-14 is to check for valid values of *id* before executing the *case* statement, as illustrated below:

```
if  (id > 0) and (id < 6)   then
   case  id  of
      1:   writeln ('ITEM IS A COMPUTER MODEM');
      2:   writeln ('ITEM IS A COMPUTER PRINTER');
      3:   writeln ('ITEM IS A COMPUTER MONITOR');
    4,5:   writeln ('ITEM IS MISCELLANEOUS SUPPLIES')
   end
```

Also, note that any of the statements in the *case* statement could be compound statements, thus giving us the capability of performing several operations when an expression matches one of the selection constants.

SUMMARY

This chapter greatly expanded the types of problems we can solve in Pascal through the use of *if* statements. We can now control the order in which statements are executed. An important property of these statements is that they are entered only at the top of the structure and that they have only one exit; this type of flow promotes the writing of simpler programs. We also learned to use both *while* loops and *for* loops to implement repetition steps. Most of the programs in the rest of the text will use either one or the other of these loop structures.

DEBUGGING AIDS

The most helpful tool in debugging is the *writeln* statement. Just knowing that your program is working incorrectly does not really tell you where to begin looking for errors. If you have the computer write the values of key variables at different points in your program, however, it becomes easier to isolate the parts of the program that are not working correctly. The location of these checkpoints, or places to write the values of key variables, depends on the program; obvious places are after reading new values for variables and after completing loops and computations.

It is also a good idea to number the checkpoints and then print the checkpoint number along with the other values. For instance, if you print the values of x and y at several checkpoints, it may not be obvious which set of x and y values have been printed. However, the following output is very clear:

If you have narrowed the problem to an *if* statement, first check the Boolean expression. Did you use $<$ when you meant $<=$? Be careful when using *not* in an expression because the relationships can get complex. For example, *not ((a = 1.0) or (b = 2.0))* is also equal to *(a $<>$ 1.0) and (b $<>$ 2.0)*.

Another possible error with *if* statements can be traced to values being very close to, but not exactly equal to, the desired value. For instance, suppose that the result of a mathematical computation should have a real value of 5.0. Since computers do have limitations on the number of digits of accuracy, the result might be 4.999 or 5.001. Yet if you check only for 5.0, you may not realize that you have the correct value. One way to address this problem is to use the *if* statement to look for values close to 5.0. For instance, if

$$|x - 5.0| < .001$$

then *x* is between 4.999 and 5.001. If this is close enough for the particular problem being solved, replace the statement

```
if  x = 5.0  then
    writeln ('X = ',x:6:3)
```

with the statement

```
if  abs(x - 5.0) < 0.001  then
    writeln ('X = ',x:6:3)
```

If you believe that a programming error lies within a *while* loop, write the values of key variables at the beginning of the loop. This information will print each time the loop executes, so you should be able to locate the trouble spot.

Most errors in a *for* loop involve the variables that specify the loop. When a program error seems to involve a *for* loop, write the value of the index or count variable immediately within the loop. After executing the loop with this output statement, you can answer the following questions:

1. Did the index start with the correct value?
2. Did the index increment by the proper amount?
3. Did the index have the correct value during the last execution of the loop?

If the answer to any of these questions is no, check the *for* statement itself. You probably have an error in the variables or expressions that you specified.

If the error is not in your original specification of the *for* statement, print the values of the index at both the beginning and end of the loop statements. After executing the loop with these two output statements, you will be able to determine if the value of the index is changed by the statements inside the loop. If the index is being modified, you have either used the index inadvertently, which can be corrected, or you should replace the *for* loop with a *while* loop.

Another common error associated with *for* loops occurs when a similar variable name is used instead of the index. For instance, if the index of the *for* loop is *index*, use *index* and not *i* inside the loop when you intend to use the index value.

STYLE/TECHNIQUE GUIDELINES

The larger a program grows in size, the more apparent becomes the programmer's style. Not only does bad style/technique become more obvious, it also becomes harder to correct. Therefore, practicing good style/technique in your small programs builds habits that will carry over into all your programming.

One of the best guidelines for good style is to use the *while* loop or the *for* loop consistently. With a little practice, you will find that all loops fit easily into one of these two forms. As we pointed out in the summary, these types of loops have one entrance and one exit, enhancing readability and adding simplicity to your program.

Another characteristic of good style is the use of indenting to emphasize the statements in *if* structures and loops. You can convince yourself of the importance of indenting if you try to read a program written by someone who has not indented statements within control structures. If loops are nested, indent each nested loop from the previous one.

Comment lines are another sign of good style; however, the use of comment lines can become excessive. Add only as many lines as are needed to show the program's organization and enhance its readability. Comment lines should be easy to distinguish from Pascal statements; thus we indent the comments from the statements around them. You should always use initial comments to describe the purpose of the program. If needed, comments may be used throughout the program to identify processes, values, variables, and so forth. You will also notice that blank lines can be very effective to separate different steps within a program. This technique is often used in our example programs.

A program exhibiting good style will save time in the long run since it is easier to debug. Programmers who may need to modify your programs in future projects will also appreciate your good style. Changing a few lines of Pascal code to achieve this will be time well spent.

KEY WORDS

Boolean data type	echo
Boolean expression	*for* loop
Boolean operator	*if* structures
compound Boolean expression	nested *for* loops
compound statement	nested *if* structures
connector	relational operator
control structure	

PROBLEMS

We begin our problem set with modifications to programs given earlier in this chapter. Give the decomposition, refined pseudocode, and Pascal program for each problem.

Problems 1–5 modify the suture packaging program *seals*, given on page 94.

1. Modify the suture packaging program so that it also writes the total number of batches rejected.
2. Modify the suture packaging program so that it also writes the number of batches in each rejection category.
3. Modify the suture packaging program so that it prints an error message if the information for a batch that should not have been rejected is entered. Do not count this batch in the overall count of rejected batches.
4. Modify the suture packaging program so that it also counts and writes the total number of batches with ranges out of bounds on more than one of the parameters.
5. Modify the suture packaging program so that it counts and prints the total number of batches with ranges out of bounds on all three parameters.

Problems 6–10 modify the cable car program *cable*, given on page 112.

6. Modify the cable car velocity program so that it uses a *while* statement instead of a *for* statement.
7. Modify the cable car velocity program so that it reads the distance increment from a data line.
8. Modify the cable car velocity program so that the report includes a fourth column giving the distance of the cable car from the nearest tower.
9. Modify the cable car velocity program so that the distance increment is 10 feet unless the cable car is less than 20 feet from a tower, in which case the distance increment should be 5 feet.
10. Modify the cable car velocity program so that there are two supporting towers between the first and last towers. The first supporting tower is 300 feet from the first tower, and the second supporting tower is 300 feet from the last tower.

Problems 11–15 modify the timber management program *timber*, given on page 115.

11. Modify the timber management program so that a value n is read from the terminal, where n represents the number of years that are to be used in printing the table.
12. Modify the timber management program so that it computes information for 20 years, but only prints information after the second year, fourth year, and so on.

13. Modify the timber management program so that a value m is read from the terminal, where m represents the number of years that should be between lines in the output table. (Problem 12 is a special case where $m = 2$.)

14. Modify the timber management program so that instead of printing data for 20 years, it continues to print yearly information until at least 10 percent of the cut area has been reforested.

15. Modify the timber management program so that it prints only the final line of data after 20 years, and then allows the user to input a different reforestation rate. The program should print the final line of data after 20 years with this new reforestation rate, and again allow the user to input a different reforestation rate. The program should end when a reforestation rate of 0.00 is entered.

For problems 16–19, write complete Pascal programs to write tables showing the values of the input variables and the function shown, using *for* loops to control the loops.

16. Print a table of values for k where

$$k = 3m$$

for values of $m = 1, 2, 3, 4$.

17. Print a table of values for k where

$$k = i^2 + 2i + 2$$

for values of $i = 0, 1, 2, \ldots, 20$.

18. Print a table of values for y where

$$y = \frac{x^2 - 9}{x^2 + 2}$$

for values of $x = 1.5, 2.0, 2.5, \ldots, 9$.

19. Print a table of values for f where

$$f = \frac{x^2 - y^2}{2xy}$$

for values of $x = 1, 2, \ldots, 9$, and for values of $y = 0.5, 0.75, 1.0, \ldots, 2.5$. (This solution requires nested *for* loops.)

Develop new programs in problems 20–28. Use the five-phase design process.

20. Write a program to print a table of consecutive even integers and their square values, beginning with 2, until the value of i is greater than 200. Use the following output format:

```
I AND I*I

2        4
4        16
.
.
.
```

21. Write a program to read a value *final*. Print a table that contains values of x and x squared, starting with x equal to zero and incrementing by 0.5, until x is greater than *final*. Use the following output format:

```
                          2
     X                   X

    0.0                 0.00
    0.5                 0.25
     .                   .
     .                   .
     .                   .
```

22. Write a program that reads student registration information from the terminal. Each line should contain a student number and the hours that the student has completed. Indicate the end of the data with student number 9999, which does not represent a student. A student's classification is based on the following table:

CLASSIFICATION	HOURS COMPLETED
Freshman	hours < 30
Sophomore	$30 \leq$ hours < 60
Junior	$60 \leq$ hours < 90
Senior	$90 \leq$ hours

After each line of input, print the correct classification in the following form:

STUDENT ID XXXX – FRESHMAN

23. Modify problem 22 so that a final summary report follows the individual classification information and has the following form:

```
REGISTRATION SUMMARY

FRESHMEN      XXXXX
SOPHOMORES    XXXXX
JUNIORS       XXXXX
SENIORS       XXXXX

TOTAL STUDENTS        XXXXXX
```

24. A retrorocket is being designed to permit softer landings. The designers have derived the following equations that they believe will predict the performance of the test rocket, where t represents the elapsed time in seconds:

$$\text{acceleration} = 4.25 - 0.015 \ t^2$$
$$\text{velocity} = 4.25 - 0.005 \ t^3$$
$$\text{distance} = 90 + 2.125 \ t^2 - 0.00125 \ t^4$$

The distance equation gives the height above ground level at time t. Thus, the first term (90) is the height in feet above ground level of the nose of the rocket at launch. To check the predicted performance, the rocket will be "flown" on a computer, using the derived equations. Write a program to print the time, height, velocity, and acceleration for the rocket from a time of zero seconds through 50 seconds, in increments of 1 second. Use the following report form:

```
                ROCKET  FLIGHT  SIMULATION

    TIME         ACCELERATION      VELOCITY      HEIGHT
    (SEC)        (FT/SEC*SEC)      (FT/SEC)      (FT)

    XXX.XX         XXXX.XX         XXXX.XX       XXXX.XX
      .
      .
      .
```

25. After discovering the omega germ, a biologist has spent five years determining the characteristics of the new virus. She has found that the germ has a constant growth rate. If 10 cells are present with a growth factor of 0.1, the next generation will have $10 + 10(0.1) = 11$ cells. Write a program that computes and prints a report with the following format:

```
                    OMEGA  GERM  GROWTH

                   NUMBER OF CELLS    PETRI DISH       GROWTH
CULTURE NUMBER        INITIALLY      DIAMETER (CM)      RATE
    XXXX                XXXX              XXX           XX.XX

GENERATION   NUMBER OF CELLS   % AREA OF PETRI DISH COVERED

    1            XXXX.X                  XXX.XX
    .
    .
    .

    5
```

Ten cells occupy 1 square millimeter. Use the following input data for four cultures:

	NUMBER OF CELLS	PETRI DISH	GROWTH
CULTURE NUMBER	INITIALLY	DIAMETER	RATE
1984	100	10 cm	0.50
1776	1300	5 cm	0.16
1812	600	15 cm	0.55
1056	700	8 cm	0.80

26. The square of the sine function can be represented by the following:

$$\sin^2 X = X^2 - \frac{2^3 X^4}{4!} + \frac{2^5 X^6}{6!} - \cdots = \sum_{n=1}^{\infty} \frac{(-1)^{n+1} 2^{2n-1} X^{2n}}{(2n)!}$$

Write a program to evaluate this series for an input value x, printing the results after 2, 4, 6, 8, ..., 14 terms and comparing each sum to the true solution. Note that the term for $n = 1$ is $x*x$, and that all consecutive terms can be obtained by multiplying the previous term by

$$\frac{-(2x)^2}{2n(2n-1)}$$

continued

The output should have the following form:

```
               COMPARISON OF VALUES OF SINE SQUARED
    NUMBER          SERIES         INTRINSIC        ABSOLUTE
   OF TERMS       SUMMATION        FUNCTION        DIFFERENCE
      2            XX.XXXX          XX.XXXX          XX.XXXX
      4            XX.XXXX          XX.XXXX          XX.XXXX
      .
      .
      .
     14            XX.XXXX          XX.XXXX          XX.XXXX
```

27. The analysis of beams is an important part of the structural analysis con-
    ducted before construction of a building begins. One type of beam that is
    frequently used is a cantilever beam, which is fixed on one end and free on
    the other. The amount of deflection when a load is applied to this type of
    beam can be computed with the following equation:

$$\text{deflection} = \frac{(l)(a^2)}{2(e)(i)} \cdot \left(\text{length} - \frac{a}{3.0} \right)$$

where l = applied load in pounds
      a = length from fixed end to applied load in feet
      e = elasticity of the material (wood, steel, etc.)
      i = moment of inertia of the beam, computed with the following
          equation:

$$i = \frac{(\text{base})(\text{height}^3)}{12}$$

The data needed in order to perform the analysis are the following real
values:

beam length	(feet)
beam base	(inches)
beam height	(inches)
elasticity constant	(lbs/sq in)
applied load	(lbs)

Write a program to read the information for a beam and print a report that
places the applied load at one-foot intervals starting at one foot from the
fixed end and moving down the length of the beam. Don't forget to ensure
that the units of measurement are consistent. The output for the beam
should contain the following information:

```
                  BEAM LENGTH = XXX.XX FT
      DISTANCE OF LOAD FROM FIXED END          DEFLECTION
                  1.0                            XXX.XX
                  2.0                            XXX.XX
                   .                               .
                   .                               .
                   .                               .
```

28. Modify the program of problem 27 so that the deflections for the beam are printed only as long as they are less than 5 percent of the beam length. When the beam deflection is greater than or equal to 5 percent, the program should stop. If the deflection distance of 5 percent is never reached, the program should print an appropriate message. The header line for the beam should also contain the 5 percent length computation. Two examples of the new output are shown below:

```
         BEAM LENGTH = 100.00 FT
          5% OF LENGTH =   5.00 FT
    DISTANCE FROM FIXED END          DEFLECTION
            1.00                        1.45
            2.00                        3.82
            3.00                        4.79


         BEAM LENGTH =    3.00 FT
          5% OF LENGTH =   0.15 FT
    DISTANCE FROM FIXED END          DEFLECTION
            1.00                        0.04
            2.00                        0.09
            3.00                        0.12
    DEFLECTION OF 5% OF LENGTH NOT REACHED
```

PASCAL STATEMENT SUMMARY

If Statement:

> if *Boolean expression* **then** *statement*

Examples:

```
if  a > 15.5   then
    count := count + 1

if  (x < 0.0) or (y >= z)   then
    begin
        total := total + x;
        writeln ('X = ',x:4:1)
    end
```

Discussion:

If the Boolean condition is true, the statement following *then* is executed. Otherwise, the statement is skipped.

If-Else Statement:

> if *Boolean expression* **then** *statement* **else** *statement*

Example:

```
if  hours <= 40.0   then
    salary := hours*rate
else
    salary := (hours - 40)*rate*1.5 + 40.0*rate
```

Discussion:

The *if-else* statement executes one statement if the Boolean condition is true, and a different statement if the condition is false.

For Statement:

> for *index* := *initial* **to** *final* **do** *statement*
> for *index* := *initial* **downto** *final* **do** *statement*

Examples:

```
for i := 1 to 50 do
    count := count + 1

for number := total downto 1 do
    begin
        y := number*number;
        writeln (y)
    end
```

Discussion:

The *for* statement defines a counting loop where *index* is the variable used as the loop counter; *initial* represents the initial value given to the loop counter; and *final* represents the final value for the index. The index is incremented by 1 after the loop is executed if *to* is chosen; the index is decremented by 1 after the loop is executed if *downto* is chosen. The loop repeats until the index is greater than the

---

final value in the *to* case, or until the index is less than the final value in the *downto* case.

While Statement:

while *Boolean expression* **do** *statement*

Examples:

```
while  count < 25  do
    begin
        readln (x);
        sum := sum + x;
        count := count + 1
    end

while  not done  do
    begin
        readln (x);
        sum := sum + x;
        count := count + 1;
        done := count >= 25
    end
```

Discussion:

The *while* statement defines a loop in which the statement is executed as long as the Boolean expression is true. If the Boolean expression is false, control passes to the statement following the *while* statement. The loop will not execute at all if the Boolean expression is initially false.

PROBLEM SOLVING—Earthquake Measurements

Engineers and scientists are hopeful that one day they will be able to predict accurately the size and location of major earthquakes. They collect data from seismometers, instruments that record the earth's motion at locations around the world. By studying this data, which is collected before, during, and after earthquakes, scientists hope to identify conditions that will aid in the prediction process.

Write a program that will sort the data collected from one seismometer during a series of recent earthquakes so that the order of the data is from smallest earthquake to largest earthquake. (See Section 4-6 for the solution.)

Photo courtesy of Dr. R. E. Wallace, U.S. Geological Survey.

4

ONE-DIMENSIONAL ARRAY PROCESSING

INTRODUCTION

In Chapter 3 we presented the control structures that are available in Pascal for implementing algorithms. We saw through a series of examples that the proper choice of a control structure is important in developing a good solution to a problem. The proper choice of a data structure is just as important in developing a good solution to a problem, and in this chapter we present one of the most useful data structures in Pascal, the one-dimensional array. In addition to studying the statements necessary to define and use this data structure, we will look at some of the common techniques used with array processing. These techniques range from the familiar ones of finding averages, minimums, and maximums to new techniques for searching and sorting with lists of data. Since many of the types of problems that we can now solve use large data sets, we also present text files. Examples illustrating methods for reading information from text files and for writing information to text files are developed.

4-1   MORE ON DATA TYPES

While the primary interest of this chapter is one-dimensional arrays, we will present several new data types in this section and then use them in examples along with one-dimensional arrays.

TEXT FILES

Up to this point, we have used the terminal keyboard to enter data that our programs needed to execute *read* or *readln* statements. Usually, the data was entered following a message that we printed to specify the input needed. Every time we ran the program, we had to reenter the data. This becomes very tedious if there are many items of data. An alternative way to enter the data is with a **data file.** You can use the editing capabilities of your computer system to create a data file, just as you use the editing capabilities to enter a Pascal program that is really a program file. Data files can also be created by other computer programs. Each line of a data file corresponds to a line of data that you would enter by hand. The data in a data file is referred to as text data, and thus our files are really **text files.**

Some special statements must be used in your program when you use data files. We will present them in this section, along with discussions of how to know when you have reached the end of your data file if you did not know ahead of time how many entries were in it. We will also show you how to write information into a file from your program instead of displaying it on the terminal screen or printing it with a line printer. (Some aspects of data file usage are system dependent. We present methods commonly used with data files, but check with your instructor if the examples we use do not seem to work on your computer system.)

Statement Extensions   In order to use data files with programs, we will need to use some new statements and some extensions of old statements. Each of these statements will reference the filename of the file that we want to use in the program. The filename is assigned when a file is built. If you build a data file with your computer system's editor, you assign a name to the file before you begin entering the data. If the system already has a file with the name that you have indicated, you generally will be given an opportunity to choose a new name or to replace the old file with the new file. The filename of each file that you wish to use in a Pascal program must be listed in the program header. Thus, a program using a data file called *experiment1* might begin with the following header:

```
program  compute (input,experiment1,output);
```

This header indicates that the program is going to use input from the keyboard, send output to the screen, and use a data file called *experiment1*.

When a data file is used in a program, its name must appear in the variable section of the program and be identified as text. (Our data files are really text files.) Thus, the variable section of the program mentioned above might include these statements:

```
var
    volume, temp: real;
    time, id: integer;
    experiment1: text;
```

At this point, the computer system knows that we are going to use a data file in the program, but it still does not know whether the file is an input file or an output file. An input file is one that already has data in it. It is accessed with *read* or *readln* statements. An output file is one that does not already have data in it; it is generated with *write* or *writeln* statements. Before we execute any input or output statements, though, we must tell the computer system which type of file we are using so that it can prepare the file for use by our program. The *reset* statement specifies that a file is an input file, while the *rewrite* statement specifies that a file is an output file. Thus, if our example file *experiment1* contained data that we wanted to read in our program, we would use the following statement to prepare the file so that we are ready to begin reading information from the beginning of the file:

```
reset (experiment1)
```

The syntax diagrams for these two new statements follow.

Reset Statement
→ **reset** → (→ *filename* →) →

Rewrite Statement
→ **rewrite** → (→ *filename* →) →

We may occasionally want to read the data in a file more than once. Each time we execute a *reset* statement, the pointers used with the file will be reset to the beginning of the file.

We have now identified the file (or files) that we want to use in our program and we have prepared them with the *reset* and *rewrite* statements. We are now ready to access the data in the files using familiar input and output statements. However, we need some means of specifying which file we want to use. For example, we may plan to read data from a file called *experiment1* and also to read data from the terminal in the same program. This problem is easily solved by including the filename of the file that we want to use in the statement itself, as shown in this statement:

```
readln (experiment1,x,y)
```

If the filename is omitted, the system automatically assumes the system input file for an input statement, and the system output file for an output statement. Thus, the two statements below are equivalent:

```
writeln (output,average)
```

```
writeln (average)
```

If error messages are generated during the execution of the program, they are printed using the system output device. Therefore, the system output file should always be included in the file list in the program header. The system input file needs to be listed only if input will be entered through the terminal keyboard.

We now look at several examples illustrating the use of these statements in programs.

EXAMPLE 4-1   Parallel Resistance

A data file *resistance* contains three data lines, each containing a resistance value from a resistor in an instrumentation circuit. Write a complete program to read the three resistances and compute their combined resistance *combined* for a parallel arrangement, as shown below:

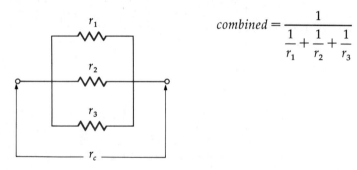

$$combined = \frac{1}{\dfrac{1}{r_1} + \dfrac{1}{r_2} + \dfrac{1}{r_3}}$$

Print the value of *combined*. The resistance is measured in ohms.

Solution

The steps to solve this problem are simple and involve no loops since we only perform the computation once.

Read three resistance values.
Compute combined resistance.
Write combined resistance.

We now add more detail to the decomposition to obtain the pseudocode.

Refinement in Pseudocode

```
compute: read r1, r2, r3
         write r1, r2, r3
         compute combined resistance
         write combined resistance
```

Converting the pseudocode steps into Pascal yields the following program.

Pascal Program

```
{---------------------------------------------------------}
program  compute (resistance,output);
    {This program reads a data file with three
     resistance values and computes their
     equivalent parallel value.}
var
    r1, r2, r3, combined: real;
    resistance: text;
begin
    reset (resistance);
    readln (resistance,r1,r2,r3);
    writeln ('INPUT VALUES ARE ',r1:7:1,r2:7:1,r3:7:1);
    combined := 1.0/(1.0/r1 + 1.0/r2 + 1.0/r3);
    writeln ('COMBINED PARALLEL RESISTANCE = ',
             combined:7:1,' OHMS')
end.
{---------------------------------------------------------}
```

Data File *resistance*

```
                    1000.0
                    1100.0
                    2000.0
```

Computer Output

```
INPUT VALUES ARE   1000.0 1100.0 2000.0
COMBINED PARALLEL RESISTANCE =    415.1 OHMS
```

Example 4-1 used a small data file, but the advantages of using a data file become more obvious when the files are large. Once the data file is built, no matter how many times you run a program that uses it, you do not have to reenter the data. It is easy to change and update a data file with the editing capabilities available on terminal systems. In addition, data files can be shared by various programs, reducing data redundancy and minimizing the memory requirements.

Data files can be built by a Pascal program with *write* or *writeln* statements; instead of using the terminal screen or line printer as our output device, we can write the information into a data file. This is often done to plot data; the data is first written into a data file, and then a program that runs the plotter can access the data file.

EXAMPLE 4-2   Parallel Resistance with Output File

Modify the program in the solution of Example 4-1 such that the combined resistance is printed and also stored in a file called *parallel*.

Solution

Since this solution is so similar to that of Example 4-1, we include only the modified Pascal program and the input and output from a sample test run.

Pascal Program

```
{------------------------------------------------------------}
program  compute (resistance,output,parallel);
    {This program reads a data file with three
    resistance values and computes their equivalent
    parallel value which is stored in a file.}
var
    r1, r2, r3, combined: real;
    resistance, parallel: text;
begin
    reset (resistance);
    rewrite (parallel);
    readln (resistance,r1,r2,r3);
    writeln ('INPUT VALUES ARE ',r1:7:1,r2:7:1,r3:7:1);
    combined := 1.0/(1.0/r1 + 1.0/r2 + 1.0/r3);
    writeln ('COMBINED PARALLEL RESISTANCE = ',
             combined:7:1,' OHMS');
    writeln (parallel,combined:7:1)
end.
{------------------------------------------------------------}
```

Data File *resistance*

```
                        1000.0
                        1100.0
                        2000.0
```

Computer Output

```
    INPUT VALUES ARE   1000.0 1100.0 2000.0
    COMBINED PARALLEL RESISTANCE =    415.1 OHMS
```

Data File *parallel*

Trailer and Sentinel Signals Many applications require the computer to read a number of data values, such as test scores or experimental results. The *for* loop can accomplish these tasks if you know exactly how many data values are in the file. For instance, if 50 data values are to be read, we could use a *for* loop of this form:

```
for count := 1 to 50 do
    begin
        readln (filename,variables);
        process data
    end
```

If the number of data values to be read is available in another variable (for example, *maximum*), we can use a *for* loop of this form:

```
for count := 1 to maximum do
    begin
        readln (filename,variables);
        process data
    end
```

However, you may not always know exactly how many data values should be read prior to executing your program. You must be careful in handling these situations, because if you execute a *read* or *readln* statement for which there is no data left in the file, an execution error will occur and program execution will stop. There are two techniques for handling an unspecified number of input data values: one uses a **trailer,** or **sentinel,** signal and the other uses an **end-of-file** Boolean function.

The first technique uses special data values called trailer or sentinel signals to indicate the end of the data. For example, a valid identification number for a student record may be three digits, ranging from 000 to 500. If we were reading student records, we could use an identification number of 999 as a trailer signal. The line with the trailer signal would also need values for the other variables in order for the input statement to work properly. As we read each data line, we test the identification number for the value 999; when we find the value 999, we exit the loop. This process can be structured easily in a *while* loop, but since the condition will use a value from the data, we must read one student record before entering the *while* loop, as shown:

```
readln (filename,id,variables);
while  id <> 999  do
    begin
        process data
        readln (filename,id,variables)
    end
```

If we need to know the number of data values read, we can put a counter in the *while* loop. Be sure not to count the trailer value as a valid data value. This

4-1 MORE ON DATA TYPES   141

technique for determining the end of a set of data should look familiar because we have already used it in some of our example programs with data entered from the terminal.

EXAMPLE 4-3 Test Scores with Trailer Signal

A group of test scores has been entered into a data file *file1*, one score per line. The last line contains a negative value to signal the end of the test scores. Write a complete program to read the data, compute the test average, and print the number of tests and the test average.

Solution

Computing an average from data read from a data file involves the same steps as computing an average from the data entered from the terminal. Thus, the decomposition should be familiar:

DECOMPOSITION

| Read and total test scores. |
| Compute average. |
| Write average. |

In the refinement of this decomposition, we include the *while* loop, which reads and totals the test scores until we read a negative value.

REFINEMENT IN PSEUDOCODE

```
average1: count ← 0
          sum ← 0
          read test
          while test ≥ 0 do
             count ← count + 1
             sum ← sum + test
             read test
          if count > 0 then
             average ← sum/count
          else
             average ← 0.0
          write count, average
```

As we convert the pseudocode into Pascal statements, remember that we are reading the test scores from a data file — thus we need to use the *reset* statement and the expanded form of the *readln* statement.

PASCAL PROGRAM

```
{------------------------------------------------------------}
program  average1 (file1,output);
    {This program computes the average of a
    group of test scores which are followed
    by a trailer line in a data file.}
var
    average: real;
    test, count, sum: integer;
    file1: text;
begin
    reset (file1);
    count := 0;
    sum := 0;
    readln (file1,test);
    while  test >= 0  do
        begin
            count := count + 1;
            sum := sum + test;
            readln (file1,test)
        end;
    if  count > 0  then
        average := sum/count
    else
        average := 0.0;
    writeln ('THE AVERAGE OF ',count:4,
            ' TEST SCORES IS ',average:5:1)
end.
{------------------------------------------------------------}
```

A sample data file and the corresponding output from this program are:

Data File *file1*

```
85
92
100
87
75
73
81
-1
```

COMPUTER OUTPUT

```
THE AVERAGE OF    7 TEST SCORES IS  84.7
```

EOF **Function** If a set of data does not have a trailer signal at the end, and if we do not know the number of data lines in the file, we must use a different technique with the *while* loop. This technique uses a built-in Boolean function *eof* which has a value of true if we have reached the end of the file, and a value of false otherwise. Our *while* loop can then be structured as shown below:

```
while  not eof(filename)  do
    begin
        readln (filename,variables);
        process data
    end
```

We must be careful not to execute a *readln* statement when *eof* is true because this will cause an execution error. Also, note that *eof* is followed by the filename in parentheses. This is necessary because there may be many files in the same program, and the system needs to know which file we are testing for end-of-file. If the filename is omitted, the system will assume you are referring to the system input file.

When a program builds an output file, the computer system automatically puts an end-of-file indicator at the end of the file. When we are reading information from this file in another program and the computer reaches this indicator, it changes the value of the *eof* function to true, allowing us to detect this situation. If you build a data file using an editor, this indicator is also at the end of your file. However, you should be sure that there are no blank lines at the end of the data file because this can make it difficult to detect the end of the file with the *eof* function.

Observe that the two techniques discussed in this section should not be used together. If you have a trailer value, test for that value to exit the loop. If you do not have a trailer signal at the end of the file, use the *eof* function in the *while* loop condition to keep you from reading past the end of the data file.

EXAMPLE 4-4   Test Scores without Trailer Signal

A group of integer test scores has been entered into a data file *file2*, one score per line, with no trailer signal. Write a complete program to read the data, compute the test average, and print the number of tests and the test average.

Solution

The decomposition steps are the same as in the previous example.

DECOMPOSITION

Read and total test scores.
Compute average.
Write average.

As we refine the solution, we must specify which technique we will use for detecting the end of the file. Because there is no trailer signal, we do not need to read the first data line outside the loop. The condition in the *while* loop determines whether or not there is more data to read. If there is no more data, we exit the *while* loop.

```
average2: count ← 0
         sum ← 0
         while not end-of-file do
            read test
            count ← count + 1
            sum ← sum + test
         if count > 0 then
            average ← sum/count
         else
            average ← 0.0
         write count, average
```

Converting this pseudocode to Pascal yields the following program.

PASCAL PROGRAM

```
{-----------------------------------------------------------}
program  average2 (file2,output);
   {This program computes the average of a
   group of test scores which are not followed
   by a trailer line in a data file.}
var
   average: real;
   test, sum, count: integer;
   file2: text;
begin
   reset (file2);
   count := 0;
   sum := 0;
   while  not eof(file2)  do
      begin
         readln (file2,test);
         count := count + 1;
         sum := sum + test
      end;
   if   count > 0  then
      average := sum/count
   else
      average := 0.0;
   writeln ('THE AVERAGE OF ',count:4,
            ' TEST SCORES IS ',average:5:1)
end.
{-----------------------------------------------------------}
```

A sample data file and the corresponding output from this program are:

Data File *file2*

```
85
92
100
87
75
73
81
```

```
 _____
(  THE  AVERAGE  OF     7 TEST SCORES IS   84.7  )
 _____/
```

SCALAR AND ORDINAL DATA TYPES

A set of values is **ordered** if there is a relationship between the values that can be used to compare them. For example, the set of integers is an ordered set because they have a relationship that can be used to determine if one integer is less than another. Similarly, the set of real values is an ordered set. Surprisingly enough, even Boolean values are ordered in Pascal. While we do not often use this property, Pascal defines the order of Boolean values to be such that false is less than true.

A **scalar** data type is a data type in which the set of values is ordered and is composed of elements that cannot be further divided into other elements. At this point we have not discussed types that can be further divided into other elements, but some of the structures presented in this chapter and in later chapters build new structures from the real, integer, and Boolean data types. All three data types that we have used thus far are ordered and cannot be further divided into other elements; therefore, scalar data types include integer, real, and Boolean data types. We will see in Chapter 8 that character data is also a scalar type since characters will have an order (similar to an alphabetic order) and since they cannot be further subdivided into other data types. (However, a character string is not scalar because it can be subdivided into individual characters.)

Ordinal data types are those in which each value (except the first) has a unique predecessor and each value (except the last) has a unique successor. For example, integers are ordinal numbers. The predecessor of 5 is 4 and the successor of 5 is 6. On the other hand, reals are not ordinal numbers. For example, what is the predecessor of 3.00? Is it 2.9, 2.99, or 2.999? The precision of a real value varies from one computer to another, and since there is no unique answer, reals cannot be ordinal numbers. In Chapter 8 we will see that characters are ordinal types. For example, the predecessor of Y is X, and the successor of Y is Z. Based on the ordering given to Boolean values, false is the predecessor of true and the successor of false is true. False does not have a predecessor, since it is first in the ordering, and true does not have a successor, since it is last in the ordering.

SUBRANGE TYPES

One of the special features of Pascal is that it allows you to define data types in addition to those that are built-in (such as real, integer, Boolean, character, and text). New data types are defined in the type section of a Pascal program, which follows the constant-definition section. The general form of a Pascal program can now be expanded to the following:

```
program   name (files);
   {This is a sample outline of a program.}
const
   constant definitions
type
   type definitions
var
   variable declarations
begin
   algorithm steps
end.
```

New types defined in the type section can be used to define variables in the variable section. It is important to recognize that defining a new type does not automatically define variables of that type; variables must be defined in the variable section.

The syntax diagram for the type section of a program follows.

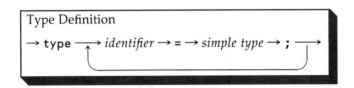

Type Definition

$\rightarrow$ **type** $\longrightarrow$ *identifier* $\rightarrow$ = $\rightarrow$ *simple type* $\rightarrow$ **;** $\longrightarrow$

A simple type is either real, integer, Boolean, character, or one of the subrange types or enumerated data types discussed next.

A **subrange** type is a new data type defined by a subrange of a previously defined ordinal data type. For example, the integer data type is a built-in data type containing all integers that can be represented by a specific computer. We can define a new data type with a subrange of the integers by specifying the beginning integer and the ending integer, separated by two periods. Then, in the variable definitions, we can specify variables with the new data type, as shown below:

```
type
   digits = 0..9;
var
   index1, index2: digits;
```

The previous subrange definition for digits is also called a **named** subrange because the subrange is defined in the type definition portion of the program; thus, *index1* and *index2* are defined as type *digits. Index1* and *index2* can also be **anonymous** data types if the subrange is not defined in a separate type definition, as shown below:

```
var
   index1, index2: 0..9;
```

Named data types are preferred to anonymous data types because they make the program more readable and allow us to refer to data types by name instead of defining them in each variable definition. When we cover procedures and functions in the next two chapters, we will find that there are also other reasons for preferring named data types to anonymous data types.

The statements below show several subrange data definitions that all contain 10 elements, but whose values are different:

```
type
    digits = 1..10;
    settings = -5..4;
    years: 1980..1989;
```

The syntax diagram for the definition of the values in a subrange data type follows.

```
Subrange Data Type Value Definition
    → value → . . → value →
```

When we define a subrange data type, the computer system will automatically check values assigned to variables that are defined as this data type to insure that they are within the proper range. A value falling outside the defined range generates an error.

In the next section of this chapter, we will see that the subrange data type is commonly used in the definition of arrays, although it does not have to be associated with an array.

ENUMERATED DATA TYPES

Another data type that we can define is the **enumerated** (or listed) data type, which is an ordered set of identifiers. The Boolean data type is an example of an enumerated data type with identifiers false and true.

An example is the best way to illustrate the use of enumerated data types. Suppose we are preparing a report summarizing the types of defects that have been detected in the assembly of computer boards for a personal computer. These defects have been divided into three categories: broken wires, defective integrated circuit chips (ICs), and defective non-IC components (such as resistors and capacitors). When we work with this data in our program, we would like to use statements like the following to enhance the program's readability:

```
if  defect = none  then
    writeln ('NO DEFECTS')
else if  defect = wire  then
    writeln ('DEFECTIVE WIRE')
else if  defect = ic  then
    writeln ('DEFECTIVE INTEGRATED CIRCUIT')
else if  defect = other  then
    writeln ('DEFECTIVE NON-IC COMPONENT')
```

In order to use statements like this one, we must define an enumerated data type that is composed of the identifiers *none, wire, ic,* and *other*. Then we define *defect* to be a variable of this enumerated data type; hence, its values can be *none, wire, ic,* or *other*. Note that the values are not in quotation marks because they are not character constants. (This is when it is handy to remember that the Boolean data type is enumerated; we use values true and false, not 'true' and 'false.') The definition of this data type and the corresponding variable *defect* is

```
type
    categories = (none,wire,ic,other);
var
    defect: categories;
```

The syntax diagram for the definition of the values in an enumerated data type follows.

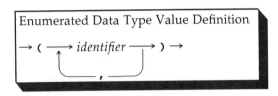

We cannot read a value directly into a variable that is an enumerated data type. Instead, we assign the variable an enumerated value based on the value of another variable. For example, suppose that a data file contains information regarding the computer board defects just discussed. Each line contains a board's identification and a code of 0 (for no defects), 1 (for wire defects), 2 (for IC defects), and 3 (for non-IC defects). If a board has more than one defect, the information will appear in a separate line in the file for each of the defects. We can read the information and assign a value to the enumerated data variable *defect* with the following statements:

```
readln (file1,id,error);
if  error = 0   then
    defect := none
else if  error = 1   then
    defect := wire
else if  error = 2   then
    defect := ic
else if  error = 3   then
    defect := other
```

The assignment of the proper value for *defect* could also have been done easily with the *case* statement.

The values of enumerated data types cannot be directly written with output statements; again, we use an *if* structure or the *case* statement to print appropriate messages. For example, if we want to print the computer board ID and the defect category that we have just read from the data file with the statements above, we could use the following statements:

```
write ('BOARD IDENTIFICATION ',id:5,'HAS ');
if  defect = none   then
    writeln ('NO DEFECTS')
else if  defect = wire   then
    writeln ('WIRE DEFECTS')
else if  defect = ic   then
    writeln ('INTEGRATED CIRCUIT CHIP DEFECTS')
else if  defect = other   then
    writeln ('NON-IC COMPONENT DEFECTS')
```

From this example, you can see the improvement in readability from enumerated data types, but you can also see that using enumerated data types requires a little more effort. Therefore, we will not use these data types in all our programs, but there definitely are programs in which they are very useful to improve readability.

Enumerated data types are ordinal, meaning that there is an order to the values. We specify the order in the type definition. In the example above, *none* is less than *wire*, *wire* is less than *ic*, and *ic* is less than *other*. While we did not use the ordering in this example, there are problem solutions in which we will want to compare enumerated values.

It is not valid to use the same value in more than one enumerated data type; for example, we could not use *other* as a value in an additional enumerated data type. Similarly, we cannot use the values true or false in our enumerated data types since they are already used in the built-in Boolean data type definition.

4-2 ONE-DIMENSIONAL ARRAY HANDLING

An **array** is a data structure composed of a group of memory locations. We give this group of memory locations a common name. Individual members of an array are called **elements** of the array and are distinguished by using the common name followed by a **subscript** or **index** in brackets. Subscripts or indices are represented by consecutive integers, usually beginning with the integer 1. A **one-dimensional array** can be visualized as either one column of data or one row of data. The memory locations and associated names for a one-dimensional integer array j of five elements and a one-dimensional real array *rate* with four elements are shown:

j[1]	2
j[2]	−5
j[3]	14
j[4]	80
j[5]	−12

1.2	−0.8	36.9	−0.07
rate[1]	rate[2]	rate[3]	rate[4]

This type of data structure is sometimes called a **list,** because it looks like a list of data values. The concept of indexing or subscripting is probably familiar to you from mathematics, where subscripted variables are often used in definitions and equations.

Defining an array really involves two definitions: a definition for the array itself and a definition for the indices or subscripts that will be used to reference the elements in the array.

When we define an array that will have 10 elements, we must specify 10 distinct values that will be used for the subscripts. The most obvious choice is probably the integers 1 through 10, although other choices may be more appropriate depending on the application. If we assume that the subscript values are to be the integers 1 through 10 and if the array is named x, we can reference individual elements in the array as *x[1]*, *x[2]*, and so on. Since we think of the array as a row or column, we know that *x[6]* comes immediately after *x[5]* and just before *x[7]*. We could use an integer variable as the subscript, but often we will want to specify that the integer variable used as a subscript has only a certain range of valid values. Thus, a definition for a subscript for the array *x* might use the subrange data type as follows:

```
type
    index = 1..10;
var
    i: index;
```

Now we are ready to define the array itself. Remember, an array is a new data type that contains a group of variables, all the same type, which are referenced with an index or subscript. Thus, the definition includes the index description (which can be a subrange of integers, a user-defined enumerated type, Boolean, or character) and the data type of the individual elements of the array.

> One-Dimensional Array Definition
> → array → [→ *index type* →] → of → *data type* → ; →

Thus, an array of 5 real values using subscripts 1 through 5 could be defined as shown below:

```
type
    index = 1..5;
    list = array[index] of real;
var
    x: list;
```

Note that we define the array as a new data type *list*, and then define the variable *x* to be of type *list*.

Arrays are very powerful data structures that we will want to use in many of our programs. Therefore, we now need to look at some examples that define, initialize, and use arrays so that we will be familiar with their use.

INITIALIZATION

Values are assigned to array elements in the same way that they are assigned to regular variables. The following are valid assignment statements, assuming that the subscript value is within the range defined for the array:

```
j[1] := 0

j[5] := new*count

distance[2] := 46.2 + sin(x)
```

It is often helpful to use variables and expressions, instead of constants, as subscripts. The following loop initializes all elements of the array *k* to the value 10. Observe that the variable *i* is used as a subscript and also as a *for* loop index:

```
type
    index = 1..5;
    list = array[index] of integer;
var
    i: index;
    k: list;
    .
    .
    .
    for i := 1 to 5 do
        k[i] := 10
```

The next loop initializes the array *k* to the values shown:

```
for i := 1 to 5 do
    k[i] := i
```

1	2	3	4	5

k[1] k[2] k[3] k[4] k[5]

The values of the array *distance* are initialized to real values with this set of statements:

```
type
    index = 1..4;
    list = array[index] of real;
var
    k: integer;
    distance: list;
    .
    .
    .
    for k := 1 to 4 do
        distance[k] := 1.5*k
```

1.5	3.0	4.5	6.0

distance[1] distance[2] distance[3] distance[4]

Note in this example that *k* was defined to be integer type, not *index* type. We might do this because we are going to use *k* for other purposes, and we do not want to restrict its value to the subrange 1..4. Remember, however, that if we use *k* as a subscript for the array *distance*, and its value is not between 1 and 4, we will get an execution error.

The previous examples illustrate that a subscript can be an integer constant or an integer variable. Subscripts can also be integer expressions, as indicated in the following statements:

```
j[2*i] := 3

r[j] := r[j-1]

b1 := tr[2*i] + tr[2*i+1]
```

Again, whenever an expression is used as a subscript, be sure the value of the expression will always lie between the starting and ending subscript values.

If we wish to move the contents of one array into another array, we can use a simple assignment statement of the following form, as long as the two arrays are the same size and type:

```
a := b
```

Note that this is really a "copy" operation because the contents of *b* are not changed, but are copied into the array *a*.

INPUT/OUTPUT

Elements of arrays can be initialized with the *readln* or *read* statement. This method is particularly useful when we want to initialize the array with data from a data file. The following examples illustrate this technique.

EXAMPLE 4-5 Temperature Measurements

A set of 50 temperature measurements has been entered into a data file named *file1*, one value per line. Give a set of statements to define an array to store these values and to read the values into the array.

Solution

We define two new data types: a subrange of integers and a one-dimensional array of real values. We then define variables using these two new data types, along with a text file. The statements following the definitions reset the file and read the data from the file into the array.

```
program  example (file1,output);
   .
   .
   .
type
    index = 1..50;
    list = array[index] of real;
var
    file1: text;
    subscript: index;
    temperature: list;
    .
    .
    .
reset (file1);
for subscript := 1 to 50 do
    readln (file1,temperature[subscript])
```

If there are several data values per line in a data file, we may need to use the *read* statement as opposed to the *readln* statement. Otherwise, for each pass through the loop, we will skip any remaining values on the current line after reading one temperature value.

EXAMPLE 4-6 Rainfall Data

A set of 28 daily rainfall measurements are stored in a data file, with 1 week of data per line. The name of the data file is *rainfall*. Give statements to read this data into an array called *rain*.

Solution

We first define new data types for the subrange and the array structure that we want to use in this solution. Then we define variables with the new data types and use the variables in the appropriate Pascal statements to read the information into the array *rain*.

```
program  precipitation (rainfall,output);
    .
    .
    .
type
    index = 1..28;
    list = array[index] of real;
var
    rainfall: text;
    k: index;
    rain: list;
    .
    .
    .
reset (rainfall);
for k := 1 to 28 do
    read (rainfall,rain[k])
```

Techniques to print values from an array are similar to those used to read values into an array. The following examples illustrate these techniques.

EXAMPLE 4-7   Mass Measurements

A group of 30 mass measurements is stored in an array *mass*. Print the values in the following tabulation:

```
MASS[ 1] = XXX.X    MASS[16] = XXX.X
MASS[ 2] = XXX.X    MASS[17] = XXX.X
 .
 .
 .
MASS[15] = XXX.X    MASS[30] = XXX.X
```

Solution

For each output line, we must reference one value in the array and then another value 15 values away from the first. Thus, if i is a subscript for the first value, $i+15$ is the subscript desired for the second value. The values for i can be generated with a *for* statement that has an index range of 1 through 15. The value of the other subscript, $i+15$, can be computed with an arithmetic expression. The output form of this solution is important; study it carefully to be sure you understand how it works.

```
type
   index = 1..30;
   list = array[index] of real;
var
   i: index;
   mass: list;
   .
   .
   .
   for i := 1 to 15 do
      writeln ('MASS[',i:2,'] = ',mass[i]:5:1,
               '    MASS[',i+15:2,'] = ',
               mass[i+15]:5:1)
```

EXAMPLE 4-8   Distance, Velocity, Acceleration

Arrays *dis, vel,* and *acc* each contain 50 values. The first value in each array represents the distance, velocity, and acceleration of a test rocket at time equal to 0 seconds. The second set of values represents data for time equal to 1 second, and so on. Print the data in the following tabulation:

```
TIME    DISTANCE    VELOCITY    ACCELERATION
(SEC)   (M)         (M/SEC)     (M/(SEC*SEC))
  0     XXX.XX      XXX.XX      XXX.XX
  .
  .
  .
 49     XXX.XX      XXX.XX      XXX.XX
```

Solution

This is an example of a situation where we might want to use an index or subscript that starts at 0 instead of 1, since the values represent times at 0 seconds, 1 second, and so on. Therefore, we will assume that the definition of the array used an index from 0 to 49, as shown below:

```
type
   index = 0..49;
   list = array[index] of real;
var
   i: index;
   dis, vel, acc: list;
   .
   .
   .
   writeln ('TIME    DISTANCE    VELOCITY    ',
            'ACCELERATION');
   writeln ('(SEC)    (M)         (M/SEC)    ',
            '(M/(SEC*SEC))');
   for i := 0 to 49 do
      writeln (i:3,dis[i]:10:2,vel[i]:11:2,
               acc[i]:11:2)
```

COMPUTATIONS

Using array elements in computations is slightly more complicated than using simple variables because we now have to use subscripts to specify which element of the array we want to use. Since many of the calculations we perform with arrays will use all the elements in the array, we will also be using loops. The index acts both as the loop counter and as the array subscript.

EXAMPLE 4-9   Sum of Filled Array

The array *area* contains 20 real values representing the area in square miles of 20 plots of land. Assume that the data has already been stored in the array. Compute and write the sum of the areas of the 20 plots of land.

Solution

To sum the data in the array, we need a counting loop that executes 20 times. The index of the loop can also be used as the subscript for the array.

```
type
    index = 1..20;
    list = array[index] of real;
var
    sum: real;
    i: index;
    area: list;
    .
    .
    .
    sum := 0.0;
    for i := 1 to 20 do
        sum := sum + area[i];
    writeln ('AREA OF 20 PLOTS OF LAND IS ',
             sum:8:2,' SQUARE MILES')
```

EXAMPLE 4-10   Sum of Partially Filled Array

The array *area* contains real values representing the area in square miles of plots of land. The actual number of plots of land varies, but never exceeds 20. Therefore, we can store the area of the plots in the array, but we need to use another variable to keep track of how many of the array elements are actually being used for data. Assume that the data has already been stored in the array and that an additional integer variable contains the number of elements in the array that contain areas. Compute and write the sum of the areas of the plots of land.

Solution

To sum the data in the array, we need a counting loop that executes the same number of times as there are valid areas stored in the array. The index of the loop can also be used as the subscript for the array.

```
type
    index = 1..20;
    list = array[index] of real;
var
    sum: real;
    i, count: index;
    area: list;
    .
    .
    .
    sum := 0.0;
    for i := 1 to count do
        sum := sum + area[i];
    writeln ('AREA OF ',count:2,' PLOTS OF LAND IS ',
            sum:8:2,' SQUARE MILES')
```

EXAMPLE 4-11   Total Defects

Assume that we have an array of data collected from one day's production of computer boards. The data contains information about errors detected in the boards. Each element of the array contains an error code. Codes 1–20 are various types of wire errors, codes 21–35 are various types of integrated circuit errors, and codes 36–49 are the remaining types of errors. The last error code in the array is followed by an array element with the value 999 to indicate the end of the actual data values. The array is an integer array with 500 elements. Give the statements necessary to determine the number of errors in each of the three categories, and write these values.

Solution 1

In this solution, we use three integer variables to accumulate the totals.

```
type
    index = 1..500;
    list = array[index] of integer;
var
    wire, ic, other: integer;
    i: index;
    error: list;
    .
    .
    .
    wire := 0;
    ic := 0;
    other := 0;
    i := 1;
    while error[i] <> 999  do
        begin
            if (1 <= error [i]) and (error[i] <= 20)  then
                wire := wire + 1
            else if  (21 <= error[i]) and
                     (error[i] <= 35)   then
                ic := ic + 1
            else if  (36 <= error[i]) and
                     (error[i] <= 49)   then
                other := other + 1
            else
                writeln ('ERROR CODE WRONG ',error[i]:5);
            i := i + 1
        end;
    writeln ('NUMBER OF WIRE ERRORS = ',wire:3);
    writeln ('NUMBER OF IC ERRORS = ',ic:3);
    writeln ('NUMBER OF OTHER ERRORS = ',other:3)
```

Solution 2

In this solution, we illustrate the use of the enumerated data type as a subscript for an additional array used to hold the error totals.

```
type
    index = 1..500;
    category = (wire,ic,other);
    list1 = array[index] of integer;
    list2 = array[category] of integer;
var
    i: index;
    defect: category;
    error: list1;
    total: list2;
    .
    .
    .
    for defect := wire to other do
        total[defect] := 0;
    i := 1;
    while  error[i] <> 999  do
        begin
            if  (1 <= error [i]) and (error[i] <= 20)  then
                defect := wire
            else if  (21 <= error[i]) and
                     (error[i] <= 35)   then
                defect := ic
            else if  (36 <= error[i]) and
                     (error[i] <=49)   then
                defect := other
            else
                writeln ('ERROR CODE WRONG ',error[i]:5);
            if  (1 <= error[i]) and (error[i] <= 49)  then
                total[defect] := total[defect] + 1;
            i := i + 1
        end;
    writeln ('NUMBER OF WIRE ERRORS = ',total[wire]:3);
    writeln ('NUMBER OF IC ERRORS = ',total[ic]:3);
    writeln ('NUMBER OF OTHER ERRORS = ',total[other]:3)
```

This self-test allows you to check quickly to see if you have remembered certain key points from Section 4-2. If you have any problems with the exercises, you should reread this section. The solutions are included at the end of the text.

Problems 1–6 contain definitions and initializations of one-dimensional arrays. Draw the array and indicate the contents of each position in the array after executing the set of statements. Assume that each set of statements is independent of the others. If no value is given to a particular position, fill it with a question mark.

1.
```
type
    index = 1..10;
    list = array[index] of integer;
var
    i: index;
    m: list;
    .
    .
    .
    for i := 1 to 10 do
        m[i] := i + 1
```

2.
```
type
    index = 1..10;
    list = array[index] of integer;
var
    i: index;
    m: list;
    .
    .
    .
    for i := 1 to 9 do
        m[i+1] := 2
```

3.
```
type
    index = 1..8;
    list = array[index] of real;
var
    kk: index;
    r: list;
    .
    .
    .
    for kk := 1 to 8 do
        r[kk] := 10 - kk
```

```
4. type
      index = 1..6;
      list = array[index] of integer;
   var
      k: index;
      data: list;
      .
      .
      .
      for k := 1 to 6 do
         data[7-k] = k
5. type
      index = 1..8;
      list = array[index] of real;
   var
      i: index;
      r: list;
      .
      .
      .
      for i := 1 to 8 do
         if  i <= 3  then
            r[i] := 2.5
         else
            r[i] := -2.5
6. type
      index = 0..9;
      list = array[index] of real;
   var
      i: index;
      r: list;
      .
      .
      .
      for i := 1 to 8 do
         if  i > 4  then
            r[i] := 4.0
```

4-3 PROBLEM SOLVING—NATIONAL PARK SNOWFALL

The daily snowfall for the month of January is stored in a data file called *january*. Each data line contains one week of snowfall amounts recorded in inches. Line 1 contains the data for the first week in January, line 2 contains the data for the second week in January, and so on. Determine the daily snowfall average and the number of days with above-average snowfall for January.

PROBLEM STATEMENT

Compute the average snowfall for January and the number of days with above-average snowfall.

INPUT/OUTPUT DESCRIPTION

The input data is contained in a file called *january* that contains the snowfall for each day in January. The output is the average daily snowfall and the number of days with above-average snowfall.

HAND EXAMPLE

For a hand-worked example, we use 1 week's data instead of 1 month's data. The values are:

Day 1	4.2 inches
Day 2	3.1 inches
Day 3	1.5 inches
Day 4	0.2 inches
Day 5	0.0 inches
Day 6	0.0 inches
Day 7	1.8 inches

To determine the average value, we total the amounts and divide by 7, which yields 10.8/7, or 1.54 inches. We compare this value to the original data values and find that 3 days had snowfalls above the average. Notice that we had to use the data values twice; thus, we will use an array because it allows us to read all the data to compute the total and still have all the values accessible for comparing them to the average.

ALGORITHM DEVELOPMENT

After completion of the hand example, the initial decomposition is straightforward.

DECOMPOSITION

Read snowfall data.
Compute average snowfall.
Determine the number of days with above-average snowfall.
Write average, number of days.

In the refinement, we need to show two loops: one to total the data and the other to compare the data to the average. Note that the loops are independent. We must complete the first loop and calculate the average before we can compare the individual values to the average.

Refinement in Pseudocode

snowfall: total ← 0
        for i=1 to 31 do
          read snow[i]
          total ← total + snow[i]
        average ← total/31
        write average
        count ← 0
        for i=1 to 31 do
          if snow[i] > average then
          count ← count + 1
        write count

Converting the steps in the pseudocode solution to Pascal yields the following program.

Pascal Program

```
{------------------------------------------------------------------}
program  snowfall (january,output);
    {This program computes the average snowfall
    for January and counts the number of days
    with above-average snowfall.}
type
    index = 1..31;
    list = array[index] of real;
var
    total, average: real;
    count: integer;
    january: text;
    i: index;
    snow: list;
begin
    reset (january);
    total := 0.0;
    count := 0;
    for i := 1 to 31 do
        begin
            read (january,snow[i]);
            total := total + snow[i]
        end;
    average := total/31.0;
    writeln ('AVERAGE SNOWFALL IS ',average:7:2,' INCHES');
    for i := 1 to 31 do
        if  snow[i] > average  then
            count := count + 1;
    writeln (count:2,' DAYS WITH ABOVE-AVERAGE SNOWFALL')
end.
{------------------------------------------------------------------}
```

Could we have used a *readln* statement in place of the *read* statement to read the values of the array? The answer is no, because the values are stored seven per line in the data file. A *readln* statement would read the first value, then skip the rest of the data values on the line.

TESTING

When testing this program, it would be important to check the actual data values being read from the data file. To do this, we can insert a *writeln* statement immediately after the *read* statement in the first loop. This *writeln* statement could easily be removed after the program has been carefully tested. Sometimes it is convenient to turn an output statement into a comment by enclosing it in braces, { and }. Then, if you make modifications to the program or if it does not seem to be working properly, it is easy to remove the braces and include the statement again. Of course, once the program is completely tested, these extra statements need to be removed because they interfere with the readability of your program, even though the compiler would ignore them (they are comments as far as the compiler is concerned).

A set of data values used in a test run is shown next, seven values per line. (Since the values are entered seven per line, and since January has 31 days, the last line in the data file contains only three values.)

Data File *january*
```
4.2 3.1 1.5 0.2 0.0 0.0 1.8
1.1 0.9 0.0 0.0 0.0 0.2 0.0
0.9 1.4 1.2 0.3 0.0 0.0 0.0
0.0 0.0 1.5 1.2 0.4 1.6 0.7
0.3 0.0 0.0
```

The corresponding output is shown below:

COMPUTER OUTPUT

```
AVERAGE SNOWFALL IS    0.73 INCHES
12 DAYS WITH ABOVE-AVERAGE SNOWFALL
```

We used an array in this solution to illustrate how to define, fill, and access the array. An alternative solution might have been to read the snowfall values and accumulate a sum without storing the values in an array. Then, after computing the average, we could reset the file back to the beginning and read the values again, comparing them to the average.

4-4 PROBLEM SOLVING—INTEGRATED CIRCUIT DEFECTS

In a manufacturing or assembly plant, quality control receives close attention. One of the key responsibilities of a quality-control engineer is to collect accurate data on the quality of the product being manufactured. This data can be used to identify problem areas in the assembly line or in the materials being used in the product.

In this section, we use information collected over a one-month period that specifies both the type of defect and the number of defects detected in the assembly of the computer board for a personal computer. These defects have been divided into three categories: broken wires, defective integrated circuit chips (ICs), and defective non-IC components (such as resistors and capacitors). The data has been stored in a file called *defects*. The first line in the data file contains the number of boards assembled in the period of time represented by the data in the file. Each line following contains a board identification number followed by three integers that represent the number of broken wires, defective ICs, and defective non-ICs, respectively, on the board. At least one of these numbers is greater than zero because the file contains only information on boards with defects. The last line in the data file contains an identification number, 9999, followed by three zero values.

Our program will read this set of information and compute the total number of defects in each category and the number of boards with defects, along with the corresponding percentages. If more than 10 percent of the total number of boards assembled had defects, then we are also to print the board identification numbers for all the boards with defects. This information will allow the quality-control engineer to identify trouble areas by using the identification numbers to determine the date of assembly and the lot of materials used in those computer boards.

PROBLEM STATEMENT

Print a report analyzing the defects in a set of computer boards.

INPUT/OUTPUT DESCRIPTION

The input to the program is to be entered from a data file *defects*. The first line in the file contains the total number of boards assembled. Each line following contains a board identification number and three integers representing the three types of defects that may occur in the board: broken wires, defective ICs, and defective non-ICs. The end of the data is indicated by 9999 board identification number. The output is a report with the following information:

```
           MONTHLY QUALITY ANALYSIS REPORT

   TOTAL NUMBER OF BOARDS ASSEMBLED = XXXX

   TOTAL BOARDS WITH DEFECTS = XXXX

         XXXX BOARDS WITH BROKEN WIRES
         XXXX BOARDS WITH DEFECTIVE IC COMPONENTS
         XXXX BOARDS WITH DEFECTIVE NON-IC COMPONENTS

   DEFECT ANALYSIS

         XXX.X% OF BOARDS HAD DEFECTS
         XXX.X% OF DEFECTS WERE BROKEN WIRES
         XXX.X% OF DEFECTS WERE DEFECTIVE IC COMPONENTS
         XXX.X% OF DEFECTS WERE DEFECTIVE NON-IC COMPONENTS
```

Also, if the total percentage of defects is greater than 10 percent, a list of all identification numbers of the computer boards with defects should be printed.

HAND EXAMPLE

Assuming that a total of 528 computer boards were assembled during the month, consider the following set of defect data:

IDENTIFICATION	DEFECTS IN THE THREE CATEGORIES
528	
145	0 0 1
188	1 1 0
410	0 1 0
312	2 0 0
366	0 0 1
368	0 0 1
279	1 1 2
407	1 0 0
9999	0 0 0

The analysis of the sample data yields the following quality analysis report:

```
           MONTHLY QUALITY ANALYSIS REPORT

   TOTAL NUMBER OF BOARDS ASSEMBLED =   528

   TOTAL BOARDS WITH DEFECTS =     8

         4 BOARDS WITH BROKEN WIRES
         3 BOARDS WITH DEFECTIVE IC COMPONENTS
         4 BOARDS WITH DEFECTIVE NON-IC COMPONENTS

   DEFECT ANALYSIS

          1.5% OF BOARDS HAVE DEFECTS
         38.5% OF DEFECTS WERE BROKEN WIRES
         23.1% OF DEFECTS WERE DEFECTIVE IC COMPONENTS
         38.5% OF DEFECTS WERE DEFECTIVE NON-IC COMPONENTS
```

Since less than 10 percent of the boards had defects, we do not need to list all the identification numbers.

ALGORITHM DEVELOPMENT

Most of the information in the report is based on totals that we need to determine as the data is read. For example, we need the following:

Total number of boards assembled

Total number of boards with defects

Total number of boards with broken wires

Total number of boards with defective ICs

Total number of boards with defective non-IC components

Total number of broken wires

Total number of defective ICs

Total number of defective non-IC components

We will not know if more than 10 percent of the boards have defects until we have read the entire file, because we don't know ahead of time how many boards with defects are in the file. Therefore, we will store the identification numbers in an array. We can print the contents of the array if the percentage of the boards is greater than 10 percent. There is no need to keep the specific defect data in arrays because we do not print it even if the percentage of boards with defects is greater than 10 percent. In order to set the size of the array, we need to know the maximum number of boards that might have defects in any month. Assume that the manufacturing process can produce a maximum of 1000 boards per month. Then, even if every board had a defect, 1000 elements in the array would be sufficient. The *while* loop for reading this data and accumulating the totals is executed "while id is not 9999," so we need to read the first set of defect data before we test this condition.

Putting these ideas into our decomposition step yields:

DECOMPOSITION

Read data and compute totals.
Compute data for defect summary.
Print corresponding report(s).

Adding more detail to these steps, our refinement in pseudocode becomes:

REFINEMENT IN PSEUDOCODE

quality: initialize all totals to zero
        read number of boards assembled
        read id, defects
        while id not equal to 9999 do
           increment appropriate totals
           read id, defects
        compute additional totals and percentages
        write summary report
        if percent of boards with defects > 10.0 then
           write report of all identification numbers

We are now ready to convert the steps in pseudocode into Pascal statements. Again we list the totals that we need, along with the identifiers we are using for them.

boards	Total number of boards assembled
defectbd	Total number of boards with defects
wirebd	Total number of boards with broken wires
icbd	Total number of boards with defective ICs
nonicbd	Total number of boards with defective non-ICs
wiretotal	Total number of broken wires
ictotal	Total number of defective ICs
nonictotal	Total number of defective non-IC components

PASCAL PROGRAM

```
{------------------------------------------------------------}
program  quality (defects,output);
    {This program uses data in a defect file to compute
    and write a Quality Analysis Report.}
type
    index = 1..1000;
    list = array[index] of integer;
var
    percdef, percwire, percic, percnonic: real;
    boards, defectbd, wirebd, icbd, nonicbd,
    wiretotal, ictotal, nonictotal, total,
    wire, ic, nonic: integer;
    defects: text;
    i: index;
    id: list;
```

```
begin
   defectbd := 0;
   wirebd := 0;
   icbd := 0;
   nonicbd := 0;
   wiretotal := 0;
   ictotal := 0;
   nonictotal := 0;
   i := 1;
   reset (defects);
   readln (defects,boards);
   readln (defects,id[i],wire,ic,nonic);
   while  id[i] <> 9999  do
      begin
         defectbd := defectbd + 1;
         if  wire > 0  then
            wirebd := wirebd + 1;
         if  ic > 0  then
            icbd := icbd + 1;
         if  nonic > 0  then
            nonicbd := nonicbd + 1;
         wiretotal := wiretotal + wire;
         ictotal := ictotal + ic;
         nonictotal := nonictotal + nonic;
         i := i + 1;
         readln (defects,id[i],wire,ic,nonic)
      end;

   percdef := defectbd/boards*100.0;
   total := wiretotal + ictotal + nonictotal;
   percwire := wiretotal/total*100.0;
   percic := ictotal/total*100.0;
   percnonic := nonictotal/total*100.0;

   writeln ('              MONTHLY QUALITY ANALYSIS REPORT');
   writeln;
   writeln ('TOTAL NUMBER OF BOARDS ASSEMBLED = ',boards:4);
   writeln;
   writeln ('TOTAL BOARDS WITH DEFECTS = ',defectbd:4);
   writeln;
   writeln (wirebd:9,' BOARDS WITH BROKEN WIRES');
   writeln (icbd:9,' BOARDS WITH DEFECTIVE IC COMPONENTS');
   writeln (nonicbd:9,' BOARDS WITH DEFECTIVE NON-IC COMPONENTS');
   writeln;
   writeln ('DEFECT ANALYSIS');
   writeln;
   writeln (percdef:10:1,'% OF BOARDS HAVE DEFECTS');
   writeln (percwire:10:1,'% OF DEFECTS WERE BROKEN WIRES');
   writeln (percic:10:1,'% OF DEFECTS WERE DEFECTIVE IC ',
            'COMPONENTS');
   writeln (percnonic:10:1,'% OF DEFECTS WERE DEFECTIVE NON-IC ',
            'COMPONENTS');

   if  percdef > 10.0  then
      begin
         writeln;
         writeln;
         writeln ('IDENTIFICATION NUMBERS FOR DEFECTIVE BOARDS');
         for i := 1 to defectbd do
            writeln (id[i])
      end
end.
{-------------------------------------------------------------}
```

Several of the literals in the output statements were too long to fit on one line and had to be separated into two lines. Instead of continuing the literal to the end of the line, we split the line between words to make it easier to read.

TESTING

If we use our sample data from the program, our output is:

```
           MONTHLY QUALITY ANALYSIS REPORT

TOTAL NUMBER OF BOARDS ASSEMBLED =   528

TOTAL BOARDS WITH DEFECTS =     8

        4 BOARDS WITH BROKEN WIRES
        3 BOARDS WITH DEFECTIVE IC COMPONENTS
        4 BOARDS WITH DEFECTIVE NON-IC COMPONENTS

DEFECT ANALYSIS

        1.5% OF BOARDS HAVE DEFECTS
       38.5% OF DEFECTS WERE BROKEN WIRES
       23.1% OF DEFECTS WERE DEFECTIVE IC COMPONENTS
       38.5% OF DEFECTS WERE DEFECTIVE NON-IC COMPONENTS
```

Once our program is working correctly with a typical set of data, we should design data sets that test special conditions. For example, we should test this program with data that does not include one of the defects. If we eliminate all the IC defects in our sample set, the preceding program produces the following report:

```
           MONTHLY QUALITY ANALYSIS REPORT

TOTAL NUMBER OF BOARDS ASSEMBLED =   528

TOTAL BOARDS WITH DEFECTS =     7

        4 BOARDS WITH BROKEN WIRES
        0 BOARDS WITH DEFECTIVE IC COMPONENTS
        4 BOARDS WITH DEFECTIVE NON-IC COMPONENTS

DEFECT ANALYSIS

        1.3% OF BOARDS HAVE DEFECTS
       50.0% OF DEFECTS WERE BROKEN WIRES
        0.0% OF DEFECTS WERE DEFECTIVE IC COMPONENTS
       50.0% OF DEFECTS WERE DEFECTIVE NON-IC COMPONENTS
```

We should also be sure to test the program with a set of data in which more than 10 percent of the boards had defects so we can test the portion of our program that should print all the board identification numbers when this condition occurs.

When entering the data in the file *defects*, is it necessary to include three zeros after the identification number 9999? Yes, because the corresponding *readln* statement lists four variables; otherwise, an execution error will occur.

4-5 COMMON TECHNIQUES USED WITH ONE-DIMENSIONAL ARRAYS

Solutions to different problems often include some of the same steps, such as computing the average of a set of values or finding the maximum of a set of values. Since these common operations often use data stored in arrays, we develop algorithms in this section to solve these problems using arrays.

AVERAGES, MINIMUMS, AND MAXIMUMS

We have already discussed algorithms for computing averages and for finding the minimum and maximum of a set of values. When the set of values is stored in an array, the solutions are the same, but they involve the array instead of a series of values entered from the keyboard or read from a data file.

To find the average of an array, we must sum the array and then divide the sum by the number of values in the array. We will assume that a variable *count* specifies how many elements in the array are actually data values. (A maximum number of elements is specified in the array definition, but we often use fewer values in the array.) The decomposition and pseudocode for finding the average follow.

DECOMPOSITION

Find average of list of values.

PSEUDOCODE FOR FINDING THE AVERAGE OF A LIST OF VALUES

(Assumes: the values are already stored in the array x; and a variable *count* specifies the number of valid data in the array.)

if count > 0 then
    sum ← 0
    for i = 1 to count do
        sum ← sum + x[i]
    average ← sum/count

If we convert this pseudocode into Pascal, we obtain the following:

PASCAL STATEMENTS

```
    .
    .
    .
if  count > 0  then
    begin
        sum := 0.0;
        for i := 1 to count do
            sum := sum + x[i];
        average := sum/count
    end
```

The algorithm shown assumes that the array contains real values, since the sum is initialized to a real zero instead of an integer zero.

We now specify the steps for finding the minimum and maximum of an array in the same routine. The algorithm that we use will initialize the minimum and maximum to the first element in the array and begin comparing array elements to the "minimum so far" and the "maximum so far." Each time we find a new minimum or maximum, we will update the "minimum so far" or the "maximum so far." The decomposition and pseudocode for finding the minimum and maximum are:

DECOMPOSITION

Find minimum and maximum in list of values.

PSEUDOCODE FOR FINDING THE MINIMUM AND MAXIMUM OF A LIST OF VALUES

(Assumes: the values are already stored in the array x, and a variable *count* specifies the number of valid data values in the array.)

if count > 0 then
   minimum ← x[1]
   maximum ← x[1]
   for i = 2 to count do
      if x[i] < minimum then
         minimum ← x[i]
      if x[i] > maximum then
         maximum ← x[i]

If we convert this pseudocode into Pascal, we obtain the following:

```
    .
    .
    .
if  count > 0  then
    begin
       minimum := x[1];
       maximum := x[1];
       for i := 2 to count do
          begin
             if  x[i] < minimum   then
                 minimum := x[i];
             if  x[i] > maximum   then
                 maximum := x[i]
          end
    end
```

If we are determining only the minimum or only the maximum, then the compound statement above is not needed since there will only be one statement in the *for* loop.

SEARCHING

Another very common operation performed with arrays is searching the array for a specific value. We may want to know if a particular value is in the array, how many times it occurs in the array, or where the value occurs in the array. Searching algorithms break into two groups: those for searching an unordered array and those for searching an ordered array.

Unordered List We first consider searching an unordered list; thus, we assume the elements are not necessarily sorted into an ascending numerical order, or any other order that may aid us in searching the array. The algorithm to search an unordered array is just a simple sequential search: check the first element, check the second element, and so on. The decomposition and pseudocode for searching an unordered list follow.

DECOMPOSITION

> Search unordered list for a specific value.

PSEUDOCODE FOR SEARCHING AN UNORDERED LIST

(Assumes: the values are already stored in the array *x*; a variable *count* specifies the number of valid data values in the array; and the variable *key* contains the value for which we are searching.)

```
if count > 0 then
   done ← false
   i ← 1
else
   done ← true
   found ← false
while not done do
   if x[i] = key then
      done ← true
      found ← true
   else
      i ← i + 1
   if i > count then
      done ← true
      found ← false
if found then
   statement to execute if key is found
else
   statement to execute if key is not found
```

Converting this to Pascal yields the following:

PASCAL STATEMENTS

```
.
.
.
if   count > 0   then
   begin
      done := false;
      i := 1
   end
else
   begin
      done := true;
      found := false
   end;
while  not done  do
   begin
      if  x[i] = key   then
         begin
            done := true;
            found := true
         end
      else
         i := i + 1;
      if  i > count   then
         begin
            done := true;
            found := false
         end
   end;
if   found   then
   statement to execute if key is found
else
   statement to execute if key is not found
```

Two conditions can cause us to exit this *while* loop: either we found the element or we have completed our search and did not find the element for which we were searching. To determine which exit condition is true, we used an *if* structure with a Boolean variable *found*. Could we have used the following *if* structure to determine which exit condition is true?

```
if   x[i] = key   then
     statement to execute when key is found
else
     statement to execute when key is not found
```

It may seem that this is equivalent to the *if* structure we used, but it is not. If the key value was not in the array, the subscript *i* will have a value that is one greater than the count of values in the array. If the count of values is equal to the number of values originally defined for the array, *x[i]* will be an invalid array reference resulting in an execution error.

Variations of this technique are used for similar problems. For example, suppose we want to count the number of occurrences of the key in the array. In this case, we don't want to stop as soon as we find the value for which we are searching; instead, we want to continue searching through the entire array. We want to use a *for* loop, as shown in the following statements:

```
found := 0;
for i := 1 to count do
    if   x[i] = key   then
         found := found + 1
```

Suppose we are interested in the location of the key value in the array. The location is specified by the subscript. The following statements will print all the locations in the array where the key appears:

```
for i := 1 to count do
    if   x[i] = key   then
         writeln ('KEY LOCATED IN POSITION ',i:3)
```

Ordered List We now consider searching an ordered, or sorted, list of values. Consider the list of ordered values below and assume that we are searching for the value 25:

−7
2
14
38
52
77
105

As soon as you reached the value 38, you know that 25 was not in the list because you knew that the list was ordered. Therefore, we do not have to search the entire list, as we would have to do for an unordered list; we only need to search past the point where the key value should have been located. If the list is in ascending order, we search until the current value in the array is larger than the key; if the list is in descending order, we search until the current value in the array is smaller than the key.

We present two common algorithms for searching an ordered list. The first searches sequentially until we either find the item or recognize that we have passed the position where it would have been in the list. The second algorithm first checks the middle of the array and decides if the item for which we are searching is in the first half of the array or the second half of the array. If it is in the first half, we then check the middle of the first half and decide whether the item is in the first fourth of the array or the second fourth of the array. The process of dividing the array into smaller and smaller pieces continues until we find the element or find the position where it should have been. Since this technique continually divides the part of the array that we are searching in half, it is sometimes called a **binary search.**

The decomposition and pseudocode for a sequential search follow.

DECOMPOSITION

> Search ordered list for a specific value.

PSEUDOCODE FOR SEQUENTIALLY SEARCHING AN ORDERED LIST

(Assumes: the values are already in an ascending order in the array x; a variable *count* specifies the number of valid data values in the array; and the variable *key* contains the value for which we are searching.)

```
if count > 0 then
    done ← false
    i ← 1
else
    done ← true
    found ← false
while not done do
    if x[i] = key then
        done ← true
        found ← true
    else if x[i] > key then
        done ← true
        found ← false
    else
        i ← i + 1
    if i > count then
        done ← true
        found ← false
if found then
    statement to execute if key is found
else
    statement to execute if key is not found
```

Converting this to Pascal yields the following:

```
.
.
.
if  count > 0  then
    begin
        done := false;
        i := 1
    end
else
    begin
        done := true;
        found := false
    end;
while  not done  do
    begin
        if  x[i] = key  then
            begin
                done := true;
                found := true
            end
        else if  x[i] > key  then
            begin
                done := true;
                found := false
            end
        else
            i := i + 1;
        if  i > count  then
            begin
                done := true;
                found := false
            end
    end;
if  found  then
    statement to execute if key is found
else
    statement to execute if key is not found
```

We now illustrate the binary search algorithm with the list used in the previous example in which we were searching sequentially for the value 25.

−7
2
14
38
52
77
105

There are seven values, the first referenced by 1 and the last referenced by 7. In a binary search, we compute the middle position by adding the first position number to the last position number and dividing by two. This should be done as an integer division. In our case, 7 plus 1 equals 8, and 8 divided by 2 is 4. Thus, we

---

check the fourth position and compare its value to the value for which we are searching. The fourth value is 38, which is larger than 25, so we can narrow our search to the top half of the array. Our new first position is still 1, and our last position is 4. We now divide that part of the array in half and compute the new midpoint to be $(1 + 4)/2$, or 2. The second value is 2, which is smaller than 25, so we can narrow our search to the second quarter of the array. Our new first position is now 2 and our last position is 4. We again divide this part of the array in half and compute the new midpoint to be $(2 + 4)/2$, or 3. The third position contains 14, which is smaller than 25, so we again narrow our search. Our new first position is 3 and our last position is 4. When the first and last positions are consecutive, we have narrowed in on the position where the value should be, but have not found it. Thus, we can exit the search algorithm. This specific example is illustrated in the diagram below. Follow through each step to be sure that you understand the sequence of steps needed.

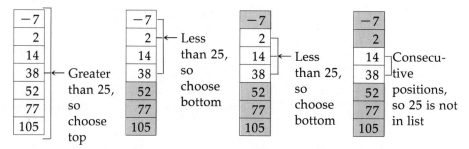

You may also want to go through an example with an even number of elements in the array to convince yourself that the algorithm will work properly for both odd and even numbers of elements. In the algorithm, we will need to check the first and last element of the list before beginning the binary search.

We now develop the detailed steps for searching an ordered list using a binary search.

DECOMPOSITION

Search ordered list for a specific value.

Pseudocode for Searching an Ordered List Using a Binary Search

(Assumes: the values are already in an ascending order in the array *x*; a variable *count* specifies the number of values in the array; and the variable *key* contains the value for which we are searching. The variable *middle* will be used to specify the position of the key value if it is in the list.)

```
if count ≤ 0 then
   found ← false
else
   done ← false
   found ← false
   first ← 1
   last ← count
   if x[first] = key then
      found ← true
      middle ← first
   else if x[last] = key then
      found ← true
      middle ← last
   else
      while not done do
         middle ← (first + last)/2
         if x[middle] = key then
            found ← true
            done ← true
         else if x[middle] > key then
            last ← middle
         else
            first ← middle
         if last = first + 1 then
            done ← true
if found then
   statement to execute if key is found
else
   statement to execute if key is not found
```

Converting this to Pascal yields the following:

PASCAL STATEMENTS

```
    .
    .
    .
if  count <= 0  then
    found := false
else
    begin
        done := false;
        found := false;
        first := 1;
        last := count;
        if  x[first] = key  then
            begin
                found := true;
                middle := first
            end
        else if  x[last] = key  then
            begin
                found := true;
                middle := last
            end
        else
            while  not done  do
                begin
                    middle := (first + last) div 2;
                    if  x[middle] = key  then
                        begin
                            found := true;
                            done := true
                        end
                    else if  x[middle] > key  then
                        last := middle
                    else
                        first := middle;
                        if  last = first + 1  then
                            done := true
                end
    end;
if  found  then
    statement to execute if key is found
else
    statement to execute if key is not found
```

While both the sequential sort and the binary search correctly search for an item in an ordered list, the sequential sort is more efficient for small lists, and the binary search is more efficient for large lists.

INSERTING AND DELETING

We now consider techniques to **insert** or **delete** an element in an ordered list. We will again assume that the list is ordered in an array and that the value of a variable *count* will specify how many of the elements in the array represent actual data values. Before we develop the pseudocode, we look at a simple hand example:

Original List

123
247
253
496

There are four valid entries in the array, although we assume that the size of the array might be much larger. Suppose we want to insert the value 147. Think through the steps as you perform them. You scan down the array until you find a value larger than 147, you move all the rest of the array elements down one position in the array, and then insert the new value in the position left open after moving the rest of the array down. (We use the terms "up one position in the array" to mean toward the top of the array, or the top of the page. "Down one position in the array" means toward the bottom of the array, or the bottom of the page.) The number of valid elements in the array has now been increased by 1. The new contents of the array are the following:

Modified List

123
147
247
253
496

Suppose we now want to insert the value 512. As we scan down the list, we find that we reach the end and the value to be inserted is greater than the last value in the list. We add the new value at the end of the list, and increment the count.

Modified List

123
147
247
253
496
512

Are there any special cases that can occur when inserting values in an ordered list? What happens if the value to be inserted is already in the list? If the list is updating the list of valid users for a computer system, we don't want to list the identification for a person more than once, so we would not insert the value again if it were already there; on the other hand, if the list represents bank transactions on a specific account, there could be multiple transactions on the same account, so we would want to add the additional information. As another special case, suppose the count equals the defined size of the array; that is, the array is full. To know how to handle this situation requires knowing more about the problem being solved. In some cases we would want to print an error message stating that the array was full and the value could not be added; in other cases we would want to insert the new value and move the rest of the elements down in the array until we reached the end of the array — thus losing the last value in the array. In our example, we will use this second alternative and lose the last value each time we insert a value in a full array.

We now develop the detailed steps for inserting in an ordered list.

DECOMPOSITION

> Add new item to ordered list.

PSEUDOCODE FOR INSERTING AN ELEMENT IN AN ORDERED LIST

(Assumes: the values are already in an ascending order in the array x; a variable *count* specifies the number of valid data values in the array; the variable *arraysize* contains the defined size of the array; the variable *new* contains the value to be inserted in the array; and we will add the new value to the array even if it is already in the array.)

INITIAL REFINEMENT

```
if count = arraysize then
    write message that last value will be lost
done ← false
i ← 1
while (i ≤ count) and (not done) then
    if x[i] < new value then
        i ← i + 1
    else
        done ← true
if i > count then
    update count
    add new value at end of list of values
else
    update count
    insert new value at this point in list
```

We still need to refine a couple of these steps. When we exit the *while* loop, the first *if* structure tests to see if *i* is greater than *count*. If the condition is true, the new element goes at the end of the values. Thus, if the array is not full, we increment the count and add the new value at the end of the list of valid values; however, if the array is already full, we do nothing because the new value would belong at the end of the list of valid values, and there is no room there.

When the new value belongs within the list, we must insert it carefully. First we go to the end of the valid data and move the last value down one position. Then we can move the next-to-the-last value in the position vacated. We continue to move values down until we have moved the value in the position where the new value is to be inserted; we can then insert the new value. If the array is full when we perform the insertion, the value in the last position will be lost. The final pseudocode refinement details these steps.

FINAL REFINEMENT

```
if count = arraysize then
   write message that last value will be lost
done ← false
i ← 1
while (i ≤ count) and (not done) then
   if x[i] < new value then
      i ← i + 1
   else
      done ← true
if i > count then
   if count < arraysize then
      count ← count + 1
      x[count] ← new value
else
   if count < arraysize then
      count ← count + 1
   for k = count downto i+1 do
      x[k] ← x[k−1]
   x[i] ← new value
```

Before we convert this to Pascal, consider the situation of inserting a value in an empty list, that is, a list which has no valid data values in it and thus has a count of zero. Look at the pseudocode and see if it will handle this situation. (It does, but be sure that you are convinced.) Converting this final refinement to Pascal yields the following:

PASCAL STATEMENTS

```
   .
   .
   .
if  count = arraysize  then
    writeln ('ARRAY IS FULL - LAST VALUE WILL BE LOST');
done := false;
i := 1;
while  (i <= count) and (not done)  do
    if  x[i] < new  then
        i := i + 1
    else
        done := true;
if  i > count  then
    begin
        if  count < arraysize  then
            begin
                count := count + 1;
                x[count] := new
            end
    end
else
    begin
        if  count < arraysize  then
            count := count + 1;
        for k := count downto i+1 do
            x[k] := x[k-1];
        x[i] := new
    end
```

The insertion technique is not trivial. It requires a thorough understanding of arrays and subscript handling. Go through the pseudocode and corresponding Pascal statements until you understand the steps.

After you master the insertion technique, you will find the deletion technique easier because there are many similarities. We again assume that the list is ordered in an array and that the value of a variable *count* will specify how many of the elements in the array represent actual data values. Let's begin with a simple hand example:

Original List
123
247
253
496

As before, there are four valid entries in the original array, but we still assume that the actual size of the array could be larger. Suppose we want to delete value 253. Think through the steps as you perform them: you scan down the array until you find the value, you remove the value, and you move the rest of the array values up one position in the array. The number of valid elements in the array has now been decreased by 1. The new contents of the array are the following:

Modified List

123
247
496

Are there any special cases that can occur when deleting values in an ordered list? What happens if the value to be deleted is not in the list? In this situation, we probably want to print a message to the user. What happens if we delete the only element in the list? In this situation, the count will be decremented to the value zero and we will have an empty list.

We are now ready to develop the detailed steps for deleting an item in an ordered list.

DECOMPOSITION

> Delete old item from ordered list.

PSEUDOCODE FOR DELETING AN ELEMENT IN AN ORDERED LIST

(Assumes: the values are already in an ascending order in the array x; a variable *count* specifies the number of valid data values in the array; and the variable *old* contains the value to be deleted from the array.)

INITIAL REFINEMENT

```
done ← false
i ← 1
while (i ≤ count) and (not done) do
    if x[i] < old then
        i ← i + 1
    else
        done ← true
if (i > count) or (x[i] > old) then
    write message that value is not in list
else
    update count
    delete old value from list
```

Will this pseudocode handle the situation in which the array is empty? Since *count* will be equal to zero, the condition in the *while* loop will be false the first time it is tested, because the value of i is 1. A message will be printed that the value is not in the list, which handles the situation properly.

We still need to refine a couple of the steps in the pseudocode. When we exit the *while* loop, the first *if* structure tests to see if the element was actually in the loop. If we searched until we reached the end of the loop *(i > count)* or until we passed the position where the element should have been *(x[i] > old)*, we write a

---

message indicating that the element was not in the list. If the element was in the list, we need to subtract one from the count and "delete old value from list." However, we really do not explicitly delete the old value. Instead, we move the value below the old value up one position in the array, the value below that one up one position in the array, and so on until we have moved all the values below the one to be deleted up one position in the array. The final pseudocode refinement details these steps.

FINAL REFINEMENT

```
done ← false
i ← 1
while (i ≤ count) and (not done) do
   if x[i] < old then
      i ← i + 1
   else
      done ← true
if (i > count) or (x[i] > old) then
   write message that value is not in list
else
   count ← count − 1
   for k = i to count do
      x[k] ← x[k+1]
```

Converting this final pseudocode to Pascal yields the following statements:

PASCAL STATEMENTS

```
.
.
.
done := false;
i := 1;
while (i <= count) and (not done)  do
   if  x[i] < old  then
      i := i + 1
   else
      done := true;
if  i > count  then
   writeln ('VALUE TO DELETE IS NOT IN LIST')
else if  x[i] > old  then
   writeln ('VALUE TO DELETE IS NOT IN LIST')
else
   begin
      count := count − 1;
      for k := i to count do
         x[k] := x[k+1]
   end
```

The compound condition (which determined whether or not the value to delete was in the list) was divided into two separate conditions in the Pascal statements because it would be invalid to examine $x[i]$ if i were greater than the array size.

The deletion technique should be easier to follow once you have mastered the insertion technique. As you have seen, both techniques require a clear understanding of how to handle arrays and subscripts. After you learn the steps involved in these techniques, you will find that all the rest of the techniques and problems that we solve with arrays are much simpler to understand.

SORTING

In this section we develop algorithms to sort a one-dimensional array into **ascending,** or low-to-high, order. (With minor alterations, the algorithm can be changed to one that sorts into **descending,** high-to-low, order. We will also see in Chapter 8 that these sort algorithms can be used to alphabetize character data.) The topic of sorting techniques is the subject of entire textbooks and courses; therefore this text will not attempt to present all the important aspects of sorting.* Instead, we present three common sorting techniques and develop pseudocode and Pascal solutions for all three so that you can compare the different techniques.

Selection sort   This is a simple sort that is based on finding the minimum value and placing it first in the list, finding the next smallest value and placing it second in the list, and so on.

Bubble sort   This is a simple sort that is based on interchanging adjacent values in the array until all the values are in the proper position. This sort is sometimes called a multipass sort.

Insertion sort   This sort begins at the top of the list, comparing adjacent elements. If an element is out of order, it is continually exchanged with the value above it in the list until it is in its proper place. The sort then continues with the next element out of order.

In all three sorts, we will use only one array. If you need to keep the original order of the data as well as the sorted data, copy the original data into a second array and sort it.

Selection Sort   We begin the discussion of the selection sort with a hand example. Consider the list of data values below:

Original List

4.1
7.3
1.7
5.2
1.3

In this algorithm, we first find the minimum value. Scanning down the list, we find that the last value, 1.3, is the minimum. We now want to put the value 1.3 in the first position of the array, but we do not want to lose the value 4.1 that is currently in the first position. Therefore, we will exchange the values.

---

* An excellent chapter on sorting is contained in *Algorithms + Data Structures = Programs*, by Niklaus Wirth (Prentice-Hall, 1976).

The switch of two values requires three steps, not two as you might imagine. Consider the statements below:

```
x[i] := x[j];
x[j] := x[i]
```

Suppose *x[i]* contained the value 3.0 and *x[j]* contained the value −1.0. The first statement will change the contents of *x[i]* from the value 3.0 to the value −1.0. The second statement will move the value in *x[i]* to *x[j]*, so that both locations contain −1.0. These steps are shown below, along with the changes in the corresponding memory locations.

	x[i]	x[j]
	3.0	−1.0
x[i] := x[j];	−1.0	−1.0
x[j] := x[i]	−1.0	−1.0

A correct way to switch the two values is shown below, along with the changes in the corresponding memory locations.

	x[i]	x[j]	hold
	3.0	−1.0	?
hold := x[i];	3.0	−1.0	3.0
x[i] := x[j];	−1.0	−1.0	3.0
x[j] := hold	−1.0	3.0	3.0

Once we have switched the first value in the array with the value that has the minimum value, we search the values in the array from the second value to the last value for the minimum in that list. We then switch the second value with the minimum. We continue this until we are looking at the next-to-last and last values. If they are out of order, we switch them. At this point, the entire array will be sorted into an ascending order, as shown in the diagram below:

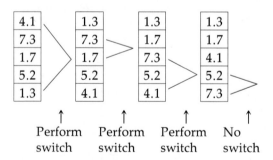

| Perform switch | Perform switch | Perform switch | No switch |

We now develop the pseudocode and Pascal statements for this selection sort.

> Sort list of data values into ascending order.

In the refinement below, notice that we do not keep track of the minimum value itself. Instead we are interested in keeping track of the index or location of the minimum value. We need its subscript in order to be able to switch positions with another element in the array. Since the portion of the array that we search for the next minimum gets smaller, we use two variables, *first* and *last*, to keep track of this array portion. *First* will start at 2 and increment by one each time we do a switch. *Last* will always be equal to *count* since we search to the bottom of the list of valid values each time.

PSEUDOCODE FOR SELECTION SORT

(Assumes: the values are already stored in the array *x*; and a variable *count* specifies the number of valid data values in the array.)

INITIAL REFINEMENT

```
for i = 1 to count−1 do
   indexmin ← i
   first ← i + 1
   last ← count
   for k = first to last do
      if x[k] < x[indexmin] then
         indexmin ← k
   switch values in x[i] and x[indexmin]
```

The only step that needs more detail is the step to switch values, because we must specify the three different moves that are necessary.

FINAL REFINEMENT

```
for i = 1 to count−1 do
   indexmin ← i
   first ← i + 1
   last ← count
   for k = first to last do
      if x[k] < x[indexmin] then
         indexmin ← k
   hold ← x[i]
   x[i] ← x[indexmin]
   x[indexmin] ← hold
```

Converting this final pseudocode to Pascal statements gives the following:

```
    .
    .
    .
for i := 1 to count-1 do
   begin
       indexmin := i;
       first := i + 1;
       last := count;
       for k := first to last do
          if  x[k] < x[indexmin]   then
              indexmin := k;
       hold := x[i];
       x[i] := x[indexmin];
       x[indexmin] := hold
   end
```

Bubble Sort The basic step to the bubble sort algorithm is a single pass through the array, comparing adjacent elements. If a pair of adjacent elements is in the correct order (that is, the first value less than or equal to the second value), we go to the next pair. If the pair is out of order, we switch the values and then go to the next pair.

The single pass through the array can be performed in a counting loop with index i. Each pair of adjacent values will be referred to by the subscripts i and $i+1$. If the number of valid data elements in the array is stored in *count*, we will make *count−1* comparisons of adjacent values in a single pass through the array.

A single pass through a one-dimensional array, switching adjacent elements which are out of order, is not guaranteed to sort the values. Consider a single pass through the following array:

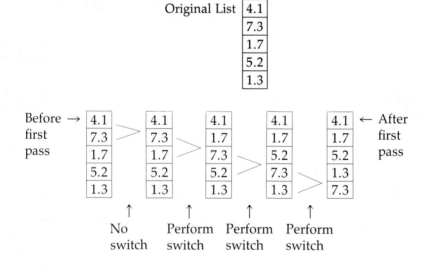

It will take two more complete passes before the array is sorted into ascending order, as shown in the diagram below:

After first pass

4.1
1.7
5.2
1.3
7.3

After second pass

1.7
4.1
1.3
5.2
7.3

After third pass

1.7
1.3
4.1
5.2
7.3

After fourth pass

1.3
1.7
4.1
5.1
7.3

A maximum of *count* passes may be necessary to sort an array with this technique. If no switches are made during a single pass through the array, however, it is in ascending order. Thus, our algorithm for sorting a one-dimensional array will be to perform single passes through the array making switches until no elements are out of order. In developing the pseudocode, we use a Boolean variable *sorted* that is initialized to true at the beginning of each pass through the data array. If any adjacent values are out of order, we switch the values and change the value of *sorted* to false because at least one pair of values was out of order on the pass. Then, at the end of a pass through the data, if the value of *sorted* is still true, the array is in ascending order.

We will make one more addition to the algorithm. Observe that during the first pass through the array, we switch any adjacent pairs that are out of order. Although this does not necessarily sort the entire array, it is guaranteed to move the largest value to the bottom of the list. During the second pass, the next-largest value will be moved to the next-to-the last position. Therefore, when we make each pass through the array, we must start at the first position, but we do not need to check values all the way to the end. In fact, with each pass, we can reduce the number of positions that we check by 1.

We now develop the pseudocode and Pascal statements for this bubble sort.

DECOMPOSITION

Sort list of data values into ascending order.

PSEUDOCODE FOR BUBBLE SORT

(Assumes: the values are already stored in the array *x*; and a variable *count* specifies the number of valid data values in the array.)

INITIAL REFINEMENT

```
sorted ← false
first ← 1
last ← count − 1
while not sorted do
   sorted ← true
   for i = first to last do
      if x[i] > x[i+1] then
         switch values
         sorted ← false
   last ← last − 1
```

The only step that needs more detail is the step to switch values, because we need to specify the three different moves that are necessary.

FINAL REFINEMENT

```
sorted ← false
first ← 1
last ← count − 1
while not sorted do
   sorted ← true
   for i = first to last do
      if x[i] > x[i+1] then
         hold ← x[i]
         x[i] ← x[i+1]
         x[i+1] ← hold
         sorted ← false
   last ← last − 1
```

Converting this final pseudocode to Pascal statements gives the following:

PASCAL STATEMENTS

```
   .
   .
   .
sorted := false;
first := 1;
last := count - 1;
while  not sorted  do
   begin
      sorted := true;
      for i := first to last do
         if  x[i] > x[i+1]  then
            begin
               hold := x[i];
               x[i] := x[i+1];
               x[i+1] := hold;
               sorted := false
            end;
      last := last - 1
   end
```

Insertion Sort The insertion sort begins at the beginning of the list, comparing adjacent elements. If an element is out of order, we switch it with the previous element and check to see if it is now in its proper place. If not, we switch it with the new previous element, and again check. We continue moving the element up in the array until it is in its proper position. We then return to the position in the list where we located the element out of order and pick up at that point, comparing the next pair of adjacent elements. When we reach the end of the list, it will be in order since each element that we found out of order was inserted in its proper position before we continued. The following diagram shows these steps with our sample array:

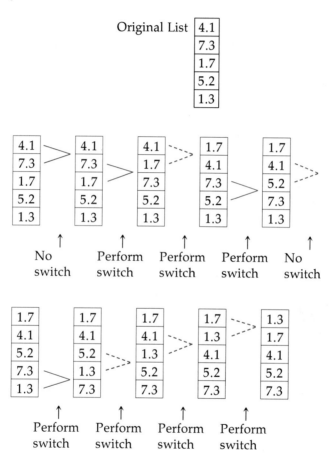

We now develop the pseudocode and Pascal statements for this insertion sort.

DECOMPOSITION

> Sort list of data values into ascending order.

In the refinement below, notice that we use the index i of the counting loop to point to our position before we begin backing up in the array to find the proper position for the element out of order. After putting the element in the correct spot, we can jump back to the next pair of elements in the list that we need to compare since the value of the index i has not been changed.

PSEUDOCODE FOR INSERTION SORT

(Assumes: the values are already stored in the array x; and a variable *count* specifies the number of valid data values in the array.)

INITIAL REFINEMENT

```
for i = 1 to count−1 do
  if x[i] > x[i+1] then
    done ← false
    k ← i
    while not done do
      switch x[k] with x[k+1]
      if (k = 1) or (x[k] ≥ x[k − 1]) then
        done ← true
      else
        k ← k − 1
```

Again, the only step that needs more detail for the final refinement is the step to switch values because of the three different moves that are necessary.

FINAL REFINEMENT

```
for i = 1 to count−1 do
  if x[i] > x[i+1] then
    done ← false
    k ← i
    while not done do
      hold ← x[k]
      x[k] ← x[k+1]
      x[k+1] ← hold
      if (k = 1) or (x[k] ≥ x[k − 1]) then
        done ← true
      else
        k ← k − 1
```

Converting this final pseudocode to Pascal statements gives the following:

PASCAL STATEMENTS

```
    .
    .
    .
for i := 1 to count-1 do
    if  x[i] > x[i+1]   then
        begin
            done := false;
            k := i;
            while  not done  do
                begin
                    hold := x[k];
                    x[k] := x[k+1];
                    x[k+1] := hold;
                    if  k = 1   then
                        done := true
                    else if  x[k] >= x[k-1]   then
                        done := true
                    else
                        k := k - 1
                end
        end
```

The final condition was separated into two separate conditions in the Pascal statements because it would be invalid to examine $x[k-1]$ if $k = 1$.

In the rest of this text, we will frequently refer to the common techniques that we have developed in this section.

This self-test allows you to check quickly to see if you have remembered certain key points from Section 4-5. If you have any problems with the exercises, you should reread this section. The solutions are included at the end of the text.

Consider the following list with six elements in it:

16
83
91
25
9
72

1. Show the sequence of changes that occur in the list if it is sorted using the selection sort algorithm.
2. Show the sequence of changes that occur in the list if it is sorted using the bubble sort algorithm.
3. Show the sequence of changes that occur in the list if it is sorted using the insertion sort algorithm.

4-6 PROBLEM SOLVING—EARTHQUAKE MEASUREMENTS

In this application we analyze data that might be collected in a field laboratory that monitors seismic (earthquake) activity. This data is collected by instruments called seismometers that are located around the world. Suppose that a particular location in California has been the site of earthquake activity for a number of years. The magnitude of each event has been recorded using the Richter scale. This data is stored in a data file *motion* in the chronological order in which the earthquakes occurred. Write a program to read this information, sort it into ascending order based on magnitude, and print the data in this new order.

The initial line of the data file contains a 5-digit integer that represents the location number for the laboratory. When new earthquakes occur, the information is added to the end of the file. Therefore, you do not know ahead of time how many data values are in the file. You can, however, assume an upper limit of 200 data values. You can also assume that a trailer signal, the last entry in the file, has a measurement of 0.0. You will need to store the data in an array since you are going to sort it.

PROBLEM STATEMENT

Sort a group of earthquake measurements into ascending order and print the values in the new order.

INPUT/OUTPUT DESCRIPTION

The earthquake measurements are stored in a data file, one value per line. The first line of the data file contains the location number of the area. The number of entries in the file is not known ahead of time, but there is a trailer signal with the value 0.0. The output is to be a listing of the same set of data, sorted into ascending order.

HAND EXAMPLE

Using the following example test file data, we sort the data into ascending order and print it.

Data File *motion*
23511
2.5810
1.5000
1.6200
3.7800
4.2500
1.7330
0.0000

Sorted Output List
1.5000
1.6200
1.7330
2.5810
3.7800
4.2500

ALGORITHM DEVELOPMENT

In Section 4-5 we presented three different sort techniques. Any of the three techniques could be used in this example; we have selected the first sort algorithm, the selection sort. You may want to review the selection sort algorithm before continuing with this development.

The decomposition of this problem solution is shown on the next page.

DECOMPOSITION

Read location number.
Write location number.
Read quake values.
Sort quake values.
Write quake values.

We now add details to these steps using pseudocode.

INITIAL REFINEMENT IN PSEUDOCODE

```
seismic: read location number
         write location number
         i ← 1
         read quake[i]
         while quake[i] > 0.0 do
            i ← i + 1
            read quake[i]
         count ← i − 1
         sort quake array
         write quake array
```

We now refine the sort step using the selection sort algorithm. The steps are copied here from the previous section, with the appropriate change in variable names.

FINAL REFINEMENT IN PSEUDOCODE

```
seismic: read location number
         write location number
         i ← 1
         read quake[i]
         while quake[i] > 0.0 do
            i ← i + 1
            read quake[i]
         count ← i − 1
         for i = 1 to count−1 do
            indexmin ← i
            first ← i + 1
            last ← count
            for k = first to last do
               if quake[k] < quake[indexmin] then
                  indexmin ← k
            hold ← quake[i]
            quake[i] ← quake[indexmin]
            quake[indexmin] ← hold
         write quake array
```

We are now ready to convert these steps into a Pascal program.

PASCAL PROGRAM

```
{- - - - - - - - - - - - - - - - - - - - - - - - - - - - - - - - - - - - - - - - - - - - - - - - - -}
program  seismic (motion,output);
    {This program reads a data file of earthquake data,
    sorts it in ascending order, and prints it.}
type
    index = 1..200;
    list = array[index] of real;
var
    hold: real;
    id, count, indexmin, first, last: integer;
    motion: text;
    i, k: index;
    quake: list;
begin
    reset (motion);
    readln (motion,id);
    i := 1;
    readln (motion,quake[i]);
    while  quake[i] > 0.0  do
        begin
            i := i + 1;
            readln (motion,quake[i])
        end;
    count := i - 1;

    for i := 1 to count-1 do
        begin
            indexmin := i;
            first := i + 1;
            last := count;
            for k := first to last do
                if  quake[k] < quake[indexmin]  then
                    indexmin := k;
            hold := quake[i];
            quake[i] := quake[indexmin];
            quake[indexmin] := hold
        end;

    writeln ('FIELD LABORATORY ',id:5,' MEASUREMENTS');
    for i := 1 to count do
        writeln (i:3,'.',quake[i]:9:3)
end.
{- - - - - - - - - - - - - - - - - - - - - - - - - - - - - - - - - - - - - - - - - - - - - - - - - -}
```

TESTING

As our programs become longer, testing becomes more of a challenge; a good plan is to test the program in pieces. For instance, test the input portion of this program without executing the rest of the program. An easy way to accomplish this is by enclosing the statements following the input portion in braces, { and }. Then add statements to write the values of the variables being read so you can see what the program is doing. When you are convinced that the input portion is working, move the braces so you can test the sort algorithm. To test the sort program, use a small data set initially so that you are not overwhelmed with data. If the sort is not working properly, insert a counting loop to print the *quake* array data elements inside the compound statement in the sort algorithm. This will allow you to see what happens each time a pair of values are switched. Notice how these pieces that we test individually correspond to the overall steps in the initial decomposition.

When you have the algorithm working, be sure to use a variety of test data sets. Use sets that are already in order and sets that are in reverse order, in addition to sequences in random order. The output from the sample set of data used in the hand example follows.

COMPUTER OUTPUT

```
FIELD LABORATORY 23511 MEASUREMENTS
   1.     1.500
   2.     1.620
   3.     1.733
   4.     2.581
   5.     3.780
   6.     4.250
```

There is one last point to make. After sorting the array *quake*, we changed the order of the values from one that was sequential in time to one that is in ascending order. In doing this, we lost the original order within our program. The data file is still in the original order, but our program has the data in ascending order only. If the program also needed the original data, we could move the original data into a second array after it was read. Then, after sorting, we would have two arrays of data—one in the original order and one in ascending order.

SUMMARY

In this chapter we learned how to use a one-dimensional array—a data structure composed of a group of memory locations that all have a common name but are distinguished by a subscript. Arrays prove to be one of the most powerful elements of Pascal because they allow us to keep large amounts of data easily accessible. Other important topics that were presented in this chapter are the common techniques used with one-dimensional arrays. The searching, inserting, deleting, and sorting algorithms are frequently used in engineering and science applications.

DEBUGGING AIDS

Because arrays are so convenient for handling large amounts of data, a natural tendency is to overuse them — and, unfortunately, arrays can also introduce new errors. As you debug programs that use arrays, consider the decision to use each array. Ask yourself, "Will I need this data more than once?" "Must this data be stored before I can use it?" If the answers to both questions are no, you should eliminate the array and replace it with simple variables. At the same time, you will probably be eliminating some loops and statements involving subscripts. These changes may not only reduce the number of errors in your program but also reduce its overall complexity.

If arrays are necessary and your program is not working correctly, consider each of the following items:

Size   The array specification must specify the maximum number of elements that are to be stored in the array. Although you do not have to use all the elements of an array, you can never use more elements than originally specified.

Subscript   Check each subscript to be sure that it represents a value that falls within the proper range of values. Particularly check for subscript values that are one value too small or one value too large.

For **Loop**   If you are using the index of a *for* loop as a subscript, be sure you have used the same variable identifier in your statements. That is, if the *for* loop index is k, did you use i instead of k as a subscript?

STYLE/TECHNIQUE GUIDELINES

Use the type section of a Pascal program to define and name all new data types used in your program. This not only documents your data structures, but also makes it easy to find new data type definitions if they are all together in the type section as opposed to being spread between the type section and the variable section.

A good program can be distinguished by the way that it uses data structures. Take the time to carefully choose the structure that best fits the data used in a program, rather than forcing the data to fit a specific structure. Pascal has a wealth of data structures, and it is well worth learning to be proficient in their use.

KEY WORDS

array

ascending order

binary search

bubble sort

data file

deletion

descending order

element

end-of-file

enumerated data type

index

insertion

insertion sort

list

one-dimensional array

ordinal data type

scalar data type

selection sort

sentinel signal

subrange data type

subscript

text files

trailer signal

PROBLEMS

We begin our problem set with modifications to programs developed in this chapter. Give the decomposition, refined pseudocode, and Pascal program for each problem.

Problems 1–5 modify the average snowfall program *snowfall*, given on page 163.

1. Modify the snowfall average program so that it prints the number of days in the month with no snowfall.
2. Modify the snowfall average program so that it prints the maximum snowfall and the day(s) on which it occurred.
3. Modify the snowfall average program so that it prints the minimum snowfall and the number of days on which it occurred.
4. Modify the snowfall average program so that it prints the longest number of consecutive days for which there was no snowfall.
5. Modify the snowfall average program so that it prints the longest number of consecutive days for which there was measurable snowfall.

Problems 6–10 modify the integrated circuit defect program *quality*, given on page 168.

6. Modify the quality analysis program so that it prints the number of broken wire defects, defective IC components, and defective non-IC components.
7. Modify the quality analysis program so that it computes and prints the total number of defects.
8. Modify the quality analysis program so that it determines and prints the number of boards with more than one defect.
9. Modify the quality analysis program so that it determines and prints the number of boards with defects in all three categories.

10. Modify the quality analysis program so that it determines and prints the identification numbers of all boards with a total of three or more defects. This list should be printed after the summary report.

Problems 11 – 15 modify the earthquake measurement program *seismic*, given on page 199.

11. Modify the earthquake measurement program so that it sorts the data values into descending order.
12. Modify the earthquake measurement program so that it prints the average earthquake value.
13. Modify the earthquake measurement program so that it prints the maximum earthquake value.
14. Modify the earthquake measurement program so that it prints the median earthquake value.
15. Modify the earthquake measurement program so that it computes and prints the number of earthquake values that are in the same position in the list both before and after the ascending sort.

For problems 16 – 19, assume that k, a one-dimensional array of 50 integer values, has already been filled with data.

16. Give Pascal statements to find and print the maximum value of k in the following form:

                    MAXIMUM VALUE IS XXXXX

17. Give Pascal statements to find and print the minimum value of k and its position or positions in the array, in the following form:

                    MINIMUM VALUE OF K IS
                    K[XX] = XXXXX

18. Give Pascal statements to count the number of positive values, zero values, and negative values in k. The output form should be:

                    XXX POSITIVE VALUES
                    XXX ZERO VALUES
                    XXX NEGATIVE VALUES

19. Give Pascal statements to replace each value of k with its absolute value; then print the array k, two values per line.

Develop these programs and program segments. Use the five-phase design process for all complete programs.

20. An array *time* contains 30 integers. Give statements that will print every other value, beginning with the second value, in this form:

```
TIME[ 2] CONTAINS XXXX SECONDS
TIME[ 4] CONTAINS XXXX SECONDS
        .
        .
        .
TIME[30] CONTAINS XXXX SECONDS
```

21. Give Pascal statements to print the last 10 elements of a real array *m* of size *n*. For instance, if *m* contains 25 elements, the output form is:

```
M[ 16] = XXX.X
M[ 17] = XXX.X
     .
     .
     .
M[ 25] = XXX.X
```

22. Give Pascal statements to interchange the first and hundredth elements, the second and ninety-ninth elements, and so on, of the array *number*, which contains 100 integer values. See the following diagram.

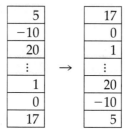

23. An array *test* contains integer test scores from 100 exams. Give the Pascal statements necessary to find the average of the first 50 exams and the second 50 exams. Print the following:

```
                AVERAGES
  1ST 50 EXAMS      2ND 50 EXAMS
     XXX.XX            XXX.XX
```

24. Write a complete program that will read as many as 20 integers from a file *numbers*, one integer per line. The last line will contain 9999. Write the data in the reverse order from which it was read. (The value 9999 will be the first value printed.)

25. When a plot is made from experimental data, sometimes the data points are so scattered that it is difficult to select a "best representative line" for the plot. In this case, the data can be adjusted to reduce the scatter by using a "moving average" mathematical method of finding the average of three points in succession and replacing the middle value with this average.

   Write a complete program to read an array *y* of 20 real values from a file *experiment* where the values are entered one per line. Build an array *z* of 20 values where *z* is the array of adjusted values. That is, $z[2]$ is the average of

$y[1]$, $y[2]$, and $y[3]$; $z[3]$ is the average of $y[2]$, $y[3]$, and $y[4]$; and so on. Notice that the first and last values of y cannot be adjusted and should be moved to z without being changed. Do not destroy the original values in y. Print the original and the adjusted values next to each other in a table.

26. A life insurance company has 12 salespeople. Each salesperson receives a commission on monthly sales that is dependent on the percentage of overall sales he or she sold. This commission is based on the following table:

PERCENT OF SALES	COMMISSION RATE
0.00–24.99	0.02
25.00–74.99	0.04
75.00–100.00	0.06

An identification number and the monthly sales in dollars are entered into a data file *sales*. Write a complete program to read the data, convert each salesperson's sales to a percentage of the total sales, and compute his or her commission. Print the following report:

```
           MONTHLY COMMISSION REPORT
    ID      SALES      PERCENT      COMMISSION
    XXX    $ XXXXX.     XXX.XX     $ XXXXX.XX
     .
     .
     .
   TOTALS  $XXXXXX.     XXX.XX     $XXXXXX.XX
```

Test your program with the following input data:

ID	SALES
002	9000
009	10050
012	550
016	1000
025	15000
036	20000
037	85000
040	4000
043	1250
044	0
045	400
046	850

27. Write a complete program to convert a Gregorian date in month-day-year form to a Julian date, which is the year followed by the number of the day in the year (1 to 366). For example, 010982 should be converted to 82009, and 052283 should be converted to 83142. Be sure to take leap years into account. (*Hint:* Use an array to store the number of days in each month.)

28. Write a complete program to convert a Julian date into a Gregorian date, again taking leap years into account. (See problem 27.)

29. When a certain telephone company monitors local calls from a given phone, it records the seven-digit number called in a data file called *dial*. Write a

program to read the data file and print each number called. If a number is called more than once, it should be printed only once. No more than 500 different numbers are ever dialed in one monitored period. The numbers are entered one per line in the data file. The last line contains a trailer signal of 9999999.

Assume that a data file called *exams* contains four integers per line. The four integers represent a student ID number and exam scores on three exams. The last line of the data file contains a student ID of 999 and exam scores of zero. Use this data file in the following problems.

30. Write a Pascal program to read the information in the data file *exams*. Sort the student ID numbers, and print the list of student ID numbers in ascending order. List the corresponding exam scores for a student on the same line as the student ID number.

31. Write a Pascal program to read the information in the data file *exams*. Compute the exam average for each student, and print the student ID number and corresponding exam average, in descending order. Also compute and print the overall class average on the combined exams.

32. Write a Pascal program to read the information in the data file *exams*. Sort the set of grades for each exam in descending order, and then print them in the following format:

```
SORTED EXAM GRADES FOR THREE EXAMS

EXAM 1        EXAM II       EXAM III
  XXX           XXX           XXX
  XXX           XXX           XXX
```

PASCAL STATEMENT SUMMARY

Reset Statement:

reset (*filename*)

Example:

reset (**experiment1**)

Discussion:

The *reset* statement prepares a data file to be used as input to a Pascal program. It must be executed before data can be read from the file. If another *reset* statement is executed after some of the data has been read, the pointers used with the file will be reset and the next input statement will begin reading at the beginning of the data file.

Rewrite Statement:

rewrite (*filename*)

Example:

rewrite (**summary**)

Discussion:

The *rewrite* statement prepares a data file to be used as output from a Pascal program. It must be executed before data can be written in the file.

PROBLEM SOLVING — Oil Well Production

Computer programs are used to analyze many types of
information. In a large oil-producing company, they would be
used to keep track of oil well production, in addition to printing a
variety of reports for internal use by the company and for
distribution outside the company. It is important that reports
distributed outside the company be designed to summarize the
important information and to be attractive. Companies often use
standardized header information at the top of each page of their
reports. This information is likely to include the company name,
report title, date printed, and a page number. The steps to print
this header must be repeated each time a new page is printed.
Write a program to print a report summarizing oil well production
and use a special header at the top of each page. (See Section 5-3
for the solution.)

5

IMPLEMENTING TOP-DOWN DESIGN WITH PROCEDURES

INTRODUCTION

As programs become longer and more complicated, it becomes harder to maintain the readability and simplicity of shorter programs. Additionally, we frequently need to repeat a set of steps at several places in the programs. Both of these problems can be solved with **procedures,** groups of statements that are defined separately and referenced when we need them in a program. In this chapter, we show you how to write procedures and how to use them in your programs. Examples illustrate the usefulness of this technique both in improving program readability and in implementing the same set of steps at several places. Since a procedure is defined as a separate set of statements, a new structure is necessary.

5-1 PROGRAM MODULARITY

In previous chapters we stressed the importance of using top-down design techniques in algorithms and programs. The *while* loop and *if* structures are essential ingredients in structured programming. Another key element in simplifying program logic is the use of modules. These **modules,** called **procedures** and **functions** in Pascal, allow us to write programs composed of nearly independent segments or routines. In fact, when we decompose the problem solution into a series of sequentially executed steps, we are decomposing the problem into a set of modules. Many of the steps in block diagrams could be structured very easily into procedures and functions. There are some important advantages to breaking programs into modules:

1. You can write and test each module separately from the rest of the program.
2. Debugging is easier because you are working with smaller sections of the program.
3. Modules can be used in other programs without rewriting or retesting.
4. Programs are more readable and thus more easily understood because of the modular structure.
5. Several programmers can work on different modules of a large program relatively independent of one another.
6. Individual parts of the program become shorter and therefore simpler.
7. A module can be used several times by the same program.

Since modules are so important in writing readable, well-structured programs, we are going to present procedures in this chapter and functions in the next chapter. The similarities and differences in the two types of modules are easier to see if we study them one at a time.

We have used the decomposition diagram to show the sequential steps necessary to solve a problem. Another type of diagram is also very useful as we decompose our problem solution into smaller problems. This new type of diagram, called a **structure chart** or **module chart,** is especially useful in decomposing the problem solution into modules. While the decomposition diagram outlines the sequential operations needed, the structure diagram outlines the modules but does not indicate the order in which they are to be executed.

The diagram below contains a structure chart for a program similar to the one described at the beginning of the chapter. In this program, we are reading oil well production data from a data file. For each oil well, we read the daily production in barrels, compute a daily average for the week, and print this information in the report. In addition, we keep summary information for all the wells and print it at the end of the report. A report heading module is used at the beginning of each page to print the header information.

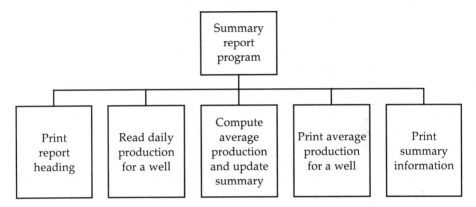

It is important to distinguish between a decomposition diagram and the structure chart. The decomposition diagram for this program, below, shows the sequential order of the steps of the solution.

DECOMPOSITION

Print heading.
Generate report.
Print summary information.

Note that the decomposition does not identify any of the steps as modules. The structure chart, on the other hand, clearly defines the module definitions for the program, but does not show the order in which the modules are used. Thus, both charts are useful in describing the algorithm that is being developed for the problem solution.

5-2 USER-WRITTEN PROCEDURES

The Pascal programs that we have written are composed of a program header (which gives the program a name and then identifies the files to be used in the program), followed by the definition of the constants and variables to be used in the program, and finally the actual statements to be executed, which are enclosed in *begin* and *end* statements. If we remove the program header, the remaining statements are referred to as a **block.** Thus, our programs have consisted of a program header and a block. Similarly, a procedure consists of a **procedure header** and a block, differing only slightly from a program. The procedure header assigns a name to the procedure and specifies the **procedure parameters,** which indicate the input and output of the procedure. The block following the procedure header includes definitions of constants and variables to be used in the procedure, along with the statements that define the steps performed by the procedure.

Since a procedure is part of the program, it is compiled at the same time that the program is compiled. Its location is inside the program block, just after the variable definition. The order of statements in a Pascal program is:

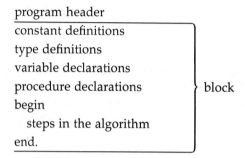

```
program header
constant definitions
type definitions
variable declarations          } block
procedure declarations
begin
    steps in the algorithm
end.
```

From the above description, you can see that we have expanded our definition of a block to include procedure definitions. Since a procedure is a procedure header and a block, it can have other procedure definitions within it. Procedures defined within another procedure are called **nested procedures.** The *end* statement for each procedure is followed by a semicolon to distinguish it from the *end* statement for the program, which is followed by a period.

To introduce procedures, we present the syntax diagrams for the procedure definition, the procedure header, and the statement that references (or **invokes**) the procedure. We then present a simple example to illustrate the process of writing and using a procedure. After the example, we give a thorough discussion of the effective use of procedures.

The syntax diagrams for the procedure definition and the procedure header follow.

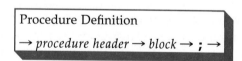

Procedure Definition

→ *procedure header* → *block* → **;** →

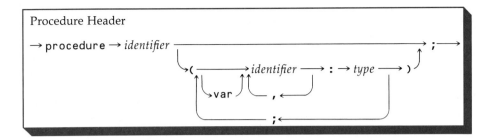

Procedure Header

The identifiers listed in parentheses in the procedure header represent both the input to the procedure and the output from the procedure. They are called the **parameters** of the procedure; they represent the information needed by the procedure in order to perform its operations. For example, if we write a procedure to sort an array of data values, the parameters for the sort procedure would probably include an array and an integer representing the number of valid data values in the array.

Once a procedure has been defined, the program references it by listing the procedure name and the corresponding parameters at the point where we want the procedure to be executed. The procedure statements are then executed as if the procedure reference was replaced by the statements in the procedure block. Thus, to include a procedure several times in a program, we merely use the procedure reference wherever we want the procedure to be executed. The syntax diagram for the statement that references or invokes the procedure follows.

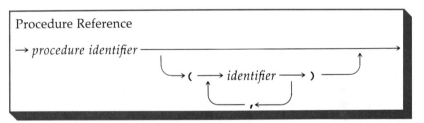

Procedure Reference

You have actually been using procedures since Chapter 1. Pascal contains several built-in procedures, just as it contains built-in functions like the square root function, *sqrt*. The most commonly used built-in procedures are those for input and output. For example, consider the following statement:

```
writeln ('THE TOTAL IS ',total)
```

This statement references the built-in procedure named *writeln*. This reference contains two parameters, the character constant 'THE TOTAL IS ' and the variable *total*. The procedure prepares the output line and causes it to be printed on the terminal screen. The *read, readln,* and *write* statements are also procedure references. Pascal also includes a built-in procedure, *page*, that causes the next line of output of a text file to be printed on a new page. This procedure is referenced with the file name as its only parameter, and if the file name is omitted, the system output file is assumed. Since the implementation of this procedure is system-dependent, we will not use it in our programs.

Before discussing the parameter list further, let's look at a simple procedure definition and the program that would use it.

EXAMPLE 5-1 Header Procedure

Write a Pascal program to read a data file *flight* that contains four numbers per line. These real values represent the time, distance, velocity, and acceleration measured during the flight of a test rocket. Print the data in a table, using column headings at the beginning of each page and including a page number on each page. Assume that 55 lines of output will be printed per page. You do not know ahead of time how many lines are in the data file, but the last data line will contain a negative value for time followed by three zero values.

Solution

We first develop the decomposition diagram for this problem solution. Since we are only reading and printing the data, the decomposition is only one step.

Decomposition

```
┌─────────────────────────────────┐
│ Read data and print report.     │
└─────────────────────────────────┘
```

To refine the decomposition, we first need to determine the appropriate data structure. Since we have just finished the chapter on arrays, you may be inclined to read the data into an array, but an array is not needed for this problem solution. We only need the data once to write each line of output information; therefore, we should use only simple variables.

Now we must consider the proper choice of control structure. Because the data file contains a trailer signal, we will use a *while* loop to read the information and exit the loop when we reach the trailer signal. Remember that we also want to print a report header at the top of every new page. The pseudocode for our first refinement follows.

First Refinement in Pseudocode

report: read time, distance, velocity, acceleration
        while time ≥ 0.0 do
           if top of page then
             write report header
          write time, distance, velocity, acceleration

The step that needs more detail is the step to determine if we are at the top of a page, and if so, to write the report header. Unfortunately, there is no Boolean function that specifies top-of-page as there is to detect end-of-file. Therefore, we will have to keep track of the number of data lines printed in order to put the header in the proper place. First we need to design the header format so we know how many lines it will use. We will use the following header:

```
                                                    PAGE XXX
                    ROCKET FLIGHT DATA

      TIME           DISTANCE          VELOCITY       ACCELERATION
    XXXX.XX          XXXX.XX           XXXX.XX          XXXX.XX
```

Because this header consists of four lines of information (count the blank line, but don't count the line of actual data), we can print 51 lines of data from the data file per page. A counter keeps track of the number of lines printed. Each time the number of lines is 51, we print the header and reset the counter to zero. Of course, we also want to print the report header at the beginning of the first page, and to initialize and update a page count. We now add these additions to the pseudocode.

FINAL REFINEMENT IN PSEUDOCODE

```
report: page ← 1
        lines ← 51
        read time, distance, velocity, acceleration
        while time ≥ 0.0 then
            if lines = 51 then
                write report header
                page ← page + 1
                lines ← 0
            write time, distance, velocity, acceleration
            lines ← lines + 1
            read time, distance, velocity, acceleration
```

After studying the pseudocode, we see that a likely choice for a procedure is the set of statements performed when we are at the top of a new page. The steps in the algorithm would otherwise be too long if we include all the steps for the header, and the longer the program becomes, the harder it is to keep it readable. Writing the report header is a simple process that is understood with only a reference to the procedure. Also, while this is a simple procedure, with slight modification it could print different headers. If the steps for printing the header are in a procedure, they are easier to integrate in other programs. As we convert the steps in the pseudocode into Pascal, note that we have included the steps to print the header, increment the page count, and reset the line count in the procedure. Also, to help distinguish procedures from the program, we added the procedure or program name as a comment after the corresponding *begin* and *end* statements.

The structure chart for this solution is shown next, along with the Pascal program.

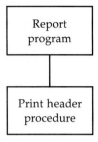

Report program

Print header procedure

PASCAL PROGRAM

```
{----------------------------------------------------------------}
program  report (flight,output);
   {This program prints the contents of a data file.}
var
   time, distance, velocity, acceleration: real;
   pages, lines: integer;
   flight: text;
{----------------------------------------------------------------}
procedure  printheader (var pagenumber,linenumber:integer);
   {This procedure prints a report heading.}
begin {printheader}
   writeln ('                                            ',
      '         PAGE ',pagenumber:3);
   writeln ('               ROCKET FLIGHT DATA');
   writeln;
   writeln ('    TIME         DISTANCE        VELOCITY',
      '      ACCELERATION');
   pagenumber := pagenumber + 1;
   linenumber := 0
end; {printheader}
{----------------------------------------------------------------}
begin {report}
   pages := 1;
   lines := 51;
   reset (flight);
   readln (flight,time,distance,velocity,acceleration);
   while  time >= 0.0  do
      begin
         if  lines = 51  then
            printheader (pages,lines);
         writeln (time:7:2,distance:15:2,velocity:15:2,
            acceleration:17:2);
         lines := lines + 1;
         readln (flight,time,distance,velocity,acceleration)
      end
end. {report}
{----------------------------------------------------------------}
```

Following are the first few lines of a sample set of output from this program.

```
                                                   PAGE   1
                    ROCKET FLIGHT DATA

     TIME         DISTANCE         VELOCITY      ACCELERATION
     0.00             0.00             0.00             0.00
     1.00            12.05            35.60            90.00
     2.00            75.32           146.25            98.05
```

PARAMETER LIST

The parameter list specifies the information flow between the program and the procedure. This information flow includes both information from the program to the procedure and information returned to the program by the procedure. As we begin to look closer at this interface between a program and a procedure, we need to explain the difference between the parameter list in the procedure header and the parameter list in the procedure reference.

Formal and Actual Parameters The parameters listed in the procedure header are **formal parameters,** those listed in the procedure reference are **actual parameters.** We can illustrate the distinction between formal and actual parameters using the previous example that printed a report header. Listed below are the procedure header and the statement that referenced the procedure:

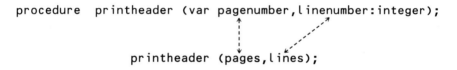

```
procedure  printheader (var pagenumber,linenumber:integer);



              printheader (pages,lines);
```

For the moment, we are going to ignore the *var* term in the procedure statement since we will discuss it in the next part of this section. The procedure header specifies that two parameters are used and that they are both integer variables. The identifiers are *pagenumber* and *linenumber;* these are formal parameters since they are in the procedure header. The identifiers used in the procedure reference are *pages* and *lines;* these are actual parameters.

It is very important that the formal parameters and the actual parameters for a procedure match in type, number, and order. Since the procedure header specified two integers as formal parameters, an error will occur if any other type is used as actual parameters when the procedure is referenced. Similarly, since the procedure header specified two integers as formal parameters, an error will occur if less than two integers or more than two integers are used as actual parameters. Finally, the order of the actual parameters must match the order of the formal parameters, as shown by the broken lines above.

Consider the following two statements. The procedure header still lists *pagenumber* and *linenumber* as formal parameters, but in the statement that references the procedure the actual parameters are reversed.

```
procedure  printheader (var pagenumber,linenumber:integer);



        printheader (lines,pages);
```

Since there are still two actual parameters and they are both integers, an error message will not be printed, but the variable *lines* will be matched to *pagenumber* and the variable *pages* will be matched to *linenumber*. The mismatch will cause the program to work improperly.

Formal parameters are always given names or identifiers in the procedure header. When writing the procedure header, you should list input parameters before output parameters. Some parameters will represent variables whose values are updated by the procedure; thus these parameters are both input and output. We will list the parameters that are both input and output after the input parameters and before the output parameters. Once the order of parameters has been specified in the procedure header, all other references must match this order exactly. While the formal parameters are always identifiers, the actual parameters for input can be constants. It is not valid for the actual parameter for output to be a constant.

Formal parameters are followed by a type specification in the procedure header. This is necessary because the formal parameters do not appear in the variable definition section of the procedure and therefore must be completely defined in the header. If a variable is not one of the built-in types, the type must be defined in the type section of the program. (Since the type section comes before the procedure definition, the formal definitions can refer to the types in the type section.) In the previous chapter, we saw that an array could be defined in the variable section, but we recommended defining an array data type in the type section and then referring to the array data type when defining the array variable. The reason for this suggestion can now be explained. Since formal parameters must be accompanied by a type identifier, if we define all new data types in the type section (as opposed to the variable section), then the new data types are available to be referenced by the formal parameters.

In the next example, we use a formal parameter that is an array. We will also reference the procedure using two different sets of actual parameters.

EXAMPLE 5-2 Temperature Conversion

Assume that a data file *datacent* contains 50 pairs of temperature measurements, with each pair of numbers entered on a different line. Each pair of measurements represents temperatures in degrees centigrade taken from two different parts of a jet engine at the same time. Assume that some of the programs that use these measurements require that the temperatures be converted from degrees centigrade to degrees Fahrenheit. Develop a program that reads these measurements into an array and converts them to degrees Fahrenheit. Use a procedure to perform the conversion on the entire array, instead of single values. The converted data values should then be written to a new data file *datafahr*. Since data files will now be available in both temperature units, a program can select the proper data file, thus avoiding the need to convert the temperatures again. (Recall that $F° = C° \cdot 1.8 + 32.0$.)

Solution

The decomposition for this program is shown below:

Decomposition

Read data from data file.
Convert data to degrees Fahrenheit.
Write data to new data file.

Since the conversion step is going to be done in a procedure, we can select the parameters for it at the same time that we develop the pseudocode.

Refinement in Pseudocode

```
conversion: read data into temp1 and temp2 arrays
            convert temp1 array
            convert temp2 array
            write converted data to new file

convert (temp): for i = 1 to 50 do
                    temp[i] ← temp[i]*1.8 + 32.0
```

The structure chart for this solution is shown next, along with the Pascal program.

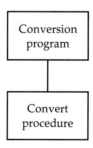

```
{------------------------------------------------------------}
program  conversion (datacent,datafahr,output);
    {This program generates an output file of temperatures
    converted from centigrade to Fahrenheit.}
type
    index = 1..50;
    list = array[index] of real;
var
    datacent, datafahr: text;
    i: index;
    temp1, temp2: list;
{------------------------------------------------------------}
procedure  convert (var temp:list);
    {This procedure converts an array of centigrade
    temperatures to Fahrenheit.}
var
    i: index;
begin {convert}
    for i := 1 to 50 do
        temp[i] := temp[i]*1.8 + 32.0
end; {convert}
{------------------------------------------------------------}
begin {conversion}
    reset (datacent);
    for i := 1 to 50 do
        readln (datacent,temp1[i],temp2[i]);
    convert (temp1);
    convert (temp2);
    rewrite (datafahr);
    for i := 1 to 50 do
        writeln (datafahr,temp1[i],temp2[i])
end. {conversion}
{------------------------------------------------------------}
```

There are several things we want to point out in this example solution. First, the formal parameter is *temp,* while *temp1* is the actual parameter in the first reference to the procedure and *temp2* is the actual parameter in the second reference. Note that the formal parameter is defined to be type *list,* which is an array defined in the type portion of the program. Also note that the parameter of the procedure is both input and output, since the array has a different set of values after the procedure is executed.

Have the values in the original data file been changed? No, the data in the array has been changed, but not the data in the data file *datacent.*

The last topic that we present on parameter lists relates to the type of reference between the actual parameter and the formal parameter. When the formal parameter is preceded by *var,* the memory address of the actual parameter is used each time the formal parameter is referenced in the procedure, and the parameter reference is called a **reference by address** or a **reference by location.** Since the memory address of the actual parameter is used each time the formal parameter is used, the contents of the actual parameter will be changed if the value in the formal parameter is changed. In general, all parameters that are to bring values back to the program should be parameter references by address; these parameters are also called **variable parameters.**

If the parameter is only supposed to supply information to the procedure, then the formal parameter should not be preceded by the term *var*. When the parameter is not preceded by *var*, the procedure works with a copy of the value of the actual parameter, so it cannot change the contents of the actual parameter. These are called **value parameters** or **references by value.** Parameters that are input parameters to the procedure should always be defined as value parameters.

Value parameter references are also used when the actual parameter is an expression as opposed to an identifier. For example, a real parameter may be the result of a computation. The expression can be used directly in the procedure reference, as shown in the following pair of statements for a procedure that uses the first three parameters to compute a new value for the fourth parameter, *x:*

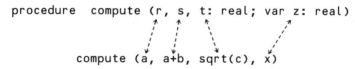

The formal parameters *r, s,* and *t* are references by value and *z* is a reference by address. The only variable in the procedure that will affect values in the rest of the program is the variable that corresponds to the formal parameter *z*, which is *x* in this example.

Although we have said that input parameters should be value parameter references and that output parameters should be references by address, there is one exception to this rule. If a file name is used as a parameter in a procedure, it must always be a reference by address; thus, it must always be preceded by the term *var.*

SCOPE OF VARIABLES

When we begin writing longer programs with several modules, it is important to be able to determine the **scope** of a variable, or the portion of the program in which it is valid to use the variable. Scope can also be defined in terms of the portion of the program where the variable is "known" or is "visible." Before we give specific rules for determining the scope of a variable, we need to define several terms that relate to the scope of a variable.

Constants and variables defined in the program (as opposed to being defined in a procedure) are **global variables** and **global constants,** which means that the scope of these variables and constants is the entire program. A **local constant** or **local variable** is one defined in the constant or variable section within a procedure. Its scope generally is limited to the procedure in which it is defined. Local variables cannot be used outside the block in which they are defined. The formal parameters in a module are also local variables.

It is valid for a local variable to have the same identifier as a global variable, although the two identifiers will refer to different variables. If the reference to the identifier occurs in the procedure, the compiler assumes we refer to the local variable; if the reference to the identifier occurs in the program, the compiler assumes we refer to the global variable. It is also valid for two different procedures to use the same identifier; however, the identifier is a local variable within each procedure.

With these definitions, we can now state the rules for determining the scope of an identifier.

1. The scope of a global variable is the program and all its procedures.
2. The scope of a local variable is the procedure in which it is defined and any other procedures that are defined in that procedure.
3. The only exception to rules 1 and 2 occur when a local variable or constant has the same identifier as another variable whose scope includes the procedure that defines the local variable. In these cases, the local variable takes precedence.

Since global variables are known in all procedures, you might be tempted to avoid passing information with a parameter list and instead use the global identifiers. This is a bad habit that can create problems (called **side effects**) that are very difficult to debug. It is much safer when all communication between the program and its procedures occurs through the parameter list. The one exception to this recommendation relates to global constants. Since the value of a constant cannot be changed, we do not have to worry about side effects, and thus it is acceptable to use global constants in the program without sending them through the parameter list.

Having defined and discussed these new terms, we now look again at the two programs we developed in this section. The program *report* is listed on page 216, and the program *conversion* is listed on page 220. Listed below are the global and local variables for each program as well as the scope of each. Work this out by yourself before comparing them to our list.

Program *report*	
global variables	variable scope
flight	report, printheader
output	report, printheader
time	report, printheader
distance	report, printheader
velocity	report, printheader
acceleration	report, printheader
pages	report, printheader
lines	report, printheader
local variables	variable scope
pagenumber	printheader
linenumber	printheader

Program *conversion*

global variables	variable scope
datacent	conversion, convert
datafahr	conversion, convert
output	conversion, convert
i	conversion
temp1	conversion, convert
temp2	conversion, convert
local variables	variable scope
temp	convert
i	convert

If you had some trouble selecting the correct type of variable or scope, review the material in this section. These are difficult concepts, and may require reading the material and studying the examples again.

SELF-TEST 5-1

This self-test allows you to check quickly to see if you have remembered certain key points from Section 5-2. If you have any problems with the exercises, you should reread this section. The solutions are included at the end of the text.

The problems refer to the following program and the procedure *sortcheck*. The program will read an array of 50 numbers from a data file called *data1*. The procedure will check to see if the array of integers is in ascending order. It will return a value of true in a Boolean variable if it is in order, and a value of false if it is not in order.

```
{- - - - - - - - - - - - - - - - - - - - - - - - - - - - - - - - - - - - - - - - -}
program  check (data1,output);
   {This program reads a set of data and checks to see
   if the data is in ascending order.}
type
   index = 1..50;
   list = array[index] of integer;
var
   i: integer;
   ordered: boolean;
   data: text;
   x: list;
{- - - - - - - - - - - - - - - - - - - - - - - - - - - - - - - - - - - - - - }
procedure  sortcheck (x:list; var sorted:boolean);
   {This procedure returns a value of true in sorted if
   the array is in ascending order; otherwise sorted is
   false.}
var
   k: integer;
   done: boolean;
```

continued

continued

```
begin {sortcheck}
   done := false;
   sorted := true;
   k := 1;
   while  not done  do
       if  x[k] > x[k+1]  then
          begin
             sorted := false;
             done := true
          end
       else if  k = 49  then
          done := true
       else
          k := k + 1
end; {sortcheck}
{- - - - - - - - - - - - - - - - - - - - - - - - - - - - - - - - - - - - - - - - - - - - - - - - - - - - - }
begin {check}
   reset (data1);
   for i := 1 to 50 do
      read (data1,x[i]);
   sortcheck (x,ordered);
   if  ordered  then
      writeln ('DATA IN FILE IS IN ASCENDING ORDER')
   else
      writeln ('DATA IN FILE NEEDS TO BE SORTED')
end. {check}
{- - - - - - - - - - - - - - - - - - - - - - - - - - - - - - - - - - - - - - - - - - - - - - - - - - - -}
```

1. List the formal parameters.
2. List the actual parameters.
3. List the global variables and give their scope.
4. List the local variables and give their scope.
5. List the parameters referenced by address.
6. List the parameters referenced by value.
7. Would the procedure work properly if all the occurrences of the variable *k* were replaced with the variable *i*? Why?

5-3 PROBLEM SOLVING—OIL WELL PRODUCTION

The daily production of oil from a group of oil wells is entered into a data file each week for analysis. One of the reports that uses this data file computes the average production from each well and prints a summary of the overall production from this group of wells. Write a Pascal program that will read the information from the data file and generate this report. Assume that the data file contains a date in the first line of the file that gives the month, day, and year of the first day of the week that corresponds to the production data. Each following line in the data file contains an integer identification number for the well and seven real numbers that represent the well's production for the week. The number of wells to be analyzed varies from week to week, so a trailer line is included at the end of the file. This trailer line contains the integer 9999. You may assume that no well will have this integer as its identification number.

The report generated should contain the following heading at the top of each page. Assume that the information for 20 wells is to be printed on one page.

```
                              PAGE XXXX

            OIL WELL PRODUCTION
            WEEK OF XX-XX-XX

        WELL ID           AVERAGE PRODUCTION
                          (IN BARRELS)

        XXXX              XXX.XX
```

Include a final line at the end of the report that gives the total number of oil wells plus their overall average.

Use the following set of data for testing the program. Assume that it has been stored in a file called *production*.

```
05 06 87
52    87    136   0     54    60    82    51
63    54    73    88    105   20    21    105
24    67    98    177   35    65    98    0
8     23    34    52    67    180   80    3
64    33    55    79    108   118   130   20
66    40    44    63    89    36    54    36
67    20    35    76    87    154   98    80
55    10    13    34    23    43    12    0
3     34    56    187   34    202   23    34
2     98    98    87    34    54    100   20
25    29    43    54    65    12    15    17
18    45    65    202   205   100   99    98
14    36    34    98    34    43    23    9
13    0     9     8     4     3     2     10
36    23    88    99    65    77    45    35
38    23    100   134   122   111   211   0
81    23    34    54    98    5     93    82
89    29    58    39    20    50    30    47
99    100   12    43    98    34    23    9
45    23    93    75    93    2     34    8
88    23    301   23    83    23    9     20
77    28    12    43    43    92    83    98
39    98    43    12    23    54    23    98
12    43    54    92    84    75    72    91
48    83    138   189   73    27    49    10
9999
```

PROBLEM STATEMENT

Generate a report on oil well production from daily production data. Give average production for individual wells and an overall average.

INPUT/OUTPUT DESCRIPTION

The input is a data file with daily production data for a group of oil wells. The first line in the file contains the date of the first day in the week. Each following line contains the identification number of the well and the seven daily production values for that well. The last line in the file contains 9999. The output is to be a report with information for 20 wells per page in the following form:

```
                              PAGE XXXX

            OIL WELL PRODUCTION
            WEEK OF XX-XX-XX

        WELL ID         AVERAGE PRODUCTION
                        (IN BARRELS)

        XXXX            XXX.XX
```

HAND EXAMPLE

For the hand example, we will use the first five lines of the data file given at the beginning of this section, along with the trailer line. Our data file is:

```
05  06  87
52      87      136     0       54      60      82      51
63      54      73      88      105     20      21      105
24      67      98      177     35      65      98      0
8       23      34      52      67      180     80      3
9999
```

The date from the first line of the data file is used in our heading. Each of the following data lines contains an identification number followed by seven numbers representing well production. We average these seven values and print this average along with the identification number. We want a final count and a final average, so we must add the averages together for each well and divide by the number of wells. For this sample data, our output is the following:

```
                          PAGE      1

            OIL WELL PRODUCTION
            WEEK OF   5- 6-87

        WELL ID         AVERAGE PRODUCTION
                        (IN BARRELS)

          52            67.14
          63            66.57
          24            77.14
           8            62.71

    OVERALL AVERAGE FOR   4 WELLS IS   68.39
```

ALGORITHM DEVELOPMENT

Before we begin considering the steps in the algorithm, we should decide the best way to store the data. For instance, do we want to store it all in arrays, do we want to store some portion of the data in an array, or can we just use simple variables? We answer these questions by looking at the way we need to use the data. To compute the individual well average, we need a sum of the individual production amounts but we do not need to keep all seven of the amounts. Similarly, to compute the overall average, we need a sum of the individual averages and a count of the number of wells, but again we do not need to keep all of the individual averages from each well. This analysis indicates that we do not need any arrays to generate this report. Using arrays would only complicate the algorithm.

We now want to decompose the algorithm into a sequence of steps.

DECOMPOSITION

Generate report.
Print summary line.

Generating the report requires reading the data, accumulating the totals, and printing the individual lines. If we refine these steps into pseudocode, our initial refinement is the following:

INITIAL REFINEMENT IN PSEUDOCODE

```
report: read date
        read id
        while id ≠ 9999 do
            determine individual well average
            if top of page then
               write header
            write individual average
            update overall average and well count
            read next id
        if top of page then
            write header
        write summary information
```

Once we have completed the initial refinement in pseudocode, we are ready to select operations that should be written as procedures. There are two guidelines that we want to remember: First, operations that will be repeated are usually good choices for procedures. Since the steps to print the header are referenced twice in our algorithm, we will make this operation into a procedure. Second, look for steps that involve detailed operations. The readability of a program suffers a great deal when the details of some of the steps become long and tedious. A likely candidate for a procedure in this algorithm is the step to determine the individual well average. This requires setting a sum to zero, reading the seven daily averages, adding them to the sum, and dividing by seven. We can reference all these steps with one procedure reference. There are other possible ways to use modules in this algorithm, but we will use only two procedures, *printheader* and *compute*. Our next refinement in pseudocode will reference these procedures, and we will also need separate pseudocode to describe the procedures.

FINAL REFINEMENT IN PSEUDOCODE

```
report: read date
        pages ← 1
        count ← 0
        total ← 0.0
        read id
        while id ≠ 9999 do
            compute (average)
            if top of page then
                printheader (month,day,year,pages)
            write individual average
            increment number of wells by 1
            add individual well average to total oil
            read next id
        if top of page then
            printheader (month,day,year,pages)
        write summary information

printheader (month,day,year,pages): print header information
                                    pages ← pages + 1

compute (average): sum ← 0.0
                   for i = 1 to 7 do
                       read oil
                       sum ← sum + oil
                   average ← sum/7
```

The structure chart for this solution is shown next, along with the Pascal program.

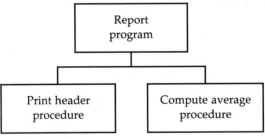

PASCAL PROGRAM

```pascal
{-------------------------------------------------------------}
program  report (production,output);
    {This program generates a report from the daily
    production information for a set of oil wells.}
var
    oiltotal, average: real;
    month, day, year, pages, wellcount, id: integer;
    production: text;
```

```
{------------------------------------------------------------}
procedure printheader (month,day,year:integer;
                       var pages:integer);
   {This procedure prints the header for an
   oil well production summary report.}
begin {printheader}
   writeln ('                          PAGE ',pages:4);
   writeln;
   writeln ('    OIL WELL PRODUCTION');
   writeln ('    WEEK OF ',month:2,'-',day:2,'-',year:2);
   writeln;
   writeln ('WELL ID        AVERAGE PRODUCTION');
   writeln ('                 (IN BARRELS)');
   writeln;
   pages := pages + 1
end; {printheader}
{------------------------------------------------------------}
procedure compute (var production:text; var average:real);
   {This procedure reads the daily production information for
   a well and computes the daily average.}
var
   sum, oil: real;
   i: integer;
begin {compute}
   sum := 0.0;
   for i := 1 to 7 do
      begin
         read (production,oil);
         sum := sum + oil
      end;
   average := sum/7.0
end; {compute}
{------------------------------------------------------------}
begin {report}
   reset (production);
   read (production,month,day,year);
   wellcount := 0;
   oiltotal := 0.0;
   pages := 1;

   read (production,id);
   while id <> 9999 do
      begin
         if wellcount mod 20 = 0 then
            printheader (month,day,year,pages);
         compute (production,average);
         writeln (id:4,average:16:2);
         wellcount := wellcount + 1;
         oiltotal := oiltotal + average;
         read (production,id)
      end;

   if wellcount mod 20 = 0 then
      printheader (month,day,year,pages);
   writeln;
   writeln ('OVERALL AVERAGE FOR',wellcount:4,' WELLS IS',
         oiltotal/wellcount:7:2);
   writeln
end. {report}
{------------------------------------------------------------}
```

TESTING

Begin testing this program using a small data set such as the one we used in the hand example. Be sure to test it with a few pages of output to be sure that the page increment steps in the header procedure work properly. Following is the output from this program using the data file given at the beginning of this section.

```
                              PAGE      1

          OIL WELL  PRODUCTION
          WEEK OF   5- 6-87

    WELL ID            AVERAGE PRODUCTION
                       (IN BARRELS)

       52                 67.14
       63                 66.57
       24                 77.14
        8                 62.71
       64                 77.57
       66                 51.71
       67                 78.57
       55                 19.29
        3                 81.43
        2                 70.14
       25                 33.57
       18                116.29
       14                 39.57
       13                  5.14
       36                 61.71
       38                100.14
       81                 55.57
       89                 39.00
       99                 45.57
       45                 46.86
 - - - - - - - - - - - - - - - - - - - - - - - - -
                              PAGE      2

          OIL WELL  PRODUCTION
          WEEK OF   5- 6-87

    WELL ID            AVERAGE PRODUCTION
                       (IN BARRELS)

       88                 68.86
       77                 57.00
       39                 50.14
       12                 73.00
       48                 81.29

    OVERALL AVERAGE FOR  25 WELLS IS  61.04
```

5-4 PROBLEM SOLVING—SIMULATION DATA

A routine to generate random numbers is useful in many engineering and science applications. Most game programs use randomly generated numbers to make the program appear to have a mind of its own—it chooses different actions each time the game is played. Programs that simulate something, such as tosses of a coin or the number of people at a bank window, also use **random number generators.**

In this application we use a random number generator to simulate (or model) electronic noise, such as static, that might occur in a piece of instrumentation. These applications of random events or random numbers use a random number generator routine. The routine presented below generates numbers between 0.0 and 1.0. The numbers are uniformly distributed across the interval between 0.0 and 1.0, which means that we are just as likely to get 0.4455 as we are to get 0.0090. This random number generator requires an argument that is a seed to the computation. When we give the routine a different seed, it returns a different random number. If we want a series of random numbers, we initialize the seed once and do not modify it again. The random number generator modifies the seed itself from one reference of the routine to the next. We will implement the random number generator with a procedure so it will be easy to include in other programs. (This random number generator will not work properly on computers with a maximum integer value of 32,767.)

Although the routine computes and returns a single value, it also needs a seed whose value is preserved from one reference of the routine to the next. Therefore, we really have two values that are being returned from the routine. While the details of this random number generator are beyond the scope of this text, it essentially causes the computer to compute integers that are too large to store. The portion of the number that can be stored is a random sequence used to determine the random number. (For more information on this algorithm, see S. D. Stearns, "A Portable Random Number Generator for Use in Signal Processing," Sandia National Laboratories Technical Report, 1981.)

Pascal Procedure

```
{------------------------------------------------------------------}
procedure  random (var seed:integer; var x:real);
   {This procedure generates random values
   between 0.0 and 1.0 using an integer seed.}
begin {random}
   seed := 2045*seed + 1;
   seed := seed - (seed/1048576)*1048576;
   x := (seed + 1)/1048577
end; {random}
{------------------------------------------------------------------}
```

The program that follows allows you to enter a seed. The program then prints the first 10 random numbers generated with that seed. Try the program with different seeds and observe that you get different numbers. An example output is shown for a seed of 12357 so that you can check to see if your procedure is working properly.

PASCAL PROGRAM

```
{-------------------------------------------------------------}
program  test (input,output);
    {This program tests the random number generator.}
var
    x: real;
    seed, i: integer;
{-------------------------------------------------------------}
                 random procedure goes here
{-------------------------------------------------------------}
begin {test}
    writeln ('ENTER A POSITIVE INTEGER SEED VALUE');
    readln (seed);
    writeln ('RANDOM NUMBERS:');
    for i := 1 to 10 do
       begin
           random (seed,x);
           writeln (x:8:6)
       end
end. {test}
{-------------------------------------------------------------}
```

COMPUTER OUTPUT

```
ENTER A POSITIVE INTEGER SEED VALUE
12357
RANDOM NUMBERS:
0.099414
0.299419
0.310731
0.442812
0.548521
0.725532
0.712078
0.199705
0.395030
0.834445
```

We are now ready to discuss the application problem. We are going to develop an algorithm for a program that generates a data file that simulates a sine wave plus noise. The program uses both the built-in sine function and the procedure to generate random numbers. The data file generated will contain values of the signal

$$f(t) = 2 \sin(2\pi t) + \text{noise}$$

for $t = 0.0, 0.01, ..., 1.00$. Each value of the sine wave is added to a random number produced by the random number generator. Because a sine wave varies from -1 to 1 and the random number generator can vary from 0 to 1, we can expect our experimental signal to vary from -2 to 3. This signal should be stored in a data file called *signal*, where each line of the data file should contain the value of *t* and the corresponding signal value.

PROBLEM STATEMENT

Generate a data file that contains samples of the function $2 \sin(2\pi t)$, with uniform random noise between 0.0 and 1.0 added to it. The data points are to be evaluated with $t = 0.0, 0.01, 0.02, ..., 1.00$.

INPUT/OUTPUT DESCRIPTION

The only input to the program is the seed to start the random number generator. The output is a data file called *signal* that contains 101 lines of data. Each line of data contains a value of time and the corresponding signal value.

HAND EXAMPLE

In our discussion of the random number generator, we illustrated the first 10 random numbers generated with seed 12357. Using these random numbers, the first 10 data points of the file *signal* are

$$f(0.00) = 2*\sin(2\pi 0.00) + 0.099414 = 0.0994144$$
$$f(0.01) = 2*\sin(2\pi 0.01) + 0.299419 = 0.4250000$$
$$f(0.02) = 2*\sin(2\pi 0.02) + 0.310731 = 0.5613975$$
$$f(0.03) = 2*\sin(2\pi 0.03) + 0.442812 = 0.8175746$$
$$f(0.04) = 2*\sin(2\pi 0.04) + 0.548521 = 1.0459008$$
$$f(0.05) = 2*\sin(2\pi 0.05) + 0.725532 = 1.3435660$$
$$f(0.06) = 2*\sin(2\pi 0.06) + 0.712078 = 1.4483271$$
$$f(0.07) = 2*\sin(2\pi 0.07) + 0.199705 = 1.0512636$$
$$f(0.08) = 2*\sin(2\pi 0.08) + 0.395030 = 1.3585374$$
$$f(0.09) = 2*\sin(2\pi 0.09) + 0.834445 = 1.9060986$$

ALGORITHM DEVELOPMENT

This program is straightforward. The only input is the random seed. The program then generates the signal values and writes them in a data file. We do not need arrays because each data value is needed only once.

DECOMPOSITION

Read random number seed.
Generate data values and write them to the file.

generate: read seed
       t ← 0.0
       while t ≤ 1.00 do
          random (seed,noise)
          f ← 2 sin (2πt) + noise
          write t, f
          t ← t + 0.01

We now convert the pseudocode to Pascal, including the procedure discussed earlier in this section for generating random numbers. The structure chart is shown next, along with the Pascal program.

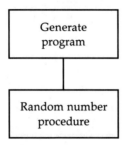

Pascal Program

```
{-----------------------------------------------------------------}
program   generate (input,output,signal);
    {This program generates a signal composed
    of a sine wave plus random noise.}
const
    pi = 3.141593;
var
    t, f, noise: real;
    seed: integer;
    signal: text;
{------------------------------------------------------------}
                random procedure goes here
{------------------------------------------------------------}
begin {generate}
    rewrite (signal);
    writeln ('ENTER A POSITIVE INTEGER SEED');
    readln (seed);
    t := 0.0;
    while  t <= 1.00   do
        begin
            random (seed,noise);
            f := 2.0*sin(2.0*pi*t) + noise;
            writeln (signal,t,f);
            t := t + 0.01
        end
end. {generate}
{------------------------------------------------------------}
```

Use the random number generator seed that we used in the hand-worked example. Check the first 10 values of the data signal in the data file; if these match the signal values computed in the hand example, we can be certain that our random number generator is working properly. It is difficult to test a program with random values thoroughly because we cannot expect (and should not get) the same values if we change the seed for the random number generator. However, the trend of the data should be the same. For example, in this problem we should be able to see the sine wave in the data even though we use different random numbers for the noise. A plot routine is helpful in looking at the general trend of a set of data. (We will develop a simple plot routine in Chapter 8 when we discuss character information.)

Some plots of the data from program *generate* are shown below. The two plots are plots of the data file using different random seeds.

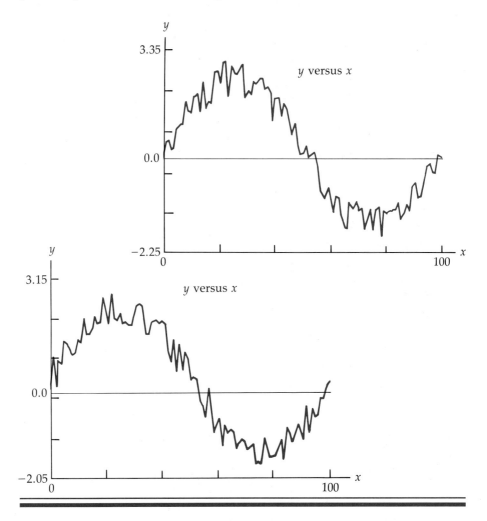

5-5 PROCEDURES FOR COMMON TECHNIQUES

In the previous chapter we presented a number of common techniques used with one-dimensional arrays. In this chapter we presented a technique for implementing top-down design — the procedure. We now combine these techniques and develop procedures for some of the common methods used with one-dimensional arrays. These procedures will be useful in a variety of programs. They are often called **software tools** because they are used so frequently. You may want to store these procedures so that they will be convenient to add to programs as you need them.

INSERTING AND DELETING

We now modify the techniques for inserting and deleting in an ordered list into procedures for inserting and deleting in an ordered list. The first decisions to be made involve the parameters of the procedures. We must determine what input information is needed to perform an insertion or deletion, and what information is returned to the program by the procedure. Consider the following:

    Insert Procedure:
      Input   — ordered list
                 — number of valid elements in the list
                 — defined size of the list
                 — new information to be added
      Output— ordered list
                 — number of valid elements in the list
    Delete Procedure:
      Input   — ordered list
                 — number of valid elements in the list
                 — old information to be deleted
      Output— ordered list
                 — number of valid elements in the list

The variables that are output or both input and output must be parameters that are referenced by address since we want to change the value in these variables. The variables that represent only input to the procedure should be value parameters. With this information, we can now determine the parameter list that goes with each procedure:

```
procedure   insert (arraysize,new:integer;
                    var count:integer;
                    var x:list);


procedure   delete (old:integer;
                    var count:integer;
                    var x:list);
```

The parameters in the procedure statement can be in any order, but once the order is specified, it must be carefully followed in any reference to the procedure.

EXAMPLE 5-3 Insert and Delete Procedure

Write Pascal procedures for inserting and deleting in an ordered list. Use the procedure headers below:

```
procedure  insert (arraysize,new:integer;
                   var count:integer;
                   var x:list);

procedure  delete (old:integer;
                   var count:integer;
                   var x:list);
```

Solution

To refresh your memory, we present the decomposition and pseudocode for each algorithm before converting to Pascal. (You may also want to reread Section 4-5 if you have questions about the pseudocode.) The assumptions made in the pseudocode for these two routines are:

The values are already in an ascending order in the array *x*.

A variable *count* specifies the number of valid data values in the array.

The variable *arraysize* contains the defined size of the array.

The variable *new* contains the value to be inserted in the array.

We will add the new value to the array even if it is already in the array.

The variable *old* contains the value to be deleted from the array.

DECOMPOSITION

Add new item to ordered list.

```
if count = arraysize then
   write message that last value will be lost
done ← false
i ← 1
while (i ≤ count) and (not done) do
   if x[i] < new then
      i ← i + 1
   else
      done ← true
if i > count then
   if count < arraysize then
      count ← count + 1
      x[count] ← new
else
   if count < arraysize then
      count ← count + 1
   for k = count downto i+1 do
      x[k] ← x[k−1]
   x[i] ← new
```

Using the procedure header determined above, we can convert this pseudocode into a Pascal procedure.

Pascal Procedure

```
{- - - - - - - - - - - - - - - - - - - - - - - - - - - - - - - - - - - - - - - - - - - - - - - - -}
procedure  insert (arraysize,new:integer;
                   var count:integer; var x:list);
   {This procedure inserts an element in an ordered list.}
var
   i, k: integer;
   done: boolean;
begin {insert}
   if  count = arraysize  then
      writeln ('ARRAY IS FULL - LAST VALUE WILL BE LOST');
   done := false;
   i := 1;
```

```
        while  (i <= count) and (not done)  do
           if  x[i] < new  then
              i := i + 1
           else
              done := true;
        if  i > count  then
           begin
              if  count < arraysize  then
                 begin
                    count := count + 1;
                    x[count] := new
                 end
           end
        else
           begin
              if  count < arraysize  then
                 count := count + 1;
              for k := count downto i+1 do
                 x[k] := x[k-1];
              x[i] := new
           end
end; {insert}
{- - - - - - - - - - - - - - - - - - - - - - - - - - - - - - - - - - - - - - - - - - - - - - - - - - - -}
```

We now present the decomposition and pseudocode for the delete algorithm, and then convert it into a Pascal procedure.

DECOMPOSITION

> Delete old item from ordered list.

PSEUDOCODE FOR DELETING AN ELEMENT IN AN ORDERED LIST

    done ← false
    i ← 1
    while (i ≤ count) and (not done) do
       if x[i] < old then
          i ← i + 1
       else
          done ← true
    if (i > count) or (x[i] > old) then
       write message that value is not in list
    else
       count ← count − 1
       for k = i to count do
          x[k] ← x[k+1]

Using the procedure header determined previously, we can convert this
pseudocode into a Pascal procedure.

```
{----------------------------------------------------------}
procedure  delete (old:integer;
                    var count:integer; var x:list);
    {This procedure deletes an element from an ordered list.}
var
    i, k: integer;
    done: boolean;
begin {delete}
    done := false;
    i := 1;
    while  (i <= count) and (not done)  do
        if  x[i] < old  then
            i := i + 1
        else
            done := true;
    if  (i > count) or (x[i] > old)  then
        writeln ('VALUE TO DELETE IS NOT IN LIST')
    else
        begin
            count := count - 1;
            for k := i to count do
                x[k] := x[k+1]
        end
end; {delete}
{----------------------------------------------------------}
```

These two procedures have been developed independently of a specific application to ensure that they will be useful in a number of applications. However, just because these routines are not part of a specific problem, we cannot skip the important step of testing the procedures. Therefore, we will write a special program (called a **driver**) to test the procedures. The driver program allows us to test modules independently of a specific program. In the driver program below, the user is asked to enter a list of ordered values. The values are stored; then the user is allowed to perform both deletions and insertions. This driver tests both procedures. It has the following structure chart:

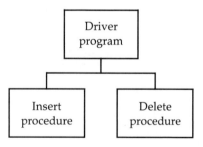

In the program, we indicate the position of the procedures to show clearly where they would be included. The order of the insertion routine and the deletion routine could be interchanged.

```
{-----------------------------------------------------------}
program  driver (input,output);
    {This driver tests both the insert and delete procedures.}
const
    arraysize = 10;
type
    index = 1..10;
    list = array[index] of integer;
var
    count, i, code, new, old: integer;
    done: boolean;
    x: list;
{-----------------------------------------------------------}
                    insert procedure goes here
{-----------------------------------------------------------}
                    delete procedure goes here
{-----------------------------------------------------------}
begin {driver}
    writeln ('ENTER COUNT (< 11) OF VALUES FOR LIST');
    readln (count);
    writeln ('ENTER VALUES IN ASCENDING ORDER');
    for i := 1 to count do
        read (x[i]);
    done := false;
    while  not done  do
        begin
            writeln ('ENTER -1 FOR DELETE, 1 TO INSERT, ',
                     '9 TO QUIT');
            readln (code);
            if  code = -1  then
                begin
                    writeln ('ENTER VALUE TO DELETE');
                    readln (old);
                    delete (old,count,x)
                end
            else if  code = 1  then
                begin
                    writeln ('ENTER VALUE TO INSERT');
                    readln (new);
                    insert (arraysize,new,count,x)
                end;
            if  code = 9  then
                done := true
            else
                begin
                    writeln ('NEW LIST:');
                    for i := 1 to count do
                        writeln (x[i]:6)
                end
        end
end. {driver}
{-----------------------------------------------------------}
```

An example of a test of the insert and delete procedures using this driver follows.

```
ENTER COUNT (< 11) OF VALUES FOR LIST
3
ENTER VALUES IN ASCENDING ORDER
5 13 17
ENTER -1 FOR DELETE, 1 TO INSERT, 9 TO QUIT
1
ENTER VALUE TO INSERT
8
NEW LIST:
      5
      8
     13
     17
ENTER -1 FOR DELETE, 1 TO INSERT, 9 TO QUIT
-1
ENTER VALUE TO DELETE
15
VALUE TO DELETE IS NOT IN LIST
NEW LIST:
      5
      8
     13
     17
ENTER -1 FOR DELETE, 1 TO INSERT, 9 TO QUIT
9
```

SORTING

In this section we modify a sort algorithm into a procedure and develop a driver program that can be used to test the sort algorithm. We will use the selection sort in our example, but any of the three sort algorithms presented in the previous chapter could be used with the same parameters and driver. (You may want to review Section 4-5 to refresh your memory on the selection sort algorithm.) We first determine the parameter list, present the pseudocode from the previous chapter, and then convert the pseudocode into a procedure.

The input and output to the sort procedure are the following:

Sort Procedure:

    Input — list of values (unordered)

             — number of valid elements in the list

    Output— list of values (new order)

Since the number or count of valid elements in the list is only input information, it should be a value parameter. The list of values will be sorted by the procedure, so the values may be in a different order when they are returned by the procedure; hence, the list should be a reference by address. Our procedure header will be

```
procedure  sort (count:integer; var x:list);
```

In the next example we will develop this Pascal sort procedure.

EXAMPLE 5-4   Sort Procedure

Write a Pascal procedure for sorting a list of values. Use the procedure header below:

```
procedure  sort (count:integer; var x:list);
```

Solution

To refresh your memory, we present the decomposition and pseudocode for the selection sort.

DECOMPOSITION

> Sort list of values into ascending order.

PSEUDOCODE FOR SELECTION SORT

(Assumes: the values are already stored in the array x; and a variable *count* specifies the number of valid data values in the array.)

```
for i = 1 to count−1 do
   indexmin ← i
   first ← i + 1
   last ← count
   for k = first to last do
      if x[k] < x[indexmin] then
         indexmin ← k
   hold ← x[i]
   x[i] ← x[indexmin]
   x[indexmin] ← hold
```

Using the procedure header determined above, we can convert this pseudocode into a Pascal procedure.

PASCAL PROCEDURE

```
{------------------------------------------------------------}
procedure  sort (count:integer; var x:list);
   {This procedure sorts an array into ascending order.}
var
   i, indexmin, first, last, k, hold: integer;
begin {sort}
   for i:= 1 to count−1 do
      begin
         indexmin := i;
         first := i + 1;
         last := count;
         for k := first to last do
            if  x[k] < x[indexmin]   then
               indexmin := k;
         hold := x[i];
         x[i] := x[indexmin];
         x[indexmin] := hold
      end
end; {sort}
{------------------------------------------------------------}
```

In order to test this procedure, we write a driver so that we can test the procedure independently of other modules and operations. In the driver program, we ask the user to enter a list of values. We store the values in an array and reference the sort procedure to reorder the values if they are out of order. The driver program has the following structure chart:

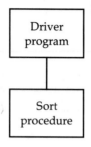

In the program, we indicate the position for the sort procedure to show clearly where it should be included.

PASCAL PROGRAM

```
{-----------------------------------------------------------}
program  driver (input,output);
    {This driver tests the sort procedure.}
type
    index = 1..10;
    list = array[index] of integer;
var
    count, i: integer;
    x: list;
{-----------------------------------------------------------}
                    sort procedure goes here
{-----------------------------------------------------------}
begin {driver}
    writeln ('ENTER COUNT (< 11) OF VALUES FOR LIST');
    readln (count);
    writeln ('ENTER VALUES');
    for i := 1 to count do
        read (x[i]);
    sort (count,x);
    writeln ('ORDERED LIST:');
    for i := 1 to count do
        writeln (x[i]:6)
end. {driver}
{-----------------------------------------------------------}
```

An example of a test of the sort procedure using this driver follows.

```
ENTER COUNT (< 11) OF VALUES FOR LIST
6
ENTER VALUES
2 -4 28 57 14 28
ORDERED LIST:
      -4
       2
      14
      28
      28
      57
```

SELF-TEST 5-2

This self-test allows you to check quickly to see if you have remembered certain key points from Section 5-5. If you have any problems with the exercise, you should reread this section. The solutions are included at the end of the text.

Write a procedure that is referenced with the following statement:

```
normalize (count,x)
```

Assume that *x* is a real array defined by the data type *list*, and that *count* specifies the number of valid data points in the array. The function is to normalize the values in *x*, which means that each value should be divided by the maximum value in *x*. The maximum value will then be replaced by the value 1.0, and all other values will be less than 1.0.

5-6 PROBLEM SOLVING—COMPUTER SECURITY

Computer security is an important issue because so much information is stored in computer systems. Some of this information is confidential. One way to maintain security is to limit access to the computer systems that store this data. A limited access system must keep a list of users that have permission to use the system. New users are added to the list as they are approved; others are deleted from the list when they no longer need access to the system. In this application, we assume that such a list uses Social Security numbers for identifying users. This list is kept in ascending order in a data file. A trailer signal of 999999999 is at the end of the file. The number of users varies, but we assume that the actual number never exceeds 500.

As we develop a program that allows Social Security numbers to be added and deleted from this list, we must be concerned about the **user interface**—the part of the program that interfaces the user to the steps in the program itself. The user interface needs to be designed to be easy to use, so that users will make fewer errors when entering the information. (Programs that are easy to use are also called **user-friendly** programs.) We will assume that the user will be entering Social Security numbers from the keyboard for additions and deletions. Since the input is probably entered from request forms, we will allow the information to be entered in any order; that is, we will not require all deletions before the insertions, and we will not assume that the Social Security numbers to be inserted or deleted are in any particular order.

Since we are inserting and deleting elements in a computer access list, it does not make sense to insert an element already in the list. Therefore, we must modify the insertion routine slightly so that a message is printed if the element is already in the list. Similarly, if the list is full, we do not want to insert another element in the list because we would lose the last element in the list. Therefore, before referencing the insert procedure, we will check to see if the list is full and, if so, print a message to the user.

PROBLEM STATEMENT

Write a program to update a computer access list.

INPUT/OUTPUT DESCRIPTION

The computer access list is stored in ascending order in a data file named *access* that has a trailer signal of 999999999. The input to the program is a set of social security numbers to be added to the list or deleted from the list. The output is an updated list of information stored in a file named *newaccess*. Error messages are also printed on the terminal screen if numbers to be added are already in the file, or if numbers to be deleted are not in the file.

Assume that the current access list contains the following Social Security numbers:

> 203294433
> 289129430
> 319330022
> 450123452
> 999999999

The updates to this list include the following insertions and deletions:

> additions: 122899823
> 244448353
> 595959591
> deletions: 289129430

After updating the list, the new computer access list is the following:

> 122899823
> 203294433
> 244448353
> 319330022
> 450123452
> 595959591
> 999999999

ALGORITHM DEVELOPMENT

The decomposition of this problem solution is

DECOMPOSITION

Read access list from file.
Perform additions and deletions to list.
Write updated list to new file.

We will use the following code to determine whether the user wants to insert a number, delete a number, or quit the program:

CODE VALUE	OPERATION DESIRED
−1	deletion
1	addition
0	quit

We now refine the decomposition steps into pseudocode.

```
update: read ssn list from data file
          done ← false
          while not done do
             write message asking for code
             read code
             if code = −1 then
                write message asking for ssn
                read old
                delete old from ssn list
             else if code = 1 then
                if count = arraysize then
                   write message that list is full
                else
                   write message asking for ssn
                   read new
                   insert new in ssn list
             else
                done ← true
          write ssn list to new file
```

We now present the pseudocode for the insertion routine. (Since the deletion procedure does not require any modifications, we do not list it again.) The parameters are listed in parenthesis after the procedure name. Recall that a slight modification was needed in the insertion routine because we do not want to insert a duplicate number in the computer access list. Instead, we will print a message that the number is already in the list. If the list is full, we will not perform an insertion because we would lose a value; instead, before we reference the insertion procedure, we will check to see if the list is full and print a message if it is. Since we will not reference the insertion procedure if the list is full, we do not need to modify the insertion routine for that situation. The pseudocode on the next page assumes the following:

The values are already in an ascending order in the array x.

A variable *count* specifies the number of valid data values in the array.

The variable *arraysize* contains the defined size of the array.

The variable *new* contains the value to be inserted in the array.

insert (arraysize,new,count,x):
    if count = arraysize then
      write message that last value will be lost
    done ← false
    i ← 1
    while (i ≤ count) and (not done) do
      if x[i] < new then
        i ← i + 1
      else
        done ← true
    if i > count then
      if count < arraysize then
        count ← count + 1
        x[count] ← new
    else
      if x[i] = new then
        write message that item is already in list
      else
        if count < arraysize then
          count ← count + 1
        for k = count downto i+1 do
          x[k] ← x[k−1]
        x[i] ← new

The structure chart for the solution is shown next, along with the Pascal program.

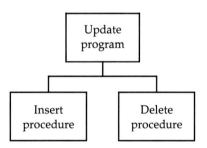

```
{------------------------------------------------------------------}
program  update (input,access,output,newaccess);
   {This program updates a computer access list.}
const
   arraysize = 500;
   trailer = 999999999;
type
   index = 1..500;
   list = array[index] of integer;
var
   i, code, count, old, new: integer;
   done: boolean;
   access, newaccess: text;
   ssn: list;
{------------------------------------------------------------------}
procedure  insert (arraysize,new:integer; var count:integer;
                   var x:list);
   {This procedure inserts an element in an ordered list.}
var
   i, k: integer;
   done: boolean;
begin {insert}
   if  count = arraysize  then
      writeln ('ARRAY IS FULL - LAST VALUE WILL BE LOST');
   done := false;
   i := 1;
   while  (i <= count) and (not done)  do
      if  x[i] < new  then
         i := i + 1
      else
         done := true;
   if  i > count  then
      begin
         if  count < arraysize  then
            begin
               count := count + 1;
               x[count] := new
            end
      end
   else
      if  x[i] = new  then
         writeln ('SSN ALREADY IN FILE')
      else
         begin
            if  count < arraysize  then
               count := count + 1;
            for k := count downto i+1 do
               x[k] := x[k-1];
            x[i] := new
         end
   end; {insert}
{------------------------------------------------------------------}
```

delete procedure goes here

```
{-------------------------------------------------------------}
begin {update}
   reset (access);
   done := false;
   i := 1
   while  not done  do
      begin
         readln (access,ssn[i]);
         if  ssn[i] = trailer  then
            done := true
         else
            i := i + 1
      end;
   count := i - 1;
   done := false;
   while  not done  do
      begin
         writeln ('ENTER -1 FOR DELETION, 1 FOR INSERTION,',
            ' 0 TO QUIT');
         readln (code);
         if  code = -1  then
            begin
               writeln ('ENTER SSN FOR DELETION');
               readln (old);
               delete (old,count,ssn)
            end
         else if  code = 1  then
            if  count = arraysize  then
               writeln ('LIST IS FULL - DO DELETIONS FIRST')
            else
               begin
                  writeln ('ENTER SSN FOR INSERTION');
                  readln (new);
                  insert (arraysize,new,count,ssn)
               end
         else
            done := true
      end;
   rewrite (newaccess);
   for i := 1 to count do
      writeln (newaccess,ssn[i]);
   writeln (newaccess,trailer)
end. {update}
{-------------------------------------------------------------}
```

TESTING

Testing this program is much simpler since we used procedures that have already been tested independently. Since we know that the procedures work properly by themselves, we can spend most of our testing time checking the interaction between the modules and the program. Of course, since we modified the insert procedure, it must be carefully tested again.

The terminal screen interaction and the input and output file contents from the hand example follow.

```
ENTER -1 FOR DELETION, 1 FOR INSERTION, 0 TO QUIT
1
ENTER SSN FOR INSERTION
122899823
ENTER -1 FOR DELETION, 1 FOR INSERTION, 0 TO QUIT
1
ENTER SSN FOR INSERTION
244448353
ENTER -1 FOR DELETION, 1 FOR INSERTION, 0 TO QUIT
1
ENTER SSN FOR INSERTION
595959591
ENTER -1 FOR DELETION, 1 FOR INSERTION, 0 TO QUIT
-1
ENTER SSN FOR DELETION
289129430
ENTER -1 FOR DELETION, 1 FOR INSERTION, 0 TO QUIT
0
```

File *access*   203294433
289129430
319330022
450123452
999999999

File *newaccess*   122899823
203294433
244448353
319330022
450123452
595959591
999999999

After writing the information from the updated array to the new data file, we wrote the trailer signal in the file. What if we had forgotten to include the trailer signal in the file? The updated list of information would still be correctly written in the file, but when we attempted to read the information from this file, we would assume that a trailer signal would follow the valid information. If the trailer signal is not in the file, we would keep reading until we reached the end of the data file or until we exceeded the limits of the array being used to hold the information. In either case, an execution error would occur.

5-7 RECURSION WITH PROCEDURES

Pascal allows a module to call itself within the module. This special type of nesting is called **recursion.** Recursion is a powerful technique that can be especially useful in solving certain types of problems. In this section we discuss the types of problems in which recursion can be applied and present an example of a **recursive procedure.** In the next chapter, we present an example of recursion with a function.

The types of problems that recursion can help solve are those in which the current problem can be defined in terms of a similar smaller problem, and the smaller problem can be defined in terms of a still smaller similar problem, until we finally reach the solution of the smallest problem. The best way to understand this is with an example. We present another sort algorithm that is one of the most efficient sorts. It is called a **quicksort** algorithm because it is generally much quicker than the types of sorts that we have already presented.

A quicksort algorithm selects some value, which we will call a **pivot value,** from the list to be sorted and separates the values into two groups — those larger than the pivot value and those smaller than the pivot value. In doing this separation, the pivot value is placed in its proper position in the list. The values in the two parts, however, are not necessarily in the proper order. We can now take the group of values smaller than the pivot, select a new pivot from this group, and separate it into two groups based on the new pivot. The new pivot value will be placed in its proper position, and we have two new groups — the group of values smaller than the new pivot value and the group of values larger than the new pivot value.

Thus, a recursion process emerges as we define a sort as the separation of a list into two groups, one with values larger than a pivot value and one with values smaller than a pivot value, while the pivot value is positioned in its proper place. Each of these new groups can be separated into two smaller groups, with the new pivot value positioned in its proper place, and so on until we get to a group of two values. This pair of values is switched if necessary to put them in the proper order. This is a very critical step in recursion. We must eventually get to a stopping point, or recursion cannot be done with the computer. Once we get to the stopping point, we reverse the process by bringing back the sorted pair of values and fitting it into the next larger group. When both halves of that group are together, it is fit into the next larger group, and so on until we are back to the original list, which will now be sorted in the proper order.

Let's look at this process with a diagram, where p represents the pivot value of a group and is selected as the first element in the group. The separation process (which we have not discussed in detail yet) will separate the group into two groups, one set of values larger than the pivot and one set smaller than the pivot, and position the pivot in its proper place. The discussion on the next page describes the steps in the diagram line by line.

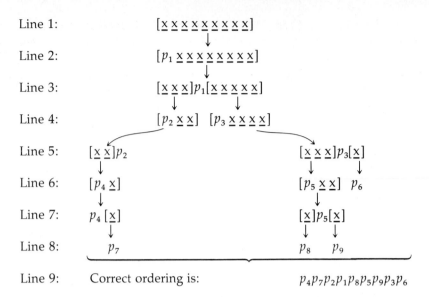

Line 1: $[\underline{x}\,\underline{x}\,\underline{x}\,\underline{x}\,\underline{x}\,\underline{x}\,\underline{x}\,\underline{x}\,\underline{x}]$

Line 2: $[p_1\,\underline{x}\,\underline{x}\,\underline{x}\,\underline{x}\,\underline{x}\,\underline{x}\,\underline{x}\,\underline{x}]$

Line 3: $[\underline{x}\,\underline{x}\,\underline{x}]p_1[\underline{x}\,\underline{x}\,\underline{x}\,\underline{x}]$

Line 4: $[p_2\,\underline{x}\,\underline{x}]\quad[p_3\,\underline{x}\,\underline{x}\,\underline{x}\,\underline{x}]$

Line 5: $[\underline{x}\,\underline{x}]p_2$ $\quad\quad\quad\quad$ $[\underline{x}\,\underline{x}\,\underline{x}]p_3[\underline{x}]$

Line 6: $[p_4\,\underline{x}]$ $\quad\quad\quad\quad\quad$ $[p_5\,\underline{x}\,\underline{x}]\quad p_6$

Line 7: $p_4\,[\underline{x}]$ $\quad\quad\quad\quad\quad$ $[\underline{x}]p_5[\underline{x}]$

Line 8: p_7 $\quad\quad\quad\quad\quad\quad\quad$ $p_8\quad\quad p_9$

Line 9: Correct ordering is: $\quad\quad\quad p_4 p_7 p_2 p_1 p_8 p_5 p_9 p_3 p_6$

Line 1: We assume that there are nine values in the list that we want to sort.

Line 2: We select the value in the first position of the list as the pivot value $p1$.

Line 3: The separation steps place the first pivot value $p1$ in its proper position (assume position 4) and group all values less than $p1$ to the left and all values greater than $p1$ to the right.

Line 4: We now apply the same steps to each of these groups. We select the first value in the group on the left as its pivot value, $p2$, and the first value in the group of the right as its pivot value, $p3$.

Line 5: The separation of the group with pivot $p2$ places $p2$ in its proper position and, in this example, places the other two values to the left of $p2$. (This would occur if both values were less than $p2$.) The separation of the group with pivot $p3$ places $p3$ in its proper position and places three values to the left of it and one value to the right.

Line 6: The first position of the group to the left of pivot $p2$ is now selected as $p4$, the pivot value for that group; the first position of the group to the left of pivot $p3$ is selected as $p5$, the pivot value for that group; and the only position in the group to the right of pivot $p3$ is selected as $p6$, and must be in its proper position since it is the only value in the group.

Line 7: The separation of the group with pivot $p4$ places $p4$ in its proper position, and the remaining element in that group forms a group to the right of $p4$. The separation of the group with pivot $p5$ places it with one position to the left and one position to the right.

Line 8: All three groups left have only one element. These elements are pivot elements for their group, and are in the proper position since there are no other elements in their group.

Line 9: Using the information from the previous lines, we can "back out" of the separations. Since the pivot values were all placed in the proper positions, when we are back to line 1, the list will be sorted in the proper order.

Each time a procedure calls itself recursively, it generates another **level of recursion.** To determine the number of levels of recursion (or nesting of recursion) for the example above, we assume that each time we separate a group, there are two more references to the sort, one for each part. This continues until the size for the separation is one—in this case the group cannot be separated and no further recursive references are made to the sort. In the example in the diagram, the assignment of a pivot position represents another level of recursion. Thus, the maximum level of recursion is four levels and occurs in several places, such as $p1,p2,p4,p7$, or $p1,p3,p5,p8$, or $p1,p3,p5,p9$.

Returning to the algorithm development, the separation process needs to separate the list into values less than the pivot and greater than the pivot, in addition to placing the pivot in its proper position. The diagram on the next page illustrates the separation process. The technique finds the first value from the left that is larger than the pivot (calling that position *up* since it represents a value that needs to be moved up), finds the first value from the right that is smaller than the pivot (calling that position *down* since it represents a value that needs to be moved down), and exchanges these values. This process of finding the next value to move up and the next value to move down and exchanging them continues until the position of *up* is greater than the position of *down*. At this point, the pivot value is moved into the position pointed to by *down* and the separation is complete. The pivot is in its proper place. All values less than the pivot are on the left and all values greater than the pivot are on the right.

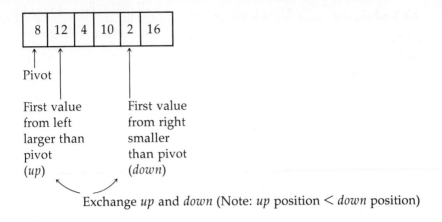

First value
from left
larger than
pivot
(*up*)

First value
from right
smaller
than pivot
(*down*)

Exchange *up* and *down* (Note: *up* position < *down* position)

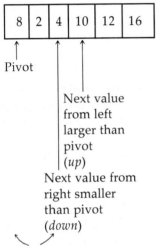

Next value
from left
larger than
pivot
(*up*)

Next value from
right smaller
than pivot
(*down*)

Exchange *pivot* and *down* (Note: *up* position > *down* position)

| 4 | 2 | 8 | 10 | 12 | 16 |

(Note: pivot value is in correct position with values
less to the left and values greater to the right)

We now have all the pieces to develop an algorithm for the quicksort technique and to implement it in Pascal.

EXAMPLE 5-5   Quicksort Procedure

Write a recursive procedure to sort a list of values using the quicksort technique. Assume that the list contains integers and that a parameter to the procedure will be the count of the valid elements in the list.

Solution

The decomposition for this problem is the following:

DECOMPOSITION

> Sort a list of data values into ascending order.

Since the solution is to be implemented in a procedure, we need to determine the procedure header and its corresponding parameter list. When we developed procedures for sorts in previous sections, we used a procedure header of the following form:

```
procedure  sort (count:integer; var x:list);
```

We cannot use this parameter list since we are writing a recursive procedure. Each recursive call to the procedure will reference a group of items within the list, but the group typically will not begin with the first item or end with the last item. For example, a recursive call to the procedure may use the group of items from position 6 through position 20. Therefore, we need to modify the procedure header so that it uses a beginning and an end position as parameters, instead of a count. The initial reference to the procedure would use 1 as the beginning position and *count* as the end position. The procedure header we use is the following:

```
procedure  quicksort (first,last:integer; var x:list);
```

The initial refinement in pseudocode will reference the separation process, which we will indicate with another procedure reference. The separation procedure needs to know the portion of the list that it is to use (specified by *first, last,* and *x*). It returns the breakpoint for that portion of the list, where the breakpoint is the proper position of its pivot value.

```
quicksort(first,last,x):
        separate(first,last,x,breakpoint)
        quicksort(first,breakpoint−1,x)
        quicksort(breakpoint+1,last,x)

separate(first,last,x,breakpoint):
        set first value to pivot value
        up ← first position from left with value
          greater than pivot value
        down ← first position from right with value
          less than pivot value
        while up < down do
          switch values pointed to by up and down
          find next values for up and down
        switch values pointed to by first and down
        breakpoint ← down
```

As we continue to refine the solution, we find that the *separate* procedure is getting long. In order to make it more readable, we are going to take several steps in it and implement them as procedures too. The *nextpair* procedure will find the next values for *up* and *down*, which are then used for switching values and determining when we have separated all the values into values greater than the pivot value and values less than the pivot value. Since values are switched in more than one place in the pseudocode, we will also use a procedure to implement the switch.

FINAL REFINEMENT IN PSEUDOCODE

```
quicksort(first,last,x):
        separate(first,last,x,breakpoint)
        quicksort(first,breakpoint−1,x)
        quicksort(breakpoint+1,last,x)

separate(first,last,x,breakpoint):
        nextpair (first,last,x,up,down)
        while up < down do
          switch (up,down,x)
          nextpair (first,last,x,up,down)
        switch (first,down,x)
        breakpoint ← down
```

nextpair(first,last,x,up,down):
      while (x[up] ≤ x[first]) and (up < last) do
        up ← up + 1
      while (x[down] ≥ x[first]) and (down > first) do
        down ← down − 1

switch(i,j,x):
      hold ← x[i]
      x[i] ← x[j]
      x[j] ← hold

We are now ready to convert the pseudocode into Pascal. We are going to include the *quicksort* procedure in a driver program that will read a list of values and then reference the *quicksort* procedure to sort the list. The driver will then print the sorted values. A structure chart for this program is shown below. It illustrates the nesting of procedures within procedures that occurs since quicksort contains the *separate* procedure, and the *separate* procedure contains both the *nextpair* procedure and the *switch* procedure.

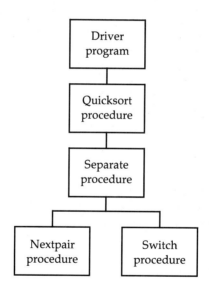

```
{-------------------------------------------------------}
program  driver (input,output);
   {This program tests the sort procedure.}
type
   index = 1..10;
   list = array[index] of integer;
var
   count, i: integer;
   x: list;
{-------------------------------------------------------}
procedure  quicksort (first,last:integer; var x:list);
   {This procedure performs a recursive sort algorithm.}
var
   breakpoint: integer;
{-------------------------------------------------------}
procedure  separate (first,last:integer; var x:list;
                     var breakpoint:integer);
   {This procedure correctly positions the first value
   in the list and separates all values less than it to
   the left and all values greater than it to the right.}
var
   up, down: integer;
{-------------------------------------------------------}
procedure  nextpair (first,last:integer; x:list;
                     var up,down:integer);
   {This procedure determines the next values less than
   and greater than the pivot value in the list.}
begin {nextpair}
   while  (x[up] <= x[first]) and (up < last)  do
      up := up + 1;
   while  (x[down] >= x[first]) and (down > first)  do
      down := down - 1
end; {nextpair}
{-------------------------------------------------------}
procedure  switch (i,j:integer; var x:list);
   {This procedure switches two values in the array.}
var
   hold: integer;
begin {switch}
   hold := x[i];
   x[i] := x[j];
   x[j] := hold
end; {switch}
{-------------------------------------------------------}
begin {separate}
   up := first;
   down := last;
   nextpair (first,last,x,up,down);
   while  up < down  do
      begin
         switch (up,down,x);
         nextpair (first,last,x,up,down)
      end;
   switch (first,down,x);
   breakpoint := down
end; {separate}
```

```
{----------------------------------------------------------}
begin {quicksort}
    if  first < last   then
        begin
            separate (first,last,x,breakpoint);
            quicksort (first,breakpoint-1,x);
            quicksort (breakpoint+1,last,x)
        end
end; {quicksort}
{----------------------------------------------------------}
begin {driver}
    writeln ('ENTER COUNT (< 11) OF VALUES FOR LIST');
    readln (count);
    writeln ('ENTER VALUES');
    for i := 1 to count do
        read (x[i]);
    quicksort (1,count,x);
    writeln ('ORDERED LIST:');
    for i := 1 to count do
        writeln (x[i]:6)
end. {driver}
{----------------------------------------------------------}
```

We could have listed the procedures independently of each other, as opposed to nesting them, provided that we listed them such that *switch* and *nextpair* preceded *separate* and *separate* preceded *quicksort*. The reason we did not list them independently is that we prefer to nest modules according to their use; otherwise, it is easy to use a module in another program and forget to include some of the modules that it needs.

An example of a test of the quicksort procedure using this driver follows.

```
ENTER COUNT (<11) OF VALUES FOR LIST
6
ENTER VALUES
2 -4 28 57 14 28
ORDERED LIST:
    -4
     2
    14
    28
    28
    57
```

SUMMARY

Procedures allow us to structure our programs by breaking them into modules that can be written and tested independently of each other. Not only do programs become simpler, but the same module can also be used in other programs without retesting. In this chapter we developed procedures for common techniques such as sorting a list of values and inserting and deleting elements in an ordered list.

DEBUGGING AIDS

Testing an individual procedure is actually testing a separate program; it generally follows the guidelines that have been summarized at the end of the previous chapters. We list here some specific guidelines to use regarding the communication link between the procedure and the program or driver.

1. Always use the parameter list to pass information back and forth between the program and the procedure.
2. Unless a variable is returning information from the procedure to the program, use references by value for all parameters to avoid side effects.
3. Be sure that the variables or expressions listed in the procedure reference match the parameter list in the procedure header, both in type and in order.
4. Define all local variables within the procedure; otherwise, you may be using a global variable (and possibly changing it) without realizing it.
5. Remember that you can put extra *write* statements in the procedure for use in debugging.
6. Always test each procedure individually.
7. Test each procedure with several sets of data to check any special conditions.

STYLE/TECHNIQUE GUIDELINES

Separating a long program into modules that transfer control smoothly from one to another becomes easier with practice. Although different sets of procedures may solve the same problem, some choices are more logical and readable than others; these are the solutions that you want to develop. Once you have selected a segment that is to be made into a procedure, you have to decide what parameters are needed and whether the parameters should be referenced by value or by address. Here are a few style suggestions to keep in mind as you make these decisions:

1. Choose descriptive names for your procedures.
2. Use comments in the procedures as you would in the program. In particular, use comments at the beginning of a procedure to describe its purpose and define its parameters if necessary.
3. For clarity, use the same variables in the parameter list of the procedure that will be used in the program, if possible. If the procedure is invoked several times with different variables, choose completely different variable identifiers in the procedure header to avoid confusion.
4. List input parameters before output parameters in the procedure list.

KEY WORDS

actual parameter	quicksort
block	random number generator
driver	recursive procedure
formal parameter	reference by address
global variable	reference by value
invoke	scope
levels of recursion	side effects
local variable	software tools
module	structure chart
nested procedures	user-friendly
parameter	user interface
procedure	value parameter
procedure header	variable parameter

PROBLEMS

We begin our problem set with modifications to programs developed earlier in this chapter. Give the decomposition, refined pseudocode, and Pascal program for each problem.

Problems 1–5 modify the oil well production program, *report*, given on page 228.

1. Modify the oil well production program so that it asks the user to enter the current date to put in the upper right-hand corner, under the page number. The report will show the date that the report was run in addition to the date of the time period for which the data was collected. Reduce the number of lines of oil well data by one line to keep the same number of lines of output per page.

2. Modify the oil well production program so that the name of the oil company, CLAYTON OIL, appears on page 1 but not on the other pages. Put a blank line in its place on the other pages. Reduce the number of lines of oil well data by one line to keep the same number of lines of output per page.

3. Modify the oil well production program so that the maximum weekly production is determined and printed after the summary line.

4. Modify the oil well production program so that it determines the maximum daily production for each oil well and returns that value to the program. Modify the program so that it prints the maximum daily production for each oil well in addition to the average.

5. Modify the oil well production program so that it determines the average oil production for an oil well based on nonzero production days. That is, if a well produced zero barrels of oil one day of the week, the average would be based on six days instead of seven.

Problems 6–10 modify the signal generating program *generate,* given on page 234.

6. Modify the signal generating program so that it increments the time by 0.25 seconds instead of 0.01.
7. Modify the signal generating program so that it reads the time increment from the terminal.
8. Modify the signal generating program so that it reads the number of data points that are to be generated from the terminal, instead of generating 101 points.
9. Modify the signal generating program so that it multiplies the noise value generated by the random generator by a constant that is read from the terminal.
10. Modify the signal generating program so that it adds the noise value to data values read from a file called *rawdata.*

Problems 11–15 modify the computer access update program *update,* given on page 250.

11. Modify the computer access program so that it writes the number of additions and deletions performed by the program on the terminal screen before exiting the program.
12. Modify the computer access program so that it writes the number of valid users in the new access file on the terminal screen before exiting the program.
13. Modify the computer access program so that it writes the number of valid users in the original access file on the terminal screen before beginning the update process.
14. Modify the computer access program so that it assumes that the access file is in descending order instead of ascending order and has a trailer value of zero.
15. Modify the computer access program so that it prints a report that lists all the valid access numbers after the access list is updated.

For problems 16–21, assume that *time,* a one-dimensional array of 100 values, has already been filled with data. Assume that the program includes the following type definitions:

```
type
    index = 1..100;
    list = array[index] of real;
```

16. Write a procedure to determine the maximum value in the array *time.*
17. Write a procedure to determine the minimum value in the array *time.*
18. Write a procedure to count the number of negative values in the array *time.*
19. Write a procedure to determine the sum of the values in the array *time.*

Write a procedure to replace all values in the array *time* with the absolute value of the corresponding value.

21. Write a procedure to return a Boolean value of true if all the values in the array *time* are zero, and false otherwise.

Here are some new programs and procedures to develop. Use the five-phase design process. Show any type statements that you assume are in the program.

22. Write a procedure called *range* that receives an integer array with 50 elements and returns the maximum and minimum values.

23. Write a procedure that will read a group of test scores from a data file *tests* until it finds a negative test score. The procedure should return the number of test scores read before the negative value was encountered and the average of those test scores.

24. Write a procedure that will compute the average, the variance, and the standard deviation of an array x of 100 data values. Use the following formulas:

$$\text{Average} \qquad \overline{X} = \frac{\sum\limits_{i=1}^{100} X_i}{100}$$

$$\text{Variance} \qquad \sigma^2 = \frac{\sum\limits_{i=1}^{100} (\overline{X} - X_i)^2}{99}$$

$$\text{Standard deviation} \qquad \sigma = \sqrt{\sigma^2}$$

25. Rewrite the procedure in the previous problem so that it will compute the average, variance, and standard deviation for an array with a maximum of 500 values. Assume that n contains the number of actual values in the array. The denominator of the expression for the variance should then be $n - 1$ instead of 99.

26. Write a procedure called *removebias* that is invoked with the following statement:

```
removebias (x,y,n)
```

Assume x is an input array with a maximum of 200 real values, and n is an integer that specifies how many of the values represent actual data values. The parameter y is an output array the same size as x whose values should be the values of x with the minimum value of the x array subtracted from each one. For example,

$$\text{If } x = \begin{array}{|c|} \hline 10 \\ \hline 2 \\ \hline 36 \\ \hline 8 \\ \hline \end{array} \text{, then } y = \begin{array}{|c|} \hline 8 \\ \hline 0 \\ \hline 34 \\ \hline 6 \\ \hline \end{array}$$

continued

Thus, the minimum value of y is always zero. This operation is referred to as removing the bias in x or adjusting for bias in x.

27. When working with experimental data, we often find that we need to scale the data for other purposes. This scaling can be a simple multiplication by a constant, or it can involve scaling the points between a new minimum and maximum. Write a procedure that has four parameters: the name of an array, the number of valid entries in the array, and the new minimum and maximum for scaling the data. Assume that the procedure header has the following form:

```
procedure scale (n:integer; minimum,maximum:real;
                 var x:list);
```

The array below contains the values before calling the procedure and then after calling the procedure with n equal to 5, minimum equal to 10, and maximum equal to 20.

Before procedure reference	After procedure reference
2.5	11.83
5.0	15.35
1.2	10.0
8.3	20.0
4.7	14.93

PASCAL STATEMENT SUMMARY

Procedure Reference:

procedure identifier (*parameters*)

Examples:

```
printheader (date,pages)

sort (count,x)
```

Discussion:

The procedure reference statement is used to transfer control to the statements in the procedure. The inputs and outputs to the procedure must be listed in the parameter list and must match in type and in number those used in the procedure header. After executing the statements in the procedure, control returns to the statement following the procedure reference.

PROBLEM SOLVING — Traffic Flow

The design of transportation systems becomes increasingly
important as the size of our population and urban areas increases.
Current as well as projected needs must be considered in these
designs. The data for determining needs and projections includes
sampled information such as the traffic flow in the current
transportation system. Write a program to analyze traffic flow
information and determine the average number of cars that pass
through an intersection per minute. (See Section 6-4 for the solution.)

6

IMPLEMENTING TOP-DOWN DESIGN WITH FUNCTIONS

INTRODUCTION

In Chapter 5, we stressed the importance of using modules in the design of our algorithms. Pascal allows two types of modules: procedures and functions. We have seen the advantages of using procedures in problem solutions. In this chapter we want to study the **function,** a module similar to a procedure but with some special advantages for computations. Since computations are so necessary in science and engineering applications, the function will be a very useful tool to use in the design of algorithms. We will review the built-in functions of Pascal, such as the absolute function and the logarithm function. We will then learn how to write our own functions to perform computations that are unique to our applications.

6-1   BUILT-IN FUNCTIONS

Pascal contains a number of built-in functions that are always available to our programs. We discussed these briefly in Chapter 1 and have frequently used some of the more common ones such as the square root function, *sqrt*. In this section we want to give a more complete discussion of these built-in functions, and to do this we will divide them into three categories: **mathematical functions, Boolean functions,** and a new type of function called **ordinal functions.**

MATHEMATICAL FUNCTIONS

Pascal contains ten built-in functions that compute a value based on input parameters to the function. Recall that the value returned by a function is returned through the function reference, not as a parameter. We now list the built-in functions with a few comments on each. A complete table listing these functions is listed on the inside back cover of the text.

ABS   The absolute value function requires one input parameter. The value returned by the function is the absolute value of the input parameter. The type of value returned is the same as the input parameter type. This function is valid only for integer and real types. An example of the use of this function is:

    `a := 3.0/abs(x)`

ARCTAN   The arctangent function requires one input parameter. The value returned by the function is the arctangent (in radians) of the input parameter. The type of value returned is real. This function accepts either real or integer input. An example of the use of this function is:

    `pi := 4.0*arctan(1.0)`

COS   The cosine function requires one input parameter. The value returned by the function is the cosine of the input parameter. The type of value returned is real. This function accepts either real or integer input and assumes that the input represents radians. An example of the use of this function is:

```
writeln (angle,cos(angle))
```

EXP   The exponential function requires one input parameter. The value returned by the function is *e* raised to the power specified by the input parameter. The type of value returned is real. This function is valid only for real and integer input parameters. An example of the use of this function is:

```
newgrowth := oldgrowth*exp(1.386*time)
```

LN   The natural logarithm function requires one input parameter. The value returned by the function is the natural logarithm of the input parameter. The type of value returned is real. This function is valid only for real and integer input parameters whose value is greater than zero. An example of the use of this function is:

```
age := (-ln(carbon14))/0.0001216
```

ROUND   The rounding function requires one input parameter. The value returned by the function is the input value rounded to the nearest integer value. This function is valid only for real input. An example of the use of this function is:

```
days := round(hours/24.0)
```

SIN   The sine function requires one input parameter. The value returned by the function is the sine of the input parameter. The type of value returned is real. This function accepts either real or integer input, but assumes that the input represents radians. An example of the use of this function is:

```
writeln (angle,sin(angle))
```

SQR   The square function requires one input parameter. The value returned by the function is the square of the input parameter. The type of value returned is the same as the input parameter type. This function is valid only for integer and real types. An example of the use of this function is:

```
area := sqr(side)
```

SQRT   The square root function requires one input parameter. The value returned by the function is the square root of the input parameter. The type of value returned is real. This function is valid only for real and integer types whose value is greater than or equal to zero. An example of the use of this function is:

```
radius := sqrt(area/pi)
```

TRUNC   The truncating function requires one input parameter. The value returned by the function is an integer whose value is the input value rounded down to the next integer value. This function is valid only for real input. An example of the use of this function is:

```
quarters := trunc(cost/0.25)
```

TABLE 6-1 Trigonometric Expressions

TRIGONOMETRIC FUNCTIONS
$$\tan x = \sin x/\cos x$$
$$\cot x = \cos x/\sin x$$
$$\sec x = 1/\cos x$$
$$\csc x = 1/\sin x$$

INVERSE TRIGONOMETRIC FUNCTIONS
$$\arcsin a = \arctan (a/\sqrt{1-a^2})$$
$$\arccos a = \arctan (\sqrt{1-a^2}/a)$$

HYPERBOLIC FUNCTIONS
$$\sinh x = (e^x - e^{-x})/2$$
$$\cosh x = (e^x + e^{-x})/2$$
$$\tanh x = (e^x - e^{-x})/(e^x + e^{-x})$$
$$\operatorname{csch} x = 2/(e^x - e^{-x})$$
$$\operatorname{sech} x = 2/(e^x + e^{-x})$$
$$\coth x = (e^x + e^{-x})/(e^x - e^{-x})$$

As we covered the mathematical built-in functions, you may have noticed that some of the mathematical functions you frequently use were not in the list. In these cases, you will have to compute the function you want using the built-in functions plus other arithmetic operations as needed. In Table 6-1 we have listed a number of expressions for computing trigonometric functions, inverse trigonometric functions, and hyperbolic functions using Pascal's built-in functions. If you only need these additional functions occasionally, we suggest that you use the equation from Table 6-1 to perform the computation. If you frequently need these additional functions, we suggest that, after reading Section 6-2 on writing your own functions, you use the equations from Table 6-1 to develop a set of user-written functions. Then, when you need them, you can refer to the user-written functions just as you refer to the built-in functions.

BOOLEAN FUNCTIONS

Pascal has three built-in Boolean functions. The *eof* function is used to detect the end of a data file, and *eoln* is used to detect the end of a data line. We discussed the *eof* function in Chapter 4. The *eoln* function will be especially useful in string manipulations, which we will discuss in detail in Chapter 8. The third Boolean function, *odd*, is used to determine if an integer is odd; it can also be used to determine if an integer is even.

EOF   The end-of-file function requires one input parameter that must be a file identifier. If the input parameter is omitted, the function assumes that the intended file is the system input file. The value returned by the function is true if the end of the file has been detected, and false otherwise. (See Chapter 4 to review the details regarding this function.) An example of the use of this function is:

```
while  not eof(data)  do
       processdata (x)
```

EOLN   The end-of-line function requires one input parameter, which must be a file identifier. If the input parameter is omitted, the function will assume that the intended file is the system input file. The value returned by the function is true if the end of the line has been detected, and false otherwise. This function will be discussed in more detail in Chapter 8. An example of the use of this function is:

```
if  not eoln  then
    read (next[i])
```

ODD   The odd function requires one input parameter, which must be an integer type. The value returned by the function is true if the input value is odd, and false otherwise. An example of the use of this function is:

```
if  odd(number)  then
    number := number + 1
```

ORDINAL FUNCTIONS

In Chapter 4 we defined an ordinal data type as one in which each value (except the first) has a unique predecessor and each value (except the last) has a unique successor. For example, integers are ordinal numbers. The predecessor of 5 is 4 and the successor of 5 is 6. However, reals are not ordinal numbers. The character data type is also an ordinal type. For example, the predecessor of *Y* is *X* and the successor of *Y* is Z. The four ordinal functions presented in this section work with ordinal data types.

The *predecessor* and *successor* functions can be used with any ordinal type. A special function for characters, *chr*, will return the character that occupies a specified location in the ordering of characters. For example, the letter *Y* occupies position 89 in the ordinal numbering of characters used by most compilers. (We will discuss this ordering more in Chapter 8.) The last ordinal function discussed below, *ord*, receives a value that is ordinal type and returns an integer that specifies the ordinal number for that value. Thus, *ord('Y')* represents the number 89. (We are presenting *chr* and *ord* here primarily to have a complete listing of the built-in functions; the motivation for their use will be seen in Chapter 8.)

PRED   The predecessor function requires one input parameter, which must be an ordinal type. The value returned by the function is the unique predecessor of the input parameter. The type of the value returned is the same as the type of the input. An example of the use of this function is:

```
previous := pred(number)
```

An execution error will occur if the parameter for this function is the first element in the order of the elements of the data type.

SUCC   The successor function requires one input parameter, which must be an ordinal type. The value returned by the function is the unique successor of the input parameter. The type of the value returned is the same as the type of the input. An example of the use of this function is:

```
next := succ(number)
```

An execution error will occur if the parameter for this function is the last element in the order of the elements of the data type.

CHR The character function requires one integer input parameter. The character returned by the function is the character whose ordinal number matches the input parameter. (See Chapter 8 for more details.) An example of the use of this function is:

```
writeln (chr(pointer))
```

ORD The ordinal function requires one input parameter which is an ordinal type. The value returned by the function is the integer that represents the ordinal number of the input parameter. (See Chapter 8 for more details.) An example of the use of this function is:

```
if  ord(':') < ord(';')  then
    sort1 (count,x)
else
    sort2 (count,x)
```

SELF-TEST 6-1

This self-test allows you to check quickly to see if you have remembered certain key points from Section 6-1. If you have any problems with the exercises, you should reread this section. The solutions are included at the end of the text.

For each of the following statements, show the output that would be printed on the terminal screen.

1. `writeln (abs(-5):6)`
2. `writeln (abs(-5.0):4:1)`
3. `writeln (round(12.6):6)`
4. `writeln (trunc(12.6):6)`
5. `if  odd(23)  then`
       `writeln ('YES')`
     `else`
       `writeln ('NO')`
6. `writeln (pred('Q'))`
7. `writeln (succ('3'))`
8. `writeln (pred(succ('T')))`

6-2 USER-WRITTEN FUNCTIONS

Writing a function is very similar to writing a procedure. Both functions and procedures are modules and follow the variable declaration section of the program. Since a function returns its value through the function name, the header line to define the function must give the type of the value that is to be returned. For example, the header line for a function called *average* that is going to compute and return the average of a real array is shown below:

```
function  average (data:list): real;
```

This function has only one parameter, the array called *data*. (We assume that *list* is a data type defined earlier to be an array.) Note that *data* is a value parameter; thus the data array cannot be modified by the function. Following the parameter list is a colon and the type specification for the function, which is real in this example. The syntax diagram for the **function header** follows.

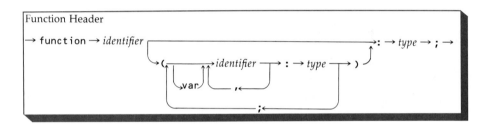

Function Header

Parameters used in the function reference must match, in type, parameters used in the function header. The corresponding order of these actual parameters and formal parameters must also match, just as in procedures.

Since the function returns a single value through the function reference, it must include a statement that assigns the function name a value. (Recall that a procedure returns values through its parameters, so the procedure name is not given a value.)

Some examples will illustrate the differences between procedures and functions. In the examples, we will develop a function and give a simple program that can be used for testing it. Remember that it is important to test any module (function or procedure) separately, before you include it in the program that is going to use it.

EXAMPLE 6-1   Median Value

The median of a list of sorted numbers is defined to be the number in the middle. In the list $-5,2,7,36,42$ the number 7 is the median. If the list has an even number of values, the median is defined to be the average of the two middle values. In the list $-5,2,7,36,42,82$ the median is $(7+36)/2$, or 21.5. Write a function called *median* that has two parameters, x (a real array that has been specified to be of type *list*) and *count* (the number of valid entries in the array x). The function should assume that the elements of x have already been sorted. Return the median value (a real number) as the function value.

Solution

The decomposition for this function is a single step:

Decomposition

> Compute median.

We now develop the details needed to write the pseudocode solution. From the problem definition we know that we will need two parameters, the array and the number of valid entries in the array. Since these parameters represent information for the function, not variables which are to return new values, they should be value parameters. Within the function, we need to determine if the value of *count* is odd or even. If *count* is odd, we need to decide which subscript refers to the middle value. For example, if *count* is 5, we want the median to refer to the third value, which is referenced by *(count/2)+1*, or *2+1*, assuming that we perform the division so that the result is an integer. If the count is even, we want to refer to the two middle values and compute their average. Thus, if *count* is 6, we want to use the third and fourth values, which can be referenced by *(count/2)* and *(count/2)+1*, again assuming we perform the division so that the result is an integer. The correponding pseudocode is shown below.

Refinement in Pseudocode

median (x,count):

    if count is odd then
        median ← x[(count/2)+1]
    else
        median ← (x[count/2] + x[count/2+1])/2

In the last section we saw that Pascal contains a built-in function for determining if a value is odd, so we will use it in our function. Also, we use the *div* operator to get an integer result from the division of two integers. With these decisions, we can now convert the pseudocode into Pascal.

Pascal Function

```
{- - - - - - - - - - - - - - - - - - - - - - - - - - - - - - - - - - - - -}
function  median (x:list; count:integer): real;
   {This function determines the median value
   in a sorted list of real values.}
begin {median}
   if  odd(count)  then
      median := x[(count div 2)+1]
   else
      median := (x[count div 2] + x[(count div 2)+1])/2.0
end; {median}
{- - - - - - - - - - - - - - - - - - - - - - - - - - - - - - - - - - - - -}
```

A program for testing this function is shown below with the proper location indicated for the function. The structure chart for this program is:

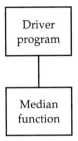

PASCAL PROGRAM

```
{------------------------------------------------------------}
program  driver (input,output);
    {This program is designed to test the median function.}
type
    index = 1..10;
    list = array[index] of real;
var
    i, count: integer;
    x: list;
{------------------------------------------------------------}
                median function goes here
{------------------------------------------------------------}
begin {driver}
    writeln ('ENTER NUMBER OF VALUES FOR ARRAY (<11)');
    readln (count);
    writeln ('NOW ENTER ARRAY VALUES ON ONE LINE');
    for i:= 1 to count do
        read (x[i]);
    writeln ('MEDIAN = ',median(x,count):7:2)
end. {driver}
{------------------------------------------------------------}
```

Output for the two sets of data given in the problem statement follows.

COMPUTER OUTPUT

```
ENTER NUMBER OF VALUES FOR ARRAY (<11)
5
NOW ENTER ARRAY VALUES ON ONE LINE
-5   2   7   36   42
MEDIAN =      7.00
```

```
ENTER NUMBER OF VALUES FOR ARRAY (<11)
6
NOW ENTER ARRAY VALUES ON ONE LINE
-5 2 7 36 42 82
MEDIAN =     21.50
```

EXAMPLE 6-2   Exponentiation

You may have noticed that Pascal does not have an exponentiation operator that will allow us to perform operations such as 3.44 raised to the 2.4 power. Certainly these types of operations arise in engineering and science applications, so we are going to develop a function to perform a general exponentiation. We will need to use logarithms for this function, so we should review the way to do this with logarithms. Remember that the logarithm of a number raised to a power is the power multiplied by the logarithm of the number. That is,

$$\ln (x^y) = y \ln (x)$$

If we now raise e to the values above, we have the following:

$$e^{\ln(x^y)} = e^{y \ln (x)}$$

which is also the same as:

$$x^y = e^{y \ln (x)}$$

Thus, we can raise x to the y power by raising e to the power of y times the logarithm of x. This may seem like a long way to go to get the answer, but we really don't have any choice. We can perform logarithms and raise e to given powers, but we cannot directly perform a general exponentiation.

Write a function called *exponentiation* that has two parameters, a base and a power, which are both real values. The function should return a value that is the base raised to the power. We will need to include an error condition test for values of the base that are equal to or less than zero since we cannot compute the logarithm of zero or of a negative number. In these instances, we will print an error message and return a value of zero.

Solution

The decomposition for this step is a single step:

Decomposition

> Compute exponentiation.

The function will need as parameters both the base and the power for the exponentiation. Using the equations developed above, we can refine this step into the following pseudocode:

Refinement in Pseudocode

exponentiation (base,power): if base ≤ 0.0 then
                    print error message
                    exponentiation ← 0.0
            else
                    compute exponentiation

We now convert these steps to Pascal.

PASCAL FUNCTION

```
{- - - - - - - - - - - - - - - - - - - - - - - - - - - - - - - - - - - - - - - - - - -}
function  exponentiation (base,power:real): real;
   {This function raises a variable base
   to a variable power.}
begin {exponentiation}
   if  base <= 0.0   then
      begin
         writeln ('BASE MUST BE GREATER THAN ZERO');
         exponentiation := 0.0
      end
   else
      exponentiation := exp(power*ln(base))
end; {exponentiation}
{- - - - - - - - - - - - - - - - - - - - - - - - - - - - - - - - - - - - - - - - -}
```

A program for testing this function is now shown, with the proper location indicated for the function. The structure chart for this program is:

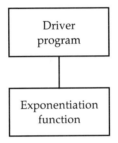

PASCAL PROGRAM

```
{- - - - - - - - - - - - - - - - - - - - - - - - - - - - - - - - - - - - - - - - - -}
program  driver (input,output);
   {This program is designed to test
   the exponentiation function.}
var
   base, power, result: real;
{- - - - - - - - - - - - - - - - - - - - - - - - - - - - - - - - - - - - - - - - - -}
              exponentiation function goes here
{- - - - - - - - - - - - - - - - - - - - - - - - - - - - - - - - - - - - - - - - - -}
begin {driver}
   writeln ('ENTER BASE AND EXPONENT');
   readln (base,power);
   result := exponentiation(base,power);
   writeln (base:6:2,' TO THE POWER ',power:7:2,
            ' = ',result:9:2)
end. {driver}
{. . . . . . . . . . . . . . . . . . . . . . . . . . . . . . . . . . . . .}
```

An example of the output of this program follows.

```
┌─────────────────────────────────────────────────────────┐
│  ENTER BASE AND EXPONENT                                  │
│  3.44  2.4                                                │
│    3.44 TO THE POWER      2.40 =       19.40              │
└─────────────────────────────────────────────────────────┘
```

In Section 2-8, we developed the pseudocode solution for a program to print a report containing the time and height information for the flight of a rocket. We could not convert the pseudocode into Pascal in Chapter 2 because we needed an exponentiation function. Since we developed an exponentiation function in this exercise, we can now give the structure chart and the Pascal solution for the rocket flight problem. (See page 68 to review the pseudocode development.)

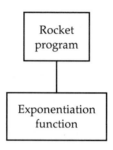

PASCAL PROGRAM

```
{----------------------------------------------------------}
program   rocket (output);
   {This program computes the time and height
   values for the flight of a rocket.}
var
   time, height: real;
{----------------------------------------------------------}
                 exponentiation function goes here
{----------------------------------------------------------}
begin {rocket}
   writeln ('TIME (SEC.)     HEIGHT (FT.)');
   writeln;
   time := 0.0;
   height := 60.0;
   while (height > 0.0) and (time <= 100.0)   do
      begin
         height := 60.0 + 2.13*sqr(time) −
                   0.0013*sqr(time)*sqr(time) +
                   0.000034*exponentiation(time,4.751);
         writeln (time:8:2,' ':8,height:9:4);
         if  height < 50.0  then
            time := time + 0.05
         else
            time := time + 2.0
      end
end. {rocket}
{----------------------------------------------------------}
```

6-3 PROBLEM SOLVING—EQUIPMENT RELIABILITY

If you have a personal computer, or if you have a friend who has one, open the back of the computer system and look at the computer board(s) that contain its circuitry. Each board contains a large number of components. You might wonder how computers can be so reliable when so many differenct pieces could malfunction. Much of their reliability is due to the quality control maintained during their manufacture. However, before the design of a computer or any complicated piece of instrumentation is actually implemented, the **reliability** of the device is analyzed. In this section we will look at one way of estimating the reliability of a piece of instrumentation that may have large numbers of the same component in it. In order to perform the computations, we must know the reliability of a single component. This number is generally available from the manufacturer. For example, a company may sell transistors that are guaranteed to be good 98 percent of the time. This information tells us how reliable one transistor is, but it does not tell us how reliable a piece of instrumentation may be if it contains 5000 of these transistors.

Equations for analyzing reliability come from the area of mathematics called statistics and probability. However, in order to select the correct equation, we must know something about the design. For example, consider the two next diagrams:

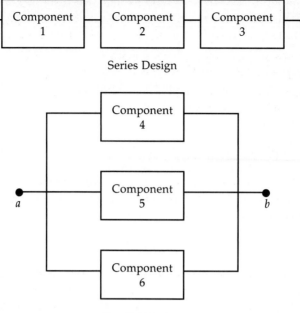

Series Design

Parallel Design

The design on the top contains three components connected serially, or in **series.** In order for information to flow from point a to point b, all three components must work properly. The design on the bottom contains three components connected in **parallel.** In order for information to flow from point a to point b, only one of the three components must work properly. If all the individual components have the same reliability, we would expect that the parallel configuration would have better overall performance. This can also be verified with mathematical equations.

In this section, we are going to estimate the reliability of a piece of equipment relative to a specific component that is used many places in the design. We are going to compute the percentage of the time that all the components will be working properly, so we are looking at a series-type design. This situation can be described using a **Bernoulli equation.** With the equation we can compute the probability that all the components will work properly. This probability can be expressed as the percentage of time that there will be no component failures. If this percentage is not high, we may not want to perform critical operations with the instrumentation or we may want to request that the instrumentation be redesigned.

Assume that p is the percentage of time that a single component will be good and n is the total number of components in the piece of equipment. Then the reliability, or percentage of the time that no component will fail, is given by the Bernoulli equation below:

$$\text{reliability} = (p/100.0)^n \cdot 100.0$$

This equation is simple to compute now that we have a function for the exponentiation operation.

Write a program that will read the reliability of a single component and the number of components in a design. Compute the percentage of time that all the components will work properly using the Bernoulli equation.

PROBLEM STATEMENT

Write a program that will compute the reliability of a piece of instrumentation relative to a specific component, using the approximation given by the Bernoulli equation.

INPUT/OUTPUT DESCRIPTION

The input will be two values: the reliability of a single component and the number of components in the instrumentation. The output will be the overall reliability of the instrumentation relative to the specific component.

HAND EXAMPLE

Suppose we are evaluating a piece of instrumentation that contains 20 transistors. Each transistor has a reliability of 96 percent. We are interested in the reliability of the instrument with no transistor failures. The calculation is performed as shown below:

$$n = 20$$
$$p = 96$$
$$\text{percentage} = (96/100)^{20} \cdot 100$$
$$= 44.20$$

where percentage is the percentage of the time that there will be no transistor failures. This number is probably lower than you expected. Even with 99 percent reliability of an individual component, the reliabilty of 20 of them at one time is 81.8 percent. Clearly, most instrumentation must have ways of improving reliability over that given by Bernoulli trials. Designs that use parallel features have greatly increased reliability, and different equations are used for the reliability computations.

ALGORITHM DEVELOPMENT

The algorithm for this problem is straightforward. After reading values for p and n, we are ready to compute the reliability. The equation uses an exponentiation, so we will use the function that we have already developed for this computation.

DECOMPOSITION

Read reliability of component and number of components.
Compute reliability of group of components.
Write reliability.

We now refine the steps in the decomposition into pseudocode.

REFINEMENT IN PSEUDOCODE

> reliability: read p, n
> percent $\leftarrow$ $(p/100.0)^n \cdot 100.0$
> write percent

The structure chart for this solution is shown next, along with the Pascal program.

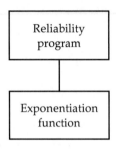

PASCAL PROGRAM

```
{-----------------------------------------------------------------}
program  reliability (input,output);
   {This program computes the reliability of
   instrumentation using a Bernoulli equation.}
var
   n: integer;
   p, percent: real;
{-----------------------------------------------------------------}
                    exponentiation function goes here
{-----------------------------------------------------------------}
begin {reliability}
   writeln ('ENTER RELIABILITY OF SINGLE COMPONENT');
   writeln ('(USE PERCENTAGE BETWEEN 0 AND 100)');
   readln (p);
   writeln ('ENTER NUMBER OF COMPONENTS IN EQUIPMENT');
   readln (n);
   percent := exponentiation(p/100.0,n)*100.0;
   writeln ('PERCENT OF THE TIME THAT THE EQUIPMENT ');
   writeln ('SHOULD WORK WITHOUT FAILURE IS ',
            percent:6:2,' %')
end. {reliability}
{-----------------------------------------------------------------}
```

TESTING

If we test this program with 20 components, each of which has a reliability of 96 percent, the output is:

```
ENTER RELIABILITY OF SINGLE COMPONENT
(USE PERCENTAGE BETWEEN 0 AND 100)
96.0
ENTER NUMBER OF COMPONENTS IN EQUIPMENT
20
PERCENT OF THE TIME THAT THE EQUIPMENT
SHOULD WORK WITHOUT FAILURE IS  44.20 %
```

If we test this program with 20 components, each of which has a reliability of 99 percent, the output is:

```
ENTER RELIABILITY OF SINGLE COMPONENT
(USE PERCENTAGE BETWEEN 0 AND 100)
99.0
ENTER NUMBER OF COMPONENTS IN EQUIPMENT
20
PERCENT OF THE TIME THAT THE EQUIPMENT
SHOULD WORK WITHOUT FAILURE IS  81.79 %
```

6-4 PROBLEM SOLVING—TRAFFIC FLOW

To study traffic flow at various intersections in large cities, the cars that pass through an intersection during certain time intervals are counted. The data collected can then be analyzed to determine the changes in traffic flow as well as to identify the intersections with the most traffic. In this application, we use traffic flow data to compute the average number of cars that pass through a specific intersection in 1 minute.

We assume that the data is contained in a file and that each line of the file contains the intersection identification, the beginning time, the ending time, and the number of cars that passed during that time interval. We assume that the data is added to the file as it is collected; thus, the file is not in order by intersection. We must read all the information in the file to be sure that we have not missed any. Because there is no special trailer line at the end of the file, we use the end-of-file indicator to detect the end of the file.

Time is stored in the data file using a 24-hour clock representation. The first two digits represent the hour and the last two digits represent the number of minutes. At midnight, the time begins at 0000 for the new day. For example, the time 0930 represents 9:30 A.M. and 2130 represents 9:30 P.M. We will assume that a single measurement does not extend from one day into the next. This representation assures that the ending time will be an integer larger than the beginning time.

PROBLEM STATEMENT

Write a program that will read an intersection identification from the terminal. Compute the average number of cars that pass through the intersection per minute, using the data in a data file named *traffic*.

INPUT/OUTPUT DESCRIPTION

The input to the program comes from two sources: an intersection identification is entered from the terminal and data is read from a traffic flow data file. The output is the average number of cars that pass through the intersection per minute.

HAND EXAMPLE

For our hand-worked example, we assume that the traffic flow data file contains the following information:

INTERSECTION	BEGINNING TIME	ENDING TIME	CARS
23	1330	1338	27
17	1422	1435	52
23	1407	1502	91
23	1507	1512	24

If we are interested in intersection 23, the average is computed as shown:

Intersection 23:
First measurement   1330 to 1338 = 8 minutes,
         27 cars
Next measurement   1407 to 1502 = 55 minutes,
         91 cars
Next measurement   1507 to 1512 = 5 minutes,
         24 cars

The average is computed by dividing the total number of cars by the total number of minutes, or

$$(27 + 91 + 24)/(8 + 55 + 5) = 142/68 = 2.09 \text{ cars/minute}$$

Note that the number of minutes in each observation is not simply the difference between the two times. For example, the difference between the integers 1502 and 1407 is 95; but if these integers represent time on a 24-hour clock, the difference is 55 minutes. Thus, we need to be careful about the steps we use to compute the number of minutes in an observation.

ALGORITHM DEVELOPMENT

The decomposition for this problem can be defined with the following steps:

DECOMPOSITION

Read intersection number.
Determine total cars and total minutes for this intersection using data file.
Compute and print average cars per minute.

The overall structure of this program is a *while* loop that is executed until we run out of data. We check each observation to see if it relates to the intersection specified, and if so, we compute the number of minutes in the observation. We can then update the total time and the total number of cars. When we exit the loop, we compute and print the average. It is possible that there will be no observations for the specified intersection, so we need to consider that case also.

The only computation we should consider further is the number of minutes in an observation. Since this computation will take several steps and since the final result is a single number, we will implement it with a function. The function converts the beginning and ending time measurements into minutes and then subtracts the two numbers. The *div* operator and the *mod* operator are useful in changing a time based on a 24-hour clock to the number of hours and minutes. For example, consider the time 1330. The number of minutes is 30, which can be computed from the expression 1330 *mod* 100; the number of hours is 13, which can be computed from the expression 1330 *div* 100. (Note that the result of the integer division is 13, not 13.3.) The total number of minutes is then computed by multiplying the number of hours by 60 and adding the number of minutes, or $13 \cdot 60 + 30$. After the function converts both the beginning time and the ending time to minutes, it can return the difference of the two values as the number of minutes in the observation.

With these steps in mind, we can develop the refinement in pseudocode for both the program and the function.

analyze: read intersection identification
        total cars ← 0
        total minutes ← 0
        while more information in file do
          read traffic information
          if traffic identification = intersection then
            add minutes to total minutes
            add cars to total cars
        if total minutes = 0 then
          write message
        else
          average ← total cars/total minutes
          write average

minutes (begintime,endtime):
        beginhour ← begintime div 100
        beginminutes ← begintime mod 100
        endhour ← endtime div 100
        endminutes ← endtime mod 100
        minutes ← (endhour*60 + endminutes) −
                (beginhour*60 + beginminutes)

The structure chart for this solution is shown next, along with the Pascal program.

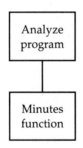

PASCAL PROGRAM

```
{---------------------------------------------------------------}
program  analyze (input,traffic,output);
   {This program reads traffic information and computes the
   average number of cars per minute through an intersection.}
var
   id, begintime, endtime, cars, totaltime,
   totalcars, fileid: integer;
   traffic: text;
```

```
{-------------------------------------------------------------------------}
function   minutes (begintime,endtime:integer): integer;
    {This function computes the number of minutes between
    the beginning time and the ending time.}
var
    beginhours, beginminutes, endhours, endminutes: integer;
begin {minutes}
    beginhours := begintime div 100;
    beginminutes := begintime mod 100;
    endhours := endtime div 100;
    endminutes := endtime mod 100;
    minutes := (endhours*60 + endminutes) -
                (beginhours*60 + beginminutes)
end; {minutes}
{-------------------------------------------------------------------------}
begin {analyze}
    totaltime := 0;
    totalcars := 0;
    reset (traffic);
    writeln ('ENTER INTERSECTION IDENTIFICATION');
    readln (id);
    while  not eof(traffic)  do
        begin
            readln (traffic,fileid,begintime,endtime,cars);
            if  fileid = id  then
                begin
                    totaltime := totaltime +
                                    minutes(begintime,endtime);
                    totalcars := totalcars + cars
                end
        end;
    if  totaltime = 0  then
        writeln ('NO OBSERVATIONS FOR INTERSECTION ',id:3)
    else
        begin
            writeln ('INTERSECTION ',id:3);
            writeln ('AVERAGE CARS PER MINUTE = ',
                    totalcars/totaltime:6:2)
        end
end.  {analyze}
{-------------------------------------------------------------------------}
```

Could we have printed *fileid* in place of *id* in the statement that prints the
intersection number? Printing *fileid* instead of *id* would be a logic error that
might be hard to identify. *Fileid* contains the last intersection number in the
data file; unless this last entry matches the identification that we entered with
the terminal, we will print the wrong identification number with the average
that was computed.

TESTING

The following output is the result of three different runs of the program using
the data given in the hand-worked example. We entered 23 as the desired
intersection number in the first run; we entered 17 as the desired intersection
number in the second run; we entered 44 as the desired intersection number
in the third run.

```
ENTER INTERSECTION IDENTIFICATION
23
INTERSECTION  23
AVERAGE CARS PER MINUTE =    2.09
```

```
ENTER INTERSECTION IDENTIFICATION
17
INTERSECTION  17
AVERAGE CARS PER MINUTE =    4.00
```

```
ENTER INTERSECTION IDENTIFICATION
44
NO OBSERVATIONS FOR INTERSECTION  44
```

What would happen if there were several observations for an intersection but no cars passed through the intersection during the observations? Because *totaltime* would not be zero, we do not have to worry about division by zero. *Totalcars* would be zero, though, and the average value would be zero. The program would print the intersection number and follow that with an average of 0.00.

6-5 FUNCTIONS FOR COMMON TECHNIQUES

In Chapter 4 we presented a number of techniques commonly used with one-dimensional arrays. In Chapter 5 we modified the insert, delete, and sort techniques into procedures, because these techniques changed values in the arrays. The techniques that are left are those that compute or determine a single value, and thus are ideal candidates for functions. In this section we will modify the techniques for averages, minimums, maximums, and searches into user-written functions.

AVERAGES

Computing the average of a one-dimensional array is a very straightforward process of summing and dividing by the number of elements in the array. If we convert this process to a function, the first step is to determine the function header, which includes the parameter list. The inputs needed are the array and the number of elements in the array that represent valid data. We will use value parameters because we do not want the function to change any of the values in the array or in the count. Therefore, the function header we will use is

```
function  average (x:list; count:integer): real;
```

We are assuming that *list* is an array data type defined in the type section. For our examples, we will assume that list is an integer array.

EXAMPLE 6-3 Average Function

Write a Pascal function to average a list of values. Use the function header below:

```
function  average (x:list; count:integer): real;
```

Solution

The decomposition for the problem is:

DECOMPOSITION

| Find average of list of values. |

To refresh your memory, we present the pseudocode for computing an average from Section 4-5. The only addition we have made is a step to print an error message if the count is less than or equal to zero. In this case, the average will also be set to zero.

PSEUDOCODE FOR FINDING THE AVERAGE OF A LIST OF VALUES

$$
\begin{aligned}
&\text{average } (x,\text{count}): \text{if count} > 0 \text{ then} \\
&\qquad\qquad\qquad \text{sum} \leftarrow 0 \\
&\qquad\qquad\qquad \text{for } i = 1 \text{ to count do} \\
&\qquad\qquad\qquad\quad \text{sum} \leftarrow \text{sum} + x[i] \\
&\qquad\qquad\qquad \text{average} \leftarrow \text{sum}/\text{count} \\
&\qquad\qquad \text{else} \\
&\qquad\qquad\qquad \text{print error message} \\
&\qquad\qquad\qquad \text{average} \leftarrow 0.0
\end{aligned}
$$

We now convert this pseudocode into a Pascal function.

```
{---------------------------------------------------------}
function  average (x:list; count:integer): real;
   {This function computes average of values in array.}
var
   sum: real;
   i: integer;
begin {average}
   if  count > 0  then
      begin
         sum := 0.0;
         for i := 1 to count do
            sum := sum + x[i];
         average := sum/count
      end
   else
      begin
         writeln ('ARRAY COUNT LESS THAN OR EQUAL TO ZERO');
         average := 0.0
      end
end; {average}
{---------------------------------------------------------}
```

We now present a driver program that could be used to test the average function. The driver will ask the user to enter a set of data to be stored in the array. After storing the data, the program will reference the function to compute the average. The structure chart for the program is shown below:

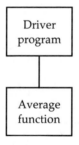

PASCAL PROGRAM

```
{---------------------------------------------------------}
program  driver (input,output);
   {This driver tests the average function.}
type
   index = 1..10;
   list = array[index] of integer;
var
   count, i: integer;
   x: list;
{---------------------------------------------------------}
```
                    average function goes here

```
{--------------------------------------------------------}
begin {driver}
   writeln ('ENTER COUNT (< 11) OF VALUES FOR LIST');
   readln (count);
   writeln ('ENTER VALUES');
   for i := 1 to count do
      read (x[i]);
   writeln ('AVERAGE = ',average(x,count):7:2)
end. {driver}
{--------------------------------------------------------}
```

An example of a test of the average function using this driver follows:

```
ENTER COUNT (< 11) OF VALUES FOR LIST
3
ENTER VALUES
26  -3  7
AVERAGE =    10.00
```

MINIMUMS AND MAXIMUMS

The steps for finding a minimum or maximum are now converted into a function. Two separate functions will be required since a function returns only a single value. We will write both functions and develop a driver to test them. The first step is to determine the function header and its corresponding parameter list. Since the functions will need the array and the count of valid elements in the array, we will use the following function headers:

```
function  minimum (x:list; count:integer): integer;
function  maximum (x:list; count:integer): integer;
```

We are assuming that *list* is an array data type defined in the type section. We also assume that the array is integer, so the minimum and maximum values would also be integer.

EXAMPLE 6-4   Minimum and Maximum Functions

Write Pascal functions for finding the minimum and maximum values in a list. Use the function headers below:

```
function  minimum (x:list; count:integer): integer;
function  maximum (x:list; count:integer): integer;
```

Solution

The decomposition for the problem is:

DECOMPOSITION

> Find the minimum and maximum in list of values.

The pseudocode from Section 4-5 provides the basis for this modified pseudocode. We have added an error message that will be printed if

---

the count is less than or equal to zero, and in these cases we will set the minimum and maximum to zero.

<small>PSEUDOCODE FOR FINDING THE MINIMUM AND MAXIMUM OF A LIST</small>

minimum (x,count): if count $>$ 0 then
    min $\leftarrow$ x[1]
    for i $=$ 2 to count do
        if x[i] $<$ min then
            min $\leftarrow$ x[i]
    else
        min $\leftarrow$ 0
        write error message
    minimum $\leftarrow$ min

maximum (x,count): if count $>$ 0 then
    max $\leftarrow$ x[1]
    for i $=$ 2 to count do
        if x[i] $>$ max then
            max $\leftarrow$ x[i]
    else
        max $\leftarrow$ 0
        write error message
    maximum $\leftarrow$ max

We now convert this pseudocode into two Pascal functions. Note that intermediate variables *min* and *max* are used to determine the minimum and maximum values, which are then moved to the function variables *minimum* and *maximum*. This is necessary because the compiler will interpret references to the function as recursive references unless they are on the left side of an equal sign.

<small>PASCAL FUNCTIONS</small>

```
{------------------------------------------------------------}
function  minimum (x:list; count:integer): integer;
    {This function determines minimum value in an array.}
var
    i, min: integer;
begin {minimum}
    if count > 0 then
        begin
            min := x[1];
            for i := 2 to count do
                if x[i] < min then
                    min := x[i]
        end
    else
        begin
            writeln ('ARRAY COUNT LESS THAN OR EQUAL TO ZERO');
            min := 0
        end;
    minimum := min
end; {minimum}
```

```
{--------------------------------------------------------------}
function  maximum (x:list; count:integer): integer;
   {This function determines maximum value in an array.}
var
   i, max: integer;
begin {maximum}
   if count > 0 then
      begin
         max := x[1];
         for i := 2 to count do
            if x[i] > max then
               max := x[i]
      end
   else
      begin
         writeln ('ARRAY COUNT LESS THAN OR EQUAL TO ZERO');
         max := 0
      end;
   maximum := max
end; {maximum}
{--------------------------------------------------------------}
```

We now present a driver program that could be used to test the minimum and maximum functions. The driver will ask the user to enter a set of data to be stored in the array. After storing the data, the program will reference the functions to determine and print the minimum and maximum. The structure chart for the program is shown below:

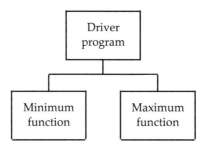

PASCAL PROGRAM

```
{--------------------------------------------------------------}
program  driver (input,output);
   {This driver tests minimum and maximum functions.}
type
   index = 1..10;
   list = array[index] of integer;
var
   count, i: integer;
   x: list;
{--------------------------------------------------------------}
                  minimum function goes here
{--------------------------------------------------------------}
                  maximum function goes here
```

continued

---

continued

```
{- - - - - - - - - - - - - - - - - - - - - - - - - - - - - - - - - - - - - - - - - - - - - - - - - -}
begin {driver}
    writeln ('ENTER COUNT (< 11) OF VALUES FOR LIST');
    readln (count);
    writeln ('ENTER VALUES');
    for i := 1 to count do
        read (x[i]);
    writeln ('MINIMUM = ',minimum(x,count):7);
    writeln ('MAXIMUM = ',maximum(x,count):7)
end. {driver}
{- - - - - - - - - - - - - - - - - - - - - - - - - - - - - - - - - - - - - - - - - - - - - - - - - -}
```

An example of a test of the minimum and maximum functions using this driver follows.

```
ENTER COUNT (< 11) OF VALUES FOR LIST
3
ENTER VALUES
26  -3  7
MINIMUM =        -3
MAXIMUM =        26
```

SEARCHING

We now convert the steps for searching for an element in an array into a function. There are several ways that we could implement this function. We could develop the function as a Boolean function that returns a value of true if the element is in the array or false if the element is not in the array. We could develop the function as an integer function that returns the first position of the element in the array if it is in the array or zero if the element is not in the array. We could develop the function as an integer function that returns the number of times the element occurs in the array. All these ideas represent valid functions, and we could think of programs that would use each of these forms. Since we have already written functions that return an integer value and functions that return a real value, we will implement this function as a Boolean function. We will call the function *found* in order to make our tests of the function read smoothly, as shown in the statement below:

```
if  found(x,count,key)  then
    access (newdata)
else
    writeln ('ACCESS TO DATA DENIED')
```

Therefore, the function header will be the following:

```
function  found (x:list; count,key:integer): boolean;
```

Note that we added to the parameter list a third parameter that represents the item for which we are searching. This item is also an integer since we are assuming that *x* is an array of integers.

As we begin to develop the solution steps for this problem, we need to decide which search algorithm we are going to use. You will recall from Section

4-5 that we presented an algorithm for searching an unordered list and two algorithms for searching an ordered list. We choose to implement the algorithm for searching an unordered list since it is the most general of the algorithms. (An algorithm for searching an unordered list will certainly work with an ordered list, even though it is not the most efficient algorithm to use if you know the list is ordered.)

EXAMPLE 6-5   Boolean Search Function

Write a Boolean function to search an unordered list for a specific value. The function should return a value of true if the specific value is found; otherwise the function should return a value of false. Use the function header below:

```
function   found (x:list; count,key:integer): boolean;
```

Solution

The decomposition for the problem is:

DECOMPOSITION

> Search unordered list for a specific value.

The pseudocode from Section 4-5 provides the basis for this modified pseudocode. We have added an error message that will be printed if the count is less than or equal to zero, and in these cases we will set the function to false.

PSEUDOCODE FOR SEARCHING AN UNORDERED LIST

```
found (x,count,key): if count > 0 then
                         done ← false
                         i ← 1
                     else
                         done ← true
                         found ← false
                         write error message
                     while not done do
                         if x[i] = key tnen
                             done ← true
                             found ← true
                         else
                             i ← i + 1
                         if i > count then
                             done ← true
                             found ← false
```

We now convert this pseudocode into a Pascal function.

```
{-----------------------------------------------------------}
function  found (x:list; count,key:integer): boolean;
    {This function determines whether or not
    key is in the array.}
var
    i: integer;
    done: boolean;
begin {found}
    if  count > 0  then
        begin
            done := false;
            i := 1
        end
    else
        begin
            done := true;
            found := false;
            writeln ('ARRAY COUNT LESS THAN OR EQUAL TO ZERO')
        end;
    while  not done  do
        begin
            if  x[i] = key  then
                begin
                    done := true;
                    found := true
                end
            else
                i := i + 1;
            if  i > count  then
                begin
                    done := true;
                    found := false
                end
        end
end; {found}
{-----------------------------------------------------------}
```

We now present a driver program that could be used to test the search function. The driver will ask the user to enter a set of data to be stored in the array. It will then ask the user to enter a specific value to be used in searching the array. The program will use the function to do the search and print a message giving the result of the search. The structure chart for the program is shown below:

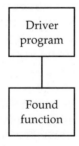

```
{------------------------------------------------------------}
program  driver (input,output);
    {This driver tests the search function.}
type
    index = 1..10;
    list = array[index] of integer;
var
    count, i, key: integer;
    x: list;
{------------------------------------------------------------}
                    found function goes here
{------------------------------------------------------------}
begin {driver}
    writeln ('ENTER COUNT (< 11) OF VALUES FOR LIST');
    readln (count);
    writeln ('ENTER VALUES');
    for i := 1 to count do
      read (x[i]);
    writeln ('ENTER VALUE FOR SEARCH');
    readln (key);
    if  found(x,count,key)  then
        writeln (key:5,' FOUND IN THE LIST');
    else
        writeln (key:5,' NOT FOUND IN THE LIST')
end. {driver}
{------------------------------------------------------------}
```

An example of a test of the function *found* using this driver follows.

```
ENTER COUNT (< 11) OF VALUES FOR LIST
3
ENTER VALUES
26  -3  7
ENTER VALUE FOR SEARCH
15
      15 NOT FOUND IN THE LIST
```

6-6 PROBLEM SOLVING—PROJECT MANAGEMENT

The timely use of resources is important to the success of any engineering project. It is often achieved by using a **critical path analysis** of a project. One method for this analysis starts by breaking a project into sequential events, then breaking each event into various tasks. Although one event must be completed before the next one is started, various tasks within an event can occur simultaneously. The time it takes to complete an event therefore depends on the number of days required to finish its longest task. Similarly, the total time it takes to finish a project is the sum of time it takes to finish each event.

Assume that the critical path information for a major project has been stored in a data file. In analyzing this information in order to make a bid on the project, company managers need some information to guide their decisions. Specifically, they would like a summary report that lists each event along with the number of days for the shortest task in that event and the number of days for the longest task in that event. In addition, they would like the total project length computed in days and converted to weeks (five days per week) and days.

The data file, named *project*, contains three integers per line. The first number is the event number, the second number is the task number, and the third number is the number of days required to complete the task. The data has been entered in the file in the order in which various project supervisors returned the information sheets on the tasks. Therefore, there is no particular order to the data. You do not know ahead of time how many entries are in the file, but there is an upper bound of 100 total tasks. There is no trailer signal in the data file.

PROBLEM STATEMENT

Write a program to determine and print a project completion timetable.

INPUT/OUTPUT

The input to the program is a data file that contains the critical path information for the events in the project. The file is not in any particular order, but the event numbers will include the numbers between 1 and some maximum event number. Each line of the file contains the event number, task number, and corresponding number of days necessary to complete the task. There is a maximum of 100 lines in the file and no trailer signal. The output is to be a summary report with the following format:

```
            PROJECT  COMPLETION  TIMETABLE

    EVENT NUMBER      MINIMUM DAYS      MAXIMUM DAYS
        XXXX              XXX               XXX
          .
          .
          .
        XXXX              XXX               XXX

     TOTAL  PROJECT  LENGTH  =  XXX  DAYS

                        =  XXX  WEEKS  X  DAYS
```

HAND EXAMPLE

Use the following set of project data for the hand example:

EVENT NUMBER	TASK NUMBER	DAYS
1	20	5
2	28	7
1	87	4
2	15	3
3	102	6
2	119	4

The corresponding report based on this data is shown below:

PROJECT COMPLETION TIMETABLE

EVENT NUMBER	MINIMUM DAYS	MAXIMUM DAYS
1	4	5
2	3	7
3	6	6

TOTAL PROJECT LENGTH = 18 DAYS

= 3 WEEKS 3 DAYS

ALGORITHM DEVELOPMENT

The decomposition of this problem solution is:

DECOMPOSITION

Read project event data.
Print summary report.

Since the data is not in any particular order, we will store it in arrays so that we can compute the information we need. The most logical way to store the data is in three arrays, one for event, one for task, and one for days.

Once the data is stored, we consider the types of information we need. Since we want to print the information in event order, we could sort the arrays. This seems like more work than necessary because we really only need minimum and maximum information within an event, not an ordered list of information. Also, if we sort the information, we need to make changes in all three arrays so that corresponding information will be in the same location in the arrays.

The algorithm we choose to implement is based on the way we did the hand problem. Since we wanted information for event 1 first, we scanned down the list looking for event 1. When we found the first line for event 1, we listed the number of days for that task. When we found the next line for event 1, we included that number of days in the list, and so on. When we reached the end of the information, we returned to the list we were making on the side and determined the minimum and maximum number of days. To implement this algorithm in pseudocode, we first read the information from the file into the arrays. While reading it, we can determine the maximum event number (we know they start at 1 and increase sequentially) and the total number of tasks that will be stored in the arrays. We can then select all the task days for event 1, store them in another array, and find the minimum and maximum of the array. We repeat these steps for event 2, and so on. Since we will be finding the minimum and maximum of an array, we can use the functions developed in the previous section.

REFINED PSEUDOCODE

```
manage: i ← 0
        maxevent ← 0
        while not eof do
           i ← i + 1
           read event[i], task[i], days[i]
           if event[i] > maxevent then
               maxevent ← event[i]
        totaltasks ← i
        totaldays ← 0
        write headers
        for i = 1 to maxevent do
           k ← 0
           for j = 1 to totaltasks do
              if event[j] = i then
                 k ← k + 1
                 hold[k] ← days[j]
           mindays ← minimum(hold,k)
           maxdays ← maximum(hold,k)
           write i, mindays, maxdays
           totaldays ← totaldays + maxdays
        weeks ← totaldays div 5
        daysleft ← totaldays mod 5
        write totaldays, weeks, daysleft
```

minimum (x,count): if count > 0 then
                             minimum ← x[1]
                             for i = 2 to count do
                                 if x[i] < minimum then
                                     minimum ← x[i]
                  else
                         minimum ← 0
                         write error message

maximum (x,count): if count > 0 then
                             maximum ← x[1]
                             for i = 2 to count do
                                 if x[i] > maximum then
                                     maximum ← x[i]
                  else
                         maximum ← 0
                         write error message

The structure chart for this solution is shown next, along with the Pascal program.

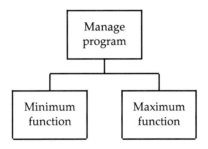

```
{-----------------------------------------------------------}
program  manage (input,project,output);
   {This program determines the timetable for a project.}
type
   index = 1..100;
   list = array[index] of integer;
var
   i, j, k, maxevent, totaltasks, totaldays,
   mindays, maxdays, weeks, daysleft: integer;
   project: text;
   event, task, days, hold: list;
{-----------------------------------------------------------}
                     minimum function goes here
{-----------------------------------------------------------}
                     maximum function goes here
{-----------------------------------------------------------}
begin {manage}
   i := 0;
   maxevent := 0;
   reset (project);
   while  not eof(project)  do
      begin
         i := i + 1;
         readln (project,event[i],task[i],days[i]);
         if  event[i] > maxevent  then
            maxevent := event[i]
      end;
   totaltasks := i;
   totaldays := 0;
   writeln ('        PROJECT COMPLETION TIMETABLE;);
   writeln;
   writeln ('EVENT NUMBER    MINIMUM TIME    MAXIMUM TIME;);
   for i := 1 to maxevent do
      begin
         k := 0;
         for j := 1 to totaltasks do
            if  event[j] = i   then
               begin
                  k := k + 1;
                  hold[k] := days[j]
               end;
         mindays := minimum(hold,k);
         maxdays := maximum(hold,k);
         writeln (i:8,mindays:16,maxdays:16);
         totaldays := totaldays + maxdays
      end;
   weeks := totaldays div 5;
   daysleft := totaldays mod 5;
   writeln;
   writeln;
   writeln ('        TOTAL PROJECT LENGTH = ',totaldays:3,
         ' DAYS');
   writeln ('                              = ',weeks:3,' WEEKS ',
            daysleft:1,' DAYS')
end. {manage}
{-----------------------------------------------------------}
```

If we run the sample set of data used in the hand example with this program, the following report is printed:

```
              PROJECT COMPLETION TIMETABLE

    EVENT NUMBER       MINIMUM DAYS       MAXIMUM DAYS
         1                  4                  5
         2                  3                  7
         3                  6                  6


        TOTAL PROJECT LENGTH  =   18 DAYS
                              =   3 WEEKS 3 DAYS
```

6-7 RECURSION WITH FUNCTIONS

Pascal allows a module to call itself within the module. This special type of nesting is called **recursion.** Recursion is a powerful technique that can be especially useful in solving certain types of problems. In this section we discuss the types of problems in which recursion can be applied and present an example of recursion.

The types of problems that recursion can help solve are those in which the current problem can be defined in terms of a similar smaller problem, and the smaller problem can be defined in terms of a still smaller similar problem, until we finally reach the solution of the smallest problem. The best way to understand this is with an example. A factorial computation occurs frequently in engineering and science applications. Recall that, by definition, n factorial, or $n!$, is computed as:

$$n! = n \cdot (n - 1) \cdot (n - 2) \cdot (n - 3) \cdot \ldots \cdot 3 \cdot 2 \cdot 1$$

Thus,

$$6! = 6 \cdot 5 \cdot 4 \cdot 3 \cdot 2 \cdot 1$$

However, note that we could also define 6! in terms of 5!, as:

$$6! = 6 \cdot 5!$$

Then 5! could be defined in terms of 4!, as:

$$5! = 5 \cdot 4!$$

Thus, a recursion process emerges as we define a factorial in terms of a smaller factorial, and that smaller factorial in terms of a still smaller factorial, until we get to 0!. By definition, 0! is equal to 1. This is a very critical step in recursion. We must eventually get to a stopping point, or recursion cannot be done with the computer. Once we get to the stopping point, we reverse the process by bringing that value back to the step that called it, compute a new value there, then back again to the step that called that one, and so on until we are back to the original problem. Let's look at this process with the following diagram:

$$6! = 6 \cdot 5!$$
$$5! = 5 \cdot 4!$$
$$4! = 4 \cdot 3!$$
$$3! = 3 \cdot 2!$$
$$2! = 2 \cdot 1!$$
$$1! = 1 \cdot 0!$$
$$0! = 1$$

We now take the value for 0! and go back one step at a time.

$$1! = 1 \cdot 1 = 1$$
$$2! = 2 \cdot 1 = 2$$
$$3! = 3 \cdot 2 = 6$$
$$4! = 4 \cdot 6 = 24$$
$$5! = 5 \cdot 24 = 120$$
$$6! = 6 \cdot 120 = 720$$

Note that this example recursively called the factorial function six times. These recursive calls are also referred to as **levels of recursion.** Thus, this example used six levels of recursion.

Now that we have seen an example worked out by hand, let's code this function in Pascal.

EXAMPLE 6-6   Factorial Function

Write a function to compute the factorial of an integer that is equal to or greater than zero. If the integer is less than zero, print an error message and return the value -1. Give two solutions, with one of the solutions using recursion.

Solution 1

We first give the nonrecursive solution, which will be based on the algorithm we developed for computing factorials in Example 3-11. (This example is on page 106 if you want to review it before continuing with this solution.)

The decomposition for this problem is the following:

DECOMPOSITION

> Compute factorial of n.

Since this is to be implemented in a function, we need to determine the function header and its corresponding parameter list. The function needs only the value of n in order to compute the factorial. Therefore, our function header is:

```
function  factorial (n:integer): integer;
```

If the value of n is negative, the function will print an error message and return a value of -1. The pseudocode for the function is then:

PSEUDOCODE FOR COMPUTING A FACTORIAL

```
factorial (n): if n < 0 then
                   write error message
                   factorial ← −1
               else
                   product ← 1
                   for k = 2 to n do
                       product ← product*k
                   factorial ← product
```

We now convert this pseudocode into a Pascal function.

PASCAL FUNCTION

```
{------------------------------------------------------------}
function  factorial (n:integer): integer;
    {This function computes the factorial of n.}
var
    k, product: integer;
begin {factorial}
    if  n < 0   then
        begin
            writeln ('N IS LESS THAN ZERO');
            factorial := -1
        end
    else
        begin
            product := 1;
            for k := 2 to n do
                product := product*k;
            factorial := product
        end
end; (factorial}
{------------------------------------------------------------}
```

Solution 2

In this solution, we use a recursive reference to the function, as illustrated in the hand example above. The decomposition for this problem is the same.

DECOMPOSITION

Compute factorial of n.

The function header also remains the same because the recursive references will also need a value in order to compute a factorial.

```
function  factorial (n:integer): integer;
```

If the value of n is negative, the function will still print an error message and return a value of -1. The pseudocode for the function is then:

PSEUDOCODE FOR COMPUTING A FACTORIAL

factorial (n): if n < 0 then
      write error message
      factorial $\leftarrow -1$
     else if n = 0 then
      factorial $\leftarrow 1$
     else
      factorial $\leftarrow$ n*factorial(n−1)

We now convert this pseudocode into a Pascal function.

PASCAL FUNCTION

```
{-----------------------------------------------------------}
function  factorial (n:integer): integer;
   {This function computes the factorial of n.}
begin {factorial}
   if  n < 0  then
      begin
         writeln ('N IS LESS THAN ZERO');
         factorial := -1
      end
   else if  n = 0  then
      factorial := 1
   else
      factorial := n*factorial(n-1)
end; {factorial}
{-----------------------------------------------------------}
```

We now present a driver program that could be used to test the recursive factorial function. The driver will ask the user to enter an integer, and the program will reference the factorial function to compute the factorial of the integer. (To test the nonrecursive factorial function, simply substitute it for the recursive factorial function.) The structure chart for the program is shown below:

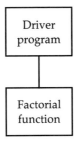

Pascal Program

```
{---------------------------------------------------------}
program  driver (input,output);
   {This driver tests the factorial function.}
var
   n, nfactorial: integer;
{---------------------------------------------------------}
                factorial function goes here
{---------------------------------------------------------}
begin {driver}
   writeln ('ENTER N TO COMPUTE N!');
   readln (n);
   nfactorial := factorial(n);
   writeln (n:2,'! = ',nfactorial:12)
end. {driver}
{---------------------------------------------------------}
```

An example of a test of the factorial function using this driver is shown below:

```
ENTER N TO COMPUTE N!
11
11! =        39916800
```

The value for 13! exceeds the upper limit for integers on most computer systems. You might want to modify the driver so that it will not reference the factorial function in these cases.

SUMMARY

A function is a module that represents a single value. Pascal contains many built-in functions that compute values such as trigonometric functions and logarithms. We can also write our own functions. In addition to developing a number of functions in the examples, we also developed functions for the common techniques of finding averages, minimums, and maximums and searching for elements in a list. Functions are especially useful in engineering and science applications because they simplify the computations in our programs.

DEBUGGING AIDS

Testing a function should be approached much like testing a complete program. You will also need a simple program, called a driver, to initialize the input to the function that you are testing. This driver program should print the output of the function so that you can determine if it is returning the proper value. If it is not, the following checks may help you locate the problem:

1. Be sure that the function is returning the proper type of value by checking the type designation on the function header.
2. Be sure that each path to the end of the function provides a value for the function.
3. Always use the parameter list to pass information to the function.
4. Always use references by value for all parameters in a function to avoid side effects.
5. Be sure that the variables or expressions listed in the function reference match the parameter list in the function header, both in type and in order.
6. Define all local variables within the function; otherwise, you may be using a global variable (and possibly changing it) without realizing it.
7. Print the values of all variables just before using the function and just after returning from the function as you debug it.
8. Remember that you can put extra output statements in the function for use in debugging.
9. Always test each function individually.
10. Test each function with several sets of data to check any special conditions.

STYLE/TECHNIQUE GUIDELINES

The use of functions to replace computations within a program can greatly improve program structure and readability. The structure of a function should receive the same attention as the structure of the program and its procedures. If a function becomes long and difficult to read, perhaps additional modules should be used. Remember that functions can reference built-in functions and other functions and procedures. Once you have decided which operations will be written as functions, follow these style suggestions:

1. Choose descriptive names for your functions.
2. Use comments in the functions as you would in the main program. In particular, use comments at the beginning of a function to describe its purpose and to define its parameters, if necessary.
3. For clarity, use the same variables in the parameter list of the function that will be used in the program, if possible. If the function is referenced several

times with different variables, choose completely different variable names in the function header to avoid confusion.

4. Since a function should compute only a single value, it should not read any new information or use variable parameters.

KEY WORDS

Boolean function	mathematical function
built-in function	ordinal function
function	parameter list
function header	recursive function

PROBLEMS

We begin our problem set with modifications to programs developed earlier in this chapter. Give the decomposition, refined pseudocode, and Pascal program for each problem.

Problems 1–5 modify the equipment reliability program *reliability*, given on page 284.

1. Modify the equipment reliability program so that it allows the user to loop through the program until zero is entered for the number of components.

2. Modify the equipment reliability program so that it checks the input percentage to be sure that the reliability is a number greater than 0.0 and less than 100.0.

3. Modify the equipment reliability program so that it reads an input reliability for a single component and then prints a table of percentages of time that the equipment should work for one component, two components, and so on, through 25 components.

4. Modify the equipment reliability program so that it reads an input reliability for a single component and the maximum number of components to be considered. Then print a table of percentages of time that the equipment should work for one component, two components, and so on, through the maximum number of components.

5. Modify the equipment reliability program so that it reads an input reliability for a single component and then prints a table of percentages of time that the equipment should work for one component, two components, and so on, until the reliability is less than 50 percent.

Problems 6–10 modify the traffic flow program *analyze*, given on page 288.

6. Modify the traffic flow program so that it prints the number of cars passing through the intersection and the total number of minutes of observation.

7. Modify the traffic flow program so that it computes an average of cars per minute for the combined data in the data file.

8. Modify the traffic flow program so that it will reset the data file after computing the average for an intersection. Continue reading intersections and computing averages until you read an intersection number of 9999 from the terminal.

9. Modify the traffic flow program so that it will count the number of different intersections that are represented by the data in the data file.

10. Modify the traffic flow program so that it will allow an observation to extend past midnight. (Thus, the ending time could be smaller than the beginning time. For example, if the beginning time is 2330 and the ending time is 0030, the total time period is 60 minutes.)

Problems 11–15 modify the project management program *manage*, given on page 304.

11. Modify the project management program so that it prints the event number and task number for the task that requires the minimum amount of time.

12. Modify the project management program so that it prints the event number and task number for the task that requires the maximum amount of time.

13. Modify the project management program so that it prints the average amount of time required for the tasks.

14. Modify the project management program so that it prints the event and task number for all tasks with required times greater than the average.

15. Modify the project management program so that it prints a list of the event numbers and the number of tasks in each event.

For problems 16–20, write the function described, assuming that the input to the function is an integer array k of 100 elements.

16. *maximum(k)*, the maximum value of the array k.
17. *minimum(k)*, the minimum value of the array k.
18. *positive(k)*, the number of values greater than or equal to zero in the array k.
19. *negative(k)*, the number of values less than zero in the array k.
20. *zero(k)*, the number of values equal to zero in the array k.

For problems 21–24, assume that you have a function *denominator* with input value x, to compute the following expression:

$$x^2 + \sqrt{1 + 2x + 3x^2}$$

Give the program statements that use this function to compute and print each of the following expressions:

21. alpha $= \dfrac{6.9 + y}{y^2 + \sqrt{1 + 2y + 3y^2}}$

22. $\text{beta} = \dfrac{\sin y}{y^4 + \sqrt{1 + 2y^2 + 3y^4}}$

23. $\text{gamma} = \dfrac{2.3z + z^4}{z^2 + \sqrt{1 + 2z + 3z^2}}$

24. $\text{delta} = \dfrac{1}{\sin^2 y + \sqrt{1 + 2\sin y + 3\sin^2 y}}$

In problems 25–30, develop these programs and functions. Use the five-phase design process.

25. Write a function whose input is a two-digit number. The function is to return a two-digit number whose digits are reversed from the input number. Thus, if 17 is the input to the function, 71 is the output.

26. Write a function *total* that will convert three parameters representing hours, minutes, and seconds to their total in seconds. For example, total(3,2,5) should return the integer value 10,925.

27. The cosine of an angle may be computed from this series, where x is measured in radians:

$$\cos x = 1 - \frac{x^2}{2!} + \frac{x^4}{4!} - \frac{x^6}{6!} + \cdots$$

Write a function *cosine* whose input is a positive angle in radians. The function should compute the first 10 terms of the series and return that approximation of the cosine. (*Hint:* The alternating sign can be obtained using the *odd* function.)

28. Rewrite the function in the previous problem so that it computes the cosine with as many terms of the series as are necessary to ensure that the absolute value of the last term is less than 0.000001.

29. Write a program that will produce a table with three columns. The first column should contain angles from 0.1 to 3.1 radians in increments of 0.1 radians. The second column should contain the cosines of the angles as computed by the built-in function. The third column should contain the cosines as computed by the function in problem 27. Print the cosine values with seven decimal positions.

30. Oil exploration and recovery is an important concern of large petroleum companies. Profitable oil recovery requires careful testing by drilling seismic holes and blasting with specific amounts of dynamite. For optimum seismic readings, a specific ratio between the amount of dynamite and the depth of the hole is required. Assume that each stick of dynamite is 2.5 feet long and weighs 5 pounds. The ideal powder charge requires a ratio of 1:3 for the dynamite to depth-of-hole ratio. Thus, a 60-foot hole would require 20 feet of dynamite, which is equal to 8 sticks or 40 pounds. The actual powder charge is not always equal to the ideal powder charge because the ideal powder charge may not be in 5-pound increments; in these cases, the actual

powder charge should be rounded down to the nearest 5-pound increment. (You cannot cut or break the dynamite into shorter lengths for field operations.)

The following example should clarify this process:

$$\text{Hole depth} = 85 \text{ feet}$$
$$\text{Ideal charge} = 85/3 = 28.33333 \text{ feet}$$
$$= 11.33333 \text{ sticks}$$
$$= 56.66666 \text{ pounds}$$
$$\text{Actual charge} = 55 \text{ pounds}$$
$$= 11 \text{ sticks}$$

Information on the depths of the holes to be tested each day is the input to the program from a data file called *drilling*. The first line contains the number of sites to be tested that day. Each following line contains integer information for a specified site that gives the site identification number and the depth of the hole in feet. Write a complete program to read this information and print the following report:

<pre>
              DAILY DRILLING REPORT

  SITE ID   DEPTH   IDEAL POWDER   ACTUAL POWDER   STICKS
             (FT)   CHARGE (LBS)   CHARGE (LBS)
  -------   -----   ------------   -------------   ------
  12980   85   56.6666   55   11
    .
    .
    .
</pre>

31. Modify the program in problem 30 so that a final summary report follows the drilling report and has the form:

<pre>
    TOTAL POWDER USED = XXXXX LBS   (XXXX STICKS)
    TOTAL DRILLING FOOTAGE = XXXXXX FT
</pre>

32. Modify the program in problem 31 so that it takes into consideration a special situation: If the depth of the hole is less than 30 feet, the hole is too shallow for testing. Instead of printing the charge values for such a hole, print the site identification number, the depth, and the message HOLE TOO SHALLOW FOR TESTING. The summary report printed at the end of the report should not include data for these shallow holes. Add an additional line to the summary report that contains the number of holes too shallow for testing.

33. Assume that a data file called *dataxy* contains a set of data coordinates that are to be used by several different programs. The first line of the file contains the number of data coordinates in the file, and each of the rest of the lines contain the x and y coordinates for one of the data points. Some of the programs must use the coordinates in polar form instead of rectangular form. Rather than have each program that needs polar coordinates convert the data, we will generate a second data file that has each point in polar form, which is a radius and an angle in radians. Then, no matter how many programs use the data, it only has to be converted to polar coordinates once,

and each program can then reference the appropriate file. Write a program to generate a new file called *polar* that contains coordinates in polar form instead of rectangular form. The following equations convert a coordinate in rectangular form to polar form:

$$r = \sqrt{x^2 + y^2}$$
$$\text{theta} = \tan^{-1}(y/x)$$

(Be sure that the first line of the new data file specifies the number of data coordinates.)

34. Rewrite the program from problem 33, assuming that the original file is *polar* and that it contains data coordinates in polar form. The new output file should be called *dataxy* and should contain data coordinates in rectangular form. The equations for converting polar coordinates to rectangular coordinates are

$$x = r \cos(\text{theta})$$
$$y = r \sin(\text{theta})$$

35. When n is an integer greater than or equal to zero, the expression $n!$ (n factorial) represents the product of all integers from 1 through n. We define $0!$ to be equal to 1. The following are a few factorials and their corresponding values:

$$0! = 1$$
$$1! = 1$$
$$2! = 1 \cdot 2 = 2$$
$$3! = 1 \cdot 2 \cdot 3 = 6$$

An approximation to $n!$ can be computed using Stirling's formula:

$$N! = \sqrt{2\pi N} \left(\frac{N}{e}\right)^N$$

where $e = 2.718282$. Write a program that reads a value of n from the terminal and then computes an approximation of $n!$ using Stirling's formula. Print the following message before you read the value of n:

ENTER N WHERE N IS BETWEEN 1 AND 12

Limiting the size of n is necessary to ensure that the value of $n!$ will fit within the limit of integers on most computers. The output of the program should be in this form:

XX! IS APPROXIMATELY XXXXXXXXXX

Continue reading values of n and computing an approximation to $n!$ until you read a negative value. If you read a value greater than 12, print a message that the input is out of the specified range and ask the user to enter a new value.

PROBLEM SOLVING — Terrain Navigation

The study of terrain navigation has become popular with the advent of remote-piloted vehicles such as planes, missiles, and tanks. The systems that guide these vehicles must be tested over a variety of land formations and topologies. Elevation information for large grids of land is available in computer databases. One way of measuring the "difficulty" of a land grid with respect to terrain navigation is to determine the number of peaks in the grid (a peak is a point that has lower elevations all around it). Write a computer program to determine the number of peaks in a grid of elevation values. (See Section 7-3 for the solution.)

7

TWO-DIMENSIONAL ARRAY PROCESSING

INTRODUCTION

In chapters 4, 5, and 6 we used one-dimensional arrays in a number of programs, procedures, and functions. In this chapter we present two-dimensional arrays and illustrate their use in programs, procedures, and functions. We have already pointed out that the proper choice of a data structure is just as important as the proper choice of a control structure in developing a good solution to a problem. Pascal allows a user to define a variety of data structures. It is important to become comfortable using them all in order to be able to make wise choices of data structures.

7-1 TWO-DIMENSIONAL ARRAY HANDLING

If we visualize a **one-dimensional array** as a single row or column of data, we can then visualize a **two-dimensional array** as a group of rows or columns, as illustrated below:

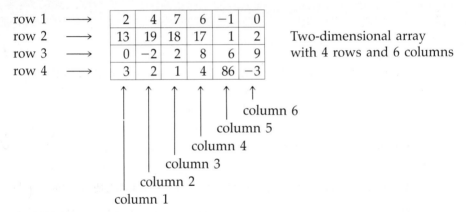

The diagram depicts an integer array with 24 elements. As in one-dimensional arrays, each of the 24 elements has the same array name. However, one subscript is not sufficient to specify an element in a two-dimensional array. For instance, if the array's name is m, it is not clear whether $m[3]$ should be the third element in the first row or the third element in the first column. To avoid any ambiguity, an element in a two-dimensional array is referenced with two subscripts, one for the row number and one for the column number. The first subscript references the row and the second subscript references the column. Thus, $m[2,3]$ refers to the number in the second row and third column. In our diagram, $m[2,3]$ contains 18.

The definition of a two-dimensional array is a direct extension of the definition of a one-dimensional array. The only difference is that we now specify the ranges of two subscripts instead of one. For example, the array m discussed in the previous paragraph has four rows and six columns. If we use values 1 through 4 for the row subscript and values 1 through 6 for the column subscript, our definition of m could be as follows:

```
type
    index1 = 1..4;
    index2 = 1..6;
    table = array[index1,index2] of integer;
var
    m: table;
```

If this array represented data taken on the 17th, 18th, 19th, and 20th days of March, we might want to use the values 17 through 20 for the row subscript and values 1 through 6 for the column subscript, as shown below:

```
type
    index1 = 17..20;
    index2 = 1..6;
    table = array[index1,index2] of integer;
var
    m: table;
```

Consider this statement:

```
type
    index1 = 0..2;
    index2 = -1..1;
    table = array[index1,index2] of integer;
var
    r: table;
```

It reserves storage for array elements r[0,−1], r[0,0], r[0,1], r[1,−1], r[1,0], r[1,1], r[2,−1], r[2,0], r[2,1].

The general form for an array definition that will allow multiple subscripts follows.

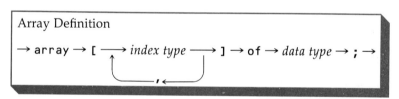

Array Definition

$\rightarrow$ array $\rightarrow$ [$\longrightarrow$ *index type* $\longrightarrow$] $\rightarrow$ of $\rightarrow$ *data type* $\rightarrow$; $\rightarrow$

Although we are primarily interested in two-dimensional arrays in this chapter, the last section will discuss **multidimensional arrays** that have more than two dimensions.

INITIALIZATION

We now look at some examples for initializing two-dimensional arrays with assignment statements.

EXAMPLE 7-1   Array Initialization

Define an array *area* with five rows and four columns. Fill it with the values shown below:

1.0	1.0	2.0	2.0
1.0	1.0	2.0	2.0
1.0	1.0	2.0	2.0
1.0	1.0	2.0	2.0
1.0	1.0	2.0	2.0

Solution

We first define two data types with the proper subranges for the subscripts. Then we use the two subrange data types in the definition of the two-dimensional data structure. In the variable section, we define an array with the new two-dimensional data structure. Then, in the initialization steps, we give values to a complete row in the array each time we execute the group of statements in the *for* loop.

```
type
    index1 = 1..5;
    index2 = 1..4;
    table = array[index1,index2] of real;
var
    area: table;
    i: integer;
      .
      .
      .
    for i := 1 to 5 do
        begin
            area[i,1] := 1.0;
            area[i,2] := 1.0;
            area[i,3] := 2.0;
            area[i,4] := 2.0
        end
```

EXAMPLE 7-2   Array Initialization

Define and fill the array *sum* as shown on the next page:

1	1	1
2	2	2
3	3	3
4	4	4

Solution

If we observe that each element of the array contains its corresponding row number, then the following solution can be used:

```
type
    index1 = 1..4;
    index2 = 1..3;
    table = array[index1,index2] of integer;
var
    sum: table;
    i, j: integer;
    .
    .
    .
for i := 1 to 4 do
    for j := 1 to 3 do
        sum[i,j] := i
```

EXAMPLE 7-3 Identity Matrix

A **matrix** is another name for a two-dimensional array. To solve engineering and science problems, we frequently use an **identity matrix.** This matrix is a two-dimensional array with the same number of rows as columns, so it is also a **square matrix.** In addition, the elements of the identity matrix are all zeros except for those on the main diagonal which are all ones, as shown in the example below of an identity matrix with five rows and five columns. Define and fill an array with these values.

1.0	0.0	0.0	0.0	0.0
0.0	1.0	0.0	0.0	0.0
0.0	0.0	1.0	0.0	0.0
0.0	0.0	0.0	1.0	0.0
0.0	0.0	0.0	0.0	1.0

Solution

Since the value 1.0 appears at different positions in each row of the array, we cannot use the type of solution that we used in Example 7-1. If we list the elements that contain the value 1.0, we find that they are positions [1,1], [2,2], [3,3], [4,4], and [5,5]. Thus, the row and the column number are the same value, and that value increments from 1 to 5. Recognizing this pattern, we can initialize the array as follows:

```
type
    index = 1..5;
    table = array[index,index] of real;
var
    identity: table;
    i, j: integer;
    .
    .
    .
    for i := 1 to 5 do
        for j := 1 to 5 do
            if i = j then
                identity[i,j] := 1.0
            else
                identity[i,j] := 0.0
```

INPUT/OUTPUT

The main difference between using values from a one-dimensional array and a two-dimensional array is that the latter requires two subscripts. Therefore, loops used in reading or printing two-dimensional arrays often contain nested loops.

EXAMPLE 7-4   Medical Data

Analysis of a medical experiment requires the use of a set of data containing the weight of 100 participants at the beginning and at the end of an experiment. The data values have been stored in a data file named *test4*. Each line in the file contains the initial weight and the final weight of a participant. Give statements to define a two-dimensional array to store the data and to read the information from the file into the array.

Solution

We first define new data types for the subranges and the array structure that we want to use in this solution. Then we define a variable with the new data type and use it in the loop that reads the information from the data file.

```
type
    index1 = 1..100;
    index2 = 1..2;
    table = array[index1,index2] of real;
```

```
var
   i: integer;
   test4: text;
   weight: table;
   .
   .
   .
   reset (test4);
   for i := 1 to 100 do
      readln (test4,weight[i,1],weight[i,2])
```

EXAMPLE 7-5   Terminal Inventory

A large technical firm keeps an inventory of the locations of its computer
terminals in a data file. Assume that this data has already been read into a
two-dimensional array. There are four types of terminals, represented by
the four columns, and 20 laboratories using the terminals, represented
by the 20 rows of the array. Thus, the number in position [5,2] represents
the number of terminals of type 2 that are located in laboratory 5. Print
the data in a form similar to the following:

```
         TERMINAL INVENTORY

         TYPE       1    2    3    4
         ----------------------------
         LAB  1     XX   XX   XX   XX
         LAB  2     XX   XX   XX   XX
         .
         .
         .
         LAB 20     XX   XX   XX   XX
```

Solution

This solution uses the *write* statement for adding values to each line of
output. The *writeln* statement then prints the line of output after four
values have been added.

```
type
   index1 = 1..20;
   index2 = 1..4;
   table = array[index1,index2] of integer;
var
   i, j: integer;
   inventory: table;
   .
   .
   .
   writeln ('TERMINAL INVENTORY');
   writeln;
   writeln ('TYPE       1    2    3    4');
   writeln ('----------------------------');
   for i := 1 to 20 do
      begin
         write ('LAB ',i:2,' ');
         for j := 1 to 4 do
            write (inventory[i,j]:5);
         writeln
      end
```

COMPUTATIONS

Using array elements in computations is slightly more complicated than using simple variables, because we must now use subscripts to specify which element of the array we want to use in the computation. With two-dimensional arrays, this means that we will need two subscripts to specify individual elements. We will generally need nested loops in order to use all the elements in the array. The next set of examples illustrates the use of array elements for computations.

EXAMPLE 7-6   Sales Average

A two-dimensional array contains the number of items sold each day from a retail store. The array has five columns, which represent the days Monday through Friday, and 52 rows, which represent the 52 weeks in the past year. Give the statements necessary to compute the overall average number of items sold per day.

Solution

We first define a data structure that is a two-dimensional array with 52 rows and 5 columns. Then, assuming that the data has already been stored in the array, we add the values in the array and divide the sum by the total number of values.

```
type
    index1 = 1..52;
    index2 = 1..5;
    table = array[index1,index2] of integer;
var
    i, j, sum: integer;
    average: real;
    sales: table;
    .
    .
    .
    sum := 0;
    for i := 1 to 52 do
       for j := 1 to 5 do
          sum := sum + sales[i,j];
    average := sum/260.0
```

EXAMPLE 7-7   Average Function

Write a function that has the following function header:

```
function  average (x:table; rows,columns:integer): real;
```

The function should compute and return the average value of an integer array x. The parameters *rows* and *columns* contain the number of rows and columns in the array that have actual data. If the array is full, the value in *rows* is the number of rows in the array and the value in *columns* is the number of columns in the array.

Solution

The steps in computing the average in a function are very similar to the steps in the previous example, which computed an average in the program instead of in a function. We will need to add local variables for the subscripts and the sum.

```
{-------------------------------------------------------}
function  average (x:table; rows,columns:integer): real;
    {This function computes the average of the
    values stored in a two-dimensional array.}
var
    i, j, sum: integer;
begin {average}
    sum := 0;
    for i := 1 to rows do
        for j := 1 to columns do
            sum := sum + x[i,j];
    average := sum/(rows*columns)
end; {average}
{-------------------------------------------------------}
```

The next example illustrates the use of a two-dimensional array in a recursive procedure. You may want to review Section 5-7, "Recursion with Procedures," before you continue with the example.

EXAMPLE 7-8 Interior Points

A problem that has a recursive nature is one to determine interior points inside a boundary. This is a problem that occurs in both graphics and image-processing applications. We will assume that we have a two-dimensional array whose values are either 0 or 1. The elements that are 1 define the boundary of a closed area within the array. A dotted line is used in the example array below to show the boundary of a closed area.

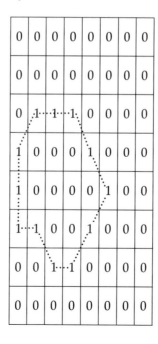

There are nine interior points in the boundary defined by this array. Write a procedure that will receive a two-dimensional array with m rows and n columns. It also receives the coordinates of one point that is known to be an interior point of the boundary. The module should fill all the interior points within the boundary with the value 2.

We start with the one interior point and look at the four points adjacent to that point. If they are zeros, we change their value to 2; if they are ones, they are boundary points and should not be changed. If we consider the four points adjacent to each interior point, we will eventually consider all points within the boundary. You can see this by looking at the small example below where we start with point i, and label its adjacent interior points a. Then we label the adjacent interior points of each of these points b, and so on. You should now begin to see the recursive nature of this problem solution.

```
0 0 1 0 0 0     0 0 1 0 0 0     0 0 1 0 0 0
0 1 0 1 0 0     0 1 a 1 0 0     0 1 a 1 0 0
1 0 i 0 1 1 → 1 a i a 1 1 → 1 a i a 1 1
1 0 0 0 0 1     1 0 a 0 0 1     1 b a b 0 1
1 1 1 1 1 1     1 1 1 1 1 1     1 1 1 1 1 1
                                       ↓
```

i denotes initial interior point
a denotes new interior points adjacent to i
b denotes new interior points adjacent to a
c denotes new interior points adjacent to b

```
0 0 1 0 0 0
0 1 a 1 0 0
1 a i a 1 1
1 b a b c 1
1 1 1 1 1 1
```

Using the outline discussed above for the solution, we can develop the decomposition steps and pseudocode.

DECOMPOSITION

Change interior values to a value of 2.

We assume that the *fill* procedure is invoked with parameters that give the array name and the position of an interior point. We want to change the value of the interior point to 2 and then check its four adjacent points. If an adjacent point is an interior point, we recursively call *fill* to change its value and to check the new adjacent points.

```
fill (i,j,x): x[i,j] ← 2
              if x[i−1,j] = 0 then
                 fill (i−1,j,x)
              if x[i+1,j] = 0 then
                 fill (i+1,j,x)
              if x[i,j−1] = 0 then
                 fill (i,j−1,x)
              if x[i,j+1] = 0 then
                 fill (i,j+1,x)
```

In addition to the Pascal procedure, we also present a program for testing it. The program will read an array and the coordinates of the interior point. It then calls the *fill* procedure, which recursively calls itself. We have included a statement at the beginning of the *fill* procedure to print the interior point it has found so that you can follow the order in which the points are changed. The program will also print the final array so that you can check to see if the interior points are all changed to 2.

```
{--------------------------------------------------------------}
program  driver (input,output);
   {This program tests the recursive fill procedure.}
type
   index = 1..10;
   table = array[index,index] of integer;
var
   i, j, m, n: integer;
   grid: table;
{--------------------------------------------------------------}
procedure  fill (i,j:integer; var x:table);
   {This procedure fills the interior points within a
   boundary with the value 2 beginning with location i,j.}
begin {fill}
   writeln (i:3,j:3);
   x[i,j] := 2;
   if  x[i-1,j] = 0  then
      fill (i-1,j,x);
   if  x[i+1,j] = 0  then
      fill (i+1,j,x);
   if  x[i,j-1] = 0  then
      fill (i,j-1,x);
   if  x[i,j+1] = 0  then
      fill (i,j+1,x)
end; {fill}
{--------------------------------------------------------------}
begin {driver}
   writeln ('ENTER ARRAY DIMENSIONS M (ROWS) AND N (COLS)');
   writeln ('(M,N < 11)');
   read (m,n);
   writeln ('ENTER ARRAY BY ROWS');
   for i := 1 to m do
      for j := 1 to n do
         read (grid[i,j]);
   writeln ('ENTER COORDINATES OF INTERIOR POINT');
   read (i,j);
   writeln;
   fill (i,j,grid);
   writeln;
   for i := 1 to m do
      begin
         for j := 1 to n do
            write (grid[i,j]:2);
         writeln
      end
end. {driver}
{--------------------------------------------------------------}
```

Shown next are the program interactions using the two example arrays.

```
ENTER ARRAY DIMENSIONS M (ROWS) AND N (COLS)
(M,N < 11)
8  8
ENTER ARRAY BY ROWS
0 0 0 0 0 0 0 0
0 0 0 0 0 0 0 0
0 1 1 1 0 0 0 0
1 0 0 0 1 0 0 0
1 0 0 0 0 1 0 0
1 1 0 0 1 0 0 0
0 0 1 1 0 0 0 0
0 0 0 0 0 0 0 0
ENTER COORDINATES OF INTERIOR POINT
4  2

   4    2
   5    2
   5    3
   4    3
   4    4
   5    4
   6    4
   6    3
   5    5

 0 0 0 0 0 0 0 0
 0 0 0 0 0 0 0 0
 0 1 1 1 0 0 0 0
 1 2 2 2 1 0 0 0
 1 2 2 2 2 1 0 0
 1 1 2 2 1 0 0 0
 0 0 1 1 0 0 0 0
 0 0 0 0 0 0 0 0
```

```
ENTER ARRAY DIMENSIONS M (ROW) AND N (COLS)
(M,N < 11)
5  6
ENTER ARRAY BY ROWS
0 0 1 0 0 0
0 1 0 1 0 0
1 0 0 0 1 1
1 0 0 0 0 1
1 1 1 1 1 1
ENTER COORDINATES OF INTERIOR POINT
3 3

   3    3
   2    3
   4    3
   4    2
   3    2
   4    4
   3    4
   4    5

 0 0 1 0 0 0
 0 1 2 1 0 0
 1 2 2 2 1 1
 1 2 2 2 2 1
 1 1 1 1 1 1
```

Before we leave this example, we would like to point out a few things. First, we assume that the boundary has been properly defined. If there is no boundary, or if there is a "hole" in the boundary, this algorithm will "flood" outside the hole and fill points outside the boundary. For this reason, this algorithm is sometimes referred to as a "flood-fill" algorithm. It is used frequently to fill objects with color in computer graphics. The other thing about this procedure is that it does not know what size array it is working with in the *fill* procedure. But, since we assume the boundary is properly specified, the algorithm should never get outside the boundary and thus should never exceed the limits of the array.

SELF-TEST 7-1

This self-test allows you to check quickly to see if you have remembered certain key points from Section 7-1. If you have any problems with the exercises, you should reread this section. The solutions are included at the end of the text.

Problems 1–5 contain definitions and initializations of two-dimensional arrays. Draw the array and indicate the contents of each position in the array after you execute the set of statements. Assume that each set of statements is independent of the others. If no value is given to a particular position, fill it with a question mark.

```
1. type
        index1 = 1..5;
        index2 = 1..4;
        table = array[index1,index2] of integer;
   var
        i, j: integer;
        results: table;
        .
        .
        .
        for i := 1 to 5 do
            for j := 1 to 4 do
                results[i,j] := i*j

2. type
        index1 = 1..5;
        index2 = 1..4;
        table = array[index1,index2] of integer;
   var
        i, j: integer;
        results: table;
        .
        .
        .
        for i := 1 to 5 do
            for j := 1 to 4 do
                results[i,j] := i
```

```
3. type
     index1 = 1..5;
     index2 = 1..4;
     table = array[index1,index2] of integer;
   var
     i, j: integer;
     results: table;
     .
     .
     .
     for i := 1 to 5 do
        for j := 1 to 4 do
           results[i,j] := j

4. type
     index1 = 1..5;
     index2 = 1..4;
     table = array[index1,index2] of integer;
   var
     i, j: integer;
     results: table;
     .
     .
     .
     for i := 1 to 5 do
        for j := 1 to 4 do
           results[i,j] := (i + j) mod 3

5. type
     index = 0..2;
     table = array[index,index] of real;
   var
     i, j: integer;
     results: table;
     .
     .
     .
     for i := 0 to 2 do
        for j := 0 to 2 do
           results[i,j] := 0.1*j
```

7-2 PROBLEM SOLVING—ANALYSIS OF POWER PLANT DATA

The following table of data represents typical power output in megawatts from a power plant over a period of eight weeks. Each row represents one week's data; each column represents data taken on the same day of the week. The data is stored one row per data line in a data file called *plant*.

	DAY 1	DAY 2	DAY 3	DAY 4	DAY 5	DAY 6	DAY 7
WEEK 1	207	301	222	302	22	167	125
WEEK 2	367	60	120	111	301	400	434
WEEK 3	211	72	441	102	21	203	317
WEEK 4	401	340	161	297	441	117	206
WEEK 5	448	111	370	220	264	444	207
WEEK 6	21	313	204	222	446	401	337
WEEK 7	213	208	444	321	320	335	313
WEEK 8	162	137	265	44	370	315	322

We need a program to read the data, analyze it, and print the results in the following composite report:

```
            COMPOSITE INFORMATION

AVERAGE DAILY POWER OUTPUT = XXX.X MEGAWATTS
NUMBER OF DAYS WITH GREATER THAN AVERAGE POWER OUTPUT = XX
DAY(S) WITH MINIMUM POWER OUTPUT:
        WEEK X    DAY X
          .
          .
          .
        WEEK X    DAY X
```

PROBLEM STATEMENT

Analyze a set of data from a power plant to determine its daily power output, the number of days with greater-than-average output, and the day or days that had minimum power output.

INPUT/OUTPUT DESCRIPTION

The input is a data file with one week's data per line in an integer form. The file contains data for eight weeks. The output should be a report as shown:

```
AVERAGE DAILY POWER OUTPUT = XXX.X MEGAWATTS
NUMBER OF DAYS WITH GREATER THAN AVERAGE POWER OUTPUT = XX
DAY(S) WITH MINIMUM POWER OUTPUT:
          WEEK X    DAY X
                .
                .
                .
          WEEK X    DAY X
```

HAND EXAMPLE

For the hand-worked example we use a smaller set of data, but one that still maintains the two-dimensional array structure. Consider this set of data:

	Day 1	Day 2
Week 1	311	405
Week 2	210	264
Week 3	361	210

First, we must sum all the values and divide by 6 to determine the average, which yields 1761/6 or 293.5 megawatts. Second, we compare each value to the average to determine how many values were greater than the average. In our small set of data, three values were greater than the average. Third, we must determine the number of days with minimum power output, which involves two steps: going through the data again to determine the minimum value and going back through the data to find the day or days with the minimum power value, then printing its/their position(s) in the array. Using the small set of data, we find that the minimum value is 210, and it occurred on two days. Thus, the output from our hand-worked example is:

```
               COMPOSITE INFORMATION

AVERAGE DAILY POWER OUTPUT = 293.5 MEGAWATTS
NUMBER OF DAYS WITH GREATER THAN AVERAGE POWER OUTPUT =  3
DAY(S) WITH MINIMUM POWER OUTPUT:
          WEEK 2    DAY 1
          WEEK 3    DAY 2
```

ALGORITHM DEVELOPMENT

Before we decompose the problem solution, it is important to spend some time considering the best way to store the data we need for the program. Unfortunately, once we become comfortable with arrays, we tend to overuse them. Using an array complicates programs because of the subscript handling. We should always stop and ask ourselves, "Should we really use an array for this data?"

If the individual data values will be needed more than once, an array is probably required. An array is also necessary if the data is not in the order needed. In general, arrays are helpful when we must read all the data before we can go back and begin processing it. However, if an average of a group of data values is all that is to be computed, we probably do not need an array; as we read the values, we can add them to a total and read the next value into the same memory location as the previous value. The individual values are not needed again because the information required is now in the total.

Now let us look at our specific problem and determine whether we need to use an array. First, we need to compute an average daily power output. Then we need to count the number of days with output greater than average, which requires that we compare each output value to the average. For this application, we need to store all the data in an array. A two-dimensional array is the best choice of data structure.

When we performed the solution by hand, we made several passes through the data to obtain different pieces of information. As we begin to develop the computer solution, we would like to minimize the number of passes through the data. We can compute the sum of the data points in the same loop in which we determine the minimum data value. However, we must make a separate pass through the data to determine how many values are greater than the average. Because we print the number of days with greater-than-average output before we print the specific day or days with minimum output, we need separate loops for these operations. For this solution, we need a total of three loops (passes) through the array. The decomposition and pseudocode for the algorithm we have discussed are:

DECOMPOSITION

Read data.
Compute and print information.

INITIAL REFINEMENT IN PSEUDOCODE

powerplant: read data
            compute average power and minimum power
            write average power
            count days with above-average power
            write count of days
            write days with minimum power

FINAL REFINEMENT IN PSEUDOCODE

powerplant: read data
            compute average and minimum value
            write heading, average
            count ← 0
            for each data value do
              if data value > average then
                count ← count + 1
            write count
            for each data value do
              if data value = minimum then
                write row position, column position

We now convert the refined pseudocode into Pascal.

PASCAL PROGRAM

```
{------------------------------------------------------------------}
program  powerplant (plant,output);
    {This program computes and prints a composite
    report covering 8 weeks for a power plant.}
type
    index1 = 1..8;
    index2 = 1..7;
    table = array[index1,index2] of integer;
var
    average: real;
    i, j, minimum, total, count: integer;
    power: table;
    plant: text;
begin
    reset (plant);
    total := 0;
    minimum := maxint;
    for i := 1 to 8 do
        for j := 1 to 7 do
            begin
                read (plant,power[i,j]);
                total := total + power[i,j];
                if  power[i,j] < minimum   then
                    minimum := power[i,j]
            end;
    average := total/56;
    count := 0;
    for i := 1 to 8 do
        for j := 1 to 7 do
            if  power[i,j] > average   then
                count := count + 1;
    writeln ('                    COMPOSITE INFORMATION');
    writeln;
    writeln ('AVERAGE DAILY POWER OUTPUT = ',
            average:5:1,' MEGAWATTS');
    writeln ('NUMBER OF DAYS WITH GREATER THAN ',
            'AVERAGE POWER OUTPUT = ',count:2);
    writeln ('DAY(S) WITH MINIMUM POWER OUTPUT:');
    for i := 1 to 8 do
        for j := 1 to 7 do
            if  power[i,j] = minimum   then
                writeln ('                WEEK ',i:2,'   DAY ',j:2)
end.
{------------------------------------------------------------------}
```

TESTING

This program should be tested in stages. Again, the decomposition gives a good idea of the overall steps involved and can be used to identify the steps that should be tested individually. Remember that one of the most useful tools for debugging is the *writeln* statement. Use it to print the values of key variables in loops that may contain errors.

The output from this program using the data file given at the beginning of this section is:

```
                    COMPOSITE INFORMATION

AVERAGE DAILY POWER OUTPUT = 254.4 MEGAWATTS
NUMBER OF DAYS WITH GREATER THAN AVERAGE POWER OUTPUT = 29
DAY(S) WITH MINIMUM POWER OUTPUT:
                WEEK   3    DAY  5
                WEEK   6    DAY  1
```

7-3   PROBLEM SOLVING — TERRAIN NAVIGATION

The study of terrain navigation has become popular with the advent of remotely piloted vehicles such as planes, missiles, and tanks. The systems that guide these vehicles must be tested over a variety of land formations and topologies. Elevation information for large grids of land is available in computer databases. One way of measuring the "difficulty" of a land grid with respect to terrain navigation is to determine the number of peaks in the grid (a peak is a point that has lower elevations all around it).

The program we develop in this section will read the elevation information for a set of grids. Then we will determine the number of peaks in each grid using the definition given above.

We assume that the file containing the elevation information is called *elevation*. The first line for each grid contains an identification number. The second line contains the number of points along the side of the grid and the number of points along the top of the grid. The elevation data for that grid then begins on the next line, with the data for the top row first, then the second row, and so on. If the data for the first row does not fit on one line, as many lines as are needed will be used. However, each new row of data will begin on a new line. The last line in the data file will contain an identification number of 9999. You can assume that the maximum grid size will be 100 points by 100 points. For each grid, print the identification number, the total number of points in the grid, and the number of peaks in the grid.

PROBLEM STATEMENT

Determine the number of peaks in a grid of elevation values, assuming that a peak is defined by a point that is higher than all four surrounding points.

INPUT/OUTPUT DESCRIPTION

The input is a data file called *elevation* that contains information on a number of grids. Each set of information contains the grid identification, the number of points along the side of the grid, the number of points along the top of the grid, and the elevations of the points in row order. The output is to be a report that lists each grid identification number, the total number of points in the grid, and the number of peaks within the grid.

HAND EXAMPLE

Assume that the following data represents the elevations for a grid that has six points along the side and eight points along the top. We have circled peaks within the data.

```
9254  8  6
25   59   63   23   21   34   21   50
32   45   43   30   (37)  32   30   27
34   38   38   39   36   28   28   35
40   (45)  42   (48)  32   30   27   25
39   39   40   42   48   (49)  25   30
31   31   31   32   32   33   44   35
```

The output for this grid would be:

```
SUMMARY OF LAND GRID ANALYSIS

IDENTIFICATION      NUMBER OF POINTS      NUMBER OF PEAKS
   9254                    48                    4
```

ALGORITHM DEVELOPMENT

You probably realized that the search for peaks need only consider interior points in the grid. A point along the edge cannot be counted as a peak since we do not know the elevation on one or more of its sides. If we are considering a point at location $map[i,j]$, then the four adjacent points are at positions $map[i-1,j]$, $map[i+1,j]$, $map[i,j-1]$, and $map[i,j+1]$ as shown:

	map[i-1,j]	
map[i,j-1]	map[i,j]	map[i,j+1]
	map[i+1,j]	

Thus, for $map[i,j]$ to be a peak, the following must be true:

$$
\begin{aligned}
map[i,j] &> map[i,j-1] \\
map[i,j] &> map[i,j+1] \\
map[i,j] &> map[i-1,j] \\
map[i,j] &> map[i+1,j]
\end{aligned}
$$

If all these conditions are met for a point $map[i,j]$, it represents a peak.

Since the number of peaks in a grid or map is a single value, we implement the searching and counting of peaks in a function. The parameters for the function are the array map and the corresponding number of rows and columns. The decomposition and refinement of this algorithm with the function for counting peaks are shown on the next page.

DECOMPOSITION

Write heading.
Read map information and generate report.

REFINEMENT IN PSEUDOCODE

topology: write heading
   read id
   while id not = 9999 do
    read rows, columns
    read array map
    print id, number of peaks
    read id

peaks(map,rows,column):
   count ← 0
   for each interior point do
    if interior point is higher than
    all four adjacent points then
     increment count

The structure chart for this solution is shown next, along with the Pascal program.

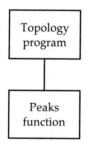

PASCAL PROGRAM

```
{---------------------------------------------------------------}
program  topology (elevation,output);
    {This program reads the elevation data for a set of
    land grids and determines the number of peaks in each.}
type
    index = 1..100;
    grid = array[index,index] of integer;
var
    i, j, id, rows, columns: integer;
    elevation: text;
    map: grid;
```

```
{------------------------------------------------------------------}
function  peaks (map:grid; rows,columns:integer): integer;
   {This function determines the number of peaks in a map.}
var
   i, j, count: integer;
begin {peaks}
   count := 0;
   for i := 2 to rows-1 do
      for j := 2 to columns-1 do
         if  (map[i,j] > map[i-1,j]) and
             (map[i,j] > map[i+1,j]) and
             (map[i,j] > map[i,j-1]) and
             (map[i,j] > map[i,j+1])   then
                  count := count + 1;
   peaks := count
end; {peaks}
{------------------------------------------------------------------}
begin {topology}
   writeln ('SUMMARY OF LAND GRID ANALYSIS');
   writeln;
   writeln ('IDENTIFICATION   NUMBER OF POINTS   ',
            'NUMBER OF PEAKS');
   reset (elevation);
   read (elevation,id);
   while  id <> 9999  do
      begin
         read (elevation,rows,columns);
         for i := 1 to rows do
            for j := 1 to columns do
               read (elevation,map[i,j]);
         writeln (id:6,rows*columns:18,
                  peaks(map,rows,columns):17);
         read (elevation,id)
      end
end. {topology}
{------------------------------------------------------------------}
```

TESTING

When using the data from the hand-worked example, our output is:

```
SUMMARY OF LAND GRID ANALYSIS

IDENTIFICATION    NUMBER OF POINTS    NUMBER OF PEAKS
   9254                  48                  4
```

Try to think of any special cases that might cause problems for this program.
You can probably think of some unique grid shapes, such as grids with one or
two rows or one or two columns. If we look at our function, we see that the
for loops used in counting peaks are:

```
for i := 2 to rows-1 do
   for j := 2 to columns-1 do
```

If we substitute 2 for rows and columns, we have

```
for i := 2 to 1 do
    for j := 2 to 1 do
```

These loops would not be executed, and because the number of peaks was initialized to zero, the number of peaks would remain at zero. Thus, the program will handle these unique grid cases correctly. If the values of *rows* and *columns* were less than 1 or greater than 100, the program would not work correctly. It might be a good idea to test *rows* and *columns* after they are read and print an appropriate error message if they are out of bounds.

Note that this program will locate individual peaks, but, it will not locate a ridge where two or more adjacent peaks are at the same elevation. The algorithm would have to be modified if we wanted to identify this type of formation.

7-4 COMMON TECHNIQUES USED WITH TWO-DIMENSIONAL ARRAYS

In previous chapters, we developed procedures and functions for some of the common techniques used with one-dimensional arrays. These techniques included averages, minimums, maximums, searches, and sorts. The solutions can be expanded to include data from a two-dimensional array. In this section we develop algorithms for row and column sums and for searches.

ROW AND COLUMN SUMS

Row and column sums are often part of the calculations needed with two-dimensional arrays. We are going to develop algorithms for row and column sums in two different types of routines. First, we develop procedures to compute row and column sums for an array and store the sums in a corresponding one-dimensional array. For example, if we have an array with 5 rows and 10 columns, the row sums could be stored in a one-dimensional array of 5 elements and the column sums could be stored in a one-dimensional array of 10 elements.

EXAMPLE 7-9 Row Sum Procedure

Write a procedure that computes the row sums of a two-dimensional integer array. Assume that the procedure has the following header:

```
procedure  sumrows (x:table; rows,columns:integer;
                    var sums:list1);
```

The parameter *x* is a two-dimensional array and the parameter *sums* is a one-dimensional array with the same number of elements as there are rows in *x*. An example of a statement that references this procedure is:

```
sumrows (data,5,10,totals)
```

Solution

To compute the sum of a single row, we hold the row number constant and vary the column number from 1 to its maximum value. Since we repeat this step for each row, we need a nested loop to compute all the row sums.

DECOMPOSITION

Compute row sums.

REFINED PSEUDOCODE

sumrows (x,rows,columns,sums):
    for i = 1 to rows do
      sums[i] ← 0
      for j = 1 to columns do
        sums[i] ← sums[i] + x[i,j]

We now convert this pseudocode to Pascal.

PASCAL PROCEDURE

```
{- - - - - - - - - - - - - - - - - - - - - - - - - - - - - - - - - - - - - - - - - - -}
procedure  sumrows (x:table; rows,columns:integer;
                        var sums:list1);
   {This procedure computes the sums of the rows
   of a two-dimensional array.}
var
   i, j: integer;
begin {sumrows}
   for i := 1 to rows do
      begin
         sums[i] := 0;
         for j := 1 to columns do
            sums[i] := sums[i] + x[i,j]
      end
end; {sumrows}
{- - - - - - - - - - - - - - - - - - - - - - - - - - - - - - - - - - - - - - - - - -}
```

EXAMPLE 7-10   Column Sum Procedure

Write a procedure that computes the column sums of a two-dimensional integer array. Assume that the procedure has the following header:

```
procedure  sumcols (x:table; rows,columns:integer;
                        var sums:list2);
```

The parameter *x* is a two-dimensional array and the parameter *sums* is a one-dimensional array with the same number of elements as there are columns in *x*. An example of a statement that references this procedure is:

```
sumcols (data,5,10,sums)
```

Solution

To compute the sum of a single column, we hold the column number constant and vary the row number from 1 to its maximum value. We repeat this step for each column, so we will need a nested loop to compute the column sums.

DECOMPOSITION

```
Compute column sums.
```

REFINED PSEUDOCODE

> sumcols (x,rows,columns,sums):
> > for j = 1 to columns do
> > > sums[j] ← 0
> > > for i = 1 to rows do
> > > > sums[j] ← sums[j] + x[i,j]

We now convert this pseudocode to Pascal.

PASCAL PROCEDURE

```
{----------------------------------------------------------}
procedure  sumcols (x:table; rows,columns:integer;
                    var sums:list2);
   {This procedure computes the sums of the columns
   of a two-dimensional array.}
var
   i, j: integer;
begin {sumcols}
   for j := 1 to columns do
      begin
         sums[j] := 0;
         for i := 1 to rows do
            sums[j] := sums[j] + x[i,j]
      end
end; {sumcols}
{----------------------------------------------------------}
```

We now develop functions for computing row sums and column sums. Since a function can return only a single value, we will not sum all the rows or all the columns; instead, one of the function parameters will specify the row or column that is to be summed.

EXAMPLE 7-11   Row Sum Function

Write a function that computes the row sum of a specific row in a two-dimensional integer array. Assume that the function has the following header:

```
function  rowsum (x:table; row,columns:integer): integer;
```

The parameter x is a two-dimensional array. The parameter *columns* specifies the number of columns in the array, and the parameter *row* specifies the row that is to be summed. An example of a statement that references this function is:

```
total := rowsum(data,3,10)
```

Solution

To compute the sum of a single row, we use the specified row number and vary the column number from 1 to its maximum value.

DECOMPOSITION

```
Compute specified row sum.
```

REFINED PSEUDOCODE

rowsum (x,row,columns): sum ← 0
          for j = 1 to columns do
            sum ← sum + x[row,j]
          rowsum ← sum

We now convert this pseudocode to Pascal.

PASCAL FUNCTION

```
{------------------------------------------------------}
function  rowsum (x:table; row,columns:integer): integer;
   {This function computes the sum of a specified row
   of a two-dimensional array.}
var
   j, sum: integer;
begin {rowsum}
   sum := 0;
   for j := 1 to columns do
      sum := sum + x[row,j];
   rowsum := sum
end; {rowsum}

{------------------------------------------------------}
```

EXAMPLE 7-12   Column Sum Function

Write a function that computes the column sum of a specific column in a two-dimensional integer array. Assume that the function has the following header:

```
function  colsum (x:table; rows,column:integer): integer;
```

The parameter x is a two-dimensional array. The parameter *rows* specifies the number of rows in the array and the parameter *column* specifies

the column that is to be summed. An example of a statement that references this function is:

```
writeln ('COLUMN SUM = ',colsum(data,5,2):5)
```

Solution

To compute the sum of a single column, we use the specified column
number and vary the row number from 1 to its maximum value.

DECOMPOSITION

> Compute specified column sum.

REFINED PSEUDOCODE

> colsum (x,rows,column): sum ← 0
> > for i = 1 to rows do
> > > sum ← sum + x[i,column]
> > colsum ← sum

We now convert this pseudocode to Pascal.

PASCAL FUNCTION

```
{- - - - - - - - - - - - - - - - - - - - - - - - - - - - - - - - - - - - - - - - - - - - - - -}
function  colsum (x:table; rows,column:integer): integer;
    {This function computes the sum of a specified column
    of a two-dimensional array.}
var
    i, sum: integer;
begin {colsum}
    sum := 0;
    for i := 1 to rows do
        sum := sum + x[i,column];
    colsum := sum
end; {colsum}
{- - - - - - - - - - - - - - - - - - - - - - - - - - - - - - - - - - - - - - - - - - - - - - -}
```

SEARCHING

We present two different techniques for searching a two-dimensional unordered
array. In Example 7-13 we assume that we are interested in whether or not a
specific item is in the array. Our solution will develop a Boolean function to
return a value of true if the value is found in the array, and a value of false
otherwise. In Example 7-14 we assume that we are interested in the number of
occurrences of the item in the array. Our solution will develop an integer function
to return the number of times that a value is found in the array; if the value is not
in the array, the function value will be zero.

EXAMPLE 7-13   Boolean Search Function

Write a function that determines whether or not a specific value occurs in a two-dimensional array. The function should return the value true if the value is found, and false otherwise. Assume that the function has the following header:

```
function found (x:table;
                rows,columns,item:integer): boolean;
```

The parameter *x* is a two-dimensional array. The parameter *rows* specifies the number of rows in the array and the parameter *columns* specifies the number of columns in the array. The parameter *item* specifies the value for which we are searching. An example of a statement that references this function is:

```
if  found(data,5,10,-1)  then
    writeln ('ERROR IN DATA')
```

Solution

Since we are interested in whether or not the value occurs in the array, not how many times it occurs, our control structure should be a *while* loop. If we find the item, there is no need to continue searching the rest of the array. In our algorithm, we will search across each row before going to the next row.

DECOMPOSITION

```
┌─────────────────────────────────┐
│  Search array for specified item.  │
└─────────────────────────────────┘
```

REFINED PSEUDOCODE

```
found (x,rows,columns,item):
                done ← false
                found ← false
                i ← 1
                j ← 1
                while not done do
                   if x[i,j] = item then
                      done ← true
                      found ← true
                   else if j < columns then
                      j ← j + 1
                   else if i < rows then
                      i ← i + 1
                      j ← 1
                   else
                      done ← true
```

We now convert this pseudocode to Pascal.

```
{- - - - - - - - - - - - - - - - - - - - - - - - - - - - - - - - - - - - - - - - - - - - - - - - - - - - -}
function   found (x:table;
                   rows,columns,item:integer): boolean;
    {This function returns a value of true if the specified
    item is in the array x, and a value of false otherwise.}
var
    i, j: integer;
    done: boolean;
begin {found}
    done := false;
    found := false;
    i := 1;
    j := 1;
    while  not done  do
        if  x[i,j] = item   then
            begin
                done := true;
                found := true
            end
        else if  j < columns   then
            j := j + 1
        else if  i < rows   then
            begin
                i := i + 1;
                j := 1
            end
        else
            done := true
end; {found}
{- - - - - - - - - - - - - - - - - - - - - - - - - - - - - - - - - - - - - - - - - - - - - - - - - - - - -}
```

EXAMPLE 7-14   Integer Search Function

Write a function that determines the number of times a specific value occurs in a two-dimensional array. The function should return the number of times that value occurs; if the value is not in the array the function should return a value of zero. Assume that the function has the following header:

```
function   count (x:table;
                   rows,columns,item:integer):  integer;
```

The parameter *x* is a two-dimensional array. The parameter *rows* specifies the number of rows in the array and the parameter *columns* specifies the number of columns in the array. The parameter *item* specifies the value for which we are searching. An example of a statement that references this function is:

```
    total := total + count(data,5,10,k)
```

Solution

Since we are interested in the number of times that the value occurs in the array, we need to check each element in the array. Our control structure should thus be a pair of nested *for* loops. Each time we find the value for which we are searching, we increment a count.

DECOMPOSITION

> Search array for specified item.

REFINED PSEUDOCODE

count (x,rows,columns,item):
>>> counter ← 0
>>> for i = 1 to rows do
>>>> for j = 1 to columns do
>>>>> if x[i,j] = item then
>>>>>> counter ← counter + 1
>>> count ← counter

We now convert this pseudocode to Pascal.

PASCAL FUNCTION

```
{- - - - - - - - - - - - - - - - - - - - - - - - - - - - - - - - - - - - - -}
function  count (x:table;
                 rows,columns,item:integer): integer;
   {This function returns the number of occurrences of
   a specific item in the array x.}
var
   i, j, counter: integer;
begin {count}
   counter := 0;
   for i := 1 to rows do
      for j := 1 to columns do
         if  x[i,j] = item  then
            counter := counter + 1;
   count := counter
end; {count}
{- - - - - - - - - - - - - - - - - - - - - - - - - - - - - - - - - - - - - -}
```

SELF-TEST 7-2

This self-test allows you to check quickly to see if you have remembered certain key points from Section 7-4. If you have any problems with the exercise, you should reread this section. The solution is included at the end of the text.

In the previous section we developed a function that computed the sum of a specific row in a two-dimensional array. We also developed a procedure that computed a one-dimensional array of row sums from a two-dimensional array. Rewrite the procedure that computes the array of row sums so that it uses the function that computes the sum of a specific row.

7-5   PROBLEM SOLVING—EXAM STATISTICS

Analyzing data and generating statistics are operations commonly performed by computers. In this problem, the data represents exam scores from an introductory computing class. Enrollment in the class has been high and additional sections have been added. The professor in charge of coordinating the classes would like a computer program to generate some statistics to help analyze the exam grades.

The particular set of available data is from an eight-week summer session in which each section took a weekly exam. The average grade from each section for each week has been stored in a data file called *summer.* The first line of the file contains a date consisting of the month, day, and year (each two digits) that represent the ending date of the summer session. The next line in the file contains eight numbers, representing the weekly exam averages for section 1. The next line in the file contains the eight weekly exam averages for section 2, and so on.

The coordinator of this class is particularly interested in analyzing the scores by weeks to see if all sections performed similarly. The first set of data to be calculated contains weekly averages for the combined group of sections, along with the minimum and maximum section scores for each week. With this data, the weekly average can be compared to the maximum and minimum for that week. If the maximum and minimum values are close to the average, there is not much difference in the performance of the sections. If the difference is large, the section's performance should be studied further. To give further information for analysis, the program should also print the numbers of the section(s) that had the minimum weekly score and the section(s) that had the maximum weekly score.

PROBLEM STATEMENT

Compute the average exam grade for the class using scores from all six sections, for each week of an eight-week summer session. In addition, determine the minimum and maximum weekly section averages.

INPUT/OUTPUT DESCRIPTION

The weekly exam averages for each section are stored in a data file called *summer,* which has the following form:

    line 1: date of the last day of summer session
    line 2: weekly averages for section 1
    line 3: weekly averages for section 2
    .
    .
    .
    line 7: weekly averages for section 6

The following output will be printed for each week:

```
WEEK X
      AVE = XXX.XX
      MIN = XXX.XX
        SECTION X
      MAX = XXX.XX
        SECTION X
```

HAND EXAMPLE

The computations work with one week's data at a time. Assume that the following is a typical data set for the first week:

section	1	2	3	4	5	6
average	86.1	92.3	85.5	100.0	96.2	100.0

The output information should then be:

```
WEEK 1
      AVE =  93.35
      MIN =  86.10
        SECTION 1
      MAX = 100.00
        SECTION 4
        SECTION 6
```

ALGORITHM DEVELOPMENT

Before we begin decomposing the problem solution into a series of steps, it is important to spend some time considering the best way to store the data we need. If we were computing an overall average for an individual section, we would need only one line of data at a time. Since we are computing the average for a week, we need the first value for section 1 (line 2), the first value for section 2 (line 3), and so on. Therefore, the data is not in the order in which we need it; we will have to read it all and then return to compute the information we need. Even if the data had been stored by weeks instead of by sections, a one-dimensional array would have been required to store an entire week's data at a time since the data is needed a second time to print the numbers of the sections whose scores were minimum or maximum for that week.

We are now ready to decompose the problem solution into a series of general steps and then do the initial refinement into pseudocode.

DECOMPOSITION

Read exam data.
Compute and print weekly statistics.

As we begin to refine the steps in the decomposition, we consider the possibility of using some of the procedures and functions for two-dimensional arrays that we developed in the previous section. For this problem we will need column averages. But since the column averages are the column sums divided by 8, we can use the procedure from the last section that computed all the column sums. Before printing each sum, we will divide it by 8 to get the proper value for the average. We are also going to need the maximum and minimum for each column, along with the corresponding section numbers. We did not develop a procedure for computing maximums and minimums in the previous section, so we will develop it for this program. The parameters of the procedure will include the array and the corresponding number of rows and columns. The output of the procedure will be two one-dimensional arrays, each with the same number of elements as the number of columns. One array will contain minimum values from each column, the other array maximum values from each column. Although these arrays contain the values we need, we still must compare them to the individual scores in order to determine the proper section number(s).

INITIAL REFINEMENT IN PSEUDOCODE

statistics: read scores
           compute column sums
           compute column minimums and maximums
           for each week do
               compute and print class average
               print minimum section averages
                   and corresponding section numbers
               print maximum section averages
                   and corresponding section numbers

In the final refinement, we will indicate the steps that are being performed by procedures.

FINAL REFINEMENT IN PSEUDOCODE

statistics: read date
      print date
      read scores into array with 6 rows and 8 columns
      sumcols (scores,6,8,sums)
      minmaxcols (scores,6,8,min,max)
      for week = 1 to 8 do
         average ← sums[week]/8
         print average
         print min[week]
         for section = 1 to 6 do
           if section average = min[week] then
             print section number
         print max[week]
         for section = 1 to 6 do
           if section average = max[week] then
             print section number

sumcols (x,rows,columns,sums):
               for j = 1 to columns do
                 sums[j] ← 0
                 for i = 1 to rows do
                    sums[j] ← sums[j] + x[i,j]

minmaxcols (x,rows,columns,min,max):
               for j = 1 to columns do
                 min[j] ← x[1,j]
                 max[j] ← x[1,j]
                 for i = 1 to rows do
                    if x[i,j] < min[j] then
                       min[j] ← x[i,j]
                    if x[i,j] > max[j] then
                       max[j] ← x[i,j]

The structure chart for this solution is shown next, along with the Pascal Program.

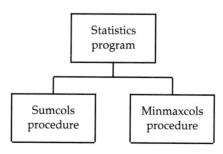

```
{---------------------------------------------------------------}
program  statistics (summer,output);
   {This program computes statistics from exam averages
   in 6 sections of a class during an 8-week session.}
type
   index1 = 1..6;
   index2 = 1..8;
   list = array[index2] of real;
   table = array[index1,index2] of real;
var
   average: real;
   month, day, year, section, week: integer;
   summer: text;
   sums, max, min: list;
   scores: table;
{---------------------------------------------------------------}
procedure  sumcols (x:table; rows,columns: integer;
                     var sums:list);
   {This procedure computes the sums of the columns
   of a two-dimensional array.}
var
   i, j: integer;
begin {sumcols}
   for j := 1 to columns do
      begin
         sums[j] := 0;
         for i := 1 to rows do
            sums[j] := sums[j] + x[i,j]
      end
end; {sumcols}
{---------------------------------------------------------------}
procedure minmaxcols (x:table; rows,columns:integer;
                      var min,max:list);
   {This procedure determines the minimum and maximum values
   in the columns of a two-dimensional array.}
var
   i, j: integer;
begin {minmaxcols}
   for j := 1 to columns do
      begin
         min[j] := x[1,j];
         max[j] := x[1,j];
         for i := 1 to rows do
            begin
               if  x[i,j] < min[j]  then
                  min[j] := x[i,j];
               if  x[i,j] > max[j]  then
                  max[j] := x[i,j]
            end
      end
end; {minmaxcols}
```

```
{----------------------------------------------------------------}
begin {statistics}
   reset (summer);
   read (summer,month,day,year);
   writeln ('SUMMER SESSION - ENDED ',month:2,'-',
            day:2,'-',year:2);
   writeln;
   for section := 1 to 6 do
      for week := 1 to 8 do
         read (summer,scores[section,week]);
   sumcols (scores,6,8,sums);
   minmaxcols (scores,6,8,min,max);
   for week := 1 to 8 do
      begin
         writeln ('WEEK',week:3);
         average := sums[week]/6;
         writeln ('       AVE = ',average:6:2);
         writeln ('       MIN = ',min[week]:6:2);
         for section := 1 to 6 do
            if  scores[section,week] = min[week]  then
               writeln ('           SECTION ',section:1);
         writeln ('       MAX = ',max[week]:6:2);
         for section := 1 to 6 do
            if  scores[section,week] = max[week]  then
               writeln ('           SECTION ',section:1)
      end
end. {statistics}
{----------------------------------------------------------------}
```

TESTING

We suggest testing this program in stages. The obvious places to insert *writeln* statements are after reading the data and after computing the sum, minimum, and maximum for each week. If sections of a program that use arrays are not working properly, print the values of the subscripts to see if you are modifying them properly. For instance, if the minimum or maximum is not correct, you might want to insert the following statement into the procedure just before it updates the minimum and maximum array values:

```
writeln (i,j,x[i,j])
```

This will print the subscripts and the corresponding array value each time through the loop.

Here is an example set of data and the output from the program.

Data File *summer*

```
08 15 87
86.1 91.4 85.5 97.2 94.0 88.4 91.9 95.7
88.3 95.0 87.1 94.4 93.8 90.0 89.9 93.5
84.5 94.6 86.7 95.3 92.2 93.1 90.0 94.1
85.6 93.7 88.2 96.7 91.6 89.2 90.3 92.0
87.7 91.4 89.3 98.1 93.2 91.8 92.0 93.8
90.2 94.1 88.3 93.8 94.7 92.9 89.4 92.6
```

```
SUMMER SESSION - ENDED  8-15-87
WEEK  1
        AVE =  87.07
        MIN =  84.50
          SECTION 3
        MAX =  90.20
          SECTION 6
WEEK  2
        AVE =  93.37
        MIN =  91.40
          SECTION 1
          SECTION 5
        MAX =  95.00
          SECTION 2
WEEK  3
        AVE =  87.52
        MIN =  85.50
          SECTION 1
        MAX =  89.30
          SECTION 5
WEEK  4
        AVE =  95.92
        MIN =  93.80
          SECTION 6
        MAX =  98.10
          SECTION 5
WEEK  5
        AVE =  93.25
        MIN =  91.60
          SECTION 4
        MAX =  94.70
          SECTION 6
WEEK  6
        AVE =  90.90
        MIN =  88.40
          SECTION 1
        MAX =  93.10
          SECTION 3
WEEK  7
        AVE =  90.58
        MIN =  89.40
          SECTION 6
        MAX =  92.00
          SECTION 5
WEEK  8
        AVE =  93.62
        MIN =  92.00
          SECTION 4
        MAX =  95.70
          SECTION 1
```

7-6 MULTIDIMENSIONAL ARRAYS

Pascal allows us to use as many dimensions as desired for arrays. We can easily visualize a three-dimensional array, such as a cube. We are also familiar with using three coordinates, x, y, and z, to locate points. This idea extends into subscripts. The three-dimensional array below could be defined with the following statements:

```
type
    index1 = 1..3;
    index2 = 1..4;
    index3 = 1..4;
    cube = array[index1,index2,index3] of real;
var
    t: cube;
```

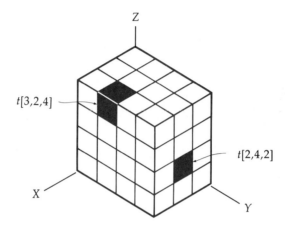

Three levels of nesting in *for* loops are often needed to access a three-dimensional array.

Most applications do not use arrays with more than three dimensions, probably because visualizing more than three dimensions seems too abstract. However, here is a simple scheme that may help you to picture even a seven-dimensional array:

Four-Dimensional Array Picture a row of three-dimensional arrays. The first subscript specifies a unique three-dimensional array. The other three subscripts specify a unique position in that array.

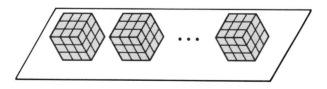

Five-Dimensional Array Picture a block or grid of three-dimensional arrays. The first two subscripts specify a unique three-dimensional array. The other three subscripts specify a unique position in that array.

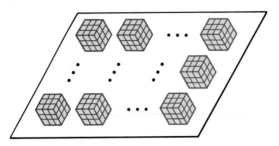

Six-Dimensional Array Picture a row of blocks or grids. One subscript specifies the grid. The other five subscripts specify the unique position in the grid.

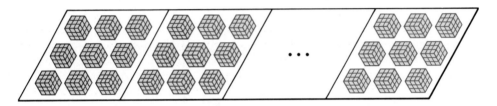

Seven-Dimensional Array Picture a grid of grids or a grid of blocks. Two subscripts specify the grid. The other five subscripts specify the unique position in the grid.

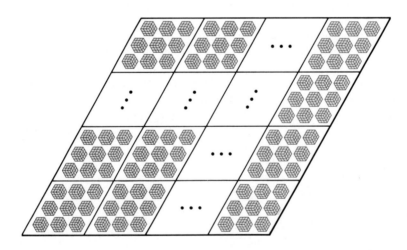

A question that frequently arises in respect to arrays is, "What dimension array do I use for solving a problem?" There is no single answer. A problem that could be solved with a two-dimensional array of four rows and three columns could also be solved with four one-dimensional arrays of three elements each. Usually the data fits one array structure better than another. Choose the structure that is easiest for you to work with in your program. For example, if you have census data from 10 countries over the period 1950–1980, you would probably use an array with 10 rows and 31 columns, or 31 rows and 10 columns. If the data represents the populations of 5 cities from each of 10 countries for the period 1950–1980, a three-dimensional array would be most appropriate. The three subscripts would represent year, country, and city.

SUMMARY

In this chapter we learned how to use a two-dimensional array, a data structure composed of rows and columns. A specific element of a two-dimensional array is referenced by using two subscripts. Arrays are one of the most powerful elements of Pascal because they allow us to keep large amounts of data easily accessible to our programs. The remaining chapters will rely heavily on arrays for storing and manipulating data. If you become comfortable using both one-dimensional and two-dimensional arrays, you can select a data structure based on the way it is to be used in the program. Other important topics that were presented in this chapter are the common techniques used with two-dimensional arrays.

DEBUGGING AIDS

Because arrays are so convenient for handling large amounts of data, a natural tendency is to overuse them — and, unfortunately, arrays can also introduce new errors. As you debug programs that use arrays, consider the decision to use each one. Ask yourself, "Will I need this data more than once? Must this data be stored before I can use it?" If the answers to both questions are no, you should eliminate the array and replace it with simple variables. At the same time, you will probably be eliminating some loops and statements involving subscripts. These changes not only may reduce the number of errors in your program but will also reduce its overall complexity.

If arrays are necessary, then consider each of the following items if your program is not working correctly:

Size The array specification must specify the maximum number of elements that are to be stored in the array. Although you do not have to use all the elements of an array, you can never use more elements than originally specified.

Subscripts Check each subscript to be sure it represents a value that falls within the proper range of values. Particularly check for subscript values that are one value too small or one value too large.

For Loop If you are using the index of a *for* loop as a subscript, be sure you have used the same variable identifier in your statements. That is, if the *for* loop index is *k*, did you use *i* instead of *k* as a subscript?

Reverse Subscripts When you work with multidimensional arrays, be sure you have the subscripts in the proper order. Do you want *x[week,section]* or *x[section,week]*?

STYLE/TECHNIQUE GUIDELINES

Use the type section of a Pascal program to define and name all new data types that you use in your program. This documents your data structures. It also makes it easy to find new data type definitions since they are all together in the type section as opposed to being spread between the type section and the variable section.

A good program can be distinguished by the way it uses data structures. Take the time to carefully choose the data structure that best fits the data used in a program rather than forcing the data to fit a specific structure. Pascal has a wealth of data structures, and you should become proficient with them all. Once you have decided that the data should be stored in an array, carefully weigh the advantages and disadvantages of several one-dimensional arrays as opposed to one two-dimensional array. If you are writing a Pascal program and the array subscripting is difficult to determine, you are probably not using the best structure for the array. Look again to see if you should change the array structure to multiple arrays or to arrays of different sizes.

KEY WORDS

array	one-dimensional array
column sums	row sums
identity matrix	square matrix
matrix	two-dimensional array
multidimensional array	

PROBLEMS

We begin our problem set with modifications to programs developed in this chapter. Give the decomposition, refined pseudocode, and Pascal program for each problem.

Problems 1–5 modify the power plant data analysis program *powerplant*, given on page 332.

1. Modify the power plant data analysis program so that it prints the minimum power output and the days on which it occurred.
2. Modify the power plant data analysis program so that it prints both the minimum and the maximum power outputs.
3. Modify the power plant data analysis program so that it reads a value n that determines the number of weeks of data to be used for the report. Assume that n will never be more than 20.
4. Modify the power plant data analysis program so that it prints a count of the number of days with the minimum power output instead of printing the specific days.
5. Modify the power plant data analysis program so that it prints the average daily power output for each week of data.

Problems 6–10 modify the terrain navigation program *topology*, given on page 338.

6. Modify the terrain navigation program so that it prints a count of the number of land grids analyzed.
7. Modify the terrain navigation program so that it prints the location (row and column subscripts) of the peaks in each land grid.
8. Modify the terrain navigation program so that it computes and prints the percentage of points in each grid that are peaks.
9. Modify the terrain navigation program so that it prints the maximum and minimum elevations for each land grid.
10. Modify the terrain navigation program so that it computes and prints the average elevation for each land grid.

Problems 11–15 modify the exam analysis program *statistics*, given on page 352.

11. Modify the exam analysis program so that it prints the overall exam average for all weeks and all sections.
12. Modify the exam analysis program so that it prints the section(s) with the highest eight-week average.
13. Modify the exam analysis program so that it prints the section(s) with the lowest eight-week average.
14. Modify the exam analysis program so that it prints the week number(s) with the highest overall average for all sections.

15. Modify the exam analysis program so that it prints the averages, minimums, and maximums by section instead of by week.

Develop these programs and modules. Use the five-phase design process for all complete programs.

16. Write a complete program that will read a two-dimensional array called *rain* containing 12 rows (one for each month) and 5 columns (one for each year, 1980–84). Read each row of real values from a data line in a file *rainfall*. Determine and print the following table of information:

```
AVERAGE YEARLY RAINFALL
1980 - XXX.XX
1981 - XXX.XX
1982 - XXX.XX
1983 - XXX.XX
1984 - XXX.XX

MAXIMUM RAINFALL
MONTH XX YEAR XXXX

MINIMUM RAINFALL
MONTH XX YEAR XXXX
```

17. Assume that the reservations for an airplane flight have been stored in a file called *flight*. The plane contains 38 rows with 6 seats in each row. The seats in each row are numbered 1–6 as follows:

1. Window seat, left side
2. Center seat, left side
3. Aisle seat, left side
4. Aisle seat, right side
5. Center seat, right side
6. Window seat, right side

The file *flight* contains 38 lines of information corresponding to the 38 rows. Each line contains 6 values corresponding to the 6 seats. The value for any seat is either 0 or 1, representing either an empty or an occupied seat.

Write a complete program to read the flight information into a two-dimensional array called *seat*. Find and print all pairs of adjacent seats that are empty. Adjacent aisle seats should not be printed. If all three seats on one side of the plane are empty, then two pairs of adjacent seats should be printed. Print this information in the following manner:

```
AVAILABLE SEAT PAIRS
   ROW      SEATS
   XX       X,X
    .
    .
    .
   XX       X,X
```

If no pairs of seats are available, print an appropriate message.

---

18. Several buyers working for a large international corporation find themselves purchasing computer terminals from several suppliers. Although they can buy the terminals for roughly the same cost from each supplier, the shipping costs vary depending on the location of both the buyer and the suppliers. A computer program is needed to compute the costs of alternative purchase schemes to select the most economical purchase plan.

Assume the program initializes a table called *cost* for five warehouses and six buyers. Let columns represent the buyers and let rows represent the warehouses. The cost for shipping an item from a particular warehouse i to a particular buyer j is stored in *cost[i,j]*. For example, if *cost(3,2)* contains 15.00, the cost for shipping each terminal from warehouse 3 to buyer 2 is $15. Assume that the *cost* table is stored by rows in a data file called *shipping*. Read the data and print it in an easily understood form similar to this:

		BUYER					
W		1	2	3	4	5	6
A R	1	$12.00	$14.34	$13.45	$12.99	$17.31	$15.81
E	2	$18.23	$13.09	$21.01	$17.33	$17.76	$ 8.73
H	3	$ 9.12	$15.00	$14.67	$16.92	$14.03	$19.17
O	4	$23.23	$ 9.09	$15.87	$17.22	$12.33	$15.75
U	5	$16.81	$14.03	$21.32	$13.56	$16.63	$10.78
S							
E							

A purchase order can be stored in another array called *order* with five rows and six columns, where *order[i,j]* represents the number of terminals from warehouse i that are bought by buyer j. Assume that a purchase order is stored in a file called *purchase*, with each line of the file corresponding to a row of the array *order*.

Your program should read the purchase order (five lines) and compute and print the cost of the solution, along with the cost to each buyer, in the following manner:

```
PURCHASE ORDER
SHIPPING COST TO BUYER 1 = XXXXX.XX
        .
        .
        .
SHIPPING COST TO BUYER 6 = XXXXX.XX

TOTAL SHIPPING COST      $XXXXXX.XX
```

19. Write a function that will determine the average of the values in a real two-dimensional array. Assume that the function header is the following:

```
function  average (x:table; rows,columns:integer): real;
```

where *rows* represents the number of rows in the array x and *columns* represents the number of columns in the array x.

20. Write a function that will determine the minimum of the values in a real two-dimensional array. Assume that the function header is the following:

```
function  minimum (x:table; rows,columns:integer): real;
```

where *rows* represents the number of rows in the array *x* and *columns* represents the number of columns in the array *x*.

21. Write a function that will determine the maximum of the values in a real two-dimensional array. Assume that the function header is the following:

```
function  maximum (x:table; rows,columns:integer): real;
```

where *rows* represents the number of rows in the array *x* and *columns* represents the number of columns in the array *x*.

22. Write a procedure that will sort the elements in a real two-dimensional array so that they are in ascending order going across the rows. Assume that the procedure header is the following:

```
procedure  sortacross (rows,columns:integer;
                   var x:table);
```

where *rows* represents the number of rows in the array *x* and *columns* represents the number of columns in the array *x*.

23. Write a procedure that will sort the elements in a real two-dimensional array, so that they are in ascending order going down the columns. Assume that the procedure header is the following:

```
procedure  sortdown (rows,columns:integer;
                  var x:table);
```

where *rows* represents the number of rows in the array *x* and *columns* represents the number of columns in the array *x*.

24. Write a procedure that will sort the elements in the first column of an array into ascending order. The sort should be done so that the values on the same row stay together. When the sort is finished, elements that were originally in the same row are still in the same row, but the order of the rows is such that the first column of the array is now in ascending order. Assume that the procedure header is the following:

```
procedure  sortcol1 (rows,columns:integer; var x:table);
```

where *rows* represents the number of rows in the array *x* and *columns* represents the number of columns in the array *x*.

25. Write a procedure that will sort into ascending order the elements in a column specified by a parameter *n*. The sort should be done so that the values in the same row stay together. When the sort is finished, elements that were originally in the same row are still in the same row, but the order of the rows is such that the *n*th column of the array is now in ascending order. Assume that the procedure header is the following:

```
procedure  sortcoln (rows,columns,n:integer; var x:table);
```

where *rows* represents the number of rows in the array *x* and *columns* represents the number of columns in the array *x*.

26. Write a procedure that will switch the *m*th row with the *n*th row in an integer two-dimensional array. Assume that the procedure header is the following:

```
procedure  rowswitch (m,n,rows,columns:integer;
                    var x:table);
```

where *rows* represents the number of rows in the array *x* and *columns* represents the number of columns in the array *x*.

27. Write a procedure that will switch the *m*th column with the *n*th column in an integer two-dimensional array. Assume that the procedure header is the following:

```
procedure  columnswitch (m,n,rows,columns:integer;
                    var x:table);
```

where *rows* represents the number of rows in the array *x* and *columns* represents the number of columns in the array *x*.

PROBLEM SOLVING — Cryptography

Computers are widely used in cryptography, which is the encoding and decoding of information to prevent unauthorized use. Codes range from simple (one character represents another character) to complicated (multiple character substitutions). A key, which specifies the substitutions being used, is generally required to decode the information. Write a program to help decipher an encoded message without the key. (See Section 8-2 for the solution.)

8

CHARACTER AND TEXT PROCESSING

INTRODUCTION

We have used three types of variables and constants in our programs up to this point—real, integer, and Boolean. The fourth data type in Pascal is **character data.** This new data type allows us to process information such as names, addresses, and descriptions. In this chapter we will look at techniques for storing and manipulating character information. In addition to using character variables to store nonnumeric information, we also investigate the use of character variables in cryptography and computer graphics.

8-1   CHARACTER INFORMATION

In Chapter 1 we learned that computers use binary languages, an internal notation composed of 0's and 1's. Information stored in integers, real numbers, and Boolean variables are converted to binary numbers when they are used in a computer. If you study computer hardware or computer architecture, you learn how to convert integer and real values such as 56 and -13.52 into binary numbers. To use Pascal, however, it is not necessary to learn this conversion.

Characters must also be converted into binary form to be used in the computer. They are converted to **binary strings,** which are also series of 0's and 1's. Several codes convert character information to binary strings, but most computers use **EBCDIC** (Extended Binary Coded Decimal Interchange Code) or **ASCII** (American Standard Code for Information Interchange). In these codes, each character can be represented by a binary string. Table 8-1 contains a few characters and their EBCDIC and ASCII equivalents.

You do not need to use the binary codes for characters in your Pascal programs. However, you must be aware that the computer stores characters differently from the numbers used in arithmetic computations; that is, the integer 5 and the character 5 are not stored the same. Thus, it is not possible to use arithmetic operations with character data even if the characters represent numbers.

TABLE 8-1   Binary Character Codes

CHARACTER	ASCII	EBCDIC
A	1000001	11000001
H	1001000	11001000
Y	1011001	11101000
3	0110011	11110011
+	0101011	01001110
$	0100100	01011011
=	0111101	01111110

INITIALIZATION

Pascal allows you to store one character in a character constant or variable. Character constants are defined by enclosing the desired character in single quotation marks. The following statements define several character constants:

```
const
   dash = '-';
   blank = ' ';
   dollarsign = '$';
   lowerz = 'z';
   upperz = 'Z';
```

Character variables are defined in the variable definition section using the type *char*. The following variable section defines several character variables:

```
var
   letter, initial, code: char;
```

Each of the variables defined above can contain only a single character, but it can be any character accepted by the computer system.

Often the character information that we wish to store has several characters in it. For example, a name may contain 25 characters. It would be very tedious to have to work with 25 different variable names, so we use arrays to store character information that is longer than one character. The variable definition below defines a name with 25 characters, an address with 30 characters, a city with 30 characters, and a state abbreviation with two characters. Since each of these pieces of information is longer than one character, we use one-dimensional arrays for the information, being careful to define the array as character information.

```
type
   list25 = array[1..25] of char;
   list30 = array[1..30] of char;
   list2 = array[1..2] of char;
var
   name: list25;
   address, city: list30;
   state: list2;
```

Values can be assigned to character variables with an assignment statement. The following statements assign a letter grade based on a numeric test score:

```
var
   score: integer;
   grade: char;
   .
   .
   .
   if  score >= 90  then
      grade := 'A'
   else if  score >= 80  then
      grade := 'B'
   else if  score >= 70  then
      grade := 'C'
   else if  score >= 60  then
      grade := 'D'
   else
      grade := 'F'
```

If *grade* and *letter* are both defined to be character types, then the following statement is also valid. It initializes *letter* with the value in *grade:*

```
letter := grade
```

INPUT/OUTPUT

Character information can be read from the terminal or from data files. For example, the following statement will read a character from the terminal and store it in the character variable *initial:*

```
read (initial)
```

Note the difference between the previous statement and the following statement:

```
readln (initial)
```

Both of the statements will read the next character (which may or may not be a blank) and store it in the variable *initial*. The *readln* statement will also cause the rest of the line to be skipped; thus, the next *read* or *readln* statement will begin with the data on the new line.

When you are entering character data from the terminal for a *read* or *readln* statement, do not enclose the data in quotation marks; if you do, the quotation marks will be read as part of the **character string.** Since the character data does not have quotation marks to indicate the beginning and ending characters, you must be careful about spaces. Any spaces that are read by the *read* or *readln* statements will be interpreted as data characters.

Recall that each data file has a special indicator at the end of the file so that we can detect the end when the data does not have a trailer signal. We used the Boolean function *eof* to detect this situation with a statement similar to the following:

```
if  not eof  then
    readln (testdata,distance,velocity)
```

A similar situation occurs when we read a line of character data. An end-of-line indicator is automatically added to the end of each line of data in a data file. When we read numeric values, we do not need to worry about the end-of-line indicator because it will not be read as a number. However, when we read character data, this end-of-line indicator will be read as a character.

To avoid reading the end-of-line indicator as part of the character data, we typically use a *while* loop to read the data, with the condition in the loop testing for the end-of-line indicator using the *eoln* function. Consider the following loop:

```
i := 1;
while  not eoln(testdata)  do
    begin
        read (testdata,name[i]);
        i := i + 1
    end;
readln
```

The *eoln* function will be true when the next character is the end-of-line indicator. Thus, we want to continue reading characters as long as the *eoln* function is false, or when *not eoln* is true. The final *readln* statement is necessary to skip the *eoln* character so that the next input statement will begin with information on the next line. If the *eoln* function is used with the system input function, the file parameter in parentheses is optional.

EXAMPLE 8-1 Read Address

Give the Pascal statements necessary to define an address that contains 25 characters. Read the address from the terminal after printing an appropriate message to the user. Echo the address after reading it.

Solution

We define *address* to be a character array containing 25 characters. Since it is more convenient to enter the entire address on one line instead of one character per line, we use the *read* statement rather than the *readln* statement. Since the address entered will often contain fewer than 25 characters, we add blanks to the data entered from the terminal if it has fewer than 25 characters.

```
const
    blank = ' ';
type
    list25 = array[1..25] of char;
var
    i: integer;
    address: list25;
    .
    .
    .
    writeln ('ENTER ADDRESS');
    writeln ('(<26 CHARACTERS)');
    i := 1;
    while  not eoln  do
        begin
            read (address[i]);
            i := i + 1
        end;
    for k := i to 25 do
        address[k] := blank;
    writeln ('ADDRESS IS:');
    for i := 1 to 25 do
        write (address[i]);
    writeln
```

There are several things to observe in this solution. First, note that we used a loop to read and print the data string because we can reference only one character at a time. It is also necessary to use the *read* and *write* statements in order to remain on the same line (either input or output) until we are finished with it. The final *writeln* is necessary to print the output line.

COMPUTATIONS

An *if* statement can be used to compare character variables. Assuming that *code* is a simple character variable, the following are valid statements:

```
if  code = 'R'  then
    regularpay (hours,salary)
else
    overtimepay (hours,salary);
if  code = 'T'  then
    temporary := temporary + 1
```

In addition to comparing a character variable to a specific character, we can also compare it to another character variable, as shown in this statement:

```
if  code1 > code2  then
    sortdata (x)
```

You might wonder why we would be interested in whether one character is "less than" another. You might even wonder how we can refer to a character as being "less than" another character. When we use terms like this, we are not really comparing the characters themselves; instead, we are comparing the binary equivalents that the computer assigns to the characters. The numeric value assigned to a character can be used to determine if a character is behind or in front of another character. These numeric values are specified by a **collating sequence,** which is an ordered list of characters that the computer recognizes. A collating sequence lists characters from the lowest to the highest value. Partial collating sequences for EBCDIC and ASCII codes are given in Table 8-2. While the ordering is not exactly the same for the EBCDIC and ASCII codes, there are some similarities:

1. Capital letters are in order from A to Z.
2. Digits are in order from 0 to 9.
3. Capital letters and digits do not overlap; either digits precede letters, or letters precede digits.
4. The blank character is less than any letter or number.

TABLE 8-2 Partial Collating Sequences for Characters

ASCII
♭ " # $ % & ( ) * + , − . /
0 1 2 3 4 5 6 7 8 9
: ; = ? @
A B C D E F G H I J K L M N O P Q R S T U V W X Y Z

EBCDIC
♭ . (+ & $ *) ; − / , % ? : # @ = "
A B C D E F G H I J K L M N O P Q R S T U V W X Y Z
0 1 2 3 4 5 6 7 8 9

Note: ♭ represents a blank.

Several pairs of characters are listed below, along with their correct relationships:

$$\begin{array}{c} \text{'1'} < \text{'2'} \\ \text{'R'} < \text{'T'} \\ \text{'\$'} < \text{'*'} \\ \text{'\%'} < \text{'@'} \end{array}$$

If we compare only letters, the order is the same as that used in a dictionary. This ordering according to the dictionary is called **lexicographic ordering.**

CHARACTER FUNCTIONS

In Chapter 6 we summarized a group of functions called **ordinal functions.** Recall that an ordinal data type is one in which each value (except the first) has a unique **predecessor** and each value (except the last) has a unique **successor.** Thus, an ordinal function is one whose input is an ordinal value, or whose function value is an ordinal value. Characters are ordinal data types since the collating sequence defines an order for the set of characters. We will review the ordinal functions and give examples of how they might be useful in character handling.

The predecessor function *pred* returns the character that precedes the input character, while the sucessor function *succ* returns the character that follows the input character. These functions might be used to determine whether a program was being run on a computer with ASCII or EBCDIC coding. By choosing a character that had a different predecessor (or successor) in the two codes, your program could compare the actual predecessor to the two possibilities and determine which code was being used on the system. A very simple secret code can also be developed by replacing each character by its predecessor (or successor), as shown in Example 8-2.

EXAMPLE 8-2   Secret Code Encryption

Write a procedure that receives a character array of length *n*. Code this array into a secret form in which each character in the array is replaced by the next character in the collating sequence. Thus, *A* will be replaced by *B*, *B* by *C*, and so on. Since the last character has no successive character in the collating sequence, it may not be used in the input character array. Assume that the procedure has the following header:

```
procedure  encode (message:list; n:integer;
                   var secret:list);
```

Solution

As shown on the next page, the solution is very simple if we use the successor function.

```
{-------------------------------------------------------------}
procedure  encode (message:list; n:integer;
                     var secret:list);
   {This procedure encodes a secret message.}
var
   i: integer;
begin {encode}
   for i := 1 to n do
      secret[i] := succ(message[i])
end; {encode}
{-------------------------------------------------------------}
```

If *message* contained MEET AT NOON AT NED'S, then *secret* would contain NFFN!BU!OPPO!BU!OFE(T assuming the computer system uses the ASCII code internally.

EXAMPLE 8-3   Secret Code Decryption

Write a procedure that receives a character array of length *n*. Decode this array from a secret form in which each character in the array has been replaced by the next character in the collating sequence. Thus, the letter *B* is really supposed to be *A*, the letter *C* is really supposed to be *B*, and so on. Assume that the procedure header is:

```
procedure  decode (secret:list; n:integer;
                     var message:list);
```

Solution

This problem is just the reverse of the previous problem. As shown below, the solution is again very simple if we use the predecessor function.

```
{-------------------------------------------------------------}
procedure  decode (secret:list; n:integer;
                     var message:list);
   {This procedure decodes a secret message.}
var
   i: integer;
begin {decode}
   for i := 1 to n do
      message[i] := pred(secret[i])
end; {decode}
{-------------------------------------------------------------}
```

If *secret* contained NFFN!BU!OPPO!BU!OFE(T, then the decoded message would be MEET AT NOON AT NED'S, again assuming that the computer system uses the ASCII code internally.

The other two ordinal functions, *chr* and *ord*, reference the collating sequence that is being used by the computer system. *Chr* returns the character that corresponds to a specified position in the collating sequence while *ord* returns the position in the collating sequence of a specified character. Thus, the functions are really inverses of each other. These functions can be used to determine the code being used on a computer system by comparing the *ord* value of a character to its value in a specific sequence. For example, the number sign is in position 35 in the ASCII collating sequence. The following statement could be used to determine if ASCII is the code in the current system, since EBCDIC does not place the number sign in the same position.

```
if  ord('#') = 35  then
    writeln ('CODE IS ASCII')
```

EXAMPLE 8-4 Another Secret Code

In this example, we write another procedure to encode a message, but we make this code more difficult to break. We use the *ord* function to give us the position in the collating sequence of an individual character. Instead of moving a fixed number of positions in the collating sequence for each character, we add the position of the character in the message to its position in the collating sequence. Then we use this new integer as the position in the collating sequence for the new character. Note that the new character may not be printable, but since we are storing its code, it is retrievable. The only caution that we need to take is to be sure that we do not come up with an integer that is larger than the length of the collating sequence. We will assume that when the message is prepared, this possibility has been eliminated. Assume that the procedure header is:

```
procedure  encrypt (message:list; n:integer;
                     var secret:list);
```

Solution

If the first character in the message is *A*, it is replaced with *B*, the character in the next position in the collating sequence. If the tenth character in the message is *A*, it will be replaced by the character that is 10 positions forward in the collating sequence. The solution below is again simple with the use of the built-in functions.

```
{-----------------------------------------------------------}
procedure  encrypt (message:list; n:integer;
                     var secret:list);
    {This procedure encodes a message.}
var
    i: integer;
begin {encrypt}
    for i := 1 to n do
        secret[i] := chr(i + ord(message[i]))
end; {encrypt}
{-----------------------------------------------------------}
```

How difficult is this coding scheme to decode? It is simple if you know the original coding scheme, but otherwise it would take some work (or luck) to decode. Computers are very useful in breaking codes such as this one, which has a regular pattern to its coding scheme.

EXAMPLE 8-5 Grade Point Average

In Section 2-7 we developed the pseudocode solution to a problem to determine the grade point average from a set of letter grades. At that time, we had not covered character information in Pascal, and so we could not convert the pseudocode to a Pascal program. We now know how to use character information in Pascal and so we convert the pseudocode to a complete program. You may want to look at the final refinement in pseudocode on page 67 before you review the following program.

PASCAL PROGRAM

```
{-----------------------------------------------------------}
program  gpa (input,output);
   {This program computes gpa from letter grades.}
var
   gradepoint: real;
   totalpts, totalhrs, points, hours,
   courses, numbergrade, count: integer;
   lettergrade: char;
begin
   totalpts := 0;
   totalhrs := 0;
   count := 0;
   writeln ('ENTER NUMBER OF COURSES');
   readln (courses);
   while  count < courses  do
      begin
         writeln ('ENTER COURSE HOURS');
         readln (hours);
         writeln ('ENTER COURSE GRADE');
         readln (lettergrade);
         if  lettergrade = 'A'   then
            numbergrade := 4.0
         else if  lettergrade = 'B'   then
            numbergrade := 3.0
         else if  lettergrade = 'C'   then
            numbergrade := 2.0
         else if  lettergrade = 'D'   then
            numbergrade := 1.0
         else if  lettergrade = 'F'   then
            numbergrade := 0.0
         else
            begin
               writeln ('ERROR IN LETTER GRADE, ',
                        'ENTER AGAIN');
               numbergrade := 0;
               hours := 0
            end;
```

```
            if  hours > 0   then
                begin
                    totalhrs := totalhrs + hours;
                    points := numbergrade*hours;
                    totalpts := totalpts + points;
                    count := count + 1
                end
        end;
    gradepoint := totalpts/totalhrs;
    writeln ('GRADE POINT AVERAGE ',gradepoint:4:2)
end.
{- - - - - - - - - - - - - - - - - - - - - - - - - - - - - - - - - - - - - - - - - - - - - - - - - - - - - - - - - - - - - - -}
```

SELF-TEST 8-1

This self-test allows you to check quickly to see if you have
remembered certain key points from Section 8-1. If you have any
problems with the exercise, you should reread this section. The
solution is included at the end of the text.

Write a complete program that asks the user to enter his or her
first name (maximum 10 letters). The program should print a message
such as the one below, which prints the name following a message.

```
HI  JOE
```

8-2 PROBLEM SOLVING—CRYPTOGRAPHY

Computers not only can encode and decode messages for a specific code, but
they also can attempt to break unknown codes. One simple test used to
analyze a code is to count the number of occurrences of each character in a
coded message. In English text, the most common letter is the letter e. If a
code simply substitutes one letter for another, the most frequently used letter
is likely to be e. Obviously, more complicated codes are more difficult to analyze.

In this application we write a program to read a coded message and
count the number of occurrences of each of the vowels, a, e, i, o, and u. We
then compare the number of occurrences using a bar graph. This program
allows us to use characters for input data and also for printing the bar graph.
Before we discuss the solution, we develop a procedure for generating a bar
graph.

Bar graphs are frequently used to compare a set of data points. For
instance, a company with an eight-person sales staff can compare the monthly
sales in a bar graph, as shown:

We cannot draw lines such as these on the printer or on the terminal screen (unless the terminal is a graphics terminal), but we can make the bars with characters such as asterisks. We will develop a procedure to print a bar graph from a set of data. The input to the procedure is an array of numeric values. The procedure uses these values to generate and print a bar graph.

We begin by looking at a simple case. Suppose the data numbers are 1, 4, 2, 3. We could then print a bar with 1 asterisk, with 4 asterisks, and so on, generating a pattern that represents a horizontal bar graph:

If the numbers were in an array *data*, this bar graph could be printed with the following statements:

```
const
   asterisk = '*';
type
   list4 = array[1..4] of integer;
var
   data: list4;
   i, j: integer;
   .
   .
   .
   writeln;
   for i := 1 to 4 do
      begin
         for j := 1 to data[i] do
            write (asterisk);
         writeln
      end
```

The value of *data[i]* is used in the inner loop to specify how many asterisks to print for each bar. Each time through the outer loop, another value in the data array is used to specify the number of asterisks to be printed. This solution works as long as we assume that the array of data values contains integer values greater than or equal to zero. Also, the data values cannot be larger than the number of positions in our output line if we want to print the corresponding bar on a single line.

Printing bar graphs with large data values can be accomplished by scaling the data values. For instance, suppose our data values are 20, 8, 40, and 32, but we want the maximum bar length to be 20. Since 40 is the maximum value, we would print a bar with 20 asterisks; other bars would be scaled accordingly. The output would be

```
**********
****
********************
****************
```

The scale factor in the example above is the length of the maximum bar divided by the maximum data value. If the maximum value is exactly the desired length of the maximum bar, the scale factor is 1 and none of the values are changed. If the maximum data value is less than the desired length of the maximum bar, the quotient will be greater than 1 and all the values will increase proportionally. If the maximum data value is greater than the length of the maximum bar, the quotient is less than 1 and all the values will decrease proportionally. The code to perform this type of scaling follows:

```
const
    asterisk = '*';
type
    list4 = array[1..4] of integer;
var
    data: list4;
    scale: real;
    i, j, k, max: integer;
    .
    .
    .
    {Find maximum value in data array.}
    max := data[1];
    for i := 2 to 4 do
        if  max < data[i]  then
            max := data[i];
    {Compute scale factor.}
    scale := 20/max;
    {Print bar graph.}
    writeln;
    for i := 1 to 4 do
        begin
            k := round(data[i]*scale);
            for j := 1 to k do
                write (asterisk);
            writeln
        end
```

When the scale factor is multiplied by a data value to determine the number of asterisks to print, we want this result to be an integer. Therefore, we used the *round* function to round the result to an integer.

By adding two more modifications, we have a versatile bar graph routine. First we allow the data to be real values. If we want to use the procedure with an integer array, we can simply move the integer values into a real array and then reference the bar graph routine with the real array. The other modification involves the line length. The optimum line length for the maximum bar will depend on the application and on the output device being

---

used. If the output device is a line printer, we may want to use the entire line of 132 characters; if the output device is a small terminal screen, we may want to use only 30 characters.

To accommodate all these possibilities, we let a parameter *line* specify the maximum bar length, up to a maximum of 132 characters. The number of asterisks to be printed for a data value is computed with the following expression, where *line/max* is the scale factor:

```
k := round(data[i]*line/max)
```

(We look at this computation more closely in the hand-worked example.)

Before we describe the design steps, we want to mention a limitation of the routine: no negative data values are permitted. We write the routine so that a value of zero will cause a bar to be skipped, but a negative value causes the routine to be exited. If needed, the routine can be modified to handle negative values by using a technique similar to that discussed in problem 26 from Chapter 5.

PROBLEM STATEMENT

Write a procedure that prints a bar graph from a real array of *n* data values. Assume that the values will be nonnegative. A parameter *line* determines the maximum bar length.

INPUT/OUTPUT DESCRIPTION

The input to the procedure is the real array of *n* values, the value of *n*, and the maximum bar length *line*. No output parameters are passed back to the procedure.

HAND EXAMPLE

For our hand example, we use the following data values:

$$data[1] = 15.0$$
$$data[2] = 26.0$$
$$data[3] = 4.0$$
$$data[4] = 8.0$$
$$data[5] = 15.8$$

Assume that the line length is to be 30. The first step in computing the scale factor is to find the maximum data value. For our set of data, the maximum value is 26.0. The scale factor can then be computed as the maximum bar length divided by the maximum data value, or 30/26.0, which yields 1.15. We then multiply each data value by the scale factor to determine the number of asterisks to print for each bar. The result must be an integer because we cannot print part of an asterisk; therefore, we can either truncate (drop) the fractional portion or round the fractional portion to the nearest integer. In this example, we choose rounding. The results are shown in the following table:

data value	$\times$ scale factor	= bar length	$\rightarrow$ rounded
15.0	$\times$ 1.15	= 17.31	$\rightarrow$ 17
26.0	$\times$ 1.15	= 29.90	$\rightarrow$ 30
4.0	$\times$ 1.15	= 4.60	$\rightarrow$ 5
8.0	$\times$ 1.15	= 9.20	$\rightarrow$ 9
15.8	$\times$ 1.15	= 18.17	$\rightarrow$ 18

The corresponding bar graph is:

```
*****************
******************************
*****
*********
******************
```

We now summarize the previous discussions in the decomposition steps and the refinement in pseudocode.

DECOMPOSITION

Determine scale factor.
Print corresponding bars of asterisks.

REFINEMENT IN PSEUDOCODE

bargraph (data,n,line):

    determine max and min data values
    if min $<$ 0 or line $<$ 0 or line $>$ 132 then
      write error message
    else
      compute scale factor
      for each data value do
        compute number of asterisks for bar
        print bar

We now convert the pseudocode into Pascal.

```
{-----------------------------------------------------------}
procedure  bargraph (data:list; n,line:integer);
    {This procedure prints a bar graph using an array of
    positive data values and a maximum line length.}
const
    asterisk = '*';
var
    min, max, scale: real;
    i, j, k: integer;
begin {bargraph}
    {Find minimum and maximum data values.}
    min := data[1];
    max := data[1];
    for i := 2 to n do
        begin
            if  data[i] < min  then
                min := data[i];
            if  data[i] > max  then
                max := data[i]
        end;
    {Check for error conditions.}
    if  (min < 0.0) or (line < 0) or (line > 132)  then
        writeln ('BARGRAPH PARAMETERS NOT VALID')
    else
        {Scale data values and print bars.}
        begin
            scale := line/max;
            writeln;
            for i := 1 to n do
                begin
                    k := round(data[i]*scale);
                    for j := 1 to k do
                        write (asterisk);
                    writeln
                end
        end
end; {bargraph}
{-----------------------------------------------------------}
```

TESTING

A driver for testing this procedure is given here:

```
{-----------------------------------------------------------}
program  driver (input,output);
    {This program tests the bargraph procedure.}
type
    list = array[1..25] of real;
var
    line, n, i: integer;
    data: list;
{-----------------------------------------------------------}
```
bargraph procedure goes here

```
{- - - - - - - - - - - - - - - - - - - - - - - - - - - - - - - - - - - - - - - - - - - - - - -}
   begin {driver}
   writeln ('ENTER MAXIMUM BAR LENGTH (MAX 132)');
   readln (line);
   writeln ('ENTER NUMBER OF DATA VALUES (MAX 25)');
   readln (n);
   writeln ('ENTER',n:3,' POSITIVE VALUES');
   for i := 1 to n do
      read (data[i]);
   writeln ('LINE = ',line:3);
   bargraph (data,n,line)
end. {driver}
{- - - - - - - - - - - - - - - - - - - - - - - - - - - - - - - - - - - - - - - - - - - - - -}
```

The following are a few examples of output (without the input portion)
illustrating different line sizes using the data values in the hand-worked
example:

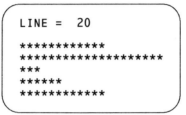

```
LINE =   10

******
*********
**
***
******
```

```
LINE =   20

************
********************
***
******
************
```

```
LINE =   30

*****************
****************************
*****
*********
******************
```

```
LINE =   40

***********************
**************************************
******
************
***********************
```

```
LINE =   50

****************************
*************************************************
********
***************
****************************
```

Can you think of ways to improve the appearance of the bar graph? How about double-row or triple-row bars instead of single-row bars? The bars could also be separated by blank lines, and headings and scales on the sides could be printed as well.

This bar graph routine is general enough to be used with many types of data but simple enough to be easily modified for specific uses. Other types of **printer plots** (ones that use the regular keyboard characters instead of a graphics plotter) are developed in the problems at the end of the chapter.

We now present a structure chart and the corresponding program that reads character strings from a data file. Each line in the data file contains a character string with a maximum length of 50 characters. Assume that the first line in the data file specifies how many lines of text follow in the file. As we read the data, we keep track of the number of occurrences of each uppercase vowel and print the numbers along with a corresponding bar graph.

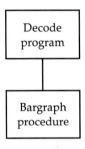

PASCAL PROGRAM

```
{- - - - - - - - - - - - - - - - - - - - - - - - - - - - - - - - - - - - - - - - - - - - - - - - - - - - -}
program   decode (secret,output);
    {This program aids in decoding a message by counting
    the number of occurrences of vowels in the message.}
type
    list = array[1..5] of real;
    list50 = array[1..50] of char;
var
    count, i, j, n, total: integer;
    secret: text;
    vowel: list;
    message: list50;
{- - - - - - - - - - - - - - - - - - - - - - - - - - - - - - - - - - - - - - - - - - - - - - - - - - - - -}
```

bargraph procedure goes here

```
{---------------------------------------------------------------}
begin {decode}
   total := 0;
   for i := 1 to 5 do
      vowel[i] := 0;
   reset (secret);
   readln (secret,n);
   for i := 1 to n do
      begin
         count := 1;
         while not eoln(secret)  do
            begin
               read (secret,message[count]);
               count := count + 1
            end;
         readln (secret);
         count := count - 1;
         total := total + count;
         for j := 1 to count do
            if  message[j] = 'A'  then
               vowel[1] = vowel[1] + 1
            else if  message[j] = 'E'  then
               vowel[2] = vowel[2] + 1
            else if  message[j] = 'I'  then
               vowel[3] = vowel[3] + 1
            else if  message[j] = 'O'  then
               vowel[4] = vowel[4] + 1
            else if  message[j] = 'U'  then
               vowel[5] = vowel[5] + 1
      end;
   writeln ('TOTAL NUMBER OF CHARACTERS = ',total:3);
   writeln;
   writeln ('OCCURRENCES OF VOWELS:');
   writeln (' A: ',vowel[1]:6:0);
   writeln (' E: ',vowel[2]:6:0);
   writeln (' I: ',vowel[3]:6:0);
   writeln (' O: ',vowel[4]:6:0);
   writeln (' U: ',vowel[5]:6:0);
   writeln;
   bargraph (vowel,5,20)
end. {decode}
{---------------------------------------------------------------}
```

```
TOTAL NUMBER OF CHARACTERS = 250

OCCURRENCES OF VOWELS:
   A:     15.
   E:     26.
   I:      4.
   O:      8.
   U:     16.


***********
*******************
***
******
***********
```

8-3 PROBLEM SOLVING—Object Manipulation

Robotics is a multidisciplinary area that involves many types of engineering. Mechanical and electrical engineering principles are used to design, build, and control a robot. Computer engineering principles are used to design the computer hardware and software interface that allows a robot to "feel" through sensors in the arms and "see" through cameras mounted on the robot. Computer simulations are used to test different aspects of robot design, such as the sequence of steps that allow a robot to manipulate an object. These steps involve defining the position of an object and then moving (or **translating**) it to another position. Write a program that will allow the user to define a two-dimensional object and to move it around on the screen using a translation operation.

In this section we develop a set of modules to define an object and then perform simple operations on the object. The types of operations we perform are the basis of a graphics package that manipulates two-dimensional objects. Before we begin defining the modules, we look at operations that we want our graphics package to contain.

First we want to be able to define a two-dimensional object. In most graphics packages, the line is the fundamental unit, so we will define our object with a set of line segments. Each line segment will be defined with a set of points. To simplify our work, we assume that the points of the object are going to be defined by row and column coordinates. For example, the arrow below is defined with the row and column coordinates shown:

Point	Row	Column
1	3	6
2	6	9
3	6	7
4	9	7
5	9	5
6	6	5
7	6	3
8	3	6

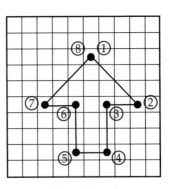

One of our modules, called *create*, will allow us to define an object by entering the row and column coordinates, as shown above. When we define the object, we also need to specify the boundaries of the grid we use to contain the object. In the example above, our grid is 10 rows by 10 columns. We will call this grid our **graphics window.** We define the object initially to be within this window, but for some of the operations defined next, the object may actually move partially or completely out of the window.

After defining an object in our graphics window, we want to draw it to be sure it was defined correctly. The *draw* module uses the arrays of row and column coordinates that defined the endpoints of the line segments to determine how to draw the line segments. Since we are assuming that we do not have a graphics terminal, we must draw the line segments by filling in characters in the approximate location of the line. For horizontal lines and vertical lines, filling in the line is straightforward. However, for other lines, we must develop an algorithm to determine which points in the window correspond to the line. The algorithm that we develop will result in the following output using our example object description. Note that the output window is outlined so that you can distinguish its boundaries.

After creating and drawing our object, we want to be able to move it using a translation, so our module is *translate*. We are not rotating or scaling the object; we are simply moving it to a new location. In our module, we assume that this translation applies to the first point of the object and that all the other points should be moved such that their positions relative to the first point are maintained. Two examples of translations of our example object are shown below, along with the defined window. Note that some translations move the object either partially or totally outside the window. Although this is a valid operation, we want our draw routine to draw only the part of the object that is within the window.

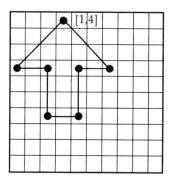
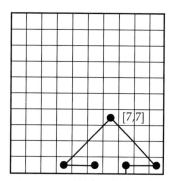

The algorithm for performing the translation is simple. We change the first point in the object definition to the new point. We then modify the other points so that they will be the same number of rows and columns from this new point as they were from the old point. Thus, the object form stays constant but it is defined in a new location.

We could add a number of other operations to this graphics software package, such as rotation, reflection, scaling, shading, and so on. A number of references on **computer graphics** are listed at the end of this section if you are interested in further study in this fascinating area.

The following is a structure chart for our software. It includes modules for creating the object, drawing the object, and translating the object. We now take each module separately and develop its Pascal solution. We also develop a program that allows the user to interact with the different modules.

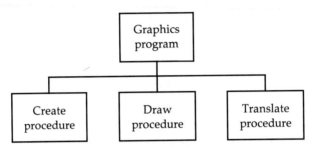

PROBLEM STATEMENT

Write a set of modules to define, draw, and translate a two-dimensional object.

INPUT/OUTPUT DESCRIPTION

Each module is listed here with its individual input and output parameters:

create no input parameters
          output parameters — arrays of row and column coordinates
                           — number of points *n*
                           — size of window, *wrow* and *wcol*

draw   input parameters — arrays of row and column coordinates
                           — number of points *n*
                           — size of window, *wrow* and *wcol*
          no output parameters

translate input parameters — arrays of row and column coordinates
                           — number of points *n*
                           — size of window, *wrow* and *wcol*
            output parameters — arrays of row and column coordinates

HAND EXAMPLE

In the initial discussion in this section, we presented an example object with eight points. We gave examples of drawing the object, translating it, and then redrawing the object. We use this example as our hand example and also as a test case after completing the software.

ALGORITHM DEVELOPMENT

Before we develop each module individually, we develop the program that will be used to interact with the modules so that you can see how they all fit together. The program will define the coordinate arrays *row* and *col*. A maximum size of 50 elements is defined for the two arrays. The program first invokes the *create* procedure. After an object has been defined by the user, the program invokes the *draw* procedure to draw the object on the screen. The program then enters a *while* loop, which allows the user to specify any of the procedures desired. The user may continue to translate the first object or create a new object and then translate it. By entering *Q* (for quit) we exit the *while* loop and the program terminates. The decomposition and refined pseudocode are shown here:

DECOMPOSITION

| Create object. |
| Draw object. |
| Perform additional operations. |

REFINEMENT IN PSEUDOCODE

graphics: create object
        action ← draw
        while not done do
           if action = create then
             create object
           else if action = draw then
             draw object
           else if action = translate then
             translate object
           write message
           read next action

We use a character code to specify the action desired: *C* for create, *D* for draw, *T* for translate, and *Q* for quit.

PASCAL PROGRAM

```
{---------------------------------------------------------------}
program  graphics (input,output);
   {This program contains a simple set of graphics routines
    for creating and manipulating a 2-dimensional object.}
type
   list50 = array[1..50] of integer;
var
   wrow, wcol, n: integer;
   code: char;
   row, col: list50;
{---------------------------------------------------------------}
               create, draw, translate procedures go here
```

```
{- - - - - - - - - - - - - - - - - - - - - - - - - - - - - - - - - - - - - - - - - - - -}
begin {graphics}
   create (n,row,col,wrow,wcol);
   code := 'D';
   while  code <> 'Q'  do
      begin
         if  code = 'C'  then
            create (n,row,col,wrow,wcol)
         else if  code = 'D'  then
            draw (n,row,col,wrow,wcol)
         else if  code = 'T'  then
            translate (n,row,col);
         writeln ('ENTER FIRST LETTER FOR DESIRED OPERATION:');
         writeln ('  CREATE, DRAW, TRANSLATE, QUIT');
         readln (code)
      end
end. {graphics}
{- - - - - - - - - - - - - - - - - - - - - - - - - - - - - - - - - - - - - - - - - - -}
```

Now that you see how the procedures work together, we develop each procedure separately.

Create The *create* procedure interacts with the user to define the window and the object within the window.

DECOMPOSITION

Write instructions.
Read window size.
Read object coordinates.

The steps in the decomposition are refined in the following pseudocode.

REFINEMENT IN PSEUDOCODE

create (n,row,col,wrow,wcol):
            write instructions
            read window size
            read number of points in object
            for each point do
                  read row and column coordinate

We now convert the refined pseudocode into Pascal.

```
{----------------------------------------------------------------------}
procedure  create (var n:integer, var row,col:list50;
                   var wrow,wcol:integer);
   {This procedure creates an object using
   row and column coordinates.}
var
   i: integer;
begin {create}
   writeln ('ENTER NUMBER OF ROWS IN WINDOW (MAX = 50)');
   readln (wrow);
   writeln ('ENTER NUMBER OF COLUMNS IN WINDOW (MAX = 50)');
   readln (wcol);
   writeln ('ENTER NUMBER OF POINTS TO DEFINE OBJECT');
   writeln ('                              (MAX = 50)');
   readln (n);
   writeln ('ROW COORDINATE MUST BE BETWEEN 1 AND ',wrow:3);
   writeln ('COLUMN COORDINATE MUST BE BETWEEN 1 AND ',
            wcol:3);
   for i := 1 to n do
      begin
         writeln ('ENTER ROW AND COLUMN COORDINATE FOR ',
                  'POINT ',i:3);
         readln (row[i],col[i])
      end
end; {create}
{----------------------------------------------------------------------}
```

Draw The *draw* procedure is the most involved of the procedures in this software package. It is not a simple process to decide which positions in the window correspond to a line drawn between two endpoints. We set up a temporary two-dimensional array called *window*. Then, for each pair of endpoints, we decide which elements of the array window correspond to the line between the endpoints and we fill those positions with asterisks. The solution that we present uses the slope of the line to determine which positions in the window array should be filled with asterisks. Since computing the slope of a vertical line requires division by zero, we handle a vertical line as a special case.

Recall that the slope of a straight line is the change in the y coordinate divided by the change in the x coordinate. Since we are using row and column coordinates, the slope is the change in row coordinates divided by the change in column coordinates.

$$\text{slope} = \frac{\text{change in row}}{\text{change in column}}$$

We can compute this slope from the two endpoints of the line segment. Assume that we begin with the leftmost point of the two points. Then, as we begin to fill in the line, we are incrementing the column number by one. The slope should remain constant, and thus the corresponding change in the row should be equal to the value of the slope.

$$\text{slope} = \frac{\text{change in row}}{\text{change in column}} = \frac{\text{slope}}{1}$$

Let's take a specific example. Assume that the endpoints of a line segment in our object are at [5,1] and [9,5]. We start at point [5,1] and increment the column number by one, so that the change in column is one. We should change the row number by the slope, which is equal to $(9 - 5)/(5 - 1)$, or $+1$. The new point is at column 2 and row 6. We increment the column to 3 and add the slope to the last row number, giving the point [7,3]. Following this procedure, we add point [8,4], and then we are at the other end point. This progression is shown in the series of steps below.

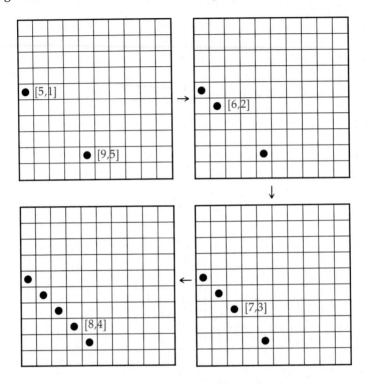

If the slope is not $+1$ or -1, the results are not as smooth. For example, consider the following case in which we wish to connect the endpoints [3,4] with [2,7]. The slope is equal to the change in row coordinates divided by the change in column coordinates, or $(2 - 3)/(7 - 4)$, or -0.33. The steps to fill in the points of this line are summarized below:

point 1   [3,4]
point 2   new column = old column + 1 = 4 + 1 = 5
          new row = old row + slope = 3 − 0.33 = 2.67 → 3
point 3   new column = old column + 1 = 5 + 1 = 6
          new row = old row + slope = 2.67 − 0.33 = 2.34 → 2
point 4   endpoint [2,7]

This process is also shown in the diagrams below:

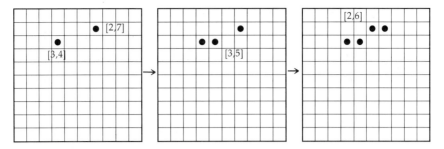

The procedure above works for both positive and negative slopes. The only special case that we need to consider occurs when the line is vertical. If we attempt to compute the slope of a vertical line, we are dividing by zero and thus will get an execution error. Therefore, we test for this case separately. For all other cases, including horizontal lines, we use the algorithm just discussed, which computes the slope. Since we start with two endpoints, we choose the point with the smallest column coordinate and work from that point to the other point. If we apply this process to the object that we defined earlier, the output on the screen is the object shown below. We have outlined the window so it is clear which part of the terminal screen corresponds to the window in which our object is defined.

We can now develop the decomposition and pseudocode for this procedure.

DECOMPOSITION

Fill window array with blanks.
Fill positions of window that correspond to the line segments.

We now refine the decomposition steps into pseudocode.

```
draw (n,row,col,wrow,wcol):
                 for each point in window array
                     fill with blank
                 for each pair of endpoints
                     if line is vertical then
                         fill corresponding window
                         positions with asterisks
                     else
                         determine corresponding window
                         positions using slope and fill
                         them with asterisks
                 print window array
```

We now convert the pseudocode to Pascal.

PASCAL PROCEDURE

```
{-----------------------------------------------------------}
procedure  draw (n:integer; row,col:list50; wrow,wcol:integer);
    {This procedure draws an object using
    coordinate arrays row and col.}
const
    asterisk = '*';
    top = '-';
    side = '|';
type
    table50x50 = array[1..50,1..50] of char;
var
    r, slope: real;
    i, j, m, r1, c1, r2, c2, c, rsub, minr, maxr: integer;
    switch: boolean;
    window: table50x50;
begin {draw}
    for i := 1 to wrow do
        for j := 1 to wcol do
            window[i,j] := ' ';
    {Set first endpoint.}
    r1 := row[1];
    c1 := col[1];
    for m := 2 to n do
        begin
            switch := false;
            {Set second endpoint.}
            r2 := row[m];
            c2 := col[m];
            {Be sure first point is leftmost.}
            if  c1 > c2  then
                begin
                    switch := true;
                    r2 := r1;
                    c2 := c1;
                    r1 := row[m];
                    c1 := col[m]
                end;
```

```
                {If vertical line, fill points between rows.}
                if  c1 = c2  then
                    begin
                        if  r1 < r2  then
                            begin
                                minr := r1;
                                maxr := r2
                            end
                        else
                            begin
                                minr := r2;
                                maxr := r1
                            end;
                        for rsub := minr to maxr do
                            if  (1 <= c1) and (c1 <= wcol) and
                                (1 <= rsub) and (rsub <= wrow)  then
                                    window[rsub,c1] := asterisk
                    end
                else
                    {If not vertical, use slope algorithm.}
                    begin
                        slope := (r2 - r1)/(c2 - c1);
                        r := r1;
                        for c := c1 to c2 do
                            begin
                                if  (1 <= c) and (c <= wcol) and
                                    (1 <= round(r)) and
                                    (round(r) <= wrow)  then
                                        window[round(r),c] := asterisk;
                                r := r + slope
                            end
                    end;
                {Set end of this line to beginning of next.}
                if  not switch  then
                    begin
                        r1 := r2;
                        c1 := c2
                    end
            end;
    {Print the contents of the window array on the screen.}
    for i := 1 to wcol+2 do
        write (top);
    writeln;
    for i := 1 to wrow do
        begin
            write (side);
            for j := 1 to wcol do
                write (window[i,j]);
            write (side);
            writeln
        end;
    for i := 1 to wcol+2 do
        write (top);
    writeln
end; {draw}
{---------------------------------------------------------------}
```

Translate In the *translate* routine, we allow the user to enter the coordinates of the point that is to be the new location of the first point in the object. Thus, this routine needs to determine the changes in row and column numbers between the old first point and the new point. We then add the changes to each pair of coordinates in the object description and the translation is finished.

DECOMPOSITION

Read coordinates of new point.
Compute changes between old point and new point.
Add changes to each point.

REFINEMENT IN PSEUDOCODE

translation (n,row,col):

> read coordinates of new point
> row change ← new row − old row
> col change ← new col − old col
> for each point do
> > new row ← old row + row change
> > new col ← old col + col change

We now convert the pseudocode to Pascal.

PASCAL PROCEDURE

```
{- - - - - - - - - - - - - - - - - - - - - - - - - - - - - - - - - - - - - - - - - - - - - - - - - -}
procedure  translate (n:integer; var row,col:list50);
   {This procedure translates the object so that the first
   point is located at the new location.}
var
   newrow, newcol, i, rchange, cchange: integer;
begin {translate}
   writeln ('ENTER THE NEW COORDINATES (ROW,COL)');
   writeln ('FOR THE FIRST POINT OF THE OBJECT');
   readln (newrow,newcol);
   rchange := newrow - row[1];
   cchange := newcol - col[1];
   for i := 1 to n do
      begin
         row[i] := row[i] + rchange;
         col[i] := col[i] + cchange
      end
end; {translate}
{- - - - - - - - - - - - - - - - - - - - - - - - - - - - - - - - - - - - - - - - - - - - - - - - - -}
```

TESTING

The object used in the hand-worked example and one of the translations that we performed on it provide our test case. The computer output from this test is shown on the next page:

```
ENTER NUMBER OF ROWS IN WINDOW (MAX = 50)
10
ENTER NUMBER OF COLUMNS IN WINDOW (MAX = 50)
10
ENTER NUMBER OF POINTS TO DEFINE OBJECT
                                 (MAX = 50)
8
ROW COORDINATE MUST BE BETWEEN 1 AND   10
COLUMN COORDINATE MUST BE BETWEEN 1 AND   10
ENTER ROW AND COLUMN COORDINATE FOR POINT   1
3 6
ENTER ROW AND COLUMN COORDINATE FOR POINT   2
6 9
ENTER ROW AND COLUMN COORDINATE FOR POINT   3
6 7
ENTER ROW AND COLUMN COORDINATE FOR POINT   4
9 7
ENTER ROW AND COLUMN COORDINATE FOR POINT   5
9 5
ENTER ROW AND COLUMN COORDINATE FOR POINT   6
6 5
ENTER ROW AND COLUMN COORDINATE FOR POINT   7
6 3
ENTER ROW AND COLUMN COORDINATE FOR POINT   8
3 6
------------
|          |
|    *     |
|   * *    |
|  *   *   |
| *** ***  |
|   * *    |
|   * *    |
|   ***    |
|          |
------------
ENTER FIRST LETTER FOR DESIRED OPERATION:
  CREATE, DRAW, TRANSLATE, QUIT
T
ENTER THE NEW COORDINATES (ROW,COL)
FOR THE FIRST POINT OF THE OBJECT
1 4
ENTER FIRST LETTER FOR DESIRED OPERATION:
  CREATE, DRAW, TRANSLATE, QUIT
D
------------
|   *      |
|  * *     |
| *   *    |
|*** ***   |
|  * *     |
|  * *     |
|  ***     |
|          |
|          |
------------
ENTER FIRST LETTER FOR DESIRED OPERATION:
  CREATE, DRAW, TRANSLATE, QUIT
Q
```

Design your own object and test the modules with it. Be sure to test the limits of each module. Examples of tests of the limits would include objects with 50 points and windows with 50 rows and columns.

The following list contains texts that will provide more detailed information on the topic of computer graphics:

1. Berger, M. *Computer Graphics with Pascal* (Menlo Park, CA: Benjamin/Cummings, 1986).
2. Demel, J. T., and M. J. Miller. *Introduction to Computer Graphics* (Monterey, CA: Brooks/Cole, 1984).
3. Foley, J. D., and A. Van Dam. *Fundamentals of Interactive Computer Graphics* (Reading, MA: Addison-Wesley, 1983).
4. Giloi, W. K. *Interactive Computer Graphics* (Englewood Cliffs, NJ: Prentice-Hall, 1978).
5. Hopgood, F. R., et al. *Introduction to the Graphical Kernal System — GKS* (New York: Academic Press, 1983).
6. Mufti, A. A. *Elementary Computer Graphics* (Reston, VA: Reston, 1983).

8-4 COMMON TECHNIQUES USED WITH CHARACTERS

Processing character information can involve many different types of operations. In this section we first present some examples of character processing as it might be applied to text material or used in word processing. Then we present a related technique for **pattern detection,** which is used when we are interested in finding specific patterns of characters in our data.

EDITING TEXT

Text processing and **word processing** refer to the processing of character information. The editor you use to build and edit your Pascal program file is an example of a sophisticated text processor. It enables you to perform steps such as deleting information, inserting information, and searching for specific characters. All these capabilities make it easy to prepare and edit files. In fact, we often forget the large number of steps that are actually performed every time we execute an edit command such as "change all occurrences of tax to taxrt." We present a couple of examples that show some of the types of steps routinely performed by editors and text processors.

EXAMPLE 8-6   Change ? to !

Give statements necessary to convert all question marks to exclamation points in a character array *string*. Assume that the number of characters in the array is contained in the variable *length*.

Solution

The solution to this problem is really a search. We sequentially search the array of characters and change any question marks to exclamation points.

```
type
    list100 = array[1..100] of char;
var
    length, i: integer;
    string: list100;
    .
    .
    .
    for i := 1 to length do
        if  string[i] = '?'  then
            string[i] := '!'
```

Assume that the value of *length* is 18 and that the string contains **WHAT? WHERE? WHEN?**. The steps below show the different values in *string* as it is processed.

VALUE OF *i*	CONTENTS OF *string*
1	WHAT? WHERE? WHEN?
.	
.	
.	
4	WHAT? WHERE? WHEN?
5	WHAT! WHERE? WHEN?
.	
.	
.	
11	WHAT! WHERE? WHEN?
12	WHAT! WHERE! WHEN?
.	
.	
.	
I7	WHAT! WHERE! WHEN?
18	WHAT! WHERE! WHEN!

EXAMPLE 8-7 Change *T* to *TH*

Give the statements necessary to convert all occurrences of *T* to *TH* in a character array called *string*. Assume that the variable *length* contains the number of characters in the string and that the changes should not affect the length of the string.

Solution

At first, this problem appears to be the same as the one that replaces ? with !. However, we now want to put two characters in the place of one character, so the rest of the characters need to be shifted one position to the right. The last character of the current character string is lost each time a new character is inserted. We give the solution and then go through it with a specific example.

```
type
    list100 = array[1..100] of char;
var
    length, i, j: integer;
    string: list100;
    .
    .
    .
for i := 1 to length-1 do
    if  string[i] = 'T'  then
        begin
            for j := length downto i+2 do
                string[j] := string[j-1];
            string[i+1] := 'H'
        end
```

Assume that *string* contains the value NOW IS THE TIME FOR and that *length* contains the integer 19. When *i* is equal to 8, the inner loop will be executed. The steps below follow the changes that occur in *string*.

Loop Indices	Contents of *string*
$i = 8$	NOW IS THE TIME FOR
$j = 19$	NOW IS THE TIME FOO
$j = 18$	NOW IS THE TIME FFO
$j = 17$	NOW IS THE TIME FO
$j = 16$	NOW IS THE TIMEE FO
$j = 15$	NOW IS THE TIMME FO
$j = 14$	NOW IS THE TIIME FO
$j = 13$	NOW IS THE TTIME FO
$j = 12$	NOW IS THE TIME FO
$j = 11$	NOW IS THEE TIME FO
$j = 10$	NOW IS THHE TIME FO

The character *H* is now placed in position 9 (note that position 9 already contained *H* in this case) and we continue the outer loop with $i = 9$. Note that the last value of *i* is $length - 1$ since this is the last position that can be followed with the letter *H*. Also note that TIME will be replaced by THIME.

PATTERN DETECTION

Typically, pattern detection involves searching for more than a single character. We are usually looking for a group of characters. We may want to count the number of occurrences or we may want to replace the pattern with a different pattern.

EXAMPLE 8-8 Count Occurrences of String *AND*

Give the statements necessary to count the number of times the characters *AND* appear in a character array called *string*. The variable *length* contains the number of elements in the character array.

Solution

Because we are looking for a group of three characters, the group cannot begin in the last or next-to-the-last positions. We must stop the *for* loop before it attempts to check these positions because otherwise our subscripts might go out of range.

```
type
    list100 = array[1..100] of char;
var
    length, count, i: integer;
    string: list100;
    .
    .
    .
    count := 0;
    for i := 1 to length-2 do
        if  string[i] = 'A'   then
            if  string[i+1] = 'N'   then
                if  string[i+2] = 'D'   then
                    count := count + 1
```

SELF-TEST 8-2

This self-test allows you to check quickly to see if you have remembered certain key points from Section 8-4. If you have any problems with the exercise, you should reread this section. The solution is included at the end of the text.

Write a complete program to read an item description that is 30 characters long. Count the number of blanks at the end of the description. Use that count so that you can print the description without the extra blanks, as shown by the following example:

`PRINTER CABLE IS THE DESCRIPTION OF THE ITEM ORDERED`

(The description might be more than one word, so blanks between words are to be printed.)

8-5 PROBLEM SOLVING — AUTHORSHIP IDENTIFICATION

Text material is sometimes analyzed carefully to determine quantities such as average word length. Such a quantity can be used to recommend the level of reading ability necessary to read the text. Average word length can even be used to help determine authorship of a literary work; it has been applied to the works of Shakespeare in an attempt to determine whether Sir Francis Bacon wrote some of the plays attributed to Shakespeare.

Write a function that receives a character array and returns the average word length of the data in the array. Assume that all words are separated from adjacent words by at least one blank. The first and last characters may or may not be blanks.

PROBLEM STATEMENT

Write a function that computes the average word length of the information stored in a character array.

INPUT/OUTPUT DESCRIPTION

The input is a character array. The output is a number that is the average word length of the input character information.

HAND EXAMPLE

Sometimes the best way to get started on a problem is to work a few cases by hand. Assume that the text for this example is 18 characters long. Then the following strings (which we have enclosed in quotation marks to show where the blanks occur) can be analyzed as follows:

'TO BE OR NOT TO BE'
> 6 words, 13 letters, 2.17 average word length

'   '
> 0 words, 0 letters, 0.0 average word length

' HELLO   '
> 1 word, 5 letters, 5.0 average word length

'IDIOSYNCRATICALLY!'
> 1 word, 18 characters, 18.0 average word length

'MR. JOHN P. BUD   '
> 4 words, 12 characters, 3.0 average word length

ALGORITHM DEVELOPMENT

From the examples done by hand, we see that the text could have no blanks or could be all blanks. The words may be separated by one or more blanks;

the text may or may not begin and end with a blank. The key part of the algorithm is to recognize words by determining where the word begins and ends.

DECOMPOSITION

| Count number of letter and words. |
| Compute average to be number of letters divided by number of words. |

We now convert the decomposition steps to pseudocode.

REFINEMENT IN PSEUDOCODE

```
wordaverage (string,n):
            words ← 0
            letters ← 0
            while more words do
                find beginning of next word
                find end of next word
                compute number of letters in word
                letters ← letters + new letters
                words ← words + 1
            if words = 0 then
                wordaverage ← 0
            else
                wordaverage ← letters/words
```

We use *words* to store the number of words and *letters* to store the number of letters. Both of these variables will be initialized to zero. Note that we are counting any nonblank character as a letter. We begin by looking through the text for the first nonblank character. If we do not find a nonblank character, we return an average word length of zero. If we do find a nonblank character, we will call the appropriate position *first.* Then we search for the first blank character following *first* and call this new position *nextblank.* If there are no blanks after first, set *nextblank* to a value one larger than the length of the character array. Then, in any case, the number of characters in the word will be *nextblank − first.* We add this value to *letters* and add 1 to *words.* We move the value of *nextblank + 1* to *first* and repeat the process until we reach the end of the array. At that point, we compute the average word length. With these steps in mind, we now convert the pseudocode to Pascal.

```
{--------------------------------------------------------}
function  wordaverage (string1:list; n:integer): real;
   {This function computes the average word length
   of character information stored in an array.}
const
   blank = ' ';
var
   first, nextblank, m, words, letters: integer;
   wordend: boolean;
begin {wordaverage}
   words := 0;
   letters := 0;
   first := 1;
   while  first <= n  do
      if  string1[first] <> blank  then
         begin
            m := first;
            wordend := false;
            while  not wordend  do
               begin
                  m := m + 1;
                  if  m > n  then
                     wordend := true
                  else
                     if  string1[m] = blank  then
                        wordend := true
               end;
            nextblank := m;
            letters := letters + (nextblank - first);
            words := words + 1;
            first := nextblank + 1
         end
      else
         first := first + 1;
   if  words = 0  then
      wordaverage := 0.0
   else
      wordaverage := letters/words
end; {wordaverage}
{--------------------------------------------------------}
```

TESTING

A driver program to test this function with the character information used in
the hand example is given next:

```
{--------------------------------------------------------}
program  driver (input,output);
   {This program tests the word average computation function.}
type
   list = array[1..18] of char;
var
   j: integer;
   string1: list;
{--------------------------------------------------------}
                   wordaverage function goes here
```

```
{- - - - - - - - - - - - - - - - - - - - - - - - - - - - - - - - - - - - - - - - - - -}
begin {driver}
   writeln ('ENTER CHARACTER INFORMATION (LENGTH = 18)');
   for j := 1 to 18 do
      read (string1[j]);
   writeln;
   writeln ('WORD AVERAGE IS ',wordaverage(string1,18):6:2)
end. {driver}
{- - - - - - - - - - - - - - - - - - - - - - - - - - - - - - - - - - - - - - - - - - -}
```

The output from one of the character strings in the hand example data is
shown here:

```
ENTER CHARACTER INFORMATION (LENGTH = 18)
TO BE OR NOT TO BE
WORD AVERAGE IS    2.17
```

Suppose we increased the length of string from 18 to 30. If the same five
examples from the hand example are used, will the word averages be
different? The answer is no, since we are adding only blanks.

8-6 PACKED CHARACTER ARRAYS

Pascal allows us to use a **packed option** when we define variables. The actual
implementation of the packing option is system-dependent, but it provides a
more efficient way of storing large amounts of information. Thus, less memory is
usually needed for packed data, but more computer time is needed when we
work with packed data. Packed data is used most often with large character
arrays. An example of a definition of a packed character array is shown below:

```
type
   list500 = packed array[1..500] of char;
var
   message: list500;
```

In addition to more efficient use of the memory, another advantage of
packed arrays is that they can be referenced as a single unit instead of one
character at a time. Thus, if we want to print a name which has been stored in a
packed array, we can use the following statements:

```
type
   list30 = packed array[1..30] of char;
var
   name: list30;
   .
   .
   .
   writeln (name)
```

Recall that to print an **unpacked array** we would need to use a *for* loop and move
each character to the output line individually. Writing packed arrays is much

simpler. Reading packed arrays must still be performed character by character, as shown in the statements below:

```
type
   list25 = packed array[1..25] of char;
var
   city: list25;
   .
   .
   .
   for i := 1 to 25 do
      read (city[i])
```

Packed arrays can also be compared as a single unit (often called a string), instead of by individual characters. The comparisons must be between arrays of the same type and length. For example, the following statements compare two names to determine if they are the same:

```
type
   list35 = packed array[1..35] of char;
var
   name1, name2: list35;
   .
   .
   .
   if  name1 = name2  then
      update (balance)
   else
      newrecord (balance)
```

To summarize, the advantages of packed arrays are the following:

1. Packed arrays provide more efficient storage of character information.
2. Packed arrays can be written or compared as single units.
3. Elements in a packed array can also be referenced as individual characters using subscripts.

Unfortunately, there are also some disadvantages to packed arrays. First, array handling takes longer because the information has to be unpacked to be used and packed again to be stored. Although we do not have to include any additional statements in the programming steps, the compiler has to add these additional steps to the program, so the compilation and the execution take longer. In most small programs, this additional time is not noticed. The main disadvantage to packing character arrays is that individual elements cannot then be used as parameters referenced by address in procedures and functions. To summarize, the disadvantages of packed arrays are the following:

1. Array operations take more time.
2. Individual elements cannot be passed as parameters referenced by address.

There are Pascal procedures for packing an unpacked array and for unpacking a packed array. You can move an array back and forth in order to use it in the

---

most advantageous form. The format of these procedures is shown below, where *u* represents an unpacked array and *p* represents a packed array.

pack(u,k,p)   This procedure packs the array *u* (starting in position *k*) into the array *p* (starting in position 1).

unpack(p,u,k)   This procedure unpacks the array *p* (starting in position 1) into the array *u* (starting in position *k*).

Most of the time we use unpacked arrays in order to avoid the steps of unpacking when we want to perform certain operations.

SUMMARY

The processing of character data plays an ever-increasing role in the analysis and presentation of information. Solutions to problems are not always numbers, so we must have the ability to handle nonnumeric information as effectively as numeric information. The character data type and its built-in functions and procedures provide the essential ingredients to write powerful text-processing algorithms.

DEBUGGING AIDS

When working with character information, echo the data after operations. You may want to print a special character just before and just after the data so that you are sure which blanks are part of your original data.

Remember that numeric characters are stored differently from numeric real or integer values. Therefore, do not attempt to perform any arithmetic with character digits.

If you are using packed arrays, be sure that any comparisons are between packed arrays of the same size. If character arrays are not packed, they can only be compared character by character. Packed arrays can be printed using the array name without subscripts, but they must be read character by character using a subscript specification.

Characters and character arrays can be used as parameters in procedures and functions. However, individual elements of packed arrays cannot be used as parameters referenced by address. You can unpack an array (using the Pascal procedure) and then use individual elements of the unpacked array as parameters to avoid this restriction.

STYLE/TECHNIQUE GUIDELINES

A programmer who is comfortable and proficient with character string manipulations will find them to be extremely useful. The ability to display information clearly and simply is valuable in communications, and the use of character strings adds a new dimension to the methods of both reading and displaying information.

Following are some guides for using character data in your programs:

1. Use character arrays of the same length where possible.
2. Use the built-in functions where feasible instead of writing your own procedures or functions.
3. Define your character constants in the constant part of your program so that they are easy to modify.
4. Take advantage of the printer-plotting routines developed in this chapter and in the problems at the end of the chapter.

KEY WORDS

ASCII code
binary string
character data
character string
collating sequence
computer graphics
EBCDIC code
lexicographic order
ordinal functions

packed arrays
pattern detection
predecessor
printer plots
successor
text processing
unpacked arrays
word processing

PROBLEMS

We begin our problem set with modifications to programs and modules developed earlier in this chapter. Give the decomposition, refined pseudocode, and Pascal statements for each problem.

The first set of problems involves modifications to the bar graph procedure, *bargraph*, given on page 380.

1. Modify the *bargraph* procedure so that it prints two lines of asterisks for each bar.
2. Modify the *bargraph* procedure so that it prints three lines of asterisks for each bar. Separate each group of three lines by a blank line.
3. Modify the *bargraph* procedure so that it has an additional parameter that is a character array of 25 elements. Print this character array as a heading before printing the bar graph.

---

4. Modify the *bargraph* procedure to allow negative values. Use the range from the smallest value to the largest value as the maximum bar size, unless the maximum bar size is greater than 50; then use a maximum size of 50. The rest of the bars should be scaled accordingly. Thus, if the range is -10 to $+10$, the maximum bar length is 21. A value of -10 should correspond to a bar with one asterisk; a value of 0 should correspond to a bar with 11 asterisks; and a value of $+10$ should correspond to a bar with 21 asterisks.

5. Modify the *bargraph* procedure so that it computes the average of the data values. In each bar, print asterisks up to the average value and print plus signs for any part of the bar that is over the average. Thus, if a data value is below average, its bar is entirely asterisks. If a data value is above average, its bar is composed of asterisks and plus signs.

This next set of problems involves modifications to the graphics program, *graphics,* and its modules, given on pages 387–94.

6. Modify the *draw* procedure so that it draws a double row of asterisks around the window.

7. Modify the *draw* procedure so that it lists the coordinates of the object after drawing it.

8. Modify the *translate* procedure so that the user can give relative movements, such as move up two rows and to the left three columns.

9. Modify the *create* procedure to draw the object after each point is entered so that the user can see what has been defined at each step.

10. Modify the *draw* procedure so that it allows the user to enter the symbol that is to be used in drawing the object. (The procedure in the text uses an asterisk to draw the object.)

For problems 11–15 modify the average word length function, *wordaverage,* given on page 402.

11. Modify the *wordaverage* function so that periods and commas are not used in the letter count.

12. Modify the *wordaverage* function so that numeric digits are not included in the letter count.

13. Modify the *wordaverage* function so that hyphenated words are counted as two words.

14. Modify the *wordaverage* function so that blanks inside quotation marks are counted as letters.

15. Modify the *wordaverage* function so that only alphabetical letters are used in the letter count.

Here are some new programs and modules to develop. Use the five-phase design process.

16. Write a complete program to read a data file *addresses* containing 50 names and addresses. The first line for each person contains the first name (10 characters), the middle name (6 characters), and the last name (21 characters). The next line in the file contains the address (25 characters), the city (10 characters), the state abbreviation (2 characters), and the zip code (5 characters). Print the information in the following label form:

First Initial. Middle Initial. Last Name
Address
City, State Zip

Skip four lines between labels. The city should not contain any blanks before the comma that follows it. A typical label might be:

```
J. D. Doe
117 Main St.
Taos, NM 87166
```

For simplicity, assume no embedded blanks in the individual data values. For example, San Jose would be entered as SanJose.

17. Write a procedure *condense* that receives a character array *in* of 50 characters and returns a character array *out*, also 50 characters, which has no adjacent blanks except at the end of the string. Thus, if the variable *in* was composed of '   HELLO   THERE' followed by blanks, the output array *out* should contain 'HELLO THERE' followed by blanks. Assume that the procedure header is the following:

```
procedure   condense (in:list50;
                      var out:list50);
```

18. Write a procedure *delete* that has a parameter list composed of a character array *string* of 100 characters and a pointer *k*. The procedure should delete the character in position *k*. The characters in the positions following the pointer should be moved one position to the left. A blank should be added at the end of *string* to keep the length of *string* consistent at 100 characters. Assume that the procedure header is the following:

```
procedure   delete (k:integer;
                    var string:list100);
```

19. Write a procedure *insert* that has a parameter list composed of a character array *string* of 100 characters, a pointer *k*, and a single character *char1*. The procedure should insert *char1* in the position pointed to by *k*. The rest of the characters should be moved one position to the right, with the last character truncated to keep the length of the string at 100 characters. Assume that the procedure header is the following:

```
procedure   insert (k:integer; char1:char;
                    var string:list100);
```

20. A data file called *cars* contains the license plate number and the number of gallons of gas that can be put into the car for each car in a certain state. The

license plate is composed of three characters followed by a space and three digits. Each line in the file contains a license number and a real number that gives the corresponding gallons of gas. The last line in the file has a license number of ZZZ 999 and is not a valid data line. Write a complete program that will help analyze the feasibility of gas rationing based on whether the license plate number is odd or even. The data to be computed and printed is the following:

```
SUM OF GAS FOR ODD CARS   XXXXX GALLONS    XX.X%
SUM OF GAS FOR EVEN CARS  XXXXX GALLONS    XX.X%
```

21. A palindrome is a word or piece of text that is spelled the same forward and backward. The word 'RADAR' is an example of a palindrome, but ' RADAR' is not a palindrome because of the unmatched blank. 'ABLE ELBA' is another palindrome. Write a Boolean function *palindrome* that receives a character array x of length 20. The function should be true if the character array is a palindrome and false otherwise. Assume that the function header is the following:

```
function  palindrome (x:list20): boolean;
```

22. Write a procedure *alpha* that receives an array of 50 lowercase letters. The procedure should alphabetize the list of letters. Assume that the function header is the following:

```
procedure  alpha (var string:list50);
```

23. Modify the procedure in the previous problem such that any duplicate letters are removed and blanks are added at the end of the array for the letters removed.

24. Write a procedure whose input is a character array of length 50. Change all punctuation marks (commas, periods, exclamations points, and question marks) to blanks. Assume that the procedure header is the following:

```
procedure  edit (var string:list50);
```

25. Write a procedure that receives a piece of text called *prose* that contains 200 characters. The procedure should print the text in lines of 30 characters each. Do not split words between two lines. Do not print any lines that are completely blank. Assume that the procedure header is the following:

```
procedure  prose (string:list200);
```

26. Write a function *consonant* that receives a character array of 100 lowercase alphabetic elements. Count the number of consonants and return that number to the main program. (It might be easiest to count the number of vowels and subtract that number from 100.) Assume that the function header is the following:

```
function  consonant (string:list100);
```

27. Write a procedure that receives an array of n real values (maximum value of n is 200) and prints a printer plot. Use an output line length of 101 characters.

Scale the line from the minimum value to the maximum value. The first line of output should be 101 periods representing the y axis. All the following lines should contain a period in the column representing x equal to 0, and the character * in the position of each data point, as shown in the following diagram:

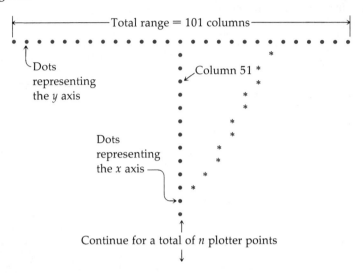

Continue for a total of n plotter points

(In this diagram, the minimum and maximum values have the same absolute value.)

Assume that the procedure has the following header:

```
procedure  plot (x:list200, n:integer);
```

28. Write a complete program that reads and stores the following two-dimensional array of characters:

```
ATIDEB
LENGTH
ECPLOT
DDUEFS
OUTPUT
CGDAER
HIRXJI
KATIMN
BHPARG
```

Now read the 11 strings listed below and find the same strings in the array above. Print the positions of characters of these hidden words that may appear forward, backward, up, down, or diagonally. For instance, the word EDIT is located in positions [1,5], [1,4], [1,3], and [1,2].

HIDDEN WORDS

PLOT	STRING
CODE	TEXT
EDIT	READ
LENGTH	GRAPH
INPUT	BAR
OUTPUT	

29. Modify the procedure of problem 25 such that the length of the output line is a parameter of the procedure. Distribute any blanks at the beginning and end of a line between words in the line so that every line begins and ends with a nonblank character. Thus, if the character string *prose* contained a portion of the Gettysburg Address and the line length is 23, the first three lines of output should be:

```
FOUR   SCORE   AND   SEVEN
YEARS AGO   OUR   FATHERS
BROUGHT FORTH UPON THIS
```

PROBLEM SOLVING — Population Data Analysis

Census data provides both historians and economists with an interesting perspective on the past. The rise and decline of the population of cities is often an accurate measure of the economy. When the economy is healthy, populations expand as new workers arrive; when the economy is faltering, populations decrease as workers and their families look elsewhere for jobs. The population rise and decline in the gold and silver mining communities of the West is particularly interesting, since many of these communities became booming cities only to collapse to virtual ghost towns in relatively short periods of time. Assume that you have files containing the population data for a mining community during the period 1850 to 1910. Write a program to determine the two consecutive years in which the population increase was the largest. (See Section 9-2 for the solution.)

9

RECORDS AND RECORD STRUCTURES

INTRODUCTION

In this chapter we present a new data structure called a **record.** The array data structure allowed us to group together items of the same type; the record data structure will allow us to group together items that may have different types. Even if we are grouping together items of the same type, we may choose the record data structure instead of an array. For example, if we have three temperature measurements from an experiment, an array is probably the best choice of data structure for these measurements; however, if we have three measurements that represent distance, velocity, and acceleration, a record may be the best choice for this data because we can group the measurements together as a unit and still indicate that they are not measurements of the same quantity.

In addition to simple records, we also learn to use record structures. There are two main types of record structures: **hierarchical records** and **arrays of records.** We present examples using both types of record structures.

9-1 SIMPLE RECORDS

In Chapter 4 we saw that the array data structure was a very powerful method for storing and accessing data. However, an array could store only one type of information; that is, we could not define an array with 50 integers followed by 50 real values. All values in an array are also referenced by the same identifier, with a subscript to specify an individual item. For some applications, though, we would like to group information together that may represent different data types. We may also want to group information together using different identifiers for items within the group. For example, if we are working with data that describes an item stored in a warehouse, this data may include a part number (integer), a part description (10 characters), the number of parts on hand (integer), and the cost of a single part (real). These four pieces of information cannot be stored in an array because they are not all the same data type, but they can be stored together as a record. Each piece of information will have a common name (similar to an array name), but instead of a subscript to identify the specific item, each item will also have its own identifier. This is best illustrated with an example. The following part description defines the data structure we have just discussed.

```
type
   inventory = record
                  number: integer;
                  description: array[1..10] of char;
                  quantity: integer;
                  price: real
               end;
var
   part: inventory;
```

A diagram of this data structure is shown below, with sample values:

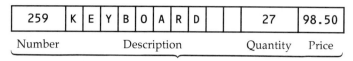

259	K	E	Y	B	O	A	R	D			27	98.50

Number · · · · · · · Description · · · · · Quantity · Price

Part record

The identifier used for an individual item in the record definition is called a **field identifier.** To reference individual items in a record, we use the record name followed by a period and the field identifier. Thus, to refer to the price within the *part* record, we use the identifier *part.price*, which is composed of the record name (*part*) and the field identifier (*price*) separated by a period. If we assume that the *part* record contains data, the following statements refer to various items within that record:

```
total := total + part.quantity

part.quantity := part.quantity - sold

if  part.number = 299   then
    for i :=\ 1 to 10 do
        write (part.description[i])
```

RECORD DEFINITION

A record can be defined in a type statement or in the variable definition portion of a Pascal program. In either case, the record is assigned a name, and then its fields or components are defined in the order in which they are to be stored. The syntax diagram for a record description follows.

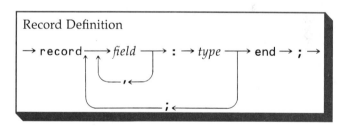

Record Definition

→ record ── → field ── : → type ── end → ; →

The following examples illustrate the use of the record data structure.

EXAMPLE 9-1   Student Record

Give the type definition for a student record that will include a student number (integer), the student name (30 characters), the student classification (2 characters), and the student grade point average (real).

Solution

Each record contains four components: student number, name, classification (FR, SO, JR, SR), and grade point average.

```
type
   data = record
              number: integer;
              name: array[1..30] of char;
              class: array[1..2] of char;
              gpa: real
           end;
var
   student: data;
```

EXAMPLE 9-2   Print Student Name and Grade Point Average

Give the statements necessary to print the student name and grade point average, assuming that the information has already been stored in the record defined in Example 9-1.

Solution

We print the student name and grade point average on the same line as shown in the following statements:

```
writeln;
for i := 1 to 30 do
   write (student.name[i]);
writeln ('   GPA:',student.gpa:6:2)
```

EXAMPLE 9-3   Print Student Number

Give the statements necessary to print the student number if the student classification is FR (freshman), again using the record definition from Example 9-1.

Solution

Because the classification is a character variable with two elements, we need to compare the two characters separately.

```
if (student.class[1] = 'F') and
   (student.class[2] = 'R')   then
      writeln ('FRESHMAN: ',student.number:5)
```

EXAMPLE 9-4   Read Record Information

Give the statements necessary to read information from the terminal into the record definition from Example 9-1.

Solution

We print a message to the user specifying the information to be entered, and then go to the next line for the user to enter the information.

```
writeln ('ENTER STUDENT NUMBER');
readln (student.number);
writeln ('ENTER STUDENT NAME (30 CHARACTERS)');
writeln ('(FILL WITH BLANKS IF NECESSARY)');
for i := 1 to 30 do
    read (student.name[i]);
readln;
writeln ('ENTER STUDENT CLASS (2 CHARACTERS)');
writeln ('(FR, SO, JR, SR)');
readln (student.class[1],student.class[2]);
writeln ('ENTER STUDENT GPA');
readln (student.gpa)
```

WITH STATEMENT

In the previous examples, the field identifiers clearly specified the items in the record we wished to use, because the identifier included the record name along with the individual field name. A unique record name is necessary because programs may contain several records; but the field identifiers are not required to be unique. Thus, a program may contain records named *student, faculty,* and *staff,* and each record may contain a field called *name.* To refer to a specific name, we use *student.name, faculty.name,* or *staff.name.* Occasionally, the use of the complete field identifier becomes tedious when several references are made to the items within a record in a single statement or block of statements. In these cases, the *with* statement is useful. The syntax diagram of the *with* statement is shown below:

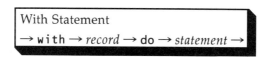

With Statement

→ **with** → *record* → **do** → *statement* →

    The purpose of the *with* statement is to specify the record name that is to be used for field identifiers without a record name. The scope of the *with* statement is only one statement, but that statement can be a compound statement. To illustrate the use of this statement, we repeat the previous examples using the *with* statement in our solutions.

EXAMPLE 9-5   Print Student Name and Grade Point Average

Give the statements necessary to print the student name and grade point average, assuming that the information has already been stored in the record defined in Example 9-1. Use the *with* statement in your solution.

Solution

```
with student do
    begin
        writeln;
        for i := 1 to 30 do
            write (name[i]);
        writeln (' GPA:',gpa:6:2)
    end
```

EXAMPLE 9-6   Print Student Number

Give the statements necessary to print the student number if the student classification is FR (freshman), again using the record definition from Example 9-1. Use the *with* statement in your solution.

Solution

```
with student do
    if (class[1] = 'F') and (class[2] = 'R')  then
        writeln ('FRESHMAN: ',number:5)
```

EXAMPLE 9-7   Read Record Information

Give the statements necessary to read information from the terminal into the record definition from Example 9-1. Use the *with* statement in your solution.

Solution

```
with student do
    begin
        writeln ('ENTER STUDENT NUMBER');
        readln (number);
        writeln ('ENTER STUDENT NAME (30 CHARACTERS)');
        writeln ('(FILL WITH BLANKS IF NECESSARY)');
        for i := 1 to 30 do
            read (name[i]);
        readln;
        writeln ('ENTER STUDENT CLASS (2 CHARACTERS)');
        writeln ('(FR, SO, JR, SR)');
        readln (class[1],class[2]);
        writeln ('ENTER STUDENT GPA');
        readln (gpa)
    end
```

If a statement or block of statements refers to fields in several records, the *with* statement has limited value because the complete field identifier must be used for all records other than the one listed in the *with* statement. In these cases, the best approach is to use the complete field identifier for each reference and omit the *with* statement.

This self-test allows you to check quickly to see if you have remembered certain key points from Section 9-1. If you have any problems with the exercise, you should reread this section. The solution is included at the end of the text.

Assume that the following record has been defined and filled with data:

```
type
    book = record
               title: array[1..30] of char;
               author: array[1..15] of char;
               year: integer;
               price: real
           end;
var
    fiction: book;
```

Give the statements necessary to print the title on one line, followed on the next line by the author, year, and price in the form below:

```
DRAGONSONG
BY MCCAFFREY          1976     $  3.95
```

9-2 PROBLEM SOLVING—POPULATION DATA ANALYSIS

Census data provides both historians and economists with an interesting perspective on the past. The rise and decline of the population of cities is often an accurate measure of the economy. When the economy is healthy, populations expand as new workers arrive; when the economy is faltering, populations decrease as workers and their families look elsewhere for jobs. The population rise and decline in the gold and silver mining communities of the West is particularly interesting, since many of these communities became booming cities only to collapse to virtual ghost towns in relatively short periods of time.

Assume that you have a data file *census* that contains the population data for a mining community during the period 1850 to 1910. Each line of the data file contains a year and the corresponding population. The data lines are in ascending order by year. Write a program to read the data and determine the two consecutive years in which the percentage increase in population was the greatest.

Find the two consecutive years in which the percentage increase in population was the greatest for the mining community.

INPUT/OUTPUT DESCRIPTION

The input is a data file with 61 lines. Each line contains a year and its corresponding population. The data is in ascending order by year. The output is the two consecutive years with the largest percentage increase in population.

HAND EXAMPLE

First we look at some typical data and compute the percentage increase in the data for each year to be sure we understand the computations involved.

YEAR	POPULATION	PERCENTAGE INCREASE
1850	82	-32% [(56 - 82)/82*100]
1851	56	27% [(71 - 56)/56*100]
1852	71	21% [(86 - 71)/71*100]
1853	86	19% [(102 - 86)/86*100]
1854	102	

During the years listed, the largest percentage increase was from 1851 to 1852. Note that this was not the largest increase in actual population, which occurred from 1853 to 1854.

ALGORITHM DEVELOPMENT

The decomposition for this problem solution is:

DECOMPOSITION

Read data and determine years with largest percentage increase.
Print result.

To compute the change in population from one year to the next, we need the previous year (old value) and the following year (new value). Thus, as we refine the decomposition, we need to read the first value (old value) outside the loop so that we can read the following year (new value) and compute the change within the loop. We execute the steps within this loop 60 times.

Initial Refinement in Pseudocode

```
analysis: read first set of data
         previous best ← 0
         for year = 1 to 60 do
             read next set of data
             compute percentage increase in population
             if new increase > previous best or year = 1 then
                 year of increase ← current year
                 best increase ← new increase
         print year of increase and its previous year
```

We need not only the information on the current line but also the information on the previous line to compute the population increase. Each line contains a year and a population. We will define a simple structure composed of a year and a population. Then we will use it to store the current information and the information from the previous line. In addition, we need to store the year in which there was the greatest percentage increase and the percentage increase itself. Note that in the final pseudocode we are initially setting the first pair of years as the ones with the greatest percentage increase. Each time through the loop, we compare this increase with the current increase; if the current increase is higher, this value is stored in *bestpercent* and the corresponding year is stored in *bestyear*.

Final Refinement in Pseudocode

```
analysis: read oldyear, oldpopulation
         bestpercent ← 0
         for i = 1 to 60 do
             read newyear, newpopulation
             percent ← (newpopulation − oldpopulation)/
                       oldpopulation*100.0
             if percent > bestpercent or i = 1 then
                 bestpercent ← percent
                 bestyear ← newyear
             oldyear ← newyear
             oldpopulation ← newpopultion
         year1 ← bestyear − 1
         year2 ← bestyear
         write year1, year2
```

We now convert the pseudocode into Pascal.

```
{-----------------------------------------------------------}
program  analysis (census,output);
    {This program reads 61 population values and determines
    the years of greatest percentage increase in population.}
type
    censusdata = record
                      year, population: integer
                 end;
var
    percent, bestpercent: real;
    i, year1, year2, bestyear: integer;
    census: text;
    old, new: censusdata;
begin {analysis}
    reset (census);
    readln (census,old.year,old.population);
    bestpercent := 0.0;
    for i := 1 to 60 do
        begin
            readln (census,new.year,new.population);
            percent := (new.population - old.population)*
                        100.0/old.population;
            if (percent > bestpercent) or (i = 1)   then
                begin
                    bestpercent := percent;
                    bestyear := new.year
                end;
            old.year := new.year;
            old.population := new.population
        end;
    year1 := bestyear - 1;
    year2 := bestyear;
    writeln ('GREATEST PERCENT INCREASE OCCURRED BETWEEN ',
             year1:4,' AND ',year2:4)
end. {analysis}
{-----------------------------------------------------------}
```

TESTING

We will not print a data file here with 61 sets of data values, but a sample output from this program is:

```
GREATEST PERCENT INCREASE OCCURRED BETWEEN 1890 AND 1891
```

If you want to test this program with a smaller data file, you can easily change the final value in the *for* loop statement to a smaller number. For example, if you build a test file with 10 sets of data, change the *for* loop statement to:

```
for i := 1 to 9 do
```

(The final value of 9 was used instead of 10 because we read one set of data before we enter the *for* loop).

In this program we updated *bestpercent* when the current percent was greater than *bestpercent*, or when *i* was equal to 1. Why is it necessary to include the case for *i* equal to 1? Because we need to initialize *bestpercent* to the first percent increase, and we won't know that value until we have read the second set of data and have computed the percentage increase. The initialization of *bestpercent* to zero was done so that the test comparing *percent* to *bestpercent* would not use a variable that had not been given a value the first time through the *for* loop.

9-3   RECORD STRUCTURES

In the previous sections we have seen a number of examples in which the record data structure was used to store information. These examples used the record as a structure that defined a group of variables within a common unit. This unit, or record, can also be used to build more complex structures. In this section we discuss **hierarchical records** (records within records) and **arrays of records.** Before we present these record structures individually, we want to remind you that the data should fit the structure you use. If you find it difficult to mold your data into a particular structure, then it probably should not be stored in that data structure. One of the unique features of Pascal is the wide variety of data structures it allows you to use. It is very likely that your data will fit one of these structures naturally; otherwise, you lose the simplicity that is characteristic of structured programs. Remember that a good program does not arbitrarily use complex features. A good program is one that is simple to follow and understand and that uses the complex features of a language only when they are warranted.

HIERARCHICAL RECORDS

Hierarchical records are formed by defining records within records. A hierarchical record is a grouping of data that has subgroupings of data within it. Probably one of the simplest examples of a hierarchical record is one that includes several dates. For example, an employee record might include a birth date, the date the employee was hired, and the date the employee was last promoted. A student record might include a birth date, the date the student graduated from high school, the date the student started undergraduate school, and the anticipated date of graduation from college. Each of these dates can be considered a record in itself that has three components, a month, a day, and a year. For example, the following statements define a student record with two dates within it:

```
type
   date = record
               month, day, year: integer
            end;
   background = record
                    name: array[1..20] of char;
                    birthdate, hsgrad: date;
                    major: array[1..5] of char;
                    gpa: real
                  end;
var
   student: background;
```

When referencing items within a hierarchical record, use the identifiers beginning with the outermost record. For example, the birth year in the student record defined above could be printed with the following statement:

```
writeln ('YEAR OF BIRTH IS ',student.birthdate.year:2)
```

Nested *with* statements may be useful to reference items in a hierarchical record. For example, the following statements print the student birthdate from the student record defined above:

```
with student do
   with birthdate do
      writeln (month:2,'-',day:2,'-',year:2)
```

EXAMPLE 9-8 Observation Record

Give the statements to define a record that will be used to store observation data collected at different traffic intersections. Each observation will contain a date in month-day-year form, an intersection identification (integer), the beginning time and ending time for the observation (24-hour time), and the number of cars that pass through the intersection. Use a hierarchical record definition with subrecords for the date and the time.

Solution

```
type
   date = record
               month, day, year: integer
            end;
   time = record
               hour, minute: integer
            end;
   traffic = record
                 datein: date;
                 id: integer;
                 begtime, endtime: time
               end;
var
   observation: traffic;
```

If information is to be read from the terminal or from a data file, the data must have blanks separating the individual parts, unless we are reading character information. For example, if we want to read values for *begtime* in the record definition in Example 9-8, the *hour* value and the *minute* value should be separated by at least one blank so that the two components can be identified separately. A statement that could be used to read *begtime* is:

```
readln (observation.begtime.hour,
        observation.begtime.minute)
```

While the use of the *with* statement would make this more readable, you can see that the identifiers accompanying a hierarchical record definition can become rather long.

ARRAYS OF RECORDS

When we need to keep a large number of pieces of similar information available to our programs, we often choose the array data structure. The elements of the array occasionally may have components themselves. When the components are similar, a multidimensional array may be the data structure to use. However, if the components are of different types or represent different quantities, an array of records may be the most logical data structure to choose. For example, suppose we have 100 measurements of time, distance, velocity, and acceleration from the flight test of a rocket. We want to have all the information available for the variety of calculations that are to be performed. An array of records will provide a good choice for the data structure. It can be defined as follows:

```
type
   data = record
               time, distance, velocity, acceleration: real
           end;
   measurements = array[1..100] of data;
var
   flight: measurements;
```

To reference a component of a record within an array, we must use the array name, the array subscript, and the field identifier. The order is easy to remember if you start from outside the data structure and work your way to the component you want. The array name and subscript specify the individual record definition; the field identifier specifies the component within the record.

EXAMPLE 9-9 Rocket Flight Data

Using the array of records defined above, give statements that would read the information for the flight array from a data file *rocket*. Assume that each line of the data file contains four numbers representing the time, distance, velocity, and acceleration values.

Solution 1

```
for i := 1 to 100 do
   with flight[i] do
        readln (rocket,time,distance,velocity,
                acceleration)
```

Solution 2:

Without the *with* statement, the solution is:

```
for i := 1 to 100 do
    readln (rocket,flight[i].time,
              flight[i].distance,flight[i].velocity,
              flight[i].acceleration)
```

SELF-TEST 9-2

This self-test allows you to check quickly to see if you have remembered certain key points from Section 9-3. If you have any problems with the exercise, you should reread this section. The solution is included at the end of the text.

Assume that a record type has been defined and then used to define an array of records as shown in the following statements:

```
type
    book = record
               title: array[1..30] of char;
               author: array[1..15] of char;
               year: integer;
               price: real
           end;
var
    library: array[1..100] of book;
```

Assume that the array has been filled with information on 100 books. Give the statements to count and print the number of books published in 1985.

9-4 PROBLEM SOLVING—INSTRUMENT USAGE LOG

The problem we consider in this section involves a large research laboratory. A number of research groups work on different problems but share the same set of instruments for field experiments. After a group runs a field experiment, the equipment and various pieces of instrumentation are returned to the technicians who maintain and store them until they are needed again. It is important that instrument usage logs be kept showing which pieces of equipment were used in each field test. If a field test must be repeated, it is then possible to use exactly the same pieces of equipment again. If the results of a field test seem incorrect, it is also possible to recheck the individual pieces of equipment and instruments to see if one of them is not working properly.

The instrument log information is kept in a data file, stored in ascending order by serial number. For example, if the laboratory has four portable oscilloscopes, each one has a different serial number. There may be several entries for a specific piece of equipment or instrumentation. The multiple entries are ordered so that the most recent returns are first. A trailer line contains a serial number of 9999.

The usage data for each week is sorted into the proper order and then **merged** with the instrument log information. The program we develop in this section will merge the two files into a new updated file. Assume that the information for each usage of a piece of equipment contains the following information:

> serial number (integer)
> date borrowed (3 integers, mo-da-yr)
> date returned (3 integers, mo-da-yr)
> group code (integer)

The serial number identifies the piece of equipment. The date borrowed and date returned indicate the period of use, and the group code identifies the research group performing the field test.

PROBLEM STATEMENT

Write a program to merge two data files.

INPUT/OUTPUT DESCRIPTION

The two input files are already sorted in ascending order by serial number. For multiple uses of a piece of equipment, the information is in descending order by date returned. The output file will contain the merged information from the two input files.

For a hand example, we use the following data for the instrumentation usage file and its update information:

INSTRUMENTATION USAGE FILE

SERIAL NUMBER	DATE BORROWED	DATE RETURNED	GROUP CODE
1253	01 13 87	02 09 87	142
1253	10 20 86	01 12 87	218
1539	01 20 87	01 23 87	317
1885	01 14 87	01 15 87	142
3119	12 02 86	02 10 87	819

UPDATE INFORMATION

SERIAL NUMBER	DATE BORROWED	DATE RETURNED	GROUP CODE
1253	02 16 87	02 18 87	142
1253	02 10 87	02 15 87	218
1885	01 19 87	02 18 87	142
3139	02 02 87	02 19 87	819

The instrumentation file is also the **master file** for this application. It is being merged with information from another file. After merging the two files, we have a new master file. For the data above, the new master file contains the following data:

UPDATED INSTRUMENTATION USAGE

SERIAL NUMBER	DATE BORROWED	DATE RETURNED	GROUP CODE
1253	02 16 87	02 18 87	142
1253	02 10 87	02 15 87	218
1253	01 13 87	02 09 87	142
1253	10 20 86	01 12 87	218
1539	01 20 87	01 23 87	317
1885	01 19 87	02 18 87	142
1885	01 14 87	01 15 87	142
3119	12 02 86	02 10 87	819
3139	02 02 87	02 19 87	819

ALGORITHM DEVELOPMENT

Several operations are commonly encountered as we process data. For instance, we have seen a number of applications that use sorting algorithms. Other operations frequently used include: finding the minimum or maximum value in a set of data, computing the average value in a set of data, inserting or deleting values in a list, and searching for a value in a list. The **merge operation** that we are using in this problem solution is another operation commonly encountered. Therefore, we consider the development of an algorithm for a merge independent of this specific problem. After developing a general merge algorithm, we return to this specific problem.

Assume that we have two lists, a and b, both sorted into the same order. We want to merge the information in these two lists into a third list, c, which preserves the order. For now, assume that the lists contain only a single number and that the numbers are in ascending order, as shown:

List a		List b	
1		7	
5		15	
8		19	
25		106	
92			

If these lists are merged into a list c, the result is:

List c	
1	
5	
7	
8	
15	
19	
25	
92	
106	

Note that list c is larger than either list a or list b; in fact, if list a contains n elements and list b contains m elements, list c should contain n+m elements.

The decomposition for the merge process consists of a single step:

DECOMPOSITION

> Merge two lists into a new list.

We now develop the detailed steps for the algorithm for merging two lists. One algorithm might be to move one list (with m elements) into the first part of a larger array with m + n elements, and then move the other array (with n elements) into the last part of the larger array. We could sort the large array and have the data items in the desired order. This idea could be extended to three or more lists. However, there are two reasons why this is not a good algorithm: It is inefficient because each individual list is already sorted; and it requires that all the data to be merged reside in memory at one time, which is impractical with large files.

If we reexamine the example with the lists above, we see that we need only the next value on each list to determine which data should be moved to the merged list. The data with the smaller number is moved to the merged list, and the next value in that list is considered. A trailer signal simplifies the algorithm's logic development because we do not need to worry about what to do when we reach the end of a list while there is data still left in the other list. When we read a trailer value that is larger than the other valid data, the rest of the values in the other list are moved to the merged list until we are positioned at the trailer signal of both lists. We then write a trailer signal to the merged list.

Let's try some simple data with this algorithm. Assume that we want to merge file 1 and file 2. Both files contain a trailer signal, 999. The arrows point to the current information (the one we have just read for the input files or the one we have just written for the output files).

File 1	File 2	Output File
→ 5	→ 2	
10	51	
82	999	
107		
999		

File 1	File 2	Output File
→ 5	2	→ 2
10	→ 51	
82	999	
107		
999		

File 1	File 2	Output File
5	2	2
→ 10	→ 51	→ 5
82	999	
107		
999		

File 1	File 2	Output File
5	2	2
10	→ 51	5
→ 82	999	→ 10
107		
999		

File 1	File 2	Output File
5	2	2
10	51	5
→ 82	→999	10
107		→ 51
999		

File 1	File 2	Output File
5	2	2
10	51	5
82	→999	10
→107		51
999		→ 82

File 1	File 2	Output File
5	2	2
10	51	5
82	→999	10
107		51
→999		82
		→107

File 1	File 2	Output File
5	2	2
10	51	5
82	→999	10
107		51
→999		82
		107
		→999

We now develop the pseudocode for this algorithm.

REFINED PSEUDOCODE FOR MERGE

merge: read first data in both files
       while more data do
          write information from file with smaller code
          read new information from file with smaller code
          write trailer signal

We now return to the instrumentation usage problem and incorporate the steps for the merge in our solution.

```
logs: read master information
      read update information
      while more data do
          if update serial < master serial then
              write update information
              read new update information
          if update serial > master serial then
              write master information
              read new update information
          if update serial = master serial then
              if master return date ≤ update return date then
                  write update information
                  read new update information
              else
                  write master information
                  read new update information
      write trailer signal
```

We use a logical variable *done* to determine when we have reached the trailer signals in both files. To avoid repeating some steps, we use another logical variable to determine which file contains the information to be written to the output file.

When the serial number in the master file matches the serial number in the update file, we must check the return date in order to determine which information should be written to the output file first. Checking the date involves first checking the year, then checking the month, and then checking the day. These checks get long, so a better solution is to compute an integer that contains the year, month, and day; that is, combine the three values in one, as in 870213, which is a combination of year 87, month 02, and day 13. Then we can compare the two combined integers in one comparison. However, if you are using a personal computer or small computer, your computer may limit integers to values less than 32,768. In these cases, the individual comparisons for year, month, and day should be used.

We now convert the pseudocode to Pascal.

PASCAL PROGRAM

```
{------------------------------------------------------------------}
program  logs (oldlog,updates,newlog,output);
   {This program merges the instrumentation log data with
   new update information to give a new master file.}
type
   date = record
             mo, da, yr: integer
          end;
   logdata = record
                serial: integer;
                out, indate: date;
                group: integer
             end;
```

```
var
   masterdate, updatedate: integer;
   done, masterout: boolean;
   oldlog, updates, newlog: text;
   master, update: logdata;
begin {logs}
   reset (oldlog);
   reset (updates);
   rewrite (newlog);
   with master do
      readln (oldlog,serial,out.mo,out.da,out.yr,
              indate.mo,indate.da,indate.yr,group);
   with update do
      readln (updates,serial,out.mo,out.da,out.yr,
              indate.mo,indate.da,indate.yr,group);
   if (master.serial = 9999) and (update.serial = 9999)  then
      done := true
   else
      done := false;
   while  not done  do
      begin
         if  update.serial < master.serial  then
            masterout := false;
         if  update.serial > master.serial  then
            masterout := true;
         if  update.serial = master.serial  then
            begin
               with master do
                  masterdate := indate.yr*10000 +
                                indate.mo*100 + indate.da;
               with update do
                  updatedate := indate.yr*10000 +
                                indate.mo*100 + indate.da;
               if  masterdate <= updatedate  then
                  masterout := false
               else
                  masterout := true
            end;
         if  masterout  then
            with master do
               begin
                  writeln (newlog,serial,out.mo,out.da,out.yr,
                           indate.mo,indate.da,indate.yr,group);
                  readln (oldlog,serial,out.mo,out.da,out.yr,
                          indate.mo,indate.da,indate.yr,group)
               end
         else
            with update do
               begin
                  writeln (newlog,serial,out.mo,out.da,out.yr,
                           indate.mo,indate.da,indate.yr,group);
                  readln (updates,serial,out.mo,out.da,out.yr,
                          indate.mo,indate.da,indate.yr,group)
               end;
         if  (master.serial = 9999) and
             (update.serial = 9999)  then
            done := true
      end;
   with master do
      writeln (newlog,serial,out.mo,out.da,out.yr,
               indate.mo,indate.da,indate.yr,group)
end. {logs}
{---------------------------------------------------------------}
```

In this solution we used records within records to represent the two different dates within the log information. The *with* statement was also useful in reducing the length of the variable names in several of the statements.

TESTING

The data files below represent the data from the hand example. Notice that the trailer lines contain zeros for the fields other than serial number. The dates are grouped together for readability, but the spacing between values will depend on the computer system used to generate the files.

Data File *oldlog*

1253	1	13	87	2	9	87	142
1253	10	20	86	1	12	87	218
1539	1	20	87	1	23	87	317
1885	1	14	87	1	15	87	142
3119	12	2	86	2	10	87	819
9999	0	0	0	0	0	0	0

Data File *updates*

1253	2	16	87	2	18	87	142
1253	2	10	87	2	15	87	218
1885	1	19	87	2	18	87	142
3139	2	2	87	2	19	87	819
9999	0	0	0	0	0	0	0

Data File *newlog*

1253	2	16	87	2	18	87	142
1253	2	10	87	2	15	87	218
1253	1	13	87	2	9	87	142
1253	10	20	86	1	12	87	218
1539	1	20	87	1	23	87	317
1885	1	19	87	2	18	87	142
1885	1	14	87	1	15	87	142
3119	12	2	86	2	10	87	819
3139	2	2	87	2	19	87	819
9999	0	0	0	0	0	0	0

This program is not completely tested with the above set of data. You should test it with data that requires merges between two sets of information for the same serial number; data with the same serial number and the same return date; and with one of the data files containing only the trailer record.

Suppose the two input data files contained only the trailer line. Would the program work properly? Yes, it would generate an output file with only a trailer line.

We assume that a merge of two files is always sufficient. If you have three files to merge, merge two of them, and then merge the combined file with the third file. If you have more than three files, continue merging two at a time until you have combined them all.

9-5   PROBLEM SOLVING—COMPUTER INVENTORY UPDATE

In this application, we develop a program to update an inventory file for a computer equipment warehouse. Each line of the inventory file contains the following information:

Stock number	Quantity	Unit price

Stock number is a numeric value that can range from 001 to 500. Quantity is the number of units of equipment that are stored in the warehouse. Unit price is the price of one item and is a real value. The number of items in the inventory file will never exceed 500, since the maximum stock number is 500. The last valid data in the file *inventory* is followed by a trailer line with a stock number 999. The items in the inventory file are ordered by stock number.

The file we use to update the inventory file is a **transaction file** called *update1*, which contains information on items received and shipped out. The order of the transactions is the order in which they occurred. The transaction record consists of a stock number and a quantity. If the quantity is positive, the transaction represents items received; if the quantity is negative, the transaction represents equipment shipped out of the warehouse.

Write a program to update the computer equipment inventory file using the transaction file. (Note that we are not adding new information to the inventory file; we are only updating information currently in the inventory file.)

PROBLEM STATEMENT

Write a program to update the quantity in an inventory file.

INPUT/OUTPUT DESCRIPTION

The input to the program is two files: the master inventory file and the transaction file. The output is an updated master inventory file.

Assume that the two files contain the following computer equipment information:

MASTER INVENTORY FILE

STOCK NUMBER	QUANTITY	UNIT PRICE
101	10	586.92
112	5	85.00
203	3	299.50
204	12	24.95

TRANSACTION FILE

STOCK NUMBER	QUANTITY
101	-2
203	-1
112	8
101	15
101	-2
112	-2

After the update, the master inventory file should be updated to contain the following information:

MASTER INVENTORY FILE

STOCK NUMBER	QUANTITY	UNIT PRICE
101	21	586.92
112	11	85.00
203	2	299.50
204	12	24.95

ALGORITHM DEVELOPMENT

The decomposition of this algorithm is a single step, as shown here:

DECOMPOSITION

Read transaction records and update master file.

As we consider algorithms for this problem solution, we could try sorting the transaction file before updating. However, since the master file is relatively small (a maximum of 500 items), we will read the information from the master file into an array and perform the updates from the transaction file in the order in which they occur. We then write the updated information back to the data file. In the initial refinement in the following pseudocode, we continue to execute the steps in a *while* loop as long as there are transactions to process.

Initial Refinement in Pseudocode

update: read master information into array
    while more transactions do
        read transaction record
        update quantity
        write updated inventory to the file

In further refining the solution, we add an error routine to print a message on the terminal screen if a match cannot be found between the inventory stock number and the transaction stock number.

Final Refinement in Pseudocode

update: read master inventory data into array
    while more transactions do
        read stock number, quantity
        if match in master array then
            update quantity
        else
            print error message
        write master inventory data to file

We now convert the pseudocode to Pascal.

Pascal Program

```
{------------------------------------------------------------}
program  update (update1,inventory,output);
   {This program updates the quantity in an inventory file.}
type
   data = record
            stocknumber, quantity: integer;
            price: real
          end;
   table = array[1..500] of data;
var
   i, count, newstock, newchange: integer;
   done, found: boolean;
   update1, inventory: text;
   item: table;
begin {update}
   reset (inventory);
   i := 1;
   done := false;
   while  not done  do
      with item[i] do
         begin
            readln (inventory,stocknumber,quantity,price);
            i := i + 1;
            if  stocknumber = 999  then
               done := true
         end;
   count := i - 1;
   reset (update1);
```

continued

```
    while  not eof(update1)  do
        begin
            readln (update1,newstock,newchange);
            i := 1;
            done := false;
            found := false;
            while  not done  do
                with item[i] do
                    begin
                        if  newstock = stocknumber   then
                            begin
                                quantity := quantity + newchange;
                                done := true;
                                found := true
                            end
                        else if  newstock < stocknumber   then
                            done := true
                        else
                            begin
                                i := i + 1;
                                if  i > count  then
                                    done := true
                            end
                    end;
            if  not found  then
                writeln ('NO MATCH FOR ',newstock:3)
        end;
    rewrite (inventory);
    for i := 1 to count do
        with item[i] do
            writeln (inventory,stocknumber,quantity,price:8:2)
end. {update}
{-----------------------------------------------------------------}
```

TESTING

The following data files represent the data from the hand example. Note that we used a format in the output statement; otherwise, the amount would be written in the file with an exponential format, and it would be more difficult to interpret visually. Also, note that the trailer lines contain zeros for the fields other than stock numbers.

Data File *inventory*

101	10	586.92
112	5	85.00
203	3	299.50
204	12	24.95
999	0	0.0

Data File *update1*

```
101  -2
203  -1
112   8
101  15
101  -2
112  -2
```

Updated File *inventory*

```
101  21  586.92
112  11   85.00
203   2  299.50
204  12   24.95
999   0    0.0
```

This program is not completely tested with the previous set of test data. For example, there are no transactions with stock numbers that are not in the master inventory file.

There is no trailer signal at the end of the transaction file. What would happen if you mistakenly added one? The trailer signal should be handled as a transaction with no match in the master inventory file.

Because this program writes a new inventory file after performing the updates, you should be careful not to lose the original inventory file while you are testing the program. You will need the original file each time you retest the program, and you don't want to have to reenter it each time.

9-6 VARIANT RECORDS

Variant records are the least-used record structure, but they are presented here for completeness and to show how they differ from the other record structures. Although seldom used, this structure may fit your data best. But before we present variant records, we will review the enumerated data type because it is frequently used in the variant record definition.

Pascal is very versatile in data types. We have used the standard data types —integer, real, character, and Boolean—and have defined subranges of these standard types. We have defined arrays and records as well as structures that combine and/or nest other structures and types. The enumerated data type is still another data type that is defined by giving an ordered list of all values that are possible for it. The term **enumerated** is applied to this data type because the values are listed. It is also an ordinal type because each value (except the first) has a unique predecessor and each value (except the last) has a unique successor.

Enumerated data types have meaning only within the program, so they cannot be read in or written out. Generally, their use is to make the program more readable, much as Boolean variables do. For example, suppose we wish to define an enumerated data type whose values are the following types of engineering specialties: electrical, mechanical, civil, chemical, computer, and nuclear. This data type can be defined with the following statements:

```
type
   department = (electrical,mechanical,civil,chemical,
                 computer,nuclear);
var
   engineering: department;
```

It is important to note that the term *civil* is not a variable; instead it represents a constant that is one of the values in the engineering data type. The variable *engineering* can be assigned one of the values using an assignment statement, such as:

```
if  major = 12  then
    engineering := electrical
```

Enumerated data types are often used in *case* statements, as shown in this example:

```
case  engineering  of
   electrical:  eetotal  := eetotal + 1;
   mechanical:  metotal  := metotal + 1;
   civil:       civtotal := civtotal + 1;
   chemical:    chmtotal := chmtotal + 1;
   computer:    cmptotal := cmptotal + 1;
   nuclear:     netotal  := netotal + 1
end
```

The use of the enumerated data type in *case* statements finally leads us to the definition of a variant record. A variant record is one that has a variable set of information. The variable portion of the record depends on the value of an ordinal data type. For example, suppose we want to define a record data structure to store student information. A large part of the record represents information that is necessary for all students, such as name, address, age, date of birth, and so on. However, there is also a portion of the student information that depends on the status of the student; that is, the additional information needed for graduate students is different from that needed for undergraduates, and that information is different from that needed for nondegree students. This fixed information and the variable information can be combined to form a variant record. Within the record definition, a statement similar to a *case* statement is used with the ordinal data type to define the portion of the record that is variable. Using the student information example, a variant record definition could be:

```
type
   category = (undergraduate,graduate,nondegree);
   data = record
               name: array[1..30] of char;
               address: array[1..25] of char;
               case status: category of
                  undergraduate:
                      (major,minor: integer);
                  graduate:
                      (research: array[1..10] of char);
                  nondegree:
                      (totalhrs: integer)
            end;
var
   student: data;
```

A diagram of this record structure is shown here:

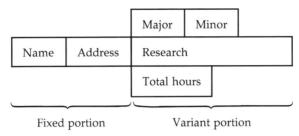

		Major	Minor
Name	Address	Research	
		Total hours	

Fixed portion　　　　　Variant portion

The variant portion of the record is determined by the identifier that follows the word *case*. This identifier, called a **tag field identifier,** must be an ordinal type. The value assigned to the tag field then determines which variant portion of the record is to be used. The list of rules that apply to the variant portion, its tag field identifier, and the tag field type are summarized as follows:

1. The variant portion of the record must follow the fixed portion, if there is one.
2. There can be only one variant portion, but it may contain nested variants.
3. Each field in the variant portion must be unique.
4. The tag field may not be defined as part of the variant portion of the record.
5. The variant portion definition does not include an *end* statement, but the variant portion is followed by the *end* statement that is part of the *record* definition.
6. The field list for each variant is enclosed in parentheses.
7. It is valid for a variant to be empty; that is, a variant may not include any fields for certain tag types.

The syntax diagram for the variant portion of a record definition follows.

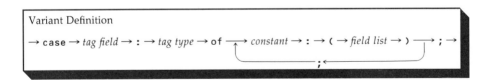

Variant Definition

→ **case** → *tag field* → : → *tag type* → **of** → *constant* → : → (→ *field list* →) → ; →

EXAMPLE 9-10　Student Record

Using the variant student record defined previously in this section, give the statements to read information from the terminal to be stored in the student record.

Solution

```
type
    category = (undergraduate,graduate,nondegree);
    data = record
               name: array[1..30] of char;
               address: array[1..25] of char;
               case status: category of
                   undergraduate:
                       (major,minor: integer);
                   graduate:
                       (research: array[1..10] of char);
                   nondegree:
                       (totalhrs: integer)
           end;
var
    letter: char;
    student: data;
    i: integer;
    .
    .
    .
    writeln ('ENTER NAME (30 CHARACTERS)');
    for i := 1 to 30 do
        read (student.name[i]);
    readln;
    writeln ('ENTER ADDRESS (25 CHARACTERS)');
    for i := 1 to 25 do
        read (student.address[i]);
    readln;
    writeln ('ENTER STATUS (1 CHARACTER)');
    writeln ('U-UNDERGRADUATE');
    writeln ('G-GRADUATE');
    writeln ('N-NONDEGREE');
    read (letter);
    readln;
    if  letter = 'U'  then
        begin
            student.status := undergraduate;
            writeln ('ENTER MAJOR & MINOR CODES');
            readln (student.major,student.minor)
        end
    else if  letter = 'G'  then
        begin
            student.status := graduate;
            writeln ('ENTER RESEARCH AREA (10 CHAR)');
            for i := 1 to 10 do
                read (student.research[i]);
            readln
        end
    else
        begin
            student.status := nondegree;
            writeln ('ENTER TOTAL HOURS COMPLETED');
            readln (student.totalhrs)
        end
```

Variant records can be implemented as fixed records by including all possible fields in the record definition. Using our student record as an example, we could define a student record so that each record contained a major and a minor code, a research area, and the total hours completed. Because some of the fields would never be used, however, it would be an inefficient method of data storage.

9-7 NONTEXT FILES

In Pascal, files are defined to be a data type that consists of a sequence of components. We have frequently used files in our example programs because they are commonly used in engineering and scientific applications to store data. The files we have used have been text files that typically have been generated using a text editor, but the concept of a file can be extended to data structures other than text. In this section we define different types of data files and discuss the difference between a **text file** and a **nontext file.** We also look at two techniques for reading and writing information in nontext files. One technique uses the familiar *read* and *write* statements, and the other presents two new statements, *get* and *put.*

Since Pascal defines a file as a data type, it is typically defined with a *type* statement. By definition, a file consists of a sequence of components, and we define these components within the file. For example, a file of integers could be defined with the following statements:

```
type
   measurements = file of integers;
var
   results: measurements;
```

With this definition, *results* is a file of integers. A file of integers is different from an array of integers in several significant ways. First, an array of integers is stored in the portion of the computer's memory that is completely accessible to our program; thus, using subscripts, we can access any integer that is stored in the array. With a file, only one component of the file is in the memory at a time. Furthermore, the components in a file can only be accessed sequentially. For example, with the file of integers we can access the first integer, then the second integer, then the third integer, and so on. We cannot access the second integer, then the last integer, and then the tenth integer. (Notice the similarity to working with text files — we access the first line of text, then the second line of text, and so on.) Access to a file is often defined as access through a **window** that contains only one component at a time. In addition, that window can move only in one direction: from the beginning of the file to the end. The diagram below illustrates this concept using a file of integers with the window identifying the component that our program can access. The window is moved from one component to the next by statements in the program.

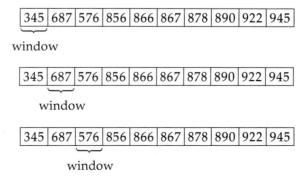

A file is also generally stored in memory that is separate from the program and often represents information to be used by other programs. This information may be stored in a file in the computer (much as we store program files), or it may be stored in another form such as magnetic tape. When data is stored as a file on magnetic tape or diskette, it is very easy to use it on different computers and with other programs.

Files of information may also be quite long. For example, earth motion measured by a seismometer might record information every second. Such information gathered over several days could represent hundreds of thousands of readings. It would not be feasible to store all this information in an array within a program. Instead, the information can be accessed one measurement at a time using the file data structure.

Files consist of a sequence of components, which can be data structures themselves. Thus, we can define many different types of files. A file of records is a particularly useful data structure. An example of a file of inventory records is defined below:

```
type
    inventory = record
                    identification: integer;
                    description: array[1..30] of char;
                    quantity: integer;
                    unitprice: real
                end;
var
    data: file of inventory;
```

This file of records consists of a sequence of records, each containing an identification, a description, a quantity, and a unit price. This data structure could be used to store the inventory information for a company's merchandise. Updates to this information can be performed sequentially to a single item at a time.

Before we discuss the statements used to read and write information from files, we need to discuss the difference between a text file and a nontext file. As discussed earlier, text files are files of characters that are usually generated with text editors. These files can represent programs or data. The information in these files is stored as lines of characters. Thus, when we read a text file with a *readln* statement, we read one complete line of data. When we read a text file with a *read* statement, we read individual characters of data. Pascal has predefined the text file data structure and the files *input* and *output*. When we define a nontext file, such as a file of records, we cannot use the *readln* and *writeln* statements. Nontext files are not defined in terms of lines, so we must use different statements to access them. Nontext files are Pascal structures that must be built and accessed with Pascal programs. Thus, since text editors are usually not Pascal programs, they cannot build a nontext file. Since we have used text files frequently, we will specifically address nontext files in the remainder of this section.

I/O WITH *READ* AND *WRITE*

To create a nontext file, we use the *rewrite* statement to initialize the window of the file to the first component. Then we can use the *write* statement to write information into that window and move the window to the next component. The following statement will write an integer *total* into the current window of a file of integers called *results* and move the window to the next component.

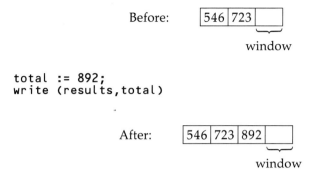

Before: | 546 | 723 | |

          window

```
total := 892;
write (results,total)
```

After: | 546 | 723 | 892 | |

          window

Note that the file name must be used as the first variable following the left parenthesis in the *write* statement; otherwise, the compiler will assume that the *write* statement applies to the file *output*. The variable following the file name must be the same type as the file component type. If the file is a file of records, then, the variable following the file name in the *write* statement must also be a record type.

To read information from a nontext file, we use the *reset* statement to position the window at the first component of the file. The *read* statement will move the information from the window to the variables that we list with the *read* statement and then move the window forward. Also, with nontext files, we cannot partially read the information in the window. All the information in the window must be read into a variable of the same type as the file component. If the file is an array of records, for example, the component must be read into another record variable.

EXAMPLE 9-11 Create File of Integers

Give the statements necessary to define a file of integers and then create the file containing the integers 1 through 1000.

Solution

```
type
    data = file of integers;
var
    numbers: data;
    i: integer;
    .
    .
    .
    rewrite (numbers);
    for i := 1 to 1000 do
        write (numbers,i)
```

I/O WITH *GET* AND *PUT*

Two new statements, *get* and *put*, may also be used to read and write information with nontext files. (*Get* and *put* are really procedures, as are *read* and *write*, although we refer to them as statements.) These statements use a **file buffer** to move information in or out of the current window of the file. This buffer area is always present with files, but its use is not apparent when using the *read* and *write* statements. The buffer area represents storage for one component of the file. Thus, in a file of integers, the file buffer is an integer; in a file of records, the file buffer is a record. The file buffer is accessed by the identifier composed of the file name followed by an **up-arrow,** ↑ . For a file called *sensor*, the file buffer variable is *sensor* ↑ . The up-arrow may be represented by different characters on different systems. The *hat* symbol (^) or the *at* symbol (@) are sometimes used in place of the up-arrow. Check with your instructor or your Pascal compiler manual to determine the correct symbol for your system. We will use the *hat* symbol in our statements.

The *get* statement causes the window to move to the next component. The information in the window is then moved into the file buffer. Since the data always goes to the file buffer, the only variable needed with the *get* statement is the file name. The syntax diagram for this statement follows.

Get Statement

→ *get* → (→ *file* →) →

Similarly, the *put* statement causes the information in the file buffer of an output file to be written into the current window of the file, and advances the window to the next component. The contents of the file buffer are undefined after the execution of the *put* statement. The syntax diagram of the *put* statement follows.

Put Statement

→ *put* → (→ *file* →) →

In order to move information into the file buffer of an output file or from the file buffer of an input file, we use the **file buffer variable.** For example, suppose we wish to write an integer *total* to an output file of integers called *results*. Using the file buffer variable, we can write this information using the following statements:

```
results^ := total;
put (results)
```

The file buffer variable is used in a similar fashion to move information from the file buffer to other variables in our programs.

EXAMPLE 9-12 Read Information from File of Records

Assume that the file data is a file of records with each record containing an integer time and a corresponding real temperature. Give a complete program that will read the data in this file and compute the average temperature measurement. Use the *get* statement rather than the *read* statement to access the information in this file.

Solution

```
{--------------------------------------------------------}
program  analyze (data,output);
    {This program computes the average temperature value
     in a file of temperature observations.}
type
    info = record
                time: integer;
                temperature: real
           end;
    observations = file of info;
var
    sum := real;
    count: integer;
    data : observations;
begin {analyze}
    reset (data);
    count := 0;
    sum := 0.0;
    while  not eof(data)  do
        begin
            sum := sum + data^.temperature;
            count := count + 1;
            get (data)
        end;
    writeln ('AVERAGE TEMPERATURE = ',sum/count:6:1)
end. {analyze}
{--------------------------------------------------------}
```

Now that we have gone through a few examples using the *read/write* statements and the *get/put* statements with nontext files, we can compare their functions. If *data* is a file of real values, then the statement

```
read (data,x)
```

is equivalent to the following statements:

```
x := data^;
get (data)
```

Also, if *results* is a file of real values, then the statement

```
write (results,total)
```

is equivalent to the following statements:

```
results^ := total;
put (results)
```

SUMMARY

A record is a data structure that allows us to group together items that may have different types. We can also define records within records and arrays of records. With the addition of records and these record structures, we have a great deal of flexibility in defining data structures that fit our information and the processes needed to analyze it. This variety of data structures makes it possible for our programs to perform highly sophisticated operations and still remain simple and readable.

DEBUGGING AIDS

As we add more complex data structures to our programs, we can make debugging easier by choosing record names and field names that clearly specify the variables in our programs. With carefully chosen names, we also avoid some of the mistakes that occur when one variable is confused with another.

The *writeln* statement, as we have pointed out before, is probably your most valuable debugging tool in any program. As you print data values at key points in your programs, give the complete label of each variable and specify the current location in the program. Printing the contents of the file buffer is often the most direct way of debugging programs with nontext files that are not working correctly.

Debugging programs with records is often simplified by careful choice of test data. Because the use of records often occurs in updating types of applications, we list some of the data sets that you should use in testing an update program. (We refer to the current information as the master file and the update information as the transaction file.)

1. Transaction data that has no matches to the master file.
2. Transaction data that includes several updates for the same master record.
3. Transaction data that has updates for several consecutive master records.
4. Transaction data that updates the first record in the master file.
5. Transaction data that updates the last record in the master file.
6. Transaction data that includes all the errors the program is supposed to identify.

This list of test data sets will certainly identify many of the errors commonly made in file updating. Remember, it is better to test with a number of small sets of data instead of one large set. Also remember that the entire set of test cases should be rerun each time a change is made in the program. It is wise to determine the expected responses from your programs before you actually run the programs.

STYLE/TECHNIQUE GUIDELINES

Style and technique are especially important in programs that use some of the more complex data structures. Some of the guidelines we have found to be useful with these data structures are listed here.

1. Use the *type* statement to define data types that you will use in your program.
2. Choose the data structure that best fits your data, and then use it consistently in all programs that use that data.
3. Use the *with* statement when you are performing a number of operations with fields within the same record.
4. If a data structure is commonly used in your programs, develop a set of procedures to perform routine operations and then use them consistently when you need the operations in your programs.
5. When using uncommon Pascal features, include more comments describing the way you are using these features.

KEY WORDS

array of records	record
field identifier	record structure
file buffer	tag field identifier
file buffer variable	transaction file
hierarchical record	up-arrow
master file	variant record
merge	window
nontext file	

PROBLEMS

We begin our problem set with modifications to programs developed in this chapter. Give the decomposition, refined pseudocode, and Pascal statements for each problem.

Problems 1–5 modify the population growth program *analysis*, given on page 422.

1. Modify the population growth program so that it finds the two consecutive years in which the percentage increase in population was the smallest.
2. Modify the population growth program so that it finds and prints the year and the corresponding population that was the smallest population value. Print all years with this minimum population.

3. Modify the population growth program so that it computes the average increase in population per year for the total period of time represented by the data in the data file.
4. Modify the population growth program so that it finds the two consecutive years in which the actual increase in population was the largest.
5. Modify the population growth program so that it prints the population values for the two consecutive years in which the actual increase in population was the smallest.

Problems 6–10 modify the instrument usage program *logs,* given on page 432.

6. Modify the instrument usage program so that it prints a report listing each serial number and the number of field tests that have used the specific piece of equipment.
7. Modify the instrument usage program so that it prints a report listing each serial number and the group numbers of all the groups that have used the specific piece of equipment.
8. Modify the instrument usage program so that after performing the updates, it prints a summary line that specifies the number of records in the new log.
9. Modify the instrument usage program so that after performing the updates it prints a summary line that specifies the number of pieces of equipment represented by the data in the new log.
10. Modify the instrument usage program so that after performing the updates it prints a summary line that specifies the number of new pieces and the number of old pieces of equipment returned. (Assume that a piece of equipment is new if there are no entries for it in the old log.)

Problems 11–15 modify the inventory update program *update* given on page 437.

11. Modify the inventory update program so that it prints the number of master records updated by the program.
12. Modify the inventory update program so that it prints the number of master records in the master file.
13. Modify the inventory update program so that it prints the identification number of any item whose quantity is zero.
14. Modify the inventory update program so that it prints a reorder report that lists all items whose quantity is less than 5 units. Include the stock number and the number of items to be ordered to bring the total quantity to 10.
15. Modify the inventory update program so that it prints the total dollar amount represented by each item. That is, if there are 10 items with a unit price of $13.52, the total dollar amount represented by that item is $135.20.

Problems 16–36 refer to the record definition and array of records defined as follows:

```
type
    book = record
              title: array[1..30] of char;
              author: array[1..15] of char;
              year: integer;
              price: real
           end;
var
    library: array[1..100] of book;
```

16. Write a procedure called *readbook* that uses the array *library* and a subscript *k* as parameters. The procedure should read the information that is to be stored in the *k*th element of the array. The procedure should prompt the user for each piece of information needed for the record (title, author, year, price). Allow the user to enter each piece of information separately.

17. Write a procedure called *printbook* that will print the information in the array of records called *library*. The parameters to the procedure are the array and an integer *n* that specifies how many records are in *library*. Use appropriate headings for the information. Include numbers from 1 through *n* on the left side of the output in order to number the books.

18. Write a procedure called *authorsearch* that has as parameters the array *library*, the variable *n* that specifies the number of books in *library*, and the array *name* that contains 15 characters. The procedure should print all book titles that have *name* as author. Include the author's name in the heading before you print the book titles. If there are no books written by *name*, print an appropriate message.

19. Write a function *authorcount* that has as parameters the array *library*, the variable *n* that specifies the number of books in *library*, and the array *name* that contains 15 characters. The function should count all book titles that have *name* as author.

20. Write a procedure called *titlesearch* that has as parameters the array *library*, the variable *n* that specifies the number of books in *library*, and the array *name* that contains 30 characters. The procedure should print all the information in the record for the books with the corresponding title. If there is no book with the title *name*, print an appropriate message.

21. Write a function called *titlecount* that has as parameters the array *library*, the variable *n* that specifies the number of books in *library*, and the array *name* that contains 30 characters. The function should count all the books with the corresponding title.

22. Write a procedure called *yearsearch* that has as parameters the array *library*, the variable *n* that specifies the number of books in *library*, and the integer *date*. The procedure should print all book titles and authors that were published in the year given by *date*. Include the integer *date* in a heading before you print the book information. If there are no books published in the year given by *date*, print an appropriate message.

23. Write a function called *yearcount* that has as parameters the array *library*, the variable *n* that specifies the number of books in *library*, and the integer *date*. The procedure should count all books that were published in the year given by *date*.

24. Write a procedure called *pricesearch* that has as parameters the array *library*, the variable *n* that specifies the number of books in *library*, and two real values, *low* and *high*. The procedure should print book titles and authors for books whose price falls between the *low* and the *high* prices. Note that if *low* is equal to *high*, the procedure should print titles and authors for books of a specific price. Include the values *low* and *high* in the heading before you print the book information. If there are no books within the specified price range, print an appropriate message.

25. Write a function called *pricecount* that has as parameters the array *library*, the variable *n* that specifies the number of books in *library*, and two real values, *low* and *high*. The function should count the number of books whose price falls between the *low* and *high* prices. Note that if *low* is equal to *high*, the procedure should count the number of books for a single specific price.

26. Write a procedure *datesort* that will sort the array *library* by the year the book was published. Use a descending sort. The input parameters are the array *library* and the variable *n* that specifies the number of books in *library*.

27. Write a procedure *pricesort* that will sort the array *library* by the price of the book. Use an ascending sort. The input parameters are the array *library* and the variable *n* that specifies the number of books in *library*.

28. Write a procedure *authorsort* that will sort the array *library* alphabetically by author. The input parameters are the array *library* and the variable *n* that specifies the number of books in *library*.

29. Write a procedure *titlesort* that will sort the array *library* alphabetically by title. The input parameters are the array *library* and the variable *n* that specifies the number of books in *library*.

30. Write a procedure called *writetext* that writes the array *library* to a text file. Each line of the file should contain the title, author, year, and price. The name of the file is *bookfile*. Include a blank between *author* and *year* and between *year* and *price*, but do not include extra blanks between the 30 characters for the title and the 15 characters for the author. The input parameters are the array *library* and the variable *n* that specifies the number of books in *library*.

31. Write a procedure called *writefile* that writes the array *library* to a file of records. Each component in the array should be a record in the file. The name of the file is *books*. The input parameters are the array *library* and the variable *n* that specifies the number of books in *library*.

32. Write a procedure called *fileread* that has the array *library* and a subscript *k* as parameters. The procedure should read book information from a line in a text file called *bookfile* and store the information in the *k*th element of the array.

33. Write a program that reads the information for a set of books from the terminal, prints the information, and then stores that information in a text file called *bookfile*. Use the procedures developed in problems 16, 17, and 30.

34. Write a program that reads the information for a set of books from a text file called *bookfile*. The information should be stored in an array *library*. The program should allow the user to search for specific books in the array by entering *T* (to specify a title search), *A* (to specify an author search), *Y* (to specify a year), or *P* (to specify a price range). The results of each search should be printed. The program should interact with the user to perform the search on the specific item and allow the search to continue until the user indicates that he or she is ready to quit. You can reference modules developed in problems 16 through 32.

35. Write a program that reads the information for a set of books from a text file called *bookfile*. The information should be stored in an array *library*. The program should then allow the user to search for specific books in the array by entering *T* (to specify a title search), *A* (to specify an author search), *Y* (to specify a year), or *P* (to specify a price range). Instead of printing the results of each search, print the number of books found in each search. The program should interact with the user to perform the search on the specific item and allow the search to continue until the user indicates that he or she is ready to quit. You can reference modules developed in problems 16 through 32.

36. Write a program that reads the information for a set of books from a text file called *bookfile*. The information should be stored in an array *library*. The program should allow the user to specify the order in which to print the data in the array (by title, author, year, or price) and then print the information in the new order. You can reference modules developed in problems 16 through 32.

PROBLEM SOLVING — Whooping Crane Migration

Each year, the migration of the whooping cranes is a special event
for wildlife researchers. Information on sightings is received by the
Wildlife Service. The information, initially a few pieces of data,
grows to hundreds of pieces of data as the cranes complete their
migration. Write a program to print the sighting information in the
order in which the sightings were made, using the date and time
recorded. (See Section 10-2 for the solution.)

10

DYNAMIC DATA STRUCTURES AND SETS

INTRODUCTION

In this chapter we present two new types of data structures: **dynamic data structures** and **sets.** The size of a dynamic data structure is determined as the program executes, as opposed to being determined when the program is compiled. (An array is not a dynamic data structure because it is defined with a specific number of elements when a program is compiled.) To define a dynamic data structure, we use a new type of variable called a **pointer variable,** which allows us to define the data structures as we need them; thus, we do not have to reserve a maximum size of memory for them. We will give examples of dynamic data structures such as **linked lists, stacks, queues,** and **trees.** The other data structure presented in this chapter is called a set. It is a collection of components that are grouped together in no particular order; that is, there is no first component, second component, and so on. We can perform special operations called **set union** and **set intersection** with sets to determine new sets.

10-1   POINTER VARIABLES AND LINKED LISTS

All the data structures that we have previously defined had a fixed size. If we defined a record, we had to define each field contained in the record. If we defined an array, we had to define an individual element of the array and specify the maximum number of elements in the array. All predefined data structures are assigned memory locations that are accessible when we begin execution of the program. For some applications, this type of memory assignment is very inefficient. For example, suppose we are using an array that occasionally may need to hold 1000 values, although most of the time we only need 50 values. With an array data structure we must always specify the maximum size, and thus we would need to reserve memory for 1000 elements.

A **dynamic data structure** is one whose memory is defined not during the compilation of the program but as it is needed during the execution of the program. Thus, with a dynamic data structure, we do not reserve memory until we need it. In the example in the previous paragraph, if we need only 50 elements, we would only use memory for 50 elements with a dynamic data structure. If we need 1000 elements, the same program would dynamically reserve the memory for 1000 elements.

In this section we define dynamic variables and illustrate the statements that manipulate them. The primary use of dynamic variables is in building a dynamic data structure. The most commonly used dynamic data structure is a linked list. We will define and give examples of linked lists and the techniques for using them.

DEFINING DYNAMIC VARIABLES

A **dynamic variable** is defined in terms of a **pointer.** This pointer is a special variable that contains the memory address of the dynamic variable. Thus, to define a dynamic variable we define the pointer variable, not the variable itself. The following diagram illustrates this relationship.

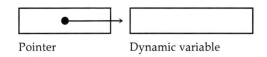

Pointer   Dynamic variable

A pointer is defined in terms of the type of variable for which it is a pointer: a pointer to an integer is defined differently from a pointer to a record, and so on. A pointer can be defined in the type section or the variable section of a program using the up-arrow (↑), followed by the type of variable for which it is a pointer. In our Pascal statements, we will use the hat symbol (^) to represent the up-arrow. In the statements below, *ptr1* is a pointer to a real value and *ptr2* is a pointer to a record:

```
type
    datarec = record
                    identification: integer;
                    gpa: real
                end;
    dataptr = ^datarec;
    realptr = ^real;
var
    ptr1: realptr;
    ptr2: dataptr;
```

Note that the up-arrow must be followed by a data type in the pointer definition; if the type is not integer, real, Boolean, or character, it must refer to a type definition in the type section of the program.

Defining the pointer variable does not automatically assign a memory address for the corresponding data variable. The *new* statement is a procedure reference that must be executed in order for a memory address to be assigned to a pointer variable. The syntax diagram for the *new* statement follows.

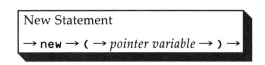

The execution of the *new* statement causes a memory address to be assigned to the pointer but does not initialize the contents of the memory address. To initialize the dynamic variable, we use the pointer identifier followed by an up-arrow. The following statements assign the value zero to the dynamic variable whose pointer is *ptr1*. The diagrams on the right show the corresponding changes in the pointer and its dynamic variable.

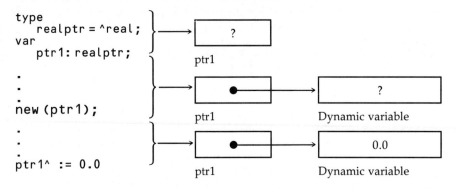

```
type
    realptr = ^real;
var
    ptr1: realptr;
.
.
.
new (ptr1);
.
.
.
ptr1^ := 0.0
```

Pointer variables may not be used in the same way that regular variables are used. For example, we cannot assign a constant value to a pointer variable (with the exception of the nil constant, which will be discussed with linked lists). We cannot print the value in a pointer variable. We can assign the contents of one pointer variable to another, and we can compare the contents of two pointer variables to determine whether they are equal. The following statements result in two different pointers referencing the same variable:

```
type
    intptr = ^integer;
var
    ptr3, ptr4: intptr;
    .
    .
    .
new (ptr3);
ptr4 := ptr3
```

Note that the variable still has not been initialized. The next diagram illustrates these results.

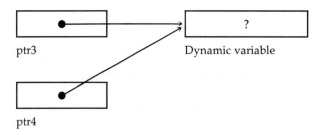

We must be careful that we do not lose the value of a dynamic variable pointer, because there is no other way to reference the variable. Consider the following sequence of steps and the memory diagrams that illustrate them:

```
type
    intptr = ^integer;
var
    ptr3, ptr4: intptr;
    .
    .
    .
    new (ptr3);
    ptr3^ := 25;
    new (ptr4);
    ptr4^ := 100
    .
    .
    .
    ptr3 := ptr4
```

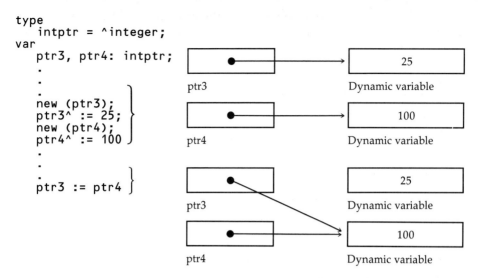

Observe that we now have two pointers referencing the variable containing 100, and no reference to the variable 25.

Consider the effect of replacing the last statement in the previous statements with a slightly different final statement:

```
type
    intptr = ^integer;
var
    ptr3, ptr4: intptr;
    .
    .
    .
    new (ptr3);
    ptr3^ := 25;
    new (ptr4);
    ptr4^ := 100
    .
    .
    .
    ptr3^ := ptr4^
```

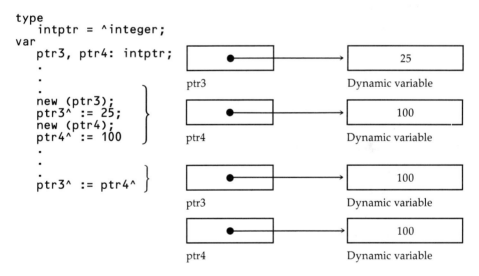

In this case, the pointers reference different variables, but both variables now contain the value 100.

If we decide that we no longer need a dynamic variable, we can release the memory assigned with the *dispose* statement, which is a procedure reference having the following syntax diagram:

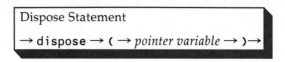

Dispose Statement

→ dispose → (→ *pointer variable* →)→

Thus, if we execute the following statement, *ptr3* no longer references a dynamic variable:

```
dispose (ptr3)
```

The memory location that *ptr3* did reference is now available for assignment later in the program.

LINKING DYNAMIC VARIABLES

The primary use of dynamic variables is not for individual variables such as those that we have used in our examples. The real power of dynamic variables is evident when we use the pointer variables to link the dynamic variables together into **linked data structures.** In the remainder of this section, we discuss **linked lists.** In Section 10-3, we discuss some variations of linked lists that have special uses.

A linked list is similar to an array because it is a group of elements that has an order: there is a first element, a second element, and so on. However, the linked list is different from an array in several ways. First, we do not use a subscript to reference an element in the linked list; instead, we use a pointer variable. Because it is composed of dynamic variables, we do not have to declare a maximum size for a linked list, whereas we do have to declare a maximum size for an array. The linked list is a group of dynamic variables linked together by pointers. Each element in the linked list has a pointer contained within it that points to the next element in the list. The diagram below of an element in a linked list shows the distinction between the data in the element and the pointer.

Linked list element

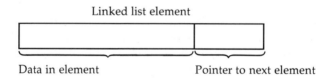

Data in element   Pointer to next element

If we assign values to the pointers so that they point to other dynamic variables, we can think of the linked list in the following way:

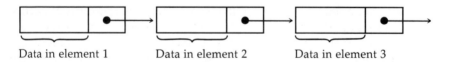

Data in element 1   Data in element 2   Data in element 3

Finally, we need a way to detect the end of a linked list. Pascal provides a special constant called **nil** that represents the end of a linked list. Our diagram of a linked list with four elements is illustrated in the next diagram:

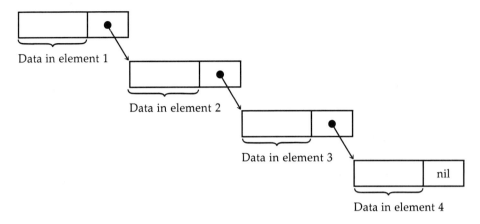

Data in element 1

Data in element 2

Data in element 3

nil

Data in element 4

We now look at the statements necessary to initialize and reference values in a linked list. We first need to define a pointer type that refers to the proper data type for the dynamic elements that are to be linked together. Then we need the definition of the dynamic variable itself, which must include the data fields and a pointer field. The following statements define a *pointer* type that references a data type called *datarec*. The type *datarec* is a record containing a real number and a pointer.

```
type
    pointer = ^datarec;
    datarec = record
                  x: real;
                  ptr: pointer
              end;
```

Note that the definition of the type *pointer* references *datarec* before *datarec* is defined. Since *datarec* contains a field defined to be type *pointer*, interchanging the pointer definition and the record definition does not avoid the forward reference. Thus, the Pascal compiler allows us to define a pointer type that refers to a type that has not yet been defined.

We can initialize the pointers using the *new* statement or by assigning the value in one pointer to another pointer. We can initialize the variables within the dynamic variable using assignment statements or input statements. The fields within the dynamic variable are referenced by using the pointer identifier followed by the up-arrow, then a period, then the field identifier. For example, if *next* currently points to a dynamic variable of the type *datarec*, we can use the following statement to read a value and store it in the field *x* within the dynamic variable:

```
readln (next^.x)
```

Assume now that we wish to read a set of values from a data file. The values represent a group of ordered temperatures taken during an experiment. We want to store this data in memory so that our program can access any of it. The number of values in the file can vary greatly from one experiment to another, so we have decided to store the data in a linked list.

We need three pointers in order to generate a linked list from data that is already in the order desired for the list. One pointer, which we call *first*, holds the reference to the first element in the list. (When a linked list is empty, *first* will contain the constant *nil*.) The other two pointers, *previous* and *next*, are used to point to the dynamic variable most recently added to the list and to the next dynamic variable to be added. The steps in generating a linked list are described here:

Initialize a pointer *first*.
Move data into the element referenced by *first*.
Initialize a pointer *previous*, and set it to point to the first data value.

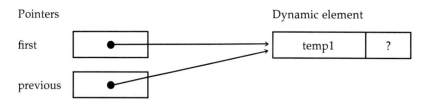

While there is more data in data file do
    initialize a pointer *next*,
    read new data into the element referenced by the pointer *next*,
    set the pointer in the previous dynamic data element so that it points to the new dynamic data element.

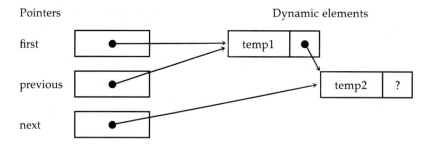

Move the value in the pointer *next* to the pointer *previous,* so they both now point to the same dynamic data element.

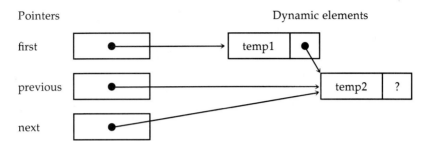

When there is no more data, do
move the value *nil* to the pointer stored in the last dynamic variable.

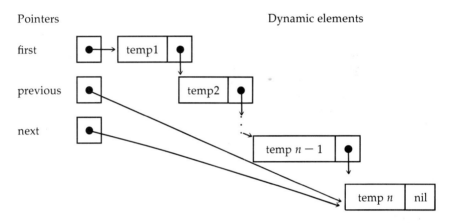

We now use these pseudocode steps and diagrams to develop the Pascal statements for building a linked list. If the data file is empty, the pointer *first* is initialized to the constant *nil.*

EXAMPLE 10-1 Initializing a Linked List

Give the statements to generate a linked list using the data from a file *tempdata,* which contains real temperature data values that have already been sorted.

Solution

The following Pascal statements utilize the algorithm developed with the previous pseudocode and diagrams.

```
type
    pointer = ^datarec;
    datarec = record
                   x: real;
                   ptr: pointer
              end;
var
    first, next, previous: pointer;
    tempdata: text;
         .
         .
         .
    if  eof(tempdata)  then
        first := nil
    else
        begin
            new (first);
            readln (tempdata,first^.x);
            previous := first;
            while  not eof(tempdata)  do
                begin
                    new (next);
                    readln (tempdata, next^.x);
                    previous^.ptr := next;
                    previous := next
                end;
            previous^.ptr := nil
        end
```

Now that we have covered the steps to build a linked list, we can use the links established to access the data. The next example illustrates the steps necessary to print the information stored in a linked list.

EXAMPLE 10-2   Printing the Data in a Linked List

Give the statements necessary to print the data stored in the linked list generated in Example 10-1. Assume that the pointer *first* points to the first element in the list.

Solution

We repeat the type statements for *datarec* and *pointer,* but we do not repeat the steps to create the linked list.

```
type
    pointer = ^datarec;
    datarec = record
                   x: real;
                   ptr: pointer
              end;
var
    first, next: pointer;
         .
         .
         .
    next := first;
    while  next <> nil  do
        begin
            writeln (next^.x:8:3);
            next := next^.ptr
        end
```

If you have trouble understanding the steps in the example that built a linked list or in the example that printed the data in a linked list, use a diagram to follow the steps with a small amount of data. Be sure you are comfortable with these two exercises before you continue to the next part of this section.

INSERTING AND DELETING WITH A LINKED LIST

In addition to building and accessing the data in a linked list, we often want to insert new items or delete old items. These types of operations are especially efficient with linked lists. When we remove an item from a linked list, all we have to do is change the previous pointer so that it points to the item following the one we want to delete, as shown in the diagram below:

Before deletion of third element:

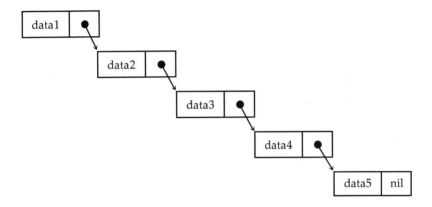

After deletion of third element:

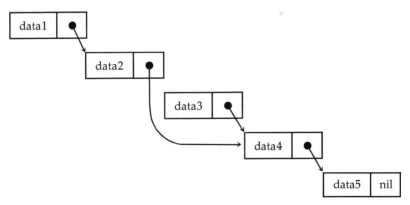

Even though the third element still points to the fourth element, the third element cannot be accessed because there is no pointer to it.

Recall that deleting an item in an array required that we move all the items following the one deleted to fill in its position. If an array is large, these steps can be time consuming. With a linked list, we only modify one value, the pointer to the item being deleted.

When we add an item to a linked list, we need to change two pointers. The pointer in the item before the new item has to be changed to point to the new item, and the pointer in the new item needs to point to the item that follows it. The following diagram illustrates these steps:

Before insertion between second and third elements:

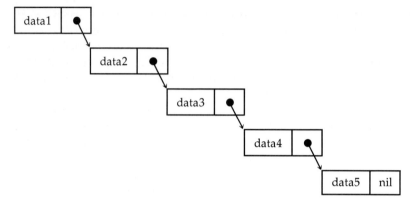

After insertion between second and third elements:

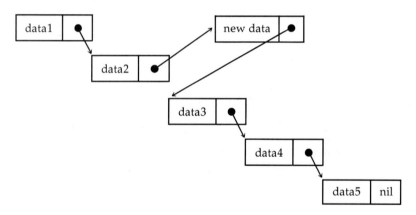

Recall that adding an item to an array required that all the items past the new item be moved one position to make room for the new item. If the array is large, these steps can also be time consuming. With a linked list, we only modify two pointers in order to insert an item.

Both inserting and deleting items with a linked list require that we access the items in the list, beginning with the first item. As we access the items, we need pointers to point to the previous item and to the next item. When we find the proper point to perform the insertion or deletion, we then perform the insertion or deletion. An insertion or deletion is really a combination of a search through the linked list to find the correct position, then the steps for the insertion or deletion itself.

EXAMPLE 10-3   Inserting in a Linked List

Give the statements necessary to insert the dynamic variable pointed to by *current* in the linked list created in Example 10-1. Assume that the temperature values are in ascending order in the list.

Solution

As we translate the steps in the previous diagrams into steps that we can define for the computer, we observe that several different situations can arise when inserting an element in a linked list. The new element can be inserted before the first element in the list, between two existing elements in the list, or after the last element in the list. All three situations involve changing two pointers. If the new element is to be inserted before the first element in the list, we need to change the value of the pointer for the beginning of the the list *(first)* so that it now points to the new element. If we assume that *current* is a pointer to the new element, we then need to change the value of the pointer in the new element (referenced by *current^.ptr*) so that it points to the value originally held in *first*. These steps are illustrated in the next diagram:

Before inserting new element at front of the list:

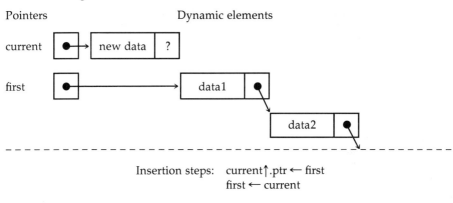

Insertion steps: current↑.ptr ← first
first ← current

After inserting new element at front of the list:

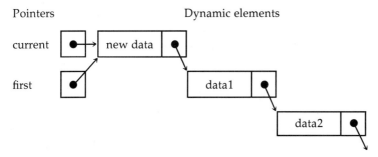

To insert a new dynamic variable between two variables, we need a pointer *previous* that points to the variable that precedes the new value. The pointer *previous*^.*ptr* points to the variable that is now to follow the new variable. Thus, the pointer in the new variable needs to be changed to point to the variable that is to follow it, and the pointer in the variable behind the new variable will need to be changed to point to the new variable. These steps are illustrated in this diagram:

Before inserting new element between two elements in the list:

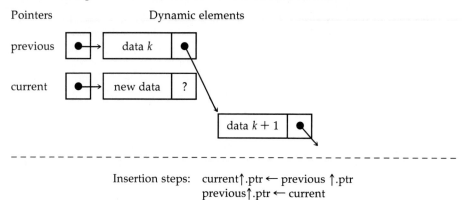

Insertion steps: current↑.ptr ← previous ↑.ptr
previous↑.ptr ← current

After inserting new element between two elements in the list:

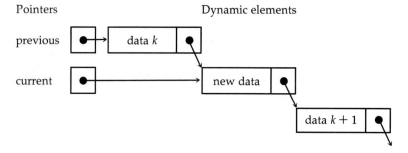

The last case, inserting at the end of the linked list, again requires changing two pointers. We must change the link at the end of the list to point to the new variable, and we must change the link in the new variable to the link in the previous variable. If we assume that *previous* points to the last variable in the list, then *previous*^.*ptr* contains the *nil* constant. These changes are illustrated in the following diagram:

Before inserting new element at the end of the list:

Pointers   Dynamic elements

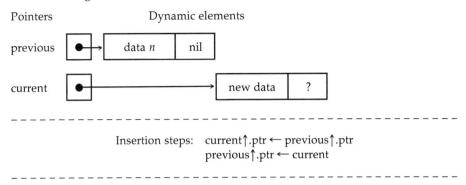

previous

current

- -

Insertion steps: current↑.ptr ← previous↑.ptr
                   previous↑.ptr ← current

- -

After inserting new element at the end of the list:

Pointers   Dynamic elements

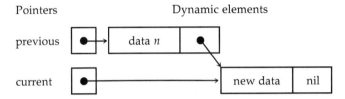

previous

current

In the pseudocode that we are now ready to develop, we use a Boolean variable *done* to determine when we have found the correct position for the insertion. Since we are assuming that the temperature data is in ascending order, any of the following conditions should cause the variable *done* to be true:

1. Insertion at the beginning of the list (occurs when current^.x < first^.x or when the list is empty)
2. Insertion between two values in the list (occurs when current^.x < next^.x)
3. Insertion at the end of the list (occurs when previous^.ptr = nil).

We now use the four pointers (*first, current, next, previous*) to develop the pseudocode for the insertion steps we have described.

(Assumes: the linked list has already been generated; the pointer *first* references the first element in the linked list; and the pointer *current* references the element to be inserted in the list.)

```
if first = nil then
    done ← true
    current^.ptr ← first
    first ← current
else if current^.x < first^.x then
    done ← true
    current^.ptr ← first
    first ← current
else
    done ← false
    previous ← first
    next ← first^.ptr
while not done do
    if current^.x < next^.x then
        done ← true
    else
        previous ← next
        next ← next^.ptr
        if next = nil then
            done ← true
if first ≠ current then
    current^.ptr ← previous^.ptr
    previous^.ptr ← current
```

In the following program we repeat the type definitions and the variable definitions used in generating the linked list. The steps here assume that the linked list has already been generated by the statements that are omitted and that *first* now points to the first element in the list. We read a new temperature value from the terminal, store it in a dynamic variable, and insert that dynamic variable into the correct position in the linked list.

```
type
   pointer = ^datarec;
   datarec = record
                  x: real;
                  ptr: pointer
              end;
var
   first, current, previous, next: pointer;
   temperature: datarec;
   done: boolean;
   .
   .
   .
   new (current);
   writeln ('ENTER NEW TEMPERATURE VALUE TO INSERT');
   readln (current^.x);
   if  first = nil  then
      begin
         done := true;
         current^.ptr := first;
         first := current
      end
   else if  current^.x < first^.x  then
      begin
         done := true;
         current^.ptr := first;
         first := current
      end
   else
      begin
         done := false;
         previous := first;
         next := first^.ptr
      end;
   while  not done  do
      if  current^.x < next^.x  then
         done := true
      else
         begin
            previous := next;
            next := next^.ptr;
            if  next = nil  then
               done := true
         end;
   if  first <> current  then
      begin
         current^.ptr := previous^.ptr;
         previous^.ptr := current
      end
```

After inserting this new value, we could use the steps from Example 10-2
to print the linked list. We will be putting all these steps together in a
complete program in the next section.

EXAMPLE 10-4   Deleting in a Linked List

Give the statements necessary to delete a dynamic variable in the linked list created in Example 10-1. Assume that the temperature values are in ascending order in the list. Read the value to be deleted from the terminal and store it in a variable *tempout*.

Solution

Deleting an item in a linked list requires changing only one pointer, as opposed to the two changes required for inserting an item. There are again three possible cases, deleting the first element in the list, deleting between two elements in the list, or deleting the last element in the list. If we delete the first element, we only need to change the pointer in *first* to point to the second element in the list, as shown in this diagram:

Before deleting the element at front of the list:

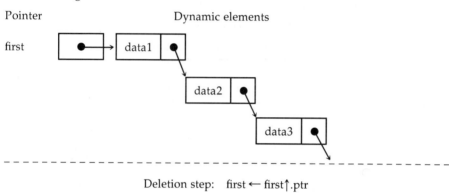

Deletion step: first ← first↑.ptr

After deleting the element at front of the list:

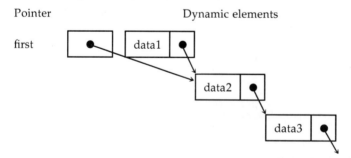

If we delete an element between two other elements in the list, we modify the pointer in the preceding element so that it points to the element following the one we are deleting. This step is illustrated in the next diagram:

Before deleting an element between two elements in the list:

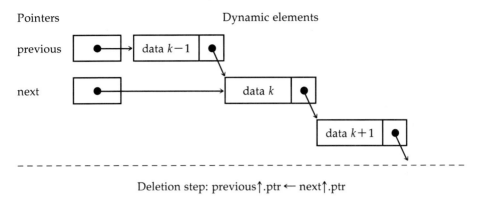

Deletion step: previous↑.ptr ← next↑.ptr

After deleting an element between two elements in the list:

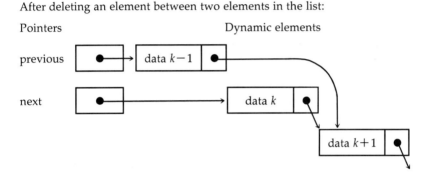

Finally, if we delete the last element, we modify the pointer in the previous element so that it contains the *nil* constant. The *nil* constant is contained in the pointer in the element to be deleted; thus the steps here are the same as the steps for deleting an element between two elements. The next diagram illustrates these steps:

Before deleting the last element in the list:

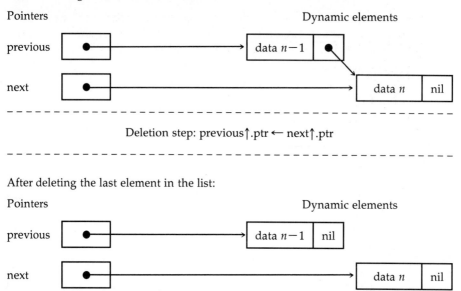

Deletion step: previous↑.ptr ← next↑.ptr

After deleting the last element in the list:

In the pseudocode that we are now ready to develop, we again use a Boolean variable *done* to determine when we have found the correct position for the deletion. We also use a Boolean variable *error* to indicate if the element that we wish to delete *(tempout)* is not in the list. If an error does occur, both *error* and *done* are given true values. We assume that the pointer *next* points to the next value in the linked list, which we are comparing to *tempout*. Since we are assuming that the temperature data is in ascending order, any of the following conditions should cause the variable *done* to be true:

1. Deletion at the beginning of the list (occurs when tempout = first^.x)

2. Deletion between two values in the list (occurs when tempout = next^.x)

3. Deletion at the end of the list (occurs when tempout = next^.x and next^.ptr = nil).

4. Error occurs if tempout > next^.x (tempout is not in the list).

We now use the two pointers *first* and *next*, along with a pointer *previous*, which points to the element previous to the one referenced by *next*, to develop the pseudocode for the deletion steps that we have described.

Pseudocode for Deleting an Element in a Linked List

(Assumes: the linked list has already been generated; the pointer *first* references the first element in the linked list; and the variable *tempout* contains the value to be deleted from the list.)

```
if first = nil then
    done ← true
    error ← true
else if tempout = first^.x then
    done ← true
    error ← false
    first ← first^.ptr
else
    done ← false
    previous ← first
    next ← first^.ptr
while not done do
    if next^.x = tempout then
        done ← true
        error ← false
    else
        previous ← next
        next ← next^.ptr
        if next = nil then
            done ← true
            error ← true
if error then
    print error message
else if tempout ≠ first ^.x then
    previous^.ptr = next^.ptr
```

In the program below we repeat the type definitions and the variable definitions used to generate the linked list. The steps here assume that the linked list has already been generated and that *first* now points to the first element in the list. We read the temperature value that is to be deleted and then delete the corresponding dynamic variable in the linked list or print an error message if it is not in the list.

```pascal
type
   pointer = ^datarec;
   datarec = record
                  x: real;
                  ptr: pointer
              end;
var
   first, next, previous: pointer;
   temperature: datarec;
   tempout: real;
   done, error: boolean;
   .
   .
   .
   writeln ('ENTER TEMPERATURE TO DELETE');
   readln (tempout);
   if  first = nil  then
      begin
         done := true;
         error := true
      end
   else if  tempout = first^.x  then
      begin
         done := true;
         error := false;
         first := first^.ptr
      end
   else
      begin
         done := false;
         previous := first;
         next := first^.ptr
      end;
   while  not done  do
      if  next^.x = tempout  then
         begin
            done := true;
            error := false
         end
      else
         begin
            previous := next;
            next := next^.ptr;
            if  next = nil  then
               begin
                  done := true;
                  error := true
               end
         end;
   if  error  then
      writeln ('TEMPERATURE ',tempout:6:1,' NOT IN LIST')
   else if  tempout <> first^.x  then
      begin
         previous^.ptr := next^.ptr;
         dispose (next)
      end
```

After deleting the value or printing the error message, we could use the steps from Example 10-2 to print the linked list to be sure that the deletion steps worked properly.

This self-test allows you to check quickly to see if you have remembered certain key points from Section 10-1. If you have any problems with the exercise, you should reread this section. The solution is included at the end of the text.

Assume that a linked list has been generated and that the elements in the list are of the type *datarec,* which is defined below. The pointer *first* points to the first element in the list. Give the statements necessary to compute the average value that is stored in the linked list. Print the average value and the number of values in the linked list. Print a special message instead of the average if the list is empty.

```
type
    pointer = ^datarec;
    datarec = record
                    x: real;
                    ptr: pointer
                end;
var
    first, next: pointer;
```

10-2 PROBLEM SOLVING — WHOOPING CRANE MIGRATION

In this section we solve the problem presented at the beginning of the chapter: printing the sighting information on whooping crane migration collected by the Wildlife Service. We want to print this information in the order of the sightings, which will not necessarily be the same order in which the Wildlife Service received it. Furthermore, the information will grow from a few sightings to hundreds of sightings by the end of the migration. The program we develop to order the data and print the current status will utilize the dynamic data structure of a linked list to handle this set of data, which does not have a fixed size but varies with the number of sightings. The program generates a linked list in order by the sighting date and time and then prints the data in the linked list to give the current status of the migration. Assume that each sighting contains the following information:

> sighting date (month, day, year)
> sighting time (using a 24-hour clock)
> grid location (two integer coordinates that give location)
> number of birds

We assume that the data is stored as a series of seven integers (*month, day, year, time, grid1, grid2, birds*) separated by blanks in a data file called *cranes.*

PROBLEM STATEMENT

Write a program to print the current migration status of the whooping cranes.

INPUT/OUTPUT DESCRIPTION

The migration data is contained in the data file *cranes* that contains the sighting information in the order in which it was received. The output is to be an ordered listing of the sighting information by the sighting date and time.

HAND EXAMPLE

For a hand example, we use the following sighting data:

Date	Time	Grids	Number of Birds
4 8 86	0830	21 7	4
4 3 86	0920	21 7	5
4 5 86	0815	21 9	4
5 1 86	1805	22 8	4
5 15 86	0730	23 7	5
5 10 86	0915	22 9	4
5 10 86	0800	22 9	4

If we order this data by date and time, the migration report should contain the following information:

```
WHOOPING CRANE MIGRATION

CURRENT SIGHTINGS
4- 3-86      920
       GRID LOCATION:  21  7
       NUMBER OF BIRDS:     5
4- 5-86      815
       GRID LOCATION:  21  9
       NUMBER OF BIRDS:     4
4- 8-86      830
       GRID LOCATION:  21  7
       NUMBER OF BIRDS:     4
5- 1-86     1805
       GRID LOCATION:  22  8
       NUMBER OF BIRDS:     4
5-10-86      800
       GRID LOCATION:  22  9
       NUMBER OF BIRDS:     4
5-10-86      915
       GRID LOCATION:  22  9
       NUMBER OF BIRDS:     4
5-15-86      730
       GRID LOCATION:  23  7
       NUMBER OF BIRDS:     5
```

Note that we may need to use part or all of the values *year, month, day,* and *time* to order the sightings correctly.

ALGORITHM DEVELOPMENT

An important part of any algorithm development is the choice of a proper data structure. In this solution, we are going to use a linked list because the data is to be ordered by date and time and because the number of sightings may vary considerably from the first time we run the program until the last time. Each element in the linked list must contain the sighting information, so we use a record as our dynamic variable. The record contains the date, time, grid locations, number of birds, and the pointer to the next record in the list. The program itself is straightforward. We want to read the data file, generate a linked list, and then print the contents of the linked list. Thus, our decomposition into sequential steps is:

DECOMPOSITION

Read sighting data and generate linked list.
Print the linked list.

In the previous section of this chapter we developed the algorithms for generating linked lists, inserting elements in linked lists, and printing linked lists. All these steps are used in this algorithm. Since the data we are reading is not in the correct order, we initialize the list with the first element and then insert each new sighting record in its correct position. Our refinement of the decomposition into more detailed pseudocode then becomes:

INITIAL REFINEMENT IN PSEUDOCODE:

```
migration: read first sighting
           create linked list with first sighting
           while more sightings do
              read sighting
              insert sighting in linked list
           print linked list
```

As we refine the solution, we want to consider implementing some of the steps in modules. We saw in the previous section that the insertion algorithm required a number of steps, so we implement it here as a procedure to improve the readability and structure of our program. As we think about determining where a new sighting fits into our linked list, we realize that we do not have a simple comparison of two data values. The time of the sighting depends on the year, month, day, and time, in that order. Therefore, we use a Boolean function to compare the data to be entered in the linked list with the next record in the list. This function returns a value of true if we have found the correct spot for the insertion, and false otherwise. In the function, we combine the year, month, and day into a single integer for comparing dates. However, if you are using a personal computer or a small computer, you may be limited to a maximum integer of 32,767. In these cases, separate comparisons for year, month, and day should be used.

Printing the linked list is another operation that fits well in a procedure. Our program contains two procedures, *insert* and *printlist*, and one function, *rightspot*. We now develop the refined pseudocode.

FINAL REFINEMENT IN PSEUDOCODE

migration: read first data
      while more data do
        read current data
        insert (current,first)
      printlist (first)

insert (current,first): next ← first
            while not rightspot(current,next) do
              next ← next data in list
            if next = first then
              first data ← current data
            else
              add current data before next data

rightspot (current,next):
      if next = end of list then
        rightspot ← true
      else
        if current date < next date then
          rightspot ← true
        else if current date > next date then
          rightspot ← false
        else if current date = next date then
          if current time < next time then
            rightspot ← true
          else
            rightspot ← false

printlist (first): print headers
        next ← first
        while more data do
          read next data
          print next data

The structure chart for the solution follows, along with the Pascal program.

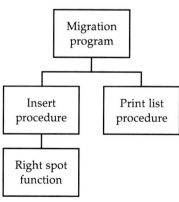

```
{----------------------------------------------------------------}
program   migration (cranes,output);
    {This program reads the migration data for the whooping
    cranes and prints the sightings in ascending order.}
type
    pointer = ^sighting;
    sighting = record
                    mo,da,yr,time,grid1,grid2,birds:integer;
                    link: pointer
               end;
var
    cranes: text;
    first, current: pointer;
{----------------------------------------------------------------}
function   rightspot (current,next:pointer): boolean;
    {This function determines whether or not the current
    data should be inserted before the next data.}
var
    currentdate, nextdate: integer;
begin {rightspot}
    if  next = nil   then
       rightspot := true
    else
       begin
          currentdate := current^.yr*10000 +
                         current^.mo*100 + current^.da;
          nextdate := next^.yr*10000 +
                      next^.mo*100 + next^.da;
          if  currentdate < nextdate   then
             rightspot := true
          else if   currentdate > nextdate   then
             rightspot := false
          else if   currentdate = nextdate   then
             if   current^.time < next^.time   then
                rightspot := true
             else
                rightspot := false
       end
end; {rightspot}
```

```
{---------------------------------------------------------------}
procedure  insert (var current,first:pointer);
   {This procedure inserts the current sighting
    in the linked list.}
var
   next, previous: pointer;
begin {insert}
   next := first;
   previous := nil;
   while  not rightspot(current,next)  do
      begin
         previous := next;
         next := next^.link
      end;
   if  previous = nil  then
      begin
         current^.link := next;
         first := current
      end
   else
      begin
         previous^.link := current;
         current^.link := next
      end
end; {insert}
{---------------------------------------------------------------}
procedure  printlist (first:pointer);
   {This procedure prints a linked list.}
var
   next: pointer;
begin {printlist}
   writeln ('WHOOPING CRANE MIGRATION');
   writeln;
   writeln ('CURRENT SIGHTINGS');
   next := first;
   while  next <> nil  do
      begin
         with next^ do
            begin
               writeln (mo:2,'-',da:2,'-',yr:2,time:8);
               writeln ('     GRID LOCATION: ',grid1:3,grid2:3);
               writeln ('     NUMBER OF BIRDS: ',birds:4)
            end;
         next := next^.link
      end
end; {printlist}
{---------------------------------------------------------------}
begin {migration}
   reset (cranes);
   new (first);
   with first^ do
      readln (cranes,mo,da,yr,time,grid1,grid2,birds);
   first^.link := nil;
   while  not eof(cranes)  do
      begin
         new (current);
         with current^ do
            readln (cranes,mo,da,yr,time,grid1,grid2,birds);
         insert (current,first)
      end;
   printlist (first)
end. {migration}
{---------------------------------------------------------------}
```

Since the dynamic variable in this example is a record, items within it can be referenced with the pointer reference and the field identifier. Items within the dynamic variable can also be referenced using the field reference and a *with* statement. In this example, we used the *with* statement at several different points to improve the readability of the *readln* or *writeln* statements.

TESTING

As we decompose our solutions into steps that can be implemented in modules, we divide the solution into smaller problems that can be solved and tested more easily than the large problem can be solved and tested. If we use modules from another program, the time spent in development is not repeated, and we can begin the testing phase sooner. Testing this program is much easier because we have already developed and tested a similar insertion module and print module.

If we use the data from the hand example in this program, the output from our program is the following:

```
WHOOPING CRANE MIGRATION

CURRENT SIGHTINGS
 4- 3-86        920
          GRID LOCATION:   21    7
          NUMBER OF BIRDS:       5
 4- 5-86        815
          GRID LOCATION:   21    9
          NUMBER OF BIRDS:       4
 4- 8-86        830
          GRID LOCATION:   21    7
          NUMBER OF BIRDS:       4
 5- 1-86        1805
          GRID LOCATION:   22    8
          NUMBER OF BIRDS:       4
 5-10-86        800
          GRID LOCATION:   22    9
          NUMBER OF BIRDS:       4
 5-10-86        915
          GRID LOCATION:   22    9
          NUMBER OF BIRDS:       4
 5-15-86        730
          GRID LOCATION:   23    7
          NUMBER OF BIRDS:       5
```

Throughout this text, we have emphasized the importance of carefully selecting test data. If you look at the examples in this set of test data, you will see that it includes data ordered so that insertions will need to be made at the beginning of the linked list, at the end of the linked list, and between items that will already be in the linked list. Although these three insertions can be tested in different test cases instead of the same one, the program will not be thoroughly tested without each of these three cases.

Because we have several variables involved in determining the correct order of the sightings, we included some sightings with the same date but different times in order to test this part of the program.

10-3 ADDITIONAL DYNAMIC DATA STRUCTURES

In this section we present five additional linked data structures that are very powerful. Although each of these data structures could reasonably be the topic of an entire chapter, we introduce them in this section to illustrate some of the special structures that can be developed with the dynamic variable. At the end of this chapter we give you further references if you wish to study these data structures in more detail.

CIRCULARLY LINKED LIST

A **circularly linked list** is generated when the last element in a linked list points to the first element in the list. The following diagram compares a regular linked list with a circularly linked list:

Linked list

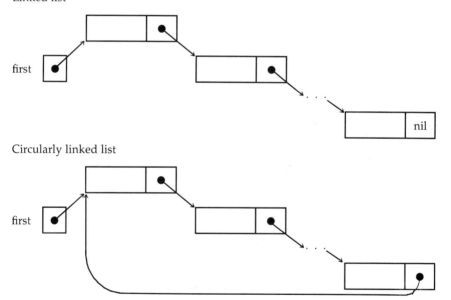

Circularly linked list

Note that the nil constant is not used with the circularly linked list because there really isn't an end to the list. However, in an empty circularly linked list the pointer *first* will contain the nil constant.

Inserting and deleting in a circularly linked list is very similar to inserting and deleting in a regular linked list. We do need to be careful that the first pointer is handled properly, because it not only points us to the beginning of the list but also determines when we have followed the links back around to the beginning.

Operating systems, which are really very sophisticated programs, have a number of applications suitable to a circularly linked list. For example, suppose that a particular program in an operating system is keeping track of the interactive users on the system. Each time a new user logs into the system, the user is added to the list, and each time a user logs off the system, the user is deleted from the list. This list has an order because new users are added at the end. When running interactive programs, the computer executes a number of steps in one user's program, then a number of steps in the next user's program, and so on until it is back to the first program. It then continues around again and again, in a circle. Thus, the information about the number of users on the system and the order in which the system will step through them is an ideal application for a circularly linked list. This type of circularly linked list is sometimes called a **round-robin** data structure.

DOUBLY LINKED LIST

We have used the linked list in several examples and have seen that the pointer in each element is used to point ahead to the next element. There are applications in which we would like to have the data linked together so that we can move forward or backward in the list. The following diagram compares a linked list with only forward links and a linked list with both forward links and backward links:

Linked list

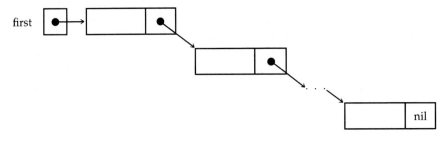

Doubly linked list

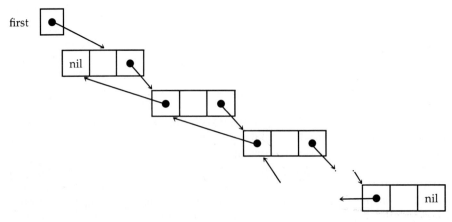

Although there is clearly an advantage to being able to move in either direction in a linked list, the routines for manipulating such a list become longer. For example, each insertion requires changing two forward links and two backward links. We must also be sure that the backward link of the first element in the list contains the *nil* constant, as does the forward link of the last element in the list.

Doubly linked lists are useful when we want to be able to insert or delete items without returning to the beginning of the list for each insertion or deletion. For example, suppose we have just inserted a new data value at the tenth item in the list. If we now wish to insert another item, instead of starting at the beginning of the list we can compare the new item to the one that we are currently accessing in the linked list. If the new item should come before the one that we are accessing, we can use the backward links to back through the list until we find the proper spot for the new insertion. If the new item should follow the one that we are accessing, we can use the forward links to continue through the list until we find the proper spot for the new insertion. This type of insertion can be very efficient in certain situations.

STACK

A **stack** is one of the most used dynamic data structures. It is often described in terms of a bucket, as shown in this diagram:

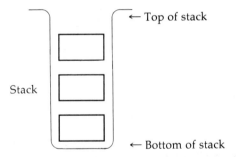

Adding an item to a stack is analogous to dropping it in the bucket. The top item on the stack is always the last item added. Thus, when we remove an item from a stack, it is the top item, or the last item that we added. This data structure is called a **lifo,** or last in, first out, structure. The routine for adding items to a stack is called a **push routine,** and the routine for removing items from a stack is called a **pop routine.** The next diagram illustrates the contents of a stack as items are added (push routine) and deleted (pop routine).

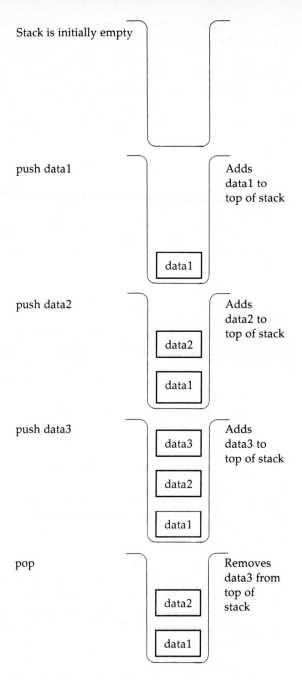

Stack is initially empty

push data1 — Adds data1 to top of stack

data1

push data2 — Adds data2 to top of stack

data2

data1

push data3 — Adds data3 to top of stack

data3

data2

data1

pop — Removes data3 from top of stack

data2

data1

From the diagram above, it is clear that a stack is a dynamic data structure. Thus, it can be implemented with a linked structure as shown following:

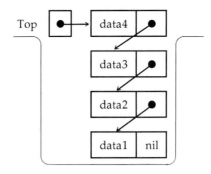

The routines for handling the push and pop routines must keep track not only of the links between elements in the stack but also of the top and bottom of the stack. The top of the stack is the position for the next insertion. Thus, if the top of the stack and the bottom of the stack point to the same position, then the stack is empty.

Stacks are used in a wide variety of applications. For example, if we want to print a set of values in reverse order, we can access the values in their regular order and place each item in the stack. When we reach the end of the values, we begin removing them from the stack. Since the last item added to the stack is the first one removed, we remove the items from the stack in the reverse order in which we added them. There are also a number of applications in which we need to hold values temporarily and then retrieve the most recently stored values first. Compilers frequently need this type of storage as they analyze the syntax in a program statement and convert it into machine language or assembly language.

QUEUE

The data structure called a **queue** is one with which we are very familiar, although we may not have realized that this structure had a name. Every time you stand in line, whether it is at the grocery store, the bank window, or the fast-food restaurant, you are in a queue. A queue is a data structure in which items are added at one end and removed from the other, as shown in the following diagram:

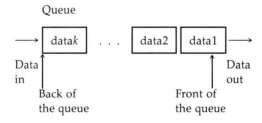

The queue is called a **fifo,** or first in, first out, structure.

Queues are commonly used in operating systems to keep track of users waiting for some computer resource. For example, suppose an interactive computer system has one printer with letter-quality type. If several users attempt to print reports at the same time, the operating system will "queue" the users so that the reports are printed one at a time, in the order that the requests are made.

The routines for handling the queue data structure must be able to handle the steps of inserting at one end of the queue and deleting from the other end. Thus, we need pointers for the front of the queue and for the back (sometimes called the **head** and **tail** of the queue). Obviously, we also need to be able to detect an empty queue. The links within the queue are similar to the regular linked list, but we can only insert at one end and delete from the other. The diagram below shows how the links and pointers are used to implement the queue:

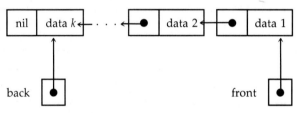

BINARY TREE

The final dynamic data structure that we are going to present is the **binary tree.** A binary tree is a data structure that begins with a single element, often called the **root** of the tree. This element has a **left branch** and a **right branch.** The element at each branch also has a left branch and a right branch. The overall structure of a binary tree is shown in the next diagram:

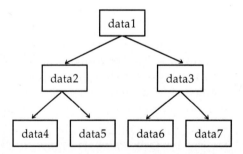

Binary trees are especially useful in certain types of searches. For example, if we assume that the data stored in the tree is ordered, with smaller values always to the left and larger values always to the right, then the algorithm to determine if a particular value is in the list is very efficient. We first compare the root to the value for which we are searching. The results of the comparison immediately determine which half of the tree is left to search. The comparison in the first branch of the correct half of the tree reduces the search to one-fourth of the tree, and so on. This process can be illustrated with the following tree:

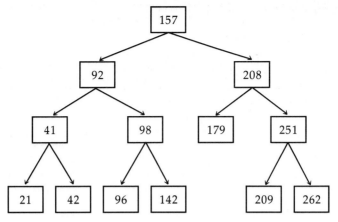

Suppose we wish to determine if the number 189 is contained in the tree. We begin with the root element. Since 189 is greater than 157, we know we must search the right branch. The first right branch contains the value 208, which is greater than the number 189. We thus take the left branch at the value 208. The branch value 179 represents the end of the branch, and we now know that the value 189 is not in the tree. If we wanted to insert it in the tree, we are now at the position to perform the insertion.

The routines to search a tree and to add and delete elements in the tree require the use of the root position and the left and right links. The implementation of the tree using our dynamic data structure can be performed like this:

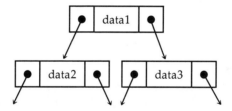

This section has introduced you to the more common dynamic data structures. As you have seen in these examples, the common thread in the structures is the use of the pointer to link the data elements together. Refer to the books listed below for information on other dynamic data structures and for more information on the routines for handling the data structures presented in this section.

1. Knuth, D. *Fundamental Algorithms,* 2d ed. (Reading, Mass.: Addison-Wesley, 1973).
2. Knuth, D. *Sorting and Searching* (Reading, Mass.: Addison-Wesley, 1973).
3. Siewiorek, D., C. Bell, and A. Newell. *Computer Structure: Principles and Examples* (New York: McGraw-Hill, 1982).
4. Tenenbaum, A., and M. Augerstein. *Data Structures Using Pascal* (Englewood Cliffs, N.J.: Prentice-Hall, 1981).
5. Wirth, N. *Algorithms + Data Structures = Programs* (Englewood Cliffs, N.J.: Prentice-Hall, 1976).

10-4 SETS

A **set** is a data type composed of a collection of elements that have the same ordinal type, called the **base type.** For example, we can specify sets of integers and sets of characters. A set differs from an array because it is not ordered; that is, it does not have a first element followed by a second element, and so on. An element is either a member of the set or it is not.

When we define a set, we must specify the base type for its elements; the base type must be an ordinal type. The maximum number of values that a set can have depends on the system, so check a manual to determine the limit for your compiler. For our examples we assume that the maximum number of values for a set is 256. The following definition describes a set of characters and a set of integers:

```
type
    charset = set of 'A'..'Z';
    intset = set of 1..25;
var
    letters: charset;
    idset: intset;
```

The set *letters* is defined with a character base type that is further restricted to the set of uppercase alphabetic letters. The set *idset* is defined with an integer base type that is further restricted to the subrange 1..25.

Defining a set does not give it any initial value, so we must give it a value before we can use its contents. If we want to initialize a set to a specific group of values, we use an assignment statement with brackets around the values to be stored in the set. The following statement initializes the set *idset* to the values 1 and 2:

```
idset := [1,2]
```

We frequently want our sets to contain no elements initially. These sets are referred to as **empty sets.** We can specify that a set is to be empty initially with the following statement:

```
idset := []
```

Note that we again use the brackets but do not include any elements within them. The statement below specifies that the set *idset* is to contain the integers 1 through 10 and 15:

```
idset := [1..10,15]
```

The elements of a set must all be of the same base type, and as we have already stated, there is no order attached to them. The elements in the set are also unique. Consider the following initialization for the set *idset:*

```
idset := [1..5,2]
```

This set has five elements, namely the integers 1, 2, 3, 4, and 5. The integer 2 will not appear twice.

We can access individual elements in an array using a subscript, but we cannot access individual elements in a set directly because of the lack of order to the elements. Instead, we compare a specific element to the set and determine whether that element is in the set. This is done using the *in* operator. For example, if we want to print the elements in a set, we must use a loop that determines if a specific element is in the set, and if so, we print that value. If *seta* is a set whose base values are the integers from 0 to 100, the following loop prints the values in the set:

```
for i := 0 to 100 do
    if  i in seta   then
        writeln (i)
```

In this example, each element in *seta* is printed on a different line. If the set contains many elements, this may not be a desirable way of printing the elements in the array. The following example illustrates a method for printing several values on the same line.

EXAMPLE 10-5   Procedure to Print Set Elements

Write a procedure with an input parameter that is an integer set whose base type is the integers 1 to 100. Print the elements of the array, five per line.

Solution

In this procedure we use a loop to compare the integers 1 to 100 to the elements in the set. When we find a match, we use the *write* statement to print the value. After every five *write* statements, we execute a *writeln* statement to print the line and begin building the next line. We assume that the type *keyset* has been defined with the following type statement:

```
type
    keyset = set of 1..100;
```

The procedure *printset* is then the following:

```
{- - - - - - - - - - - - - - - - - - - - - - - - - - - - - - - - - - - - - - - - - - - - -}
procedure  printset (x:keyset);
    {This procedure prints the elements of the
    set x, five values per line.}
var
    count, i: integer;
begin {printset}
    count := 0;
    for i := 1 to 100 do
        if  i in x   then
            begin
                write (i:5);
                count := count + 1;
                if  count mod 5 = 0   then
                    writeln
            end;
    writeln
end; {printset}
{- - - - - - - - - - - - - - - - - - - - - - - - - - - - - - - - - - - - - - - - - - - - -}
```

The *in* operation is useful in determining if a particular value is in a set, but we also want to be able to perform operations with the sets themselves. The next part of this section covers the operations that can be performed with sets.

SET OPERATIONS

We can perform three operations with sets. Each of these operations yields a new set. The operation **union** adds elements to a set, the operation **difference** subtracts elements from a set, and the operation **intersection** forms a set of elements common to different sets. We now look at each of these operations with some examples.

One set is added to another with the union operation, which is specified with a plus sign. Thus, if *seta, setb,* and *setc* represent sets with the same base type, the statement below forms a set called *setc,* which is the combination of the two sets:

```
seta := [1..5];
setb := [2..8,10];
setc := seta + setb
```

After executing the statements above, *setc* contains the following elements: 1, 2, 3, 4, 5, 6, 7, 8, 10. Set union is used to add elements to a set, as shown in the statements below:

```
readln (number);
setc := setc + [number]
```

A value is read into the variable number. We then perform a set union between the set *setc* and the set composed of *number* (note the brackets around the variable name to specify that *number* is being used as a set). Thus, if *number* is not already in *setc,* it is added to *setc;* if *number* is already in *setc, setc* does not change.

The difference operation, used to remove elements from a set, is specified with the minus sign. Consider the statement below, which assumes that *setd* is defined with the same type definition as *seta* and *setb:*

```
setd := setb - seta
```

In this statement, *setd* is defined as the set difference of *setb* and *seta.* Thus, we can define *setd* as the set of elements that are in *setb* but that are not in *seta.* If *setb* and *seta* contain exactly the same set of elements, *setd* is the empty set. If *setb* and *seta* contain no elements in common, *setd* contains the same set of elements as *setb.* What is the value of *setd* if *setb* is the empty set? The answer is the empty set, because *setd* cannot contain any more elements than the set *setb.* What is the value of *setd* if *setb* and *seta* are both empty? The answer is again the empty set. Consider the following statements:

```
seta := [1..20];
setb := [5,10,15,20,25]
setc := seta - setb;
setd := setb - seta
```

After executing these statements, *setc* contains the integers 1, 2, 3, 4, 6, 7, 8, 9, 11, 12, 13, 14, 16, 17, 18, 19, and *setd* contains the integer 25.

The set formed by the intersection of two sets is the set of elements that are common to both sets. Thus, if two sets have exactly the same elements, their intersection is the same set of elements. If two sets have no elements in common, their intersection is the empty set. The intersection is specified with an asterisk. The following statements compute *setc* as the intersection of *seta* and *setb:*

```
setc := seta*setb
```

If *seta* is the set [1..5] and *setb* is the set [5,10], then the intersection is the set [5].

Venn diagrams are often used to illustrate set operations. With Venn diagrams, we represent a set by a circle, drawn within a rectangle. This rectangle, representing all elements of the base type of the set, is called the **universal set.** For example, if a set *a* is defined with a base type of integers [1..100], the rectangle represents all integers from 1 through 100 (the universal set) and the circle within the rectangle represents the elements of the universal set that are within *a.*

Universal set

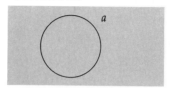

The following set of diagrams uses two sets, *a* and *b,* to illustrate the three set operations. The area darkened in the first diagram represents the set formed by the set union *a+b,* which is the same set as the set union *b+a.* The area darkened in the second diagram represents the set formed by the set difference *a—b.* The area darkened in the third diagram represents the set formed by the set difference *b—a.* The area darkened in the fourth diagram represents the set formed by the set intersection *a*b,* which is the same set as the set intersection *b*a.*

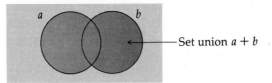

Universal set

Set union $a + b$

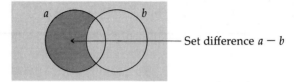

Universal set

Set difference $a - b$

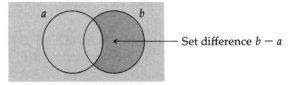

Universal set

Set difference $b - a$

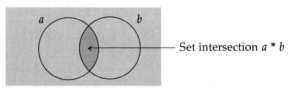

Universal set

Set intersection $a * b$

The elements in the darkened areas of all the diagrams depend on the values in the sets a and b. It is possible that a darkened area could represent the empty set. For example, if the set a contained the elements 2, 4, 6, 8, and the set b contained the elements 1..10, then the set difference $a-b$ would be the empty set. If we included these elements in the Venn diagram circles and assumed that the universal set was the integers 1..15, then our diagram of this set difference would be the following:

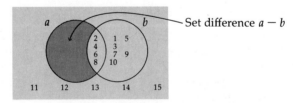

Universal set

Set difference $a - b$

EXAMPLE 10-6   Count the Elements in an Intersection

Give the steps necessary to count the number of elements in the intersection of sets a and b and store the intersection in a set called ab. Assume that the sets *a*, *b*, and *ab* have been defined as type *keyset*, which includes integers from 1 to 200.

Solution

The following statements define the set *ab* as the intersection of *a* and *b*, and store in the integer *count* the number of elements in *ab*.

```
ab := a*b;
count := 0;
for i := 1 to 200 do
    if  i in ab  then
        count := count + 1
```

RELATIONAL OPERATORS

Before defining relational operators with sets, we need to define the concept of **subset.** A set *a* is a subset of the set *b* if every element of *a* is also an element of *b*. In the following example, *a* is a subset of *b*:

```
type
    keyset = set of 1..100;
var
    a, b: keyset;
    .
    .
    .
a := [1..50];
b := [1..75];
```

We use the condition $a <= b$ to determine whether *a* is a subset of *b*. Another way of specifying the same thing is to use the notation $b >= a$. If the condition $a <= b$ is true, then *a* is a subset of *b*.

Two sets *a* and *b* are equal if they contain exactly the same elements. We use the condition $a = b$ to test for set equality and the condition $a <> b$ to test for set inequality.

In mathematical set theory, a set *a* is a **proper subset** of *b* when *a* is a subset of *b* and there is at least one element of *b* that does not appear in *a*. In Pascal, to determine if *a* is a proper subset of *b*, we first need to determine if *a* is equal to *b*. If *a* is not equal to *b*, then we determine if *a* is a subset of *b*. The following statements print a message if the set *a* is a proper subset of *b*:

```
if  a <> b  then
    if  a <= b  then
        writeln ('A IS A PROPER SUBSET OF B')
```

Some compilers allow the use of the relational operators $<$ and $>$ to test for proper subsets, but the ISO standard specifies only the relational operators $=$, $<>$, $<=$, and $>=$ for sets.

The Venn diagrams on the next page illustrate some of the different subset relationships possible with two nonempty sets *a* and *b*:

Universal set

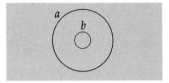

Universal set

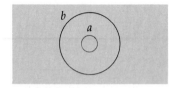

Universal set

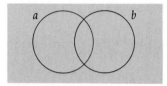

Universal set

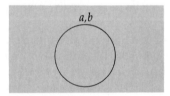

Universal set

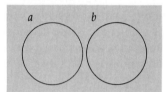

Note that it is possible for two nonempty sets to be unequal, and for neither to be a subset of the other.

EXAMPLE 10-7   Print the Elements Common to Two Sets

Give the statements necessary to print the elements that are common to both sets *a* and *b*. Print the values one per line. If there are no elements in common, print the message 'NO ELEMENTS IN COMMON'. Assume that the sets *a* and *b* are defined such that their base type is the set of integers from 1 to 200.

Solution

In the statements below, we store the intersection of *a* and *b* in a separate set *c;* otherwise, we would need to compute the set intersection for each test within the *for* loop.

```
type
   keyset = set of 1..200;
var
   a, b, c: keyset;
   .
   .
   .
   c := a*b;
   if  c = []  then
      writeln ('NO ELEMENTS IN COMMON')
   else
      for i := 1 to 200 do
          if  i in c  then
             writeln (i:5)
```

SELF-TEST 10-2

This self-test allows you to check quickly to see if you have remembered certain key points from Section 10-4. If you have any problems with the exercises, you should reread this section. The solutions are included at the end of the text.

The following statements define sets *a, b,* and *c.* New sets are then defined using set operations with *a, b,* and *c.* After each new set is defined, give the elements that are in the new set.

```
type
   numbers = set of -10..10;
var
   a, b, c, d, e, f, g, h: numbers;
   .
   .
   .
   a := [2,4,6,8];
   b := [0,1,2,3,4];
   c := [-2,0,2];
```

1. d := a - b
2. e := (a*b)*c
3. f := (a + b) + c
4. g := (c - b)*a
5. h := (b - a) - c

10-5 PROBLEM SOLVING—ACCIDENT SURVEY

In this section, we use information collected from traffic accidents that occurred within the limits of a large city to determine some statistics on injury accidents. The data collected has been stored in a data file in the order in which the accidents occurred, with one line of data per accident. The information for an accident is summarized in six integers, which represent the following information:

> Identification number for the accident
> Number of cars involved in the accident
> Number of trucks involved in the accident
> Number of other vehicles (bicycles, motorcycles, etc.) involved in the accident
> Number of pedestrians involved in the accident
> Number of people injured in the accident

The identification number is between 1 and 250. There is no trailer signal at the end of the data file.

We are interested in summarizing some of the information from this file regarding accidents with injuries. Specifically, we want to compute the following items:

> Average number of vehicles per accident
> Average number of vehicles per accident with injuries
> Percent of accidents with injuries
> Percent of accidents with injuries involving pedestrians
> Percent of accidents with injuries involving vehicles other than cars and trucks
> Percent of accidents with injuries involving only cars

As we consider the steps necessary to compute these values, we find that we are grouping the accidents according to categories: accidents with vehicles, accidents with vehicles and injuries, and so on. Within a category, there is no order to the information; thus, a good choice of data structure is a set.

PROBLEM DESCRIPTION

Print a report summarizing data on accidents with injuries.

INPUT/OUTPUT DESCRIPTION

The accident data is contained in a data file *survey*, which contains information for each accident. The output is a report with the following information:

```
            SURVEY OF ACCIDENTS WITH INJURIES

    AVERAGE NUMBER OF VEHICLES PER ACCIDENT = XX.X

    AVERAGE NUMBER OF VEHICLES PER ACCIDENT
                           WITH INJURIES = XX.X

    PERCENT OF ACCIDENTS WITH INJURIES = XXX.X %

    PERCENT OF ACCIDENTS WITH INJURIES
              INVOLVING PEDESTRIANS = XXX.X %

    PERCENT OF ACCIDENTS WITH INJURIES
            INVOLVING VEHICLES OTHER
                THAN CARS AND TRUCKS = XXX.X %

    PERCENT OF ACCIDENTS WITH INJURIES
                INVOLVING ONLY CARS = XXX.X %
```

HAND EXAMPLE

For a hand example, we use the following accident survey information:

ACCIDENT ID	CARS INVOLVED	TRUCKS INVOLVED	OTHER VEHICLES INVOLVED	PEDESTRIANS INVOLVED	INJURIES INVOLVED
142	2	0	0	0	1
144	0	1	1	0	2
145	1	0	0	1	0
150	0	1	1	0	0
152	1	2	0	0	1
156	0	0	1	0	1
159	1	0	1	1	3

Using this data, the report information is the following:

```
            SURVEY OF ACCIDENTS WITH INJURIES

    AVERAGE NUMBER OF VEHICLES PER ACCIDENT =  1.9

    AVERAGE NUMBER OF VEHICLES PER ACCIDENT
                           WITH INJURIES =  2.0

    PERCENT OF ACCIDENTS WITH INJURIES =  71.4 %

    PERCENT OF ACCIDENTS WITH INJURIES
              INVOLVING PEDESTRIANS =  14.3 %

    PERCENT OF ACCIDENTS WITH INJURIES
            INVOLVING VEHICLES OTHER
                THAN CARS AND TRUCKS =  42.9 %

    PERCENT OF ACCIDENTS WITH INJURIES
                INVOLVING ONLY CARS =  14.3 %
```

ALGORITHM DEVELOPMENT

As we have already discussed, sets are good choices for data structures for this algorithm because we are working with categories of information that have no particular order. We do not need sets to compute the averages because we can accumulate this data as we read the information; the sets are used for storing accident identification numbers for the various categories. The decomposition of the solution is:

DECOMPOSITION

Read data and compute averages.
Determine percentages.
Print report.

We can count the number of accidents as we read the data. We can also generate sets with identification numbers for the various categories in which we are interested—accidents involving cars, accidents involving trucks, accidents involving other vehicles, accidents involving pedestrians, and accidents involving injuries. The same identification number may occur in one or more of the sets. We can use the set operations of union, intersection, and difference to find identification numbers that meet certain specifications. Since we want to count the number of elements in several sets, we use a function to determine the number of elements in a set. With this in mind, we develop the pseudocode for the solution.

```
accident: totalid ← 0
            vehicles ← 0
            vehinjury ← 0
            initialize sets to empty sets
            while  more data  do
               read id,ncars,ntrucks,nother,npedestrian,ninjuries
               totalid ← totalid + 1
               vehicles ← vehicles + ncars + ntrucks + nother
               if  ninjuries > 0  then
                  vehinjury ← vehinjury + ncars + ntrucks + nother
                  add id to injury set
               if  ncars > 0  then
                  add id to car set
               if  ntrucks > 0  then
                  add id to truck set
               if  nother > 0  then
                  add id to other set
               if  npedestrian > 0  then
                  add id to pedestrian set
            ave ← vehicles/totalid
            injcount ← setcount(injuries)
            injpedcount ← setcount(injury set*pedestrian set)
            injothercount ← setcount(injury set*other set)
            onlycars ← cars − ((trucks set+other set)
                                    +pedestrian set)
            injcarcount ← setcount(injury set*onlycars)
            aveinjury ← vehinjury/injcount
            percinj ← injcount/totalid*100.0
            percped ← injpedcount/totalid*100.0
            percother ← injothercount/totalid*100.0
            perccars ← injcarcount/totalid*100.0
            write report using averages and percents calculated

setcount (x):  count ← 0
               for i = 1 to 250 do
                  if  i is in set  then
                     count ← count + 1
```

The structure chart for the solution is shown next, along with the Pascal program.

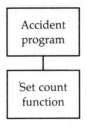

PASCAL PROGRAM

```
{------------------------------------------------------------}
program   accident (survey,output);
    {This program uses the data in an accident survey file
    to summarize information regarding accidents with injuries.}
type
    id = set of 1..250;
var
    ave,aveinjury,percinj,percped,percother,perccars: real;
    injothercount, injpedcount, injcount, totalid,
    vehicles, idnum, vehinjury, injcarcount,
    ncars, ntrucks, nother, npedestrian, ninjuries: integer;
    survey: text;
    cars, trucks, other, pedestrians, injuries, onlycars: id;
{------------------------------------------------------------}
function   setcount (x:id): integer;
    {This function counts the number of elements in the set x.}
var
    count, i: integer;
begin {setcount}
    count := 0;
    for i := 1 to 250 do
        if   i in x   then
            count := count + 1;
    setcount := count
end; {setcount}
{------------------------------------------------------------}
begin {accident}
    totalid := 0;
    vehicles := 0;
    vehinjury := 0;
    cars := [];
    trucks := [];
    other := [];
    pedestrians := [];
    injuries := [];
    reset (survey);
```

```
        while  not eof(survey)  do
          begin
              readln (survey,idnum,ncars,ntrucks,nother,
                      npedestrian,ninjuries);
              totalid := totalid + 1;
              vehicles := vehicles + ncars + ntrucks + nother;
              if  ninjuries > 0  then
                begin
                    vehinjury := vehinjury + ncars + ntrucks + nother;
                    injuries := injuries + [idnum]
                end;
              if  ncars > 0  then
                  cars := cars + [idnum];
              if  ntrucks > 0  then
                  trucks := trucks + [idnum];
              if  nother > 0  then
                  other := other + [idnum];
              if  npedestrian > 0  then
                  pedestrian := pedestrian + [idnum]
          end;
      ave := vehicles/totalid;
      injcount := setcount(injuries);
      injpedcount := setcount(injuries*pedestrian);
      injothercount := setcount(injuries*other);
      onlycars := cars - ((trucks+other)+pedestrians);
      injcarcount := setcount(injuries*onlycars);
      aveinjury := vehinjury/injcount;
      percinj := injcount/totalid*100.0;
      percped := injpedcount/totalid*100.0;
      percother := injothercount/totalid*100.0;
      perccars := injcarcount/totalid*100.0;
      writeln ('     SURVEY OF ACCIDENTS WITH INJURIES');
      writeln;
      writeln ('AVERAGE NUMBER OF VEHICLES PER ACCIDENT = ',
              ave:4:1);
      writeln;
      writeln ('AVERAGE NUMBER OF VEHICLES PER ACCIDENT');
      writeln ('                         WITH INJURIES = ',
              aveinjury:4:1);
      writeln;
      writeln ('PERCENT OF ACCIDENTS WITH INJURIES = ',
              percinj:5:1,' %');
      writeln;
      writeln ('PERCENT OF ACCIDENTS WITH INJURIES');
      writeln ('              INVOLVING PEDESTRIANS = ',
              percped:5:1,' %');
      writeln;
      writeln ('PERCENT OF ACCIDENTS WITH INJURIES');
      writeln ('           INVOLVING VEHICLES OTHER');
      writeln ('            THAN CARS AND TRUCKS = ',
              percother:5:1,' %');
      writeln;
      writeln ('PERCENT OF ACCIDENTS WITH INJURIES');
      writeln ('              INVOLVING ONLY CARS = ',
              perccars:5:1,' %')
end. {accidents}
{-------------------------------------------------------------}
```

If we use the sample data in the program, our output is the following:

```
        SURVEY OF ACCIDENTS WITH INJURIES

    AVERAGE NUMBER OF VEHICLES PER ACCIDENT =   1.9

    AVERAGE NUMBER OF VEHICLES PER ACCIDENT
                         WITH INJURIES =   2.0

    PERCENT OF ACCIDENTS WITH INJURIES =   71.4 %

    PERCENT OF ACCIDENTS WITH INJURIES
               INVOLVING PEDESTRIANS =   14.3 %

    PERCENT OF ACCIDENTS WITH INJURIES
            INVOLVING VEHICLES OTHER
               THAN CARS AND TRUCKS =   42.9 %

    PERCENT OF ACCIDENTS WITH INJURIES
               INVOLVING ONLY CARS =   14.3 %
```

SUMMARY

This chapter presented two unique types of data structures, the dynamic data structure and the set. The dynamic data structure is extremely powerful for linking together components that have some order. The size of the data structure is determined as the program executes and thus enables very efficient use of memory. The many different ways of linking the components together allows us to define the data structure in such a way that it fits the data naturally, thus making the linked list very useful in writing programs that solve complicated problems with straightforward solutions. The set is a collection of components that are grouped together but that do not have any specified order. The set data structure is especially useful when we want to determine elements that have special relationships with other sets, such as the set of elements each contained in a group of other sets.

DEBUGGING AIDS

Probably the most useful debugging aid for a data structure is a module for printing the values in the data structure in a convenient form. This module can then be referenced at key points in your program. As it shows you the current contents of the data structure, you can locate the problem areas in your program. Examples of modules for printing a linked list and for printing the contents of a set were developed in this chapter.

When you use one of the data structures in this chapter, it is also a good idea to use the same set of procedures that you have used in other programs. For example, do not rewrite an insertion routine every time you write a program that uses a linked list. Write and carefully test one insertion routine that is general enough to be adapted for most uses. Then modify it and use it when you need an insertion routine. Not only do you save time in the development and testing of the routine, but you will also find that your programs have fewer problems because you are using similar logic and similar variables to work with the data structure. Some of the routines that you may want to have available for linked lists and for sets are the following:

Linked list — procedure to print a linked list,
              procedure to insert in a linked list,
              procedure to delete from a linked list,
              function to count elements in a linked list

Sets — procedure to print the contents of a set,
              procedure to print the union of two sets,
              procedure to print the difference of two sets,
              procedure to print the intersection of two sets,
              function to count the elements in a set

In addition to having a set of common routines, be sure that you are consistent in the identifiers you use for referencing key elements in the data structure. For example, don't call the previous item *previous* in one program, *behind* in another program, and *past* in still another. You will be able to write programs and routines with fewer problems if you do not have to worry about which identifiers you are using in the current program.

STYLE/TECHNIQUE GUIDELINES

Good style and technique follow naturally in a program if the correct data structure has been chosen. If you are having difficulties writing statements that have good readability and good technique in a program with a dynamic data structure or a set, you should reconsider your choice of data structure. The power of these structures lies in their ability to take an otherwise complicated problem and make it straightforward. If we try to mold the data into the wrong structure, we compromise this power and often find that it is very difficult to write programs and procedures with good style and technique.

Some of the suggestions from the debugging aids also apply to style and technique. Use similar routines in programs that use dynamic data structures or sets. A set of common routines makes it easier for you and others to read your programs. Similarly, a common set of variable names also adds to the style that you incorporate in your programs.

We recommend that all new data types and pointers be defined in the type section of your program. This groups all the new types together. Later you can add procedures and functions to your programs that use these new data types and pointers as parameters without having to change other parts of your program.

KEY WORDS

base type	push routine
binary tree	queue
circularly linked list	set
doubly linked list	set difference
dynamic data structure	set intersection
dynamic variable	set union
empty set	stack
linked list	subset
nil constant	universal set
pointer variable	Venn diagram
pop routine	

PROBLEMS

We begin our problem set with modifications to the programs and modules developed earlier in this chapter. Give the decomposition, refined pseudocode, and Pascal program for each problem.

Problems 1-5 modify the whooping crane migration program, *migration*, given on page 482.

1. Modify the whooping crane migration program so that it prints a count of the number of sightings at the end of the report.
2. Modify the whooping crane migration program so that it prints the maximum number of birds that have been sighted in the current report.
3. Modify the whooping crane migration program so that it prints a list of all grid locations of sightings. Even if a location occurs more than once, it should only be printed once.
4. Modify the whooping crane migration program so that it tracks only a certain size group. For example, the program could ask the user to enter the size group of cranes in which the user is interested. If the user enters the number 5, then the program will link together and print a report only for the data that included five birds in the sighting data.

5. Modify the whooping crane migration program so that it prints the longest period of time (in days) between sightings within the file. Print this at the end of the report.

Problems 6 – 10 modify the accident survey program *accident,* given on page 504.

6. Modify the accident survey program so that it prints a list of accident identification numbers for all accidents with injuries.
7. Modify the accident survey program so that it prints the number of accidents with injuries in addition to printing the percentage of accidents with injuries.
8. Modify the accident survey program so that it prints the number of pedestrians involved in accidents with injuries in addition to printing the percentage of accidents with injuries involving pedestrians.
9. Modify the accident survey program so that it prints the total number of vehicles involved in accidents with injuries and then prints the percentage of the vehicles that are cars, the percentage that are trucks, and the percentage that are other vehicles.
10. Modify the accident survey program so that it prints the average number of injuries per accident with injuries.

The next set of problems uses the data entered from the terminal to display the status of orders at a computer warehouse. As people come by to pick up an item, the information is added to a linked list, displayed on a screen in the warehouse so that the stock people can bring the items to the pick-up door. Once an order is picked up, the information is entered at the terminal so that the order can be removed from the list. Note that the items in this list are in the order in which they are received.

11. Write a procedure *neworder* that has an order number and item number as parameters. Add a record containing these two numbers to the end of a linked list that has two pointers, *first* and *last,* where *first* points to the first element in the list and *last* points to the last element in the list. If *first* contains the constant *nil,* the list is empty. If *first* and *last* point to the same item, the list contains one item. Assume that *first* and *last* also are parameters to the procedure. The following type statements are included in the program:

```
type
    pointer = ^order;
    order = record
                number, item: integer;
                ptr: pointer
            end;
```

12. Write a procedure *printorder* to print the contents of the linked list pointed to by the parameter *first.* If the list is empty, print an appropriate message.
13. Write a procedure *orderfilled* that has an order number and the pointer *first* as parameters. The procedure should delete the entry in the linked list that

corresponds to the order number that is the input parameter. If the corresponding entry is not in the linked list, print an error message.

14. Write a program using the modules defined in problems 11, 12, and 13 to accept information from the terminal, either to add data to the end of the linked list or to remove data from the linked list. Assume that the terminal interaction has the following form. First, this message is printed:

```
ENTER N FOR NEW ORDER TO ADD TO LIST
      D TO DELETE ORDER FROM LIST
      Q TO QUIT PROGRAM
```

If the character N is read, the program should print the message ENTER ORDER NUMBER AND ITEM NUMBER. After reading the appropriate information, it should use the procedure *neworder* to add the information to the list. If the character D is read, the program should print the message ENTER ORDER NUMBER. After reading the order number, it should use the procedure *orderfilled* to remove the order from the list. If the character Q is read, the program should print either ORDER LIST EMPTY or ORDER LIST NOT EMPTY. If the list is not empty, the list should be printed before the program terminates. The program should be built around a main loop that accepts the character N, D, or Q from the terminal and then takes the appropriate action. After adding or deleting an item, it should print the contents of the list and return to wait for the next character to be entered.

15. Modify the program in problem 14 so that it prints a final total of orders filled before terminating.

16. Assume that a linked list is going to be used to store the item numbers and quantities sold for the computer warehouse, in addition to the linked list that is being used to keep track of orders being filled. This new linked list is to contain the item number and the quantity of that item that has been sold. Each time an order is received, information is added to the order linked list and to the item linked list. Write a procedure *newitem* whose input parameters are a pointer *item1* to the first item in the item linked list and the item number. The new linked list is to be ordered by item number, and each element of the linked list is to contain an item number, the quantity of that item that has been sold, and a pointer to the next item in the list. Assume that *item1* contains the constant *nil* if the list is empty. The following type statements are included in the program:

```
type
    itemptr = ^itemrec;
    itemrec = record
                 item, quantity: integer;
                 nextitem: itemptr
              end;
```

The procedure should insert a new item if it is not in the list and should increment the quantity by 1 if the item is already in the list.

17. Write a procedure *printitem* to print the contents of the linked list pointed to by *item1*. If the list is empty, print an appropriate message.

18. Modify the program in problem 14 so that it correctly updates the item linked list when new orders are received. Print a summary of the information in the item linked list when the program terminates.

The next set of problems uses the data in a data file called *software* that contains the information on software sales for a small computer store. Each line in the file contains the following information:

   Sales receipt number
   Identification code for the software package sold

The sales receipt number is an integer less than 200. The identification code is an integer representing the following packages:

   1 — Word processor
   2 — Pascal compiler
   3 — F77 compiler
   4 — C compiler
   5 — Graphics package

If a sale involves more than one package, there is more than one line in the file with the same sales receipt number.

19. Write a procedure called *readsets* that reads the data from the file *software* and generates five sets. One set should contain the sales receipt numbers from sales of word processors, another should contain the sales receipt numbers from sales of Pascal compilers, and so on.
20. Write a procedure called *printset* that prints sales receipt numbers contained in a set that is an input parameter. (Assume that the sets have already been initialized with the procedure described in problem 19.)
21. Write a function called *countset* that returns a count of the sales receipts contained in a set that is an input parameter.
22. Using the modules in problems 19, 20, and 21, write a program to read and initialize the five sets of receipt numbers. Print a summary report giving the number of sales for each category of software. Use the following format:

```
          MONTHLY SOFTWARE SALES SUMMARY

          CATEGORY               NUMBER OF SALES
          ------------------------------------
          WORD PROCESSOR              XXXX
          PASCAL COMPILER             XXXX
          F77 COMPILER                XXXX
          C COMPILER                  XXXX
          GRAPHICS PACKAGE            XXXX
```

23. Modify the program in problem 22 so that it also prints the total number of sales receipts and the number of software packages sold.

24. Modify the program in problem 22 so that it also includes the following analysis information in the summary report:

```
NUMBER OF COMPILERS SOLD                   XXXX
NUMBER OF RECEIPTS WITH ONE COMPILER       XXXX
NUMBER OF RECEIPTS WITH TWO COMPILERS      XXXX
NUMBER OF RECEIPTS WITH THREE COMPILERS    XXXX
```

25. Modify the program in problem 22 so that it includes the following summary information in the summary report:

```
NUMBER OF WORD PROCESSORS SOLD               XXXX
NUMBER OF WORD PROCESSORS SOLD SEPARATELY    XXXX
NUMBER OF WORD PROCESSORS SOLD WITH A COMPILER  XXXX
```

26. Write a program that uses the modules from problems 19 and 20 to read the information in the file software. Print the sales receipt numbers for sales in each set, four numbers per line (you may need to modify the procedure *printset*). Use the following heading format for each set:

```
SALES RECEIPTS FOR WORD PROCESSORS

XXXXX XXXXX XXXXX XXXXX
           .
           .
           .
```

The next set of problems uses the data in a file called *training* that contains the employee information for a training program conducted during work hours. The training program offers courses in four topics: electronics, computer literacy, digital logic design, and microprocessors. The codes for these courses are, respectively, E, C, D, and M. Each time an employee completes one of these programs, a line is added to the file that contains the code for the course completed followed by the employee number (an integer between 500 and 750). The order of the information in the file is the order in which courses were completed.

27. Write a procedure *readcourse* that reads the information in this file and generates four sets that contain the employee numbers of the employees who took the electronics course, the computer literacy course, the digital logic design course, and the microprocessor course.

28. Write a procedure *printstudent* that prints the employee numbers in a set that is an input parameter. The employee numbers should be printed in descending order, three numbers per line.

29. Write a function called *countstudent* that returns a count of the employee numbers contained in a set that is an input parameter.

30. Using the modules in problems 27, 28, and 29, write a program to read and initialize the four sets of employee numbers. Print a summary report giving the percentage of students taking each course. Use the following format:

```
SUMMARY OF TRAINING PROGRAM COURSES

COURSE                    PERCENTAGE
------------------------------------
ELECTRONICS               XXX.X
COMPUTER LITERACY         XXX.X
DIGITAL LOGIC DESIGN      XXX.X
MICROPROCESSORS           XXX.X
```

31. Modify the program in problem 30 so that it also prints the total enrollment in the courses and the number of students involved. (Remember, one student may take several courses.)

32. Modify the program in Problem 30 so that it also prints the number of students who took only one course, the number of students who took two courses, the number of students who took three courses, and the number of students who took all four courses.

PROBLEM SOLVING — Coil Deflection Model

One of the greatest achievements of engineers and scientists has been the manned expeditions to the moon. Sophisticated sensors and computer equipment provide the astronauts and the NASA staff with the information they need to make decisions during the flights. Collecting data and then using that data to develop an equation or model is important in analyzing a complex system. Write a program to determine a linear model for a set of coil deflection data that has been collected from a spacecraft accelerometer. (See Section 11-2 for the solution.)

11

NUMERICAL TECHNIQUES AND APPLICATIONS

INTRODUCTION

The strengths of Pascal are often described in terms of its data structures. We have seen many different ways to describe and manipulate data with these structures. Using these data structures and the Pascal statements and procedures that we have already discussed, we find that Pascal can perform the numerical computations needed by engineers and scientists. In this chapter we discuss some of the common numerical techniques used to solve engineering and science problems along with some suggestions for avoiding or minimizing errors that are due to the precision of the computer.

11-1 APPROXIMATIONS

In this section we present several numerical techniques for **approximating** values or functions. Many engineering problems in complex environments use data samples to compute another value or to construct a model for the system being studied. For example, in weather forecasts the meteorologist uses the temperature and humidity values plus general weather conditions around the country to predict tomorrow's weather. Computer modeling is a similar process. We use the available information to determine an equation that "best fits" the data, and then we use that model to predict additional data values. When we use interpolation to find a logarithm or trigonometric value between entries in a table, we assume that the values are connected by a straight line. Interpolation computes a specific value on that line. In Section 11-2, we present an application in which we determine a **linear model** (or linear equation) for a set of data. We can use that model to determine values anywhere on the line. Other techniques to find polynomial models for a set of data are discussed in the references at the end of this section.

An important aspect of creating a model for a set of data is evaluating the usefulness of the model. A linear model for a set of data may not work well if the data is better represented by a quadratic model (or quadratic equation). It is important that our techniques allow us not only to derive the model but also to evaluate its quality.

Approximations are also needed when we want to compute information related to the data. For example, a set of data may represent values of a function over a particular interval, and we want to approximate the area under this function in the interval. Although here we discuss this problem in terms of approximating an area, it is really a technique for **numerical integration,** because an integral represents the area under a curve. Many techniques can approximate the area under a curve, but the most common is the **trapezoidal approximation.** In Section 11-3, we develop a program to compute points on a curve and then approximate the area under the curve. We present a technique for **numerical differentiation** in the problems at the end of the chapter.

Before we proceed, we discuss some general methods for minimizing precision errors in numerical calculations. These methods are presented through examples that do not include a detailed analysis of the error propagation. Although most computer systems have seven- or eight-digit precision, our examples assume three-digit precision for ease in computing.

Our first guideline relates to adding (or subtracting) long lists of numbers. Work with smaller numbers first to reduce precision errors. If you are concerned about keeping as much accuracy in the data as possible, you may want to sort the numbers and then begin adding with the smallest value. For example, consider the following set of numbers that have three-digit precision (recall that the computer stores real values in exponential form, thus we begin counting digits of precision with the first nonzero digit):

$$
\begin{aligned}
&0.0336\\
&0.0356\\
&0.3290\\
&0.5190
\end{aligned}
$$

If we add these values by hand, the sum is 0.9172. If we add these numbers as the computer would, we add them two at a time, each partial sum being truncated to three digits of precision. This process is illustrated below. The addition starts with the smallest numbers on the left side and with the largest numbers on the right side. As you can see, the more accurate sum started with the smaller numbers:

ADDING FROM TOP	ADDING FROM BOTTOM
0.0336	0.519
+ 0.0356	+ 0.329
0.0692	0.848
+ 0.329	+ 0.0356
0.398	0.883
+ 0.519	+ 0.0336
0.917	0.916

The second guideline relates to numbers of nearly equal value. If possible, avoid subtracting nearly equal values. Expressions can sometimes be written to avoid this subtraction; for example, consider the expression

$$a + b + (c - d)$$

If c and d are nearly equal in value, we can rewrite the expression as

$$(a + c) + (b - d)$$

As a specific example, assume that we are working with three-digit precision and that the variables have the following values:

$$a = 0.919,\ b = 0.829,\ c = 0.0356,\ d = 0.0330$$

We now substitute these values in both expressions and truncate all intermediate steps to three digits. The correct value is 1.7506, but only one of the computations produces a result that is accurate to three-digit precision:.

$a + b + (c - d)$	$0.919 + 0.829$	$= 1.74$
	$0.0356 - 0.0330$	$= 0.00260$
		1.74
$(a + c) + (b - d)$	$0.919 + 0.0356$	$= 0.954$
	$0.829 - 0.0330$	$= 0.796$
		1.75

The third guideline minimizes the number of arithmetic operations. Because precision errors can occur with each operation, we minimize these effects when we minimize the number of operations. For example, the following expressions are equivalent, but the one on the left uses two operations and the one on the right uses three:

$$3.0*x*y \qquad (x + x + x)*y$$

If you use the computer for numerical applications, you may want further information on numerical techniques and their analysis. The following list contains texts that provide detailed information on this topic:

1. Acton, F. *Numerical Methods That Work* (New York: Harper & Row, 1970).
2. Cheney, W., and D. Kincaid. *Numerical Mathematics and Computing* (Monterey, Calif.: Brooks/Cole, 1980).
3. Conte, S. D., and C. deBoor. *Elementary Numerical Analysis* (New York: McGraw-Hill, 1972).
4. Hornbeck, R. W. *Numerical Methods* (New York: Quantum, 1975).
5. James, M., G. Smith, and J. Wolford. *Applied Numerical Methods for Digital Computation* (New York: Harper & Row, 1985).
6. Pennington, R. H. *Introductory Computer Methods and Numerical Analysis* (London: Macmillan, 1970).
7. Shoup, T. *A Practical Guide to Computer Methods for Engineers* (Englewood Cliffs, N.J.: Prentice-Hall, 1979).

11-2 PROBLEM SOLVING—COIL DEFLECTION MODEL

When working with experimental or empirical data, we often want to determine the equation of a straight line that represents a good fit to the data. If the data values are linear, a linear equation can estimate values for which we have no data. Suppose for instance that the following data represents the load-deflection curve of a coil spring, where the length of the spring is measured in millimeters and the load (or weight applied to the spring) is measured in dynes:

LOAD	LENGTH
0.28	6.62
0.50	5.93
0.67	4.46
0.93	4.25
1.15	3.30
1.38	3.15
1.60	2.43
1.98	1.46

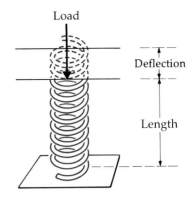

Given a linear equation that represents a good fit to the data, we could estimate the initial length of the spring by substituting a value of zero for the load in the equation. Similarly, the load that causes the spring to have a length of 5 millimeters could also be calculated. The following plot contains the original data points plus an estimate of the position of the straight line that represents a good fit to the data:

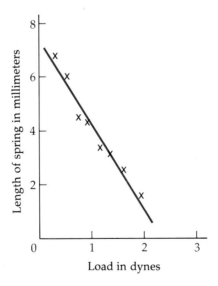

The **method of least squares** is a standard technique used for determining the equation of a straight line from a set of data. Recall that the equation of a straight line is

$$y = mx + b$$

where m is the slope of the line and b is the y-intercept. Given a set of data, such as the load-versus-length values for the spring problem, the slope and y-intercept for the least-squares line can be calculated using the following equations (derived from differential calculus). The symbol Σ represents summation. Therefore, given the set of points $\{(x_1,y_1), (x_2,y_2), \ldots, (x_n,y_n)\}$, let

$$\sum x = x_1 + x_2 + \cdots + x_n$$
$$\sum y = y_1 + y_2 + \cdots + y_n$$
$$\sum xy = x_1 y_1 + x_2 y_2 + \cdots + x_n y_n$$
$$\sum x^2 = x_1^2 + x_2^2 + \cdots + x_n^2$$

The slope and y-intercept can be calculated using these equations:

$$\text{Slope} = \frac{\sum x \sum y - n \sum (x \cdot y)}{\left(\sum x\right)^2 - n \sum (x^2)}$$

$$y\text{-intercept} = \frac{\sum y - \text{slope} \cdot \sum x}{n}$$

Once the slope and y-intercept have been calculated, the equation of the line can be obtained.

If the data points and the straight line were drawn on graph paper, it would be possible to see how closely the line fits the data. Another way to test how well the line fits the data would be to substitute an x value in the equation to calculate a new y value. This new y value, designated $\tilde{y}$, would be an estimate for the value of y when x is given. For example, suppose the least-squares technique yielded the following linear equation for a set of data:

$$y = 4.2x - 3.1$$

Then, for the data coordinate $(1.0,.9)$, the estimate for y would be:

$$\tilde{y} = 4.2(1.0) - 3.1 = 1.1$$

The **residual** for a data point is the difference between the actual data value and its estimated value, $y - \tilde{y}$. The residual for the preceding data point is $(0.9 - 1.1)$, or -0.2. The sum of the squares of the residuals, called the **residual sum,** gives an estimate of the quality of fit of the data to the linear equation without plotting the data. When the data is exactly linear, the residual sum is zero. The residual sum becomes larger as the data deviates from the linear equation. If we want to compare two linear equations that both seem good estimates for the same data, we can compare residual sums to determine the better estimate.

The accelerometer used in a spacecraft to measure acceleration contains a spring that must be tested at different temperatures to determine the effects of temperature on the load-deflection model. Accurate measurements of this model are needed in order to determine accurate acceleration measurements for the spacecraft. Write a program to determine the load-deflection linear model from a set of data values taken with a constant temperature.

PROBLEM STATEMENT

Find the linear equation that best fits a set of data values stored in a data file. Print a report that gives the linear equation and the residual sum.

INPUT/OUTPUT DESCRIPTION

The input is a data file *xydata*. We do not know how many values are in the file, and it does not contain a trailer signal. Each line of the file contains an experimentally measured x and y value. The output should be a report in the following form:

```
THE LINEAR EQUATION IS
Y = xxx.xx X + xxx.xx

ORIGINAL       ORIGINAL      ESTIMATED      RESIDUAL
   X              Y             Y

XXX.XX         XXX.XX        XXX.XX         XXX.XX
 .
 .
 .
RESIDUAL SUM = XXX.XX
```

HAND EXAMPLE

For a hand-worked example, we use the first three data values given for the load-deflection curve at the beginning of the section. The corresponding sums are:

$$\sum x \ \ = 0.28 + 0.50 + 0.67 = 1.45$$
$$\sum y \ \ = 6.62 + 5.93 + 4.46 = 17.01$$
$$\sum xy = 0.28*6.62 + 0.50*5.93 + 0.67*4.46 = 7.8068$$
$$\sum x*x = 0.28*0.28 + 0.50*0.50 + 0.67*0.67 = 0.7773$$

Using the slope and y-intercept equations, we determine the following equation:

$$y = -5.42x + 8.29$$

Using this equation to compute the residuals gives the following table:

```
THE LINEAR EQUATION IS
Y =  -5.42 X +    8.29

ORIGINAL       ORIGINAL      ESTIMATED      RESIDUAL
   X              Y             Y

  0.28           6.62          6.77          -0.15
  0.50           5.93          5.58           0.35
  0.67           4.46          4.66          -0.20

RESIDUAL SUM =    0.19
```

ALGORITHM DEVELOPMENT

The decomposition of this problem solution into general steps is shown here:

DECOMPOSITION

Read x and y data.
Compute slope and y-intercept.
Compute residuals.
Print report.

As we refine the decomposition, we recognize that we need a loop to read the x and y data. Because we are reading each pair of data values from a single line, we can also add the values to the sums that we are going to need for the calculations. We also need to use arrays for the x and y data because the data is needed for the report. If we only wanted the values for the slope and y-intercept of the linear model, we would not need arrays for the x and y data.

The residuals are used for computing the residual sum and for printing the report. However, in one loop we can compute the residual, print it, and add the squared value to the sum. Thus, we do not need an array for the residual values.

REFINEMENT IN PSEUDOCODE

```
linear: i ← 1
        sumx ← 0
        sumy ← 0
        sumxy ← 0
        sumxx ← 0
        while  more data  do
          read x[i],y[i]
          sumx ← sumx + x[i]
          sumy ← sumy + y[i]
          sumxy ← sumxy + x[i]*y[i]
          sumxx ← sumxx + x[i]*x[i]
          i ← i + 1
        count ← i − 1
        compute slope and y-intercept
        write slope, y-intercept
        sumresidual ← 0
        for i = 1 to count do
          ynew ← slope*x[i] + y-intercept
          residual ← y[i] − ynew
          sumresidual ← sumresidual + residual*residual
          write x[i], y[i], ynew, residual
        write sumresidual
```

We now convert the refined pseudocode into Pascal.

PASCAL PROGRAM

```
{------------------------------------------------------------------}
program  linear (xydata,output);
   {This program computes a linear model for a set of data and
   then computes the residual sum to evaluate the model.}
type
   list500 = array[1..500] of real;
var
   slope, intercept, ynew, residual, sumx, sumy,
   sumxy, sumxx, sumresidual: real;
   i, count: integer;
   xydata: text;
   x, y: list500;
begin {linear}
   sumx := 0.0;
   sumy := 0.0;
   sumxy := 0.0;
   sumxx := 0.0;
   sumresidual := 0.0;
   i := 1;
   reset (xydata);
   while  not eof(xydata)  do
      begin
         readln (xydata,x[i],y[i]);
         sumx := sumx + x[i];
         sumy := sumy + y[i];
         sumxy := sumxy + x[i]*y[i];
         sumxx := sumxx + x[i]*x[i];
         i := i + 1
      end;
   count := i - 1;
   slope := (sumx*sumy - count*sumxy)/
            (sumx*sumx - count*sumxx);
   intercept := (sumy - slope*sumx)/count;
   writeln ('THE LINEAR EQUATION IS');
   writeln ('Y = ',slope:6:2,' X + ',intercept:6:2);
   writeln;
   writeln ('ORIGINAL    ORIGINAL    ESTIMATED    RESIDUAL');
   writeln ('   X           Y            Y                ');
   writeln;
   for i := 1 to count do
      begin
         ynew := slope*x[i] + intercept;
         residual := y[i] - ynew;
         sumresidual := sumresidual + residual*residual;
         writeln (x[i]:6:2,y[i]:12:2,ynew:13:2,residual:13:2)
      end;
   writeln;
   writeln ('RESIDUAL SUM = ',sumresidual:6:2)
end. {linear}
{------------------------------------------------------------------}
```

TESTING

If we test this program with the data set given at the beginning of this section, the following report is printed:

```
THE LINEAR EQUATION IS
Y =  -2.93 X +    7.06

ORIGINAL      ORIGINAL      ESTIMATED      RESIDUAL
   X             Y             Y

  0.28          6.62          6.24           0.38
  0.50          5.93          5.59           0.34
  0.67          4.46          5.10          -0.64
  0.93          4.25          4.33          -0.08
  1.15          3.30          3.69          -0.39
  1.38          3.15          3.02           0.13
  1.60          2.43          2.37           0.06
  1.98          1.46          1.26           0.20

RESIDUAL SUM =    0.88
```

Note that the residual sum for the hand-worked example, which used the first three data points, was 0.19, and the residual sum for the full set of data was 0.88; this indicates that a linear equation better approximated the first three data points than the full set of data points.

11-3   PROBLEM SOLVING—POWER IN FREQUENCY BANDS

The operations of integration and differentiation give engineers and scientists important information about functions or data sets. For example, distance, velocity, and acceleration all relate to each other through integrals (integration) and derivatives (differentiation). The derivative of distance is velocity, and the derivative of velocity is acceleration; the integral of acceleration is velocity, and the integral of velocity is distance. These topics are covered in detail in calculus courses, but the underlying principles are simple enough to apply independently. Integrating a function over an interval can be approximated by computing the area under the graph of the function; differentiation can be approximated by computing tangents to the graph of the function. Both of these numerical approximations are easily performed with Pascal.

In this application, we use a numerical technique to estimate the area under a curve. Problems 24–25 at the end of the chapter use a numerical technique to estimate tangents to a curve.

Assume that we want to estimate the area under the curve in the interval [a,b], as shown in the diagram on the next page.

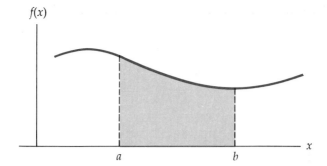

If we are given the function that represents the curve, we can evaluate that function at points spaced along the interval of interest, as shown:

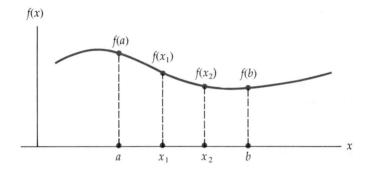

If we assume that the points on the curve we have computed are joined by straight line segments, we have formed a group of trapezoids whose combined area approximates the area under the curve. As we compute points closer together on the curve, we acquire more trapezoids in the interval. The following two diagrams illustrate that our estimate of the area (which is the sum of the areas of the trapezoids) should improve as the number of trapezoids increases:

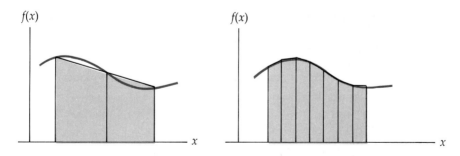

Consider a single trapezoid with a base and two side heights. The equation for the area of the trapezoid is:

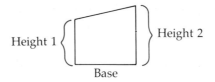

$$\text{area} = 0.5 \cdot \text{base} \cdot (\text{height1} + \text{height2})$$

If we assume that the base length represents the increment along the x-axis, this value is constant if we divide the interval into a number of equally spaced points. The heights represent the function value on the left- and right-hand sides of the small interval.

Before we develop this solution, note that the data points on the curve could come from several sources. If we have the equation for the curve, the program can compute the data points that we then use as sides for our trapezoids; in this case, we can choose the data points to be as close together or as far apart as we want. Another possibility is that the data represents experimentally collected data; in this case, we have a set of (x,y) coordinates but no general equation. We can use the increment in the x coordinates as the base values and the y coordinates as the heights of the trapezoids.

Both cases are important, and we give Pascal programs for both situations. Because the programs are similar in the algorithm development phases, we assume the case where we have an equation for the curve.

Assume that the following equation describes the power in a signal with respect to frequency:

$$f(x) = y = 4e^{-(x-2)^2}$$

We can find the power of the signal over a band of frequencies by integrating or by computing the area under the curve in the desired frequency range. Write a program to compute the area under this curve between two specified points. Use the trapezoidal rule, and allow the user to choose the number of trapezoids used to approximate the area.

PROBLEM STATEMENT

Determine the area under the curve defined by the following equation:

$$f(x) = y = 4e^{-(x-2)^2}$$

INPUT/OUTPUT DESCRIPTION

The input values give the interval of x values to be used and the number of trapezoids in that interval. The output is the estimate of the area under the curve.

For a hand-worked example, we assume that we are interested in the area in the interval [1,2] and that we want to break the interval into five trapezoids, as shown:

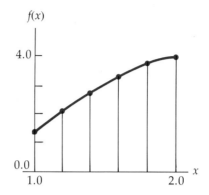

The following table shows the x and y coordinates and the computations for the areas of the five trapezoids:

x	y	Trapezoid Area	
1.0	1.47	$0.5 \cdot 0.2 \cdot (1.47 + 2.11)$	= 0.36
1.2	2.11	$0.5 \cdot 0.2 \cdot (2.11 + 2.79)$	= 0.49
1.4	2.79	$0.5 \cdot 0.2 \cdot (2.79 + 3.41)$	= 0.62
1.6	3.41	$0.5 \cdot 0.2 \cdot (3.41 + 3.84)$	= 0.73
1.8	3.84	$0.5 \cdot 0.2 \cdot (3.84 + 4.00)$	= 0.78
2.0	4.00		

Sum of trapezoid areas = 2.98

(The value of this integral is not easy to compute, even using calculus, because it does not have a closed form. The value of the integral is 2.9873.)

ALGORITHM DEVELOPMENT

The decomposition of the solution into general steps is the following:

DECOMPOSITION

Read interval endpoints and number of trapezoids.
Compute estimate of area.
Write estimate of area.

We can compute the length of the entire interval by subtracting the left endpoint from the right endpoint. This length is then divided by the number of trapezoids, giving us the size of each base. For each trapezoid, we also need a left height and a right height; however, after computing the heights of the first trapezoid, we do not need to compute both heights for each following trapezoid because the left height is computed as the right height of the previous trapezoid. In order to easily change the function that defines the curve, we implement the computation in a Pascal function. The function can be referenced when it is needed, and since it is defined in only one place in the program, it is easy to change. We now describe these steps in pseudocode.

REFINEMENT IN PSEUDOCODE

```
area1: read a, b, n
          base ← (b − a)/n
          left ← f(a)
          right ← f(a + base)
          for i = 1 to n do
             area ← 0.5*base*(left + right)
             sum ← sum + area
             left ← right
             right ← f(base*(i+1)+a)
          write n, sum


f(x): f ← 4.0*exp(−sqr(x−2))
```

The structure chart for the solution is shown next, along with the Pascal program.

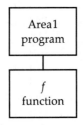

PASCAL PROGRAM

```
{------------------------------------------------------------}
program  area1 (input,output);
    {This program estimates the area under a given curve.}
var
    a, b, base, left, right, area, sum: real;
    n, i: integer;
{------------------------------------------------------------}
function  f (x:real): real;
    {This function computes a value using an equation.}
begin {f}
    f := 4.0*exp(-sqr(x-2))
end; {f}
```

```
{--------------------------------------------------------}
begin {area1}
   writeln ('ENTER THE INTERVAL ENDPOINTS');
   readln (a,b);
   writeln ('ENTER THE NUMBER OF TRAPEZOIDS');
   readln (n);
   sum := 0.0;
   base := (b - a)/n;
   left := f(a);
   right := f(a + base);
   for i := 1 to n do
      begin
         area := 0.5*base*(left + right);
         sum := sum + area;
         left := right;
         right := f(base*(i + 1) + a)
      end;
   writeln ('USING ',n:3,' TRAPEZOIDS, THE ESTIMATED AREA IS ',
            sum:7:3)
end. {area1}
{--------------------------------------------------------}
```

We now modify the program so that the data is read from a data file instead of computed from an equation. Note that the number of data points determines the number of trapezoids. We also recompute the base of the trapezoid for each new pair of data points because not all of the x coordinates may have the same increment. We do not need the data points after we have computed the area of the corresponding trapezoid; thus, no array is needed to store the data.

PASCAL PROGRAM

```
{--------------------------------------------------------}
program  area2 (xydata,output);
   {This program estimates the area under a given curve.}
var
   xl, yl, xr, yr, base, area, sum: real;
   n: integer;
   xydata: text;
begin {area2}
   sum := 0.0;
   n := 0;
   reset (xydata);
   readln (xydata,xl,yl);
   while  not eof(xydata)  do
      begin
         readln (xydata,xr,yr);
         base := xr - xl;
         area := 0.5*base*(yl + yr);
         sum := sum + area;
         xl := xr;
         yl := yr;
         n := n + 1
      end;
   writeln ('USING ',n:3,' TRAPEZOIDS, THE ESTIMATED AREA IS ',
            sum:7:3)
end. {area2}
{--------------------------------------------------------}
```

TESTING

The first version of the program was used for testing. The following sets of output represent estimates of the function over the interval [1,2], using 5, 10, 50, and 100 trapezoids.

```
ENTER THE INTERVAL ENDPOINTS
1.0 2.0
ENTER THE NUMBER OF TRAPEZOIDS
5
USING   5 TRAPEZOIDS, THE ESTIMATED AREA IS   2.977
```

```
ENTER THE INTERVAL ENDPOINTS
1.0 2.0
ENTER THE NUMBER OF TRAPEZOIDS
10
USING  10 TRAPEZOIDS, THE ESTIMATED AREA IS   2.985
```

```
ENTER THE INTERVAL ENDPOINTS
1.0 2.0
ENTER THE NUMBER OF TRAPEZOIDS
50
USING  50 TRAPEZOIDS, THE ESTIMATED AREA IS   2.987
```

```
ENTER THE INTERVAL ENDPOINTS
1.0 2.0
ENTER THE NUMBER OF TRAPEZOIDS
100
USING 100 TRAPEZOIDS, THE ESTIMATED AREA IS   2.987
```

Note that we do not see any change from 50 trapezoids to 100 trapezoids when we use three decimal positions to print our area.

This technique for numerical integration is referred to as integration using the **trapezoidal rule.** Another rule, called **Simpson's rule,** is used in numerical integration to approximate the area under a curve by assuming that the points on the curve are joined by parabolas instead of straight lines. For the same number of divisions of a curve into smaller segments, Simpson's rule gives a more accurate approximation than the trapezoidal rule. Simpson's rule is slightly more complicated to compute; details can be found in the references given for numerical techniques at the end of Section 11-1.

11-4 ITERATIVE SOLUTIONS

In many of the applications in this text, the solution to the problem involved direct computation of a value or several values. Sometimes, an **iterative** or **repetitive technique** is needed to compute the desired information. In several problems at the end of Chapter 6, we approximated the value of the cosine function by computing and adding terms of an infinite series that were equivalent to the cosine function. This technique is iterative because we continue computing terms to add to our approximation until we have added a specified number of terms, or until the terms become so small that they are insignificant.

Iterative techniques are often used in situations not easily described with equations. For example, the following applications require computing the **roots of polynomials:** designing the control system for a robot arm, designing spring and shock absorbers in an automobile, analyzing the response characteristic of a motor, and analyzing the stability of an electric circuit. Recall that the roots are the values of x for which the polynomial $p(x)$ is equal to zero. If the polynomial is linear, it is easy to solve for the single root, as shown:

$$p(x) = 5x - 3$$
$$p(x) = 0 \Rightarrow 5x = 3$$
$$x = 0.6$$

If the polynomial is quadratic, the quadratic formula can be used to determine the roots of a polynomial. There could be no real roots (the quadratic curve does not cross the x-axis), two distinct real roots, or a double root. Thus, determining the roots for the linear or quadratic case is not difficult. However, suppose the polynomial equation is the following:

$$p(x) = 4.5x^8 + 0.5x^4 - 2.1x^3 - 0.6$$

Finding the roots of this polynomial by hand is laborious, but if we use an iterative method, we have several techniques for finding the roots of a general polynomial. One of these techniques, called **interval halving** or bisection, is presented in Section 11-5. Another common technique is the **Newton method** (also called the Newton-Rhapson method); this technique uses the derivative of the polynomial to determine the next approximation for the root. To use the Newton method, we must also be able to compute or approximate the derivative. The **Secant method** is a variation of the Newton method that uses linear interpolation to approximate the derivative. These techniques are discussed in the references listed at the end of Section 11-1.

Some of the root-finding techniques that we have discussed can also be applied to **transcendental** functions, which are not polynomials but functions that contain trigonometric or other special functions such as logarithmic or exponential functions. For example, suppose we wanted to solve the following equation:

$$x = \tan x$$

One way to solve for the value of x is to rewrite the equation as shown and then to find the roots, or values of x for which the equation is equal to zero:

$$f(x) = x - \tan x$$

These techniques do not always lead to a solution. A more detailed study of iterative solutions is required to solve for roots of transcendental functions.

11-5 PROBLEM SOLVING — ROBOT ARM STABILITY

Computers are often used to find the roots of equations. In a few cases, such as in the quadratic equation, simple formulas can find the roots. In most situations of practical interest, however, no such formulas exist, and it is necessary to use iterative (repetitive) methods that lead to an approximate answer. In this application, we study the simplest such method: interval halving.

Suppose we have an equation that is represented by the following curve on a given interval:

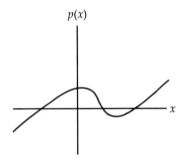

A root of the equation is a point at which the curve crosses the x-axis. At such a point, the y value of the curve is zero. Suppose that we have two points, a and b, such that $p(a)$ and $p(b)$ are of different signs, as shown:

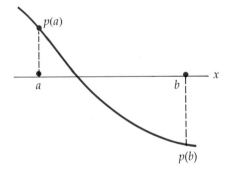

We can be sure that there is at least one root in the interval between a and b because the curve must cross the x-axis. There may also be three roots, or another odd number of roots, in the interval between a and b.

For now, assume that there is only one root in the interval between a and b. Also assume that $p(a)$ is positive and that $p(b)$ is negative. If the equation is evaluated at m, the midpoint of the interval, there are three possible outcomes. If the equation value at the midpoint, represented by $p(m)$, is zero, it represents the root; if the equation value at the midpoint is negative, the root falls in the interval between a and m; if the equation value at the midpoint is positive, the root falls in the interval between m and b. We have halved the interval within which the root must lie. We now repeat the steps in this iterative algorithm, halving the interval of interest with each iteration.

There are many ways to decide when to stop the iterative process. In this application, we stop the process when we find the root or when the interval of interest is less than 0.01.

Because there can be more than one root in the overall interval being considered, we suggest starting at the left-hand side of the overall interval and begin moving across it in small intervals. If the left and right polynomial values for one of the small intervals have different signs, assume that there is one root in the interval and perform the iterations to narrow in on it; then proceed to the next interval, searching for new roots. There are special cases in which this algorithm can miss roots, but a completely general algorithm for finding roots is too long for this example.

The design of a control system for a robot arm involves a careful analysis of the stability of the design. One step in the stability analysis uses the roots of polynomials that are used in the control system. Write a program to estimate the real roots of a fourth-degree polynomial over the interval $[-5,5]$ by using the interval-halving technique. (A polynomial has as many roots as the maximum degree of the polynomial, but some of the roots can be complex. In this example, we are only concerned with real roots, which can be detected by the interval-halving technique.)

PROBLEM STATEMENT

Write a program to determine the roots of a polynomial $p(x)$ within the interval $[-5,5]$, where $p(x)$ has the following form:

$$p(x) = ax^4 + bx^3 + cx^2 + dx + e$$

INPUT/OUTPUT DESCRIPTION

The input to the program is the polynomial coefficients a, b, c, d, and e. The output should be the equation for the polynomial and any roots that were found. If there are no roots for the polynomial in the given interval, print an appropriate message.

We use small intervals of 0.25 for the initial test to determine whether a root is in the interval. For this test case, assume that the polynomial is:

$$p(x) = 3x - 2.5$$

This is a linear equation, but it is also a special case of a quartic polynomial with the following coefficients:

$$a = 0.0,\ b = 0.0,\ c = 0.0,\ d = 3.0,\ e = -2.5$$

We begin by evaluating $p(x)$ at the endpoints of the following intervals:

$$[-5.0,-4.75],[-4.75,-4.5],...,[4.75,5.0]$$

When the value of the polynomial at the left endpoint, $p(left)$, has a different sign than its value at the right endpoint, $p(right)$, there is a real root in the interval. We also need to check the polynomial evaluated at the endpoints for the value of zero in case an endpoint is a root. For the specific example, both endpoints have negative polynomial values until we reach the interval $[0.75,1.00]$, where $p(0.75) = -0.25$ and $p(1.0) = 0.5$. The following steps show the iterative technique that halves the interval, determines which half contains the root, halves the new interval, and so on until the root is found or the interval is less than 0.01:

Interval $[0.75,1.0]$
$p(0.75) = -0.25,\ p(1.0) = 0.5$
Midpoint: $p(0.875) = 0.125$
Iteration 1: Interval $[0.75,0.875]$
$p(0.75) = -0.25,\ p(0.875) = 0.125$
Midpoint: $p(0.8125) = -0.0625$
Iteration 2: Interval $[0.8125,0.875]$
$p(0.8125) = -0.0625,\ p(0.875) = 0.125$
Midpoint: $p(0.8438) = 0.0314$
Iteration 3: Interval $[0.8125,0.8438]$
$p(0.8125) = -0.0625,\ p(0.8438) = 0.0314$
Midpoint: $p(0.8282) = -0.0154$
Iteration 4: Interval $[0.8282,0.8438]$
$p(0.8282) = -0.0154,\ p(0.8438) = 0.0314$
Midpoint: $p(0.836) = 0.008$
Iteration 5: Interval $[0.8282,0.836]$
This interval is less than 0.01; thus, our estimate of the root is the midpoint of this interval, or 0.8321. The polynomial value, $p(x)$, at this point is -0.0037.

ALGORITHM DEVELOPMENT

The decomposition of this algorithm involves reading coefficients and then finding roots.

DECOMPOSITION

> Read coefficients and find roots.

We develop this program so that it reads the coefficients of a polynomial, determines the roots in the interval $[-5,5]$, and reads coefficients for another polynomial. We continue the process until the values of all the coefficients are zero.

REFINEMENT IN PSEUDOCODE

```
roots: read coefficients
        while all coefficients are not zero do
            count ← 0
            left ← −5.0
            right ← −4.75
            for i = 1 to 40 do
              if p(left) = 0 then
                  write left
                  count ← count + 1
              else if p(left)*p(right) < 0.0 then
                  iterate for root
                  write root
                  count ← count + 1
              left ← right
              right ← left + 0.25
            if p(left) = 0.0 then
                print left
                count ← count + 1
            if count = 0 then
                print 'NO ROOTS IN INTERVAL'
            read new coefficients
```

We must further refine the iteration step. Recall that the iteration continues until the process finds the root or until the interval of interest is less than 0.01. Since the iteration involves several steps, we are going to implement it as a procedure. The polynomial needs to be evaluated for several points in both the program and the iteration procedure, so we implement it as a function. Note that we will need to include the polynomial coefficients in the parameter list for both modules. Following is the pseudocode for these two modules:

iterate (a,b,c,d,e,left,right,root):
    done ← false
    size ← right − left
    while size > 0.01 and not done do
      midpoint ← (left + right)/2
      if p(a,b,c,d,e,midpoint) = 0.0 then
        done ← true
      else if p(a,b,c,d,e,midpoint)*
          p(a,b,c,d,e,left)< 0.0 then
       right ← midpoint
      else
       left ← midpoint
    if size ≤ 0.01 then
     root ← (left + right)/2
    else
     root ← midpoint

p(a,b,c,d,e,x): p ← a*x*x*x*x + b*x*x*x + c*x*x + d*x + e

The structure chart for the solution is shown next, along with the Pascal program.

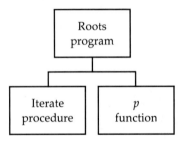

```
{----------------------------------------------------------------}
program  roots (input,output);
   {This program determines the roots in the interval [-5,5]
   for a quartic polynomial using interval halving.}
var
   a, b, c, d, e, left, right, root: real;
   count: integer;
{----------------------------------------------------------------}
function  p (a,b,c,d,e,x:real): real;
   {This function evaluates a quartic polynomial at x.}
begin {p}
   p := a*x*x*x*x + b*x*x*x + c*x*x + d*x + e
end; {p}
{----------------------------------------------------------------}
procedure iterate (a,b,c,d,e,left,right:real; var root:real);
   {This procedure uses interval halving to find a root.}
var
   size, midpoint: real;
   done: boolean;
begin {iterate}
   done := false;
   size := right - left;
   while  (size > 0.01) and (not done)  do
      begin
         midpoint := (left + right)/2;
         if  p(a,b,c,d,e,midpoint) = 0.0  then
            done := true
         else if  (p(a,b,c,d,e,midpoint)*
                   p(a,b,c,d,e,left)) < 0.0  then
            right := midpoint
         else
            left := midpoint
      end;
   if  size > 0.01  then
      root := midpoint
   else
      root := (left + right)/2
end; {iterate}
```

continued

```
{-------------------------------------------------------------}
begin {roots}
    writeln ('ENTER COEFFICIENTS A, B, C, D, E');
    readln (a,b,c,d,e);
    while   (a <> 0.0) or (b <> 0.0) or (c <> 0.0) or
            (d <> 0.0) or (e <> 0.0)   do
       begin
          writeln;
          writeln ('POLYNOMIAL:');
          writeln ('        4               3              2');
          writeln (a:7:3,' X  + ',b:7:3,' X  + ',c:7:3,' X  + ',
                   d:7:3,' X + ',e:7:3);
          writeln;
          count := 0;
          left := -5.0;
          right := -4.75;
          for i := 1 to 40 do
             begin
                if  p(a,b,c,d,e,left) = 0.0   then
                   begin
                      writeln ('ROOT = ',left:7:3,'    P(ROOT)',
                               ' = ',p(a,b,c,d,e,left):7:3);
                      count := count + 1
                   end
                else if  (p(a,b,c,d,e,left)*
                          p(a,b,c,d,e,right)) < 0.0   then
                   begin
                      iterate (a,b,c,d,e,left,right,root);
                      writeln ('ROOT = ',root:7:3,'    P(ROOT)',
                               ' = ',p(a,b,c,d,e,root):7:3);
                      count := count + 1
                   end;
                left := right;
                right := left + 0.25
             end;
          if  p(a,b,c,d,e,left) = 0.0   then
             begin
                writeln ('ROOT = ',left:7:3,'    P(ROOT) = ',
                         p(a,b,c,d,e,left):7:3);
                count := count + 1
             end;
          if  count = 0   then
             writeln ('NO ROOTS IN INTERVAL [-5,5]');
          writeln;
          writeln ('ENTER COEFFICIENTS A, B, C, D, E');
          writeln ('(ALL ZEROS TO QUIT)');
          readln (a,b,c,d,e)
       end
end. {roots}
{-------------------------------------------------------------}
```

TESTING

Five different polynomials were used as test data. These polynomials covered the cases with no roots, one root, and three roots. Some of the roots fell on interval endpoints. The last polynomial is the one we used in the hand-worked example. The output from the program is shown. Following the output, we have also included plots of the polynomials in the same order as they were entered in the program.

```
ENTER COEFFICIENTS A, B, C, D, E
0.0  1.0  -2.125  -25.0  53.125

POLYNOMIAL:
         4            3            2
  0.000 X  +   1.000 X  +  -2.125 X  + -25.000 X +  53.125

ROOT =  -5.000     P(ROOT) =    0.000
ROOT =   2.125     P(ROOT) =    0.000
ROOT =   5.000     P(ROOT) =    0.000

ENTER COEFFICIENTS A, B, C, D, E
(ALL ZEROS TO QUIT)
0.0  0.0  1.0  14.0  3.0

POLYNOMIAL:
         4            3            2
  0.000 X  +   0.000 X  +   1.000 X  +  14.000 X +   3.000

ROOT =  -0.215     P(ROOT) =    0.038

ENTER COEFFICIENTS A, B, C, D, E
(ALL ZEROS TO QUIT)
3.0  -12.4  -26.29  29.766  0.0

POLYNOMIAL:
         4            3            2
  3.000 X  + -12.400 X  + -26.290 X  +  29.766 X +   0.000

ROOT =  -2.137     P(ROOT) =   -0.131
ROOT =   0.000     P(ROOT) =    0.000
ROOT =   0.855     P(ROOT) =    0.068

ENTER COEFFICIENTS A, B, C, D, E
(ALL ZEROS TO QUIT)
0.0  0.0  1.234  -1.2  10.44

POLYNOMIAL:
         4            3            2
  0.000 X  +   0.000 X  +   1.234 X  +  -1.200 X +  10.440

NO ROOTS IN INTERVAL [-5,5]

ENTER COEFFICIENTS A, B, C, D, E
(ALL ZEROS TO QUIT)
0.0  0.0  0.0  3.0  -2.5

POLYNOMIAL:
         4            3            2
  0.000 X  +   0.000 X  +   0.000 X  +   3.000 X +  -2.500

ROOT =   0.832     P(ROOT) =   -0.004

ENTER COEFFICIENTS A, B, C, D, E
(ALL ZEROS TO QUIT)
0.0  0.0  0.0  0.0  0.0
```

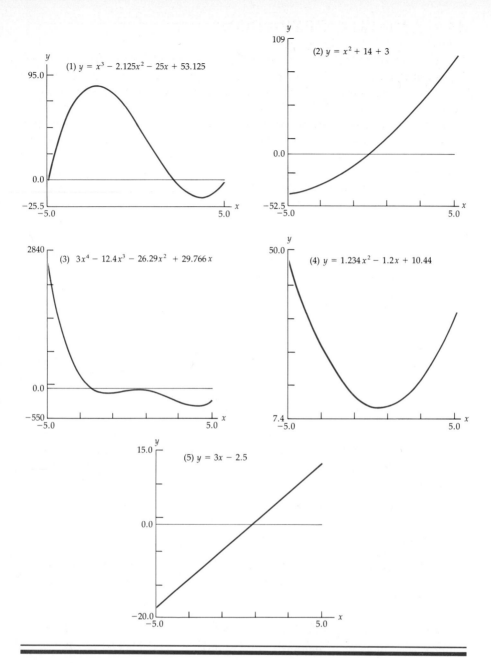

(1) $y = x^3 - 2.125x^2 - 25x + 53.125$

(2) $y = x^2 + 14 + 3$

(3) $3x^4 - 12.4x^3 - 26.29x^2 + 29.766x$

(4) $y = 1.234x^2 - 1.2x + 10.44$

(5) $y = 3x - 2.5$

11-6 MATRIX OPERATIONS

Many engineering and science computations use a **matrix** as a convenient way to represent data. In Pascal, a matrix is easily represented in a two-dimensional array. Operations performed with matrices require more than a single statement because the operations generally must be able to access all elements of the matrix; thus, loops are needed. In this section we define a number of the common operations performed with matrices and develop Pascal modules to compute them. In these examples we assume that the size of the matrix is included as two parameters, *rows* and *cols*. Recall that these arguments should contain values that match the number of rows and columns used in the array definition in the program.

EXAMPLE 11-1   Scalar Multiplication

Multiplying each element in a matrix by a scalar is referred to as **scalar multiplication.** Write a procedure whose arguments are a matrix a, its size in terms of rows and columns, and a scalar c. The procedure should multiply the matrix a by the scalar c and return the result in the matrix a, as shown in the following matrix notation:

$$[a[i,j]] \leftarrow [c[a[i,j]]]$$

To illustrate, matrix a is multiplied by a scalar value of 4:

$$a = \begin{bmatrix} 1.0 & 2.2 \\ 3.0 & 4.0 \\ -1.0 & 0.0 \end{bmatrix} \qquad 4 \cdot a = \begin{bmatrix} 4.0 & 8.8 \\ 12.0 & 16.0 \\ -4.0 & 0.0 \end{bmatrix}$$

Assume that the two-dimensional array a has been defined with the data type *matrix* in the program. Therefore, the procedure header has the following form:

```
procedure  scalar (rows,cols:integer; c:real;
                   var a:matrix);
```

Solution

The steps in this solution involve defining a pair of nested loops to access each element of the array, then multiplying each element by the scalar or constant c:

```
{-------------------------------------------------------}
procedure  scalar (rows,cols:integer; c:real;
                   var a:matrix);
   {This procedure multiplies an array by a scalar.}
var
   i, j: integer;
begin {scalar}
   for i := 1 to rows do
      for j := 1 to cols do
         a[i,j] := c*a[i,j]
end; {scalar}
{-------------------------------------------------------}
```

EXAMPLE 11-2 Matrix Addition

Matrix addition can be performed only with matrices of the same size. The result of the addition is another matrix of the same size in which the elements are the sum of the elements in the corresponding positions of the original matrices, as shown in the matrix notation:

$$[c[i,j]] \leftarrow [a[i,j]] + [b[i,j]]$$

To illustrate, matrix a is added to matrix b, and the result is a new matrix c:

$$a = \begin{bmatrix} 1.0 & 2.2 \\ 3.0 & 4.0 \\ -1.0 & 0.0 \end{bmatrix} \qquad b = \begin{bmatrix} 4.0 & -3.0 \\ 2.0 & 6.0 \\ -4.0 & 0.5 \end{bmatrix}$$

$$a + b = c = \begin{bmatrix} 5.0 & -0.8 \\ 5.0 & 10.0 \\ -5.0 & 0.5 \end{bmatrix}$$

Write a procedure called *add* that has five parameters. Three parameters represent matrices (two to be added and one to hold the sum), and the other two parameters give the size of the matrices. Assume that the two-dimensional arrays a, b, and c have been defined with the data type *matrix* in the program. Therefore, the procedure header has the following form:

```
procedure  add (rows,cols:integer; a,b:matrix;
                var c:matrix);
```

Solution

This procedure is written so that the matrix that represents the sum is a separate matrix. If we wanted to store the sum in one of the original matrices, the procedure header and parameters would have to be modified.

```
{------------------------------------------------------}
procedure  add (rows,cols:integer; a,b:matrix;
                var c:matrix);
    {This procedure adds matrices a and b, and stores
    the result in matrix c.}
var
    i, j: integer;
begin {add}
    for i := 1 to rows do
        for j := 1 to cols do
            c[i,j] := a[i,j] + b[i,j]
end; {add}
{------------------------------------------------------}
```

EXAMPLE 11-3 Matrix Subtraction

Matrix subtraction can also be performed only with matrices of the same size. The result of the subtraction is another matrix of the same size in

which the elements are the difference of the elements in the corresponding positions of the original matrices, as shown in the matrix notation:

$$[c[i,j]] \leftarrow [a[i,j]] - [b[i,j]]$$

To illustrate, matrix b is subtracted from matrix a, and the result is a new
matrix c:

$$a = \begin{bmatrix} 1.0 & 2.2 \\ 3.0 & 4.0 \\ -1.0 & 0.0 \end{bmatrix} \qquad b = \begin{bmatrix} 4.0 & -3.0 \\ 2.0 & 6.0 \\ -4.0 & 0.5 \end{bmatrix}$$

$$a - b = c = \begin{bmatrix} -3.0 & 5.2 \\ 1.0 & -2.0 \\ 3.0 & -0.5 \end{bmatrix}$$

Although the order in adding matrices does not matter, the order in
subtracting matrices is important.

Write a procedure called *subtract* that has five parameters. Three
parameters represent matrices (two to be subtracted and one to hold the
difference), and the other two parameters give the size of the matrices.
Assume that the two-dimensional arrays a, b, and c have been defined
with the data type *matrix* in the program. Therefore, the procedure
header has the following form:

```
procedure  subtract (rows,cols:integer; a,b:matrix;
                     var c:matrix);
```

Solution

This procedure is written so that the matrix that represents the difference
is a separate matrix. If we want to store the difference in one of the
original matrices, the procedure header and parameters would have to
be modified.

```
{-----------------------------------------------------}
procedure  subtract (rows,cols:integer; a,b:matrix;
                     var c:matrix);
   {This procedure subtracts matrix b from matrix a
    and stores the result in matrix c.}
var
   i, j: integer;
begin {subtract}
   for i := 1 to rows do
      for j := 1 to cols do
         c[i,j] := a[i,j] - b[i,j]
end; {subtract}
{-----------------------------------------------}
```

EXAMPLE 11-4   Dot Product

The **dot product** is an operation performed between two vectors, or
one-dimensional arrays, with the same dimension. This is not actually a
matrix operation; however, it is often used in computations that also

involve matrices, so we include it here. The dot product between two one-dimensional arrays of the same size is a number computed by adding the products of values in corresponding positions in the arrays, as shown in the summation equation:

$$\text{Dot product} \leftarrow \sum a[i] \cdot b[i]$$

To illustrate, the dot product of one-dimensional arrays a and b is computed:

$$a = \begin{bmatrix} 3.0 \\ 1.5 \\ -0.5 \end{bmatrix} \quad b = \begin{bmatrix} 1.0 \\ 2.0 \\ 3.0 \end{bmatrix}$$

$$\begin{aligned} \text{Dot product of } a \text{ and } b &= 3.0 \cdot 1.0 + 1.5 \cdot 2.0 + (-0.5) \cdot 3.0 \\ &= 3.0 + 3.0 - 1.5 \\ &= 4.5 \end{aligned}$$

Write a function to compute the dot product of two arrays with a common size n. Assume that the one-dimensional arrays a and b have been defined with the data type *list* in the program. Therefore, the function header has the following form:

```
function  dotproduct (n:integer; a,b:list): real;
```

Solution

Note that this module is written as a function instead of as a procedure because it returns a single value.

```
{-------------------------------------------------------}
function  dotproduct (n:integer; a,b:list): real;
    {This function computes the dot product of a and b.}
var
    i: integer;
    sum: real;
begin {dotproduct}
    sum := 0.0;
    for i := 1 to n do
        sum := sum + a[i]*b[i];
    dotproduct := sum
end; {dotproduct}
{-------------------------------------------------------}
```

EXAMPLE 11-5   Matrix Multiplication

In contrast to earlier operations, matrix multiplication is not computed by multiplying corresponding elements of the matrices. The value in position i,j of the product of two matrices is the dot product of row i of the first matrix and column j of the second matrix, as shown in the summation equation:

$$[c[i,j] \leftarrow \sum_k a[i,k] \cdot b[k,j]$$

In the equation, i and j are fixed values, and k varies in the summation.

Because dot products require that the arrays have the same number of elements, we must have the same number of elements in each row of the first matrix as we have in each column of the second matrix to compute the product of the two matrices. The product matrix has the same number of rows as the first matrix and the same number of columns as the second matrix. Thus, if a and b both have five rows and five columns, their product has five rows and five columns. If a has three rows and two columns and b has two rows and two columns, their product has three rows and two columns. To illustrate, matrix a is multiplied by matrix b, and the result is a new matrix c:

$$a = \begin{bmatrix} 1.0 & 2.2 \\ 3.0 & 4.0 \\ -1.0 & 0.0 \end{bmatrix} \qquad b = \begin{bmatrix} 4.0 & -3.0 \\ 2.0 & 6.0 \end{bmatrix}$$

$$a \cdot b = c = \begin{bmatrix} 8.4 & 10.2 \\ 20.0 & 15.0 \\ -4.0 & 3.0 \end{bmatrix}$$

A procedure to multiply two matrices must have the sizes of both input arrays as parameters in addition to the arrays themselves. The result of the multiplication must be an additional array because it can be a different size from either of the two arrays to be multiplied.

Write a procedure called *multiply* that has nine parameters. Three parameters represent matrices (two to be multiplied and one to hold the product), and the other six parameters give the size of the three matrices. Assume that the two-dimensional arrays a, b, and c have been defined with the data types *matrix1*, *matrix2*, and *matrix3* in the program. Therefore, the procedure header has the following form:

```
procedure  multiply (arows,acols,brows,bcols,
                     crows,ccols:integer;
                     a:matrix1; b:matrix2;
                     var c:matrix3);
```

Solution

In the procedure, we print an error message if the input sizes are not correct:

```
{-------------------------------------------------------}
procedure  multiply (arows,acols,brows,bcols,
                     crows,ccols:integer;
                     a:matrix1; b:matrix2;
                     var c:matrix3);
   {This procedure multiplies arrays a and b and
   stores the product in array c.}
var
   i, j, k: integer;
   error: boolean;
begin {multiply}
   error := false;
   if  (acols <> brows)  or  (arows <> crows)  or
       (bcols <> ccols)  then
      error := true;
   if  error  then
      writeln ('ERROR IN ARRAY SIZES')
   else
      for i := 1 to crows do
         for j := 1 to ccols do
            begin
               c[i,j] := 0.0;
               for k := 1 to acols do
                  c[i,j] := c[i,j] + a[i,k]*b[k,j]
            end
end; {multiply}
{-------------------------------------------------------}
```

In Section 11-7, our application solves **simultaneous equations** using matrices. Systems of simultaneous equations are often used for such computations as the stress analysis of mechanical systems, the analysis of a fluid-flow system, or the analysis of currents or voltages in an electrical circuit. The design of airplane control systems may also require the solution of systems of simultaneous equations. The information from these applications is stored in a matrix, and we solve the system of simultaneous equations represented by this matrix to complete the desired analysis.

11-7 PROBLEM SOLVING—ELECTRICAL CURRENT ANALYSIS

In this application, we develop a program to solve three simultaneous equations. A general set of three simultaneous equations can be written in the following form:

$$a[1]x + b[1]y + c[1]z = d[1]$$
$$a[2]x + b[2]y + c[2]z = d[2]$$
$$a[3]x + b[3]y + c[3]z = d[3]$$

There are many ways to solve a system of three simultaneous equations. The method used here is **Cramer's rule,** which uses **determinants.** Recall that a determinant is a number that is computed from a matrix. Specifically, the determinant of the matrix formed from the set of coefficients of x, y, and z is computed as:

$$\begin{vmatrix} a1 & b1 & c1 \\ a2 & b2 & c2 \\ a3 & b3 & c3 \end{vmatrix} = \begin{matrix} a1 \cdot b2 \cdot c3 + b1 \cdot c2 \cdot a3 + c1 \cdot a2 \cdot b3 \\ - a3 \cdot b2 \cdot c1 - b3 \cdot c2 \cdot a1 - c3 \cdot a2 \cdot b1 \end{matrix}$$

The x, y, and z values that form the solution of the set of three simultaneous equations can be computed from determinants, using Cramer's rule, as shown:

$$x = \frac{\begin{vmatrix} d1 & b1 & c1 \\ d2 & b2 & c2 \\ d3 & b3 & c3 \end{vmatrix}}{\begin{vmatrix} a1 & b1 & c1 \\ a2 & b2 & c2 \\ a3 & b3 & c3 \end{vmatrix}} \qquad y = \frac{\begin{vmatrix} a1 & d1 & c1 \\ a2 & d2 & c2 \\ a3 & d3 & c3 \end{vmatrix}}{\begin{vmatrix} a1 & b1 & c1 \\ a2 & b2 & c2 \\ a3 & b3 & c3 \end{vmatrix}} \qquad z = \frac{\begin{vmatrix} a1 & b1 & d1 \\ a2 & b2 & d2 \\ a3 & b3 & d3 \end{vmatrix}}{\begin{vmatrix} a1 & b1 & c1 \\ a2 & b2 & c2 \\ a3 & b3 & c3 \end{vmatrix}}$$

Note that all three equations have the same denominator, which is the determinant formed from the coefficients of x, y, and z. When this determinant is equal to zero, a unique solution does not exist.

Write a program that reads the coefficients from three simultaneous equations with three variables that represent the current analysis equations in an electrical circuit. Solve the system of equations for the three unknown currents.

PROBLEM STATEMENT

Use determinants to find the x, y, and z values that solve a set of three simultaneous equations from an electrical circuit.

INPUT/OUTPUT DESCRIPTION

The input is the set of coefficients for the equations. There are four coefficients for each equation; thus, 12 coefficients are needed. The output is the set of values for x, y, and z that solve each equation.

HAND EXAMPLE

Assume that the following set of equations is to be solved using determinants:

$$2x + 3y - 1z = 1$$
$$3x + 5y + 2z = 8$$
$$1x - 2y - 3z = -1$$

We first compute the determinant of the matrix formed from the coefficients of x, y, and z to determine if a unique solution exists:

$$\begin{vmatrix} 2 & 3 & -1 \\ 3 & 5 & 2 \\ 1 & -2 & -3 \end{vmatrix} = -30 + 6 + 6 + 5 + 8 + 27 = 22$$

Because the determinant is nonzero, a unique solution exists. We now compute the specific values for x, y, and z.

$$x = \frac{\begin{vmatrix} 1 & 3 & -1 \\ 8 & 5 & 2 \\ -1 & -2 & -3 \end{vmatrix}}{22} = \frac{-15 - 6 + 16 - 5 + 4 + 72}{22} = \frac{66}{22} = 3$$

$$y = \frac{\begin{vmatrix} 2 & 1 & -1 \\ 3 & 8 & 2 \\ 1 & -1 & -3 \end{vmatrix}}{22} = \frac{-48 + 2 + 3 + 8 + 4 + 9}{22} = \frac{-22}{22} = -1$$

$$z = \frac{\begin{vmatrix} 2 & 3 & 1 \\ 3 & 5 & 8 \\ 1 & -2 & -1 \end{vmatrix}}{22} = \frac{-10 + 24 - 6 - 5 + 32 + 9}{22} = \frac{44}{22} = 2$$

ALGORITHM DEVELOPMENT

The decomposition of our solution in general steps is the following:

DECOMPOSITION

Read coefficients.
Compute solution.
Write solution.

As we refine these steps, we realize that we need to compute several determinants in the solution. This computation can be performed in a function that is referenced each time we need it. We want to think carefully about the parameters to this function; it is cumbersome to list nine different variables that represent the matrix elements. Because the elements in the matrix vary with each computation, a two-dimensional array is not a good choice: we must change its values before each function reference. If you refer to the hand-worked example, you see that the matrix is composed of three columns, and each time the matrix changes, one of these columns changes. Therefore, if we send the three columns of the matrix to the determinant function as three one-dimensional arrays, we only need three parameters. It will also be easy to change parameters because we only need to change one-dimensional array names.

REFINEMENT IN PSEUDOCODE

solution: read coefficient arrays a, b, c, d
        compute determinant (a,b,c)
        if coefficient determinant = 0 then
           write 'NO UNIQUE SOLUTION'
        else
           compute x, y, z using determinants
           write x, y, z
determinant (p,q,r): compute determinant

As we convert the pseudocode into Pascal, we want to make it as easy as possible to enter the coefficients. This is important because we have 12 values to enter, and if they are entered out of order, the solution will be incorrect.

The structure chart for the solution is shown next, along with the Pascal program.

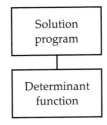

```
{------------------------------------------------------------------}
program  solution (input,output);
   {This program computes the solution to three simultaneous
    equations using determinants.}
type
   list3 = array[1..3] of real;
var
   denominator, x, y, z: real;
   a, b, c, d: list3;
{------------------------------------------------------------------}
function  determinant (p,q,r:list3): real;
   {This function computes the determinant of a 3X3 matrix
    where p, q, r represent the three columns of the matrix.}
begin {determinant}
   determinant := p[1]*q[2]*r[3] + q[1]*r[2]*p[3] +
                  r[1]*p[2]*q[3]-p[3]*q[2]*r[1]
                  q[3]*r[2]*p[1]-r[3]*p[2]*q[1]
end; {determinant}
{------------------------------------------------------------------}
begin {solution}
   writeln ('EACH EQUATION SHOULD BE IN THIS FORM:');
   writeln ('A*X + B*Y + C*Z = D');
   writeln ('ENTER A,B,C,D FOR EQUATION 1');
   readln (a[1],b[1],c[1],d[1]);
   writeln ('ENTER A,B,C,D FOR EQUATION 2');
   readln (a[2],b[2],c[2],d[2]);
   writeln ('ENTER A,B,C,D FOR EQUATION 3');
   readln (a[3],b[3],c[3],d[3]);
   writeln;
   denominator := determinant(a,b,c);
   if  denominator = 0.0   then
      writeln ('NO UNIQUE SOLUTION EXISTS')
   else
      begin
         x := determinant(d,b,c)/denominator;
         y := determinant(a,d,c)/denominator;
         z := determinant(a,b,d)/denominator
      end;
   writeln ('SOLUTION: X = ',x:7:2);
   writeln ('          Y = ',y:7:2);
   writeln ('          Z = ',z:7:2)
end. {solution}
{------------------------------------------------------------------}
```

Note that we did not use *a*, *b*, and *c* as variable names in the function. It would be confusing to use *a*, *b*, *c*, or *d* as variable names in the function because different combinations of those names were used as parameters.

TESTING

The output of this program with the data from the hand example is:

```
EACH EQUATION SHOULD BE IN THIS FORM:
A*X + B*Y + C*Y = D
ENTER A,B,C,D FOR EQUATION 1
2.0 3.0 -1.0 1.0
ENTER A,B,C,D FOR EQUATION 2
3.0 5.0 2.0 8.0
ENTER A,B,C,D FOR EQUATION 3
1.0 -2.0 -3.0 -1.0

SOLUTION: X =    3.00
          Y =   -1.00
          Z =    2.00
```

This technique is a simple one for solving systems of three equations, but it is not generally used for systems with four, five, or more equations because the determinant becomes more complicated to compute. The **Gauss-Jordan method** for solving a system of equations is a frequently used technique that requires a number of row manipulations to solve the system of equations. The **Gauss-Siedel method** is an iterative technique that is often used for a sparse system (one in which many of the coefficients are zero). Both of these techniques are discussed in the references listed at the end of Section 11-1.

SUMMARY

Some of the numerical techniques commonly used by engineers and scientists were introduced in this chapter. A set of data was modeled using a linear equation and evaluated using a sum of squared residuals. Numerical integration was discussed, and a program for estimating the integral of a function over a given interval was developed using the trapezoidal technique. Iterative techniques were illustrated with a program for finding the roots of a general polynomial. A number of matrix operations were implemented in Pascal, and a program for solving a system of three linear equations was developed using determinants.

DEBUGGING AIDS

Some important suggestions to ensure accuracy in your computations were presented in the chapter. We list these again:

1. When adding or subtracting long lists of numbers, work with the smaller numbers first.
2. If possible, avoid subtraction of nearly equal values.
3. Minimize the number of arithmetic operations.

At the end of Section 11-1, we gave a reference list for further information on numerical techniques. These references not only describe a number of numerical techniques but also discuss the limitations that apply to the techniques.

STYLE/TECHNIQUE GUIDELINES

Numerical applications may often use techniques that are not familiar to all programmers; thus, be sure to document your program and its modules carefully. If certain numerical applications are going to be used frequently, develop a set of modules that apply to the application. For example, if you are using matrices frequently, develop a set of modules to perform the operations that you need, and use this set consistently.

Pascal does not have a standard set of numerical approximation functions and procedures. In this chapter we wrote our own programs, functions, and procedures. However, a number of excellent software packages include routines to find matrix inverses, to solve differential equations and large systems of simultaneous equations, and to fit curves to a set of data. In general, if a routine to perform the operation that you need exists in a numerical package, it is usually better to use that routine than to write one yourself. The general routine is written to handle special cases and to perform operations so that precision errors and computation time are minimized.

KEY WORDS

approximations	method of least squares
Cramer's rule	numerical differentiation
determinant	numerical integration
dot product	residual
interval-halving technique	roots of polynomials
iterative technique	simultaneous equations
linear model	trapezoidal rule
matrix operations	

PROBLEMS

We begin our problem set with modifications to programs developed earlier in this chapter. Give the decomposition, refined pseudocode, and Pascal solution for each problem.

Problems 1–5 modify the program *linear*, given on page 523, which computed a linear model for a set of data.

1. Modify the linear modeling program so that it prints the point that has the largest residual (in absolute value). This is the point that deviates the most from the approximate straight line.

2. Modify the linear modeling program so that it computes the residual sum as the sum of the absolute value of the difference between the actual data value for y and its estimated value.

3. Modify the linear modeling program so that it computes the slope and y-intercept in a procedure.

4. Modify the linear modeling program so that it reads a data file that has a trailer record containing $(-999, -999)$ as the coordinates of the data point.

5. Modify the linear modeling program so that it asks the user to enter an x value and then uses the linear equation that has been computed to predict the corresponding y value.

Problems 6–10 modify the program *area1*, given on page 528, which estimated the area under a curve.

6. Modify the integration program so that the user can continue specifying the number of trapezoids until he or she is satisfied with the accuracy of the area estimate.

7. Modify the integration program so that the number of trapezoids is initially set to 10 and the corresponding area is computed. Then the number of trapezoids is doubled and the area is recomputed. This process continues until the change in the area is less than 0.01.

8. Modify the integration program so that the number of trapezoids is initially set to 10 and the corresponding area is computed. Then the number of trapezoids is doubled and the area is recomputed. This process continues until the change in the area is less than a user-entered tolerance.

9. Modify the integration program so that the area is computed in a function.

10. Modify the integration program so that it stores the x and y coordinates of the endpoints of the trapezoids in a data file so that they can be plotted later.

Problems 11–15 modify the program *roots*, given on page 537, which determines the roots of a polynomial in a given interval.

11. Modify the root-finding program so that it allows the user to enter the interval endpoints instead of using $[-5,5]$.

12. Modify the root-finding program so that it allows the user to enter the size of the small intervals used to search initially for the roots.

13. Modify the root-finding program so that it prints the maximum and minimum polynomial values over the interval.

14. Modify the root-finding program so that it prints the number of iterations performed to find the root.

15. Modify the root-finding program so that it continues halving the interval until the function value for the root is less than 0.01.

Problems 16–18 modify the program *solution*, given on page 550, which determines a solution for three linear equations.

16. Modify the simultaneous equations program so that the data is read from a data file instead of from the terminal.

17. Modify the simultaneous equations program so that it solves a system of two simultaneous equations. The determinant of a matrix with two rows and two columns is defined as:

$$\begin{vmatrix} a[1] & b[1] \\ a[2] & b[2] \end{vmatrix} = a[1] \cdot b[2] - a[2] \cdot b[1]$$

18. Modify the simultaneous equations program so that it determines if two of the equations represent the same plane when the determinant is equal to zero. In these cases, print an additional message that specifies which of the planes are the same. Recall that the same plane can be represented by two equations in which one of the equations is multiplied by a constant to get the other. Thus, the following equations represent the same plane:

$$3x + 2y - z = 5$$
$$6x + 4y - 2z = 10$$

In problems 19–20, use the five-phase design process to develop programs.

19. Write a procedure to compute the transpose of a matrix, where a transpose is defined to be another matrix that is generated by interchanging the rows with the columns of the original matrix. An example of a matrix a and its transpose a^T is given here:

$$a = \begin{bmatrix} 2 & 5 & 1 & 1 \\ 3 & 1 & 0 & 5 \\ 8 & 9 & 9 & 4 \end{bmatrix} \qquad a^T = \begin{bmatrix} 2 & 3 & 8 \\ 5 & 1 & 9 \\ 1 & 0 & 9 \\ 1 & 5 & 4 \end{bmatrix}$$

Assume that the procedure has the following header:

```
procedure  transpose (arows,acols,trows,tcols:integer;
                      a:matrix1; var t:matrix2);
```

where t represents the transpose matrix.

20. Write a procedure that normalizes the values in a matrix to values between 0 and 1. Thus, the maximum value is scaled to 1, the minimum value is scaled to 0, and all values in between are scaled accordingly. Assume that the procedure has four parameters: the matrix a, two integers that specify the size of a, and the output matrix b. Assume that the procedure has the following header:

```
procedure  normalize (a:matrix; rows,cols:integer;
                      var b:matrix);
```

Problems 21 – 23 refer to the following algorithm for computing pi. The area of a circle with radius 1 is equal to pi, and thus the area of a quarter circle with radius 1 is equal to pi/4. If we compute an estimate of the area of this quarter circle and multiply that value by 4, we have an estimate for the value of pi. To compute the area of the quarter circle, we sum the area of the subsections of the circle that are approximated by trapezoids, as shown in the following diagram. The values for y_1 and y_2 can be computed using the Pythagorean theorem because they represent the length of one side of a right triangle. If we assume that the areas of the subsections are added, starting with the subsections on the right, the appropriate equations are:

$$SUB_i = \frac{Y_2 + Y_1}{2} \cdot DX$$

$$Y_2 = \sqrt{R^2 - X_i^2}$$

$$Y_1 = \sqrt{R^2 - (X_i + DX)^2}$$

$$X_i = R - i \cdot DX$$

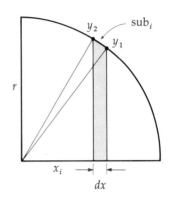

21. Write a program to compute pi using the technique just described. Let the user enter the number of subsections.

22. Modify the program in problem 21 so that the computation of pi is performed in a function that has the number of subsections as a parameter.

23. Modify the program in problem 21 so that the number of subsections is initialized to 100. Print the number of subsections and the estimate of pi, then repeat the process, increasing the number of subsections by 100. Continue until the number of subsections is equal to 1000.

Problems 24 – 25 refer to the following discussion on **numerical differentiation.** A **derivative** of a function at a given point can be approximated by the tangent or slope of the function at the given point, as shown in this diagram:

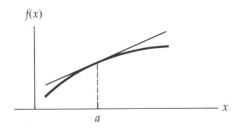

If we are given the x and y coordinates of two points on a curve, we can compute the slope of the line joining the two points. This slope is then an estimate of the derivative of the function at the midpoint of the two given points, as shown in the diagram:

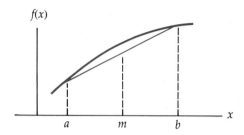

This technique uses a symmetric difference to approximate the derivative because it computes the derivative at a point, using the function values on both sides of it. Other common techniques for approximating the derivative use a forward difference (which computes the derivative at a point, using function values at that point and at the next point) or a backward difference (which computes the derivative at a point, using function values at that point and at the previous point).

24. Write a program to read a set of (x,y) coordinates and compute the slope between consecutive pairs of points. Print the coordinates of the midpoint of the interval generated by each pair of points and the value of the slope that corresponds to it.

25. Modify the program in problem 24 so that instead of printing a table of values, it prints a message that says 'POINT OF MAXIMUM OR MINIMUM IN CURVE OCCURS NEAR X COORDINATE VALUE xxx.xx' when the sign of the slope changes.

APPENDIX A

SYNTAX DIAGRAMS

The syntax diagrams in this appendix describe the main elements in a Pascal program, as shown in this block diagram:

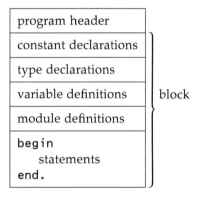

Reference the corresponding text material for additional details and specific examples. Rarely used items are not included here, but references to the text material on these items are included in the index.

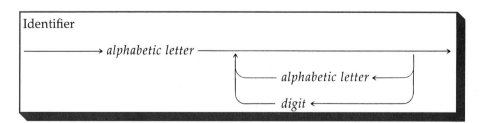

Numeric Constant

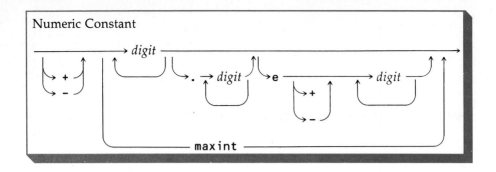

Constant

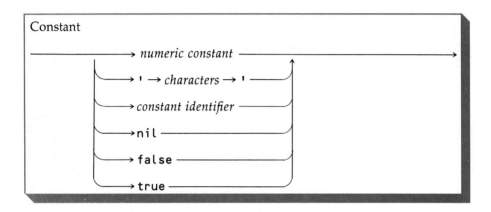

Expression

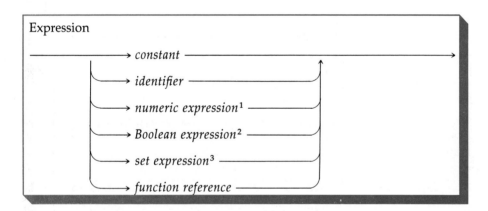

[1] An expression that can be evaluated to be a number.
[2] An expression that can be evaluated to be true or false.
[3] An expression that can be evaluated to be a set or nil.

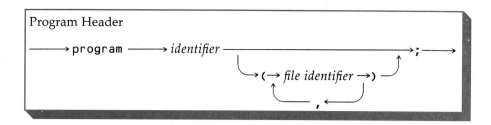

Program Header

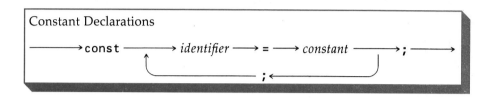

Constant Declarations

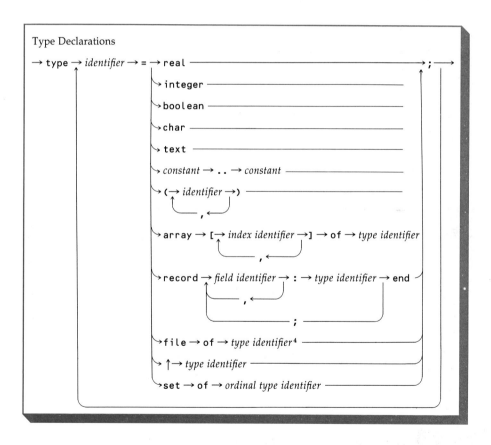

Type Declarations

[4] Any type identifier that does not include the type file.

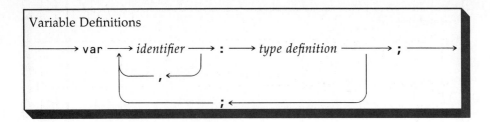

Variable Definitions

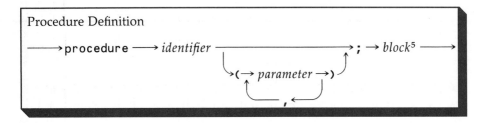

Procedure Definition

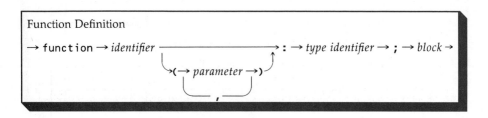

Function Definition

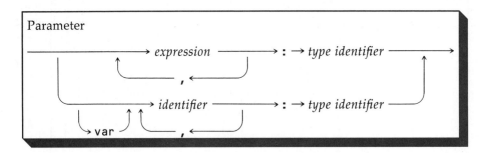

Parameter

[5] Blocks in procedure and function definitions end with a semicolon instead of a period.

Statement

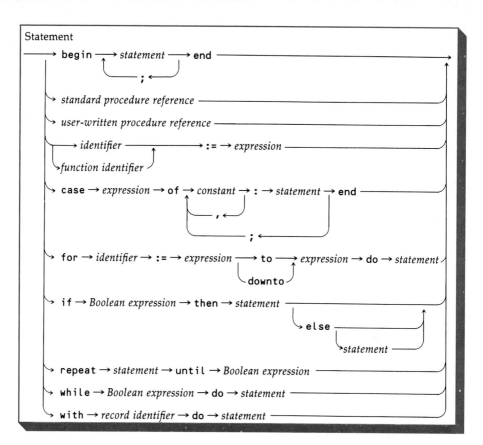

Standard Procedure Reference

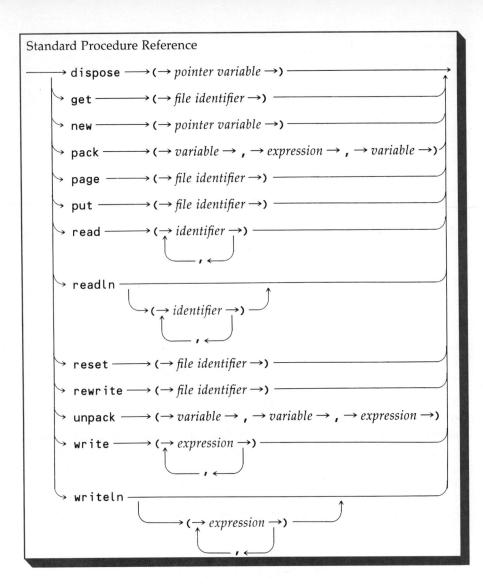

APPENDIX B

FLOWCHARTS

INTRODUCTION

Flowcharts are occasionally used instead of pseudocode to describe the steps in an algorithm. Whereas pseudocode uses English-like statements to define these steps, flowcharts use a graphic method. Your choice of which tool you use to describe your algorithms should be based on which form works best for you. Most people consistently use either one or the other, although some switch back and forth depending on which form seems to best fit a particular algorithm. We suggest that you try both so that you are able to read algorithms in either form. Then choose the form that you find easiest to use. In this appendix we first present the basic flowchart symbols and illustrate their use in *if* structures and *while* loops. This is followed by a section with flowcharts to accompany selected problem-solving sections in the text.

B-1 FLOWCHART SYMBOLS AND STRUCTURES

Algorithms are described in terms of steps such as input, output, and computations. Decisions are made by testing Boolean expressions that are evaluated to be true or false. The flowchart symbols for these processes, along with a symbol to indicate the beginning or end of a flowchart, are shown here:

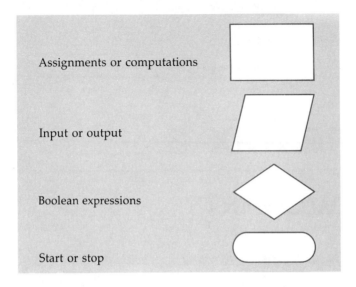

Assignments or computations

Input or output

Boolean expressions

Start or stop

These symbols can be combined to show the steps in *if* structures and *while* loops as shown below. The Pascal statements that correspond to the structures are shown above the flowchart segments.

If **Statement**

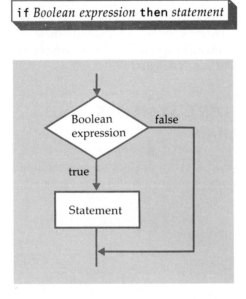

if *Boolean expression* **then** *statement*

Boolean expression — false

true

Statement

If-Else Statement

```
if Boolean expression then
     statement 1
else
     statement 2
```

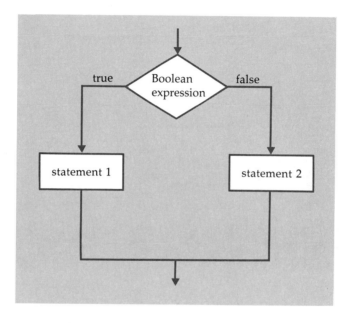

Nested *If-Else* Statements

(This form can also have a final *else* clause.)

> if *Boolean expression 1* then
>   *statement 1*
> else if *Boolean expression 2* then
>   *statement 2*
> else if *Boolean expression 3* then
>   *statement 3*

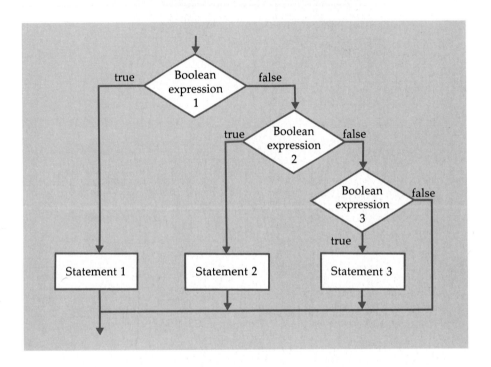

The *while* loop is shown below:

> **while** *Boolean expression* **do**
> *statement*

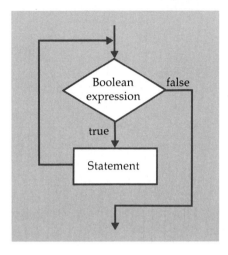

The flowchart symbol for a counting loop represents the three steps initializing the index, testing the index, and modifying the index. In Pascal, this counting loop corresponds to a *for* loop.

> **for** *index* := *initial* **to** *final* **do** *statement*
> **for** *index* := *initial* **downto** *final* **do** *statement*

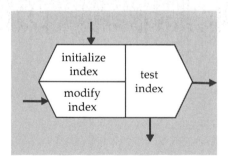

An example of a counting loop and its corresponding flowchart are shown below:

for i := 1 to 50 do *statement*

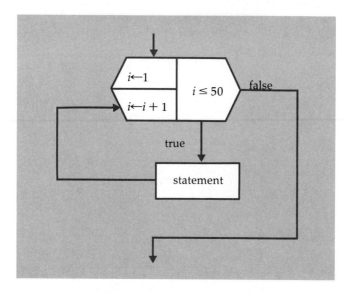

Procedures and functions are described by the following symbol in the program. A separate flowchart can also be done for the individual modules.

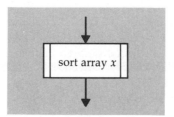

These symbols describe all basic operations needed to develop algorithms. Just as many algorithms can be developed to solve the same problem, many flowchart solutions also exist. Therefore, do not be surprised if your flowchart is somewhat different from one developed by another student to describe the same algorithm. The flowchart is a tool to aid you in describing your algorithms, and if too many rules are applied to it, the tool is no longer a quick and easy one to use.

B-2 FLOWCHARTS FOR SELECTED PROBLEM-SOLVING SECTIONS

The following flowcharts accompany selected problem-solving sections from the text. The algorithm development process still starts with the decomposition. The decomposition steps are then refined into a flowchart. Just as several pseudocode solutions may be necessary to refine the algorithm into sufficient detail, several flowcharts may also be necessary. The flowcharts shown here represent the final algorithm description before proceeding to the Pascal solution.

FOREIGN CURRENCY EXCHANGE (Section 1-7)

PROGRAM *convert*

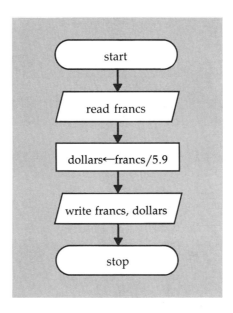

BACTERIA GROWTH (Section 1-8)

PROGRAM *growth*

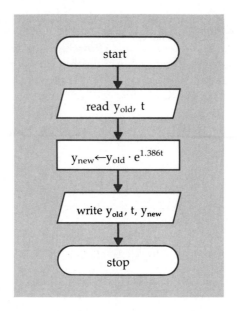

DEGREE TO RADIAN CONVERSION (Section 2-6)

PROGRAM *table*

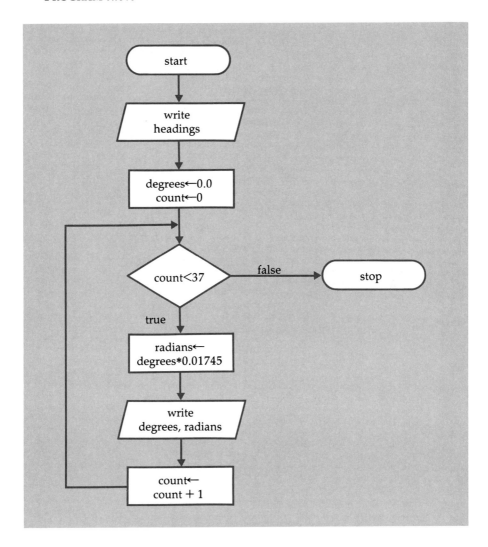

ROCKET TRAJECTORY (Section 2-8)

PROGRAM *rocket*

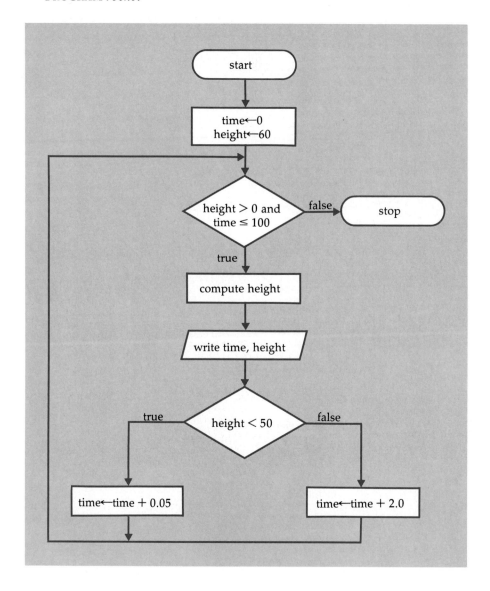

CABLE CAR VELOCITY (Section 3-5)

PROGRAM *cable*

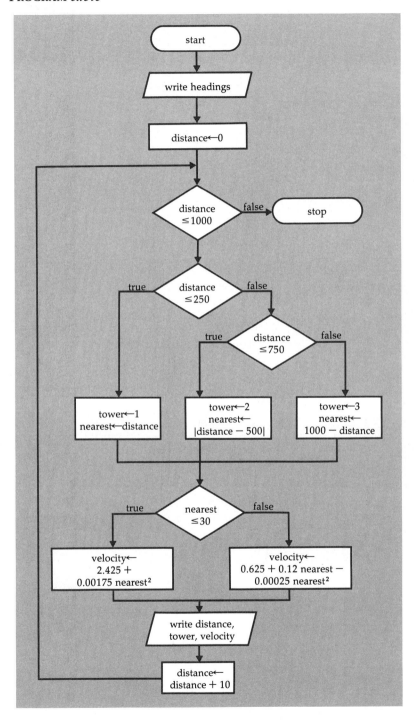

TIMBER MANAGEMENT (Section 3-6)

PROGRAM *timber*

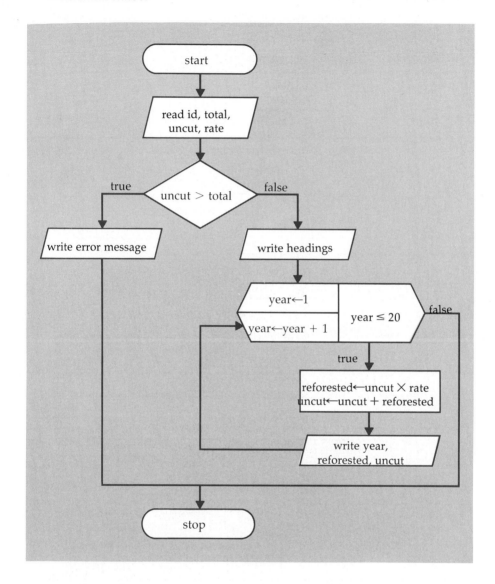

NATIONAL PARK SNOWFALL (Section 4-3)

PROGRAM *snowfall*

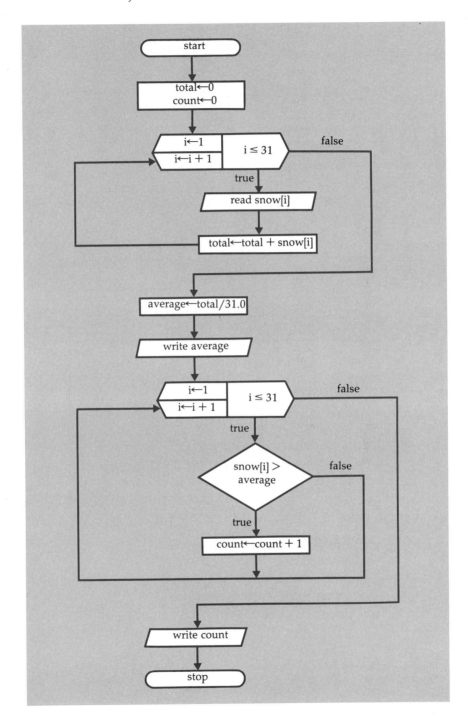

SIMULATION DATA (Section 5-4)

PROGRAM *generate*

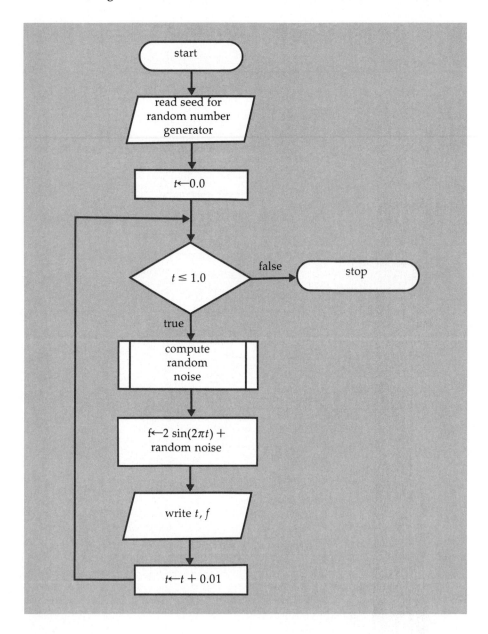

AUTHORSHIP IDENTIFICATION (Section 8-5)

FUNCTION *wordaverage*

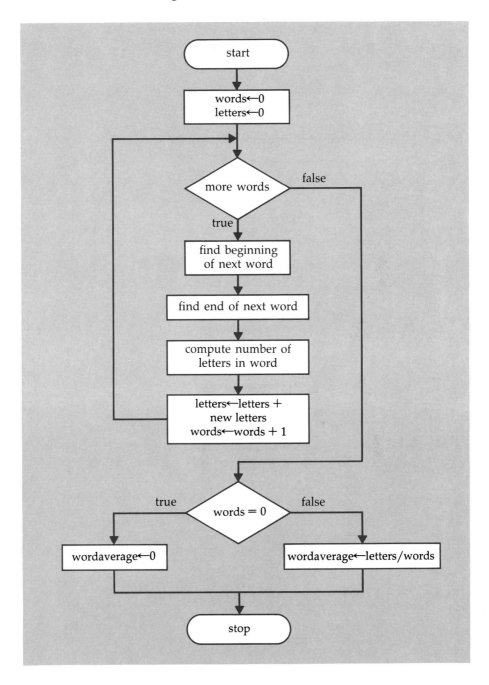

POPULATION DATA ANALYSIS (Section 9-2)

PROGRAM *analysis*

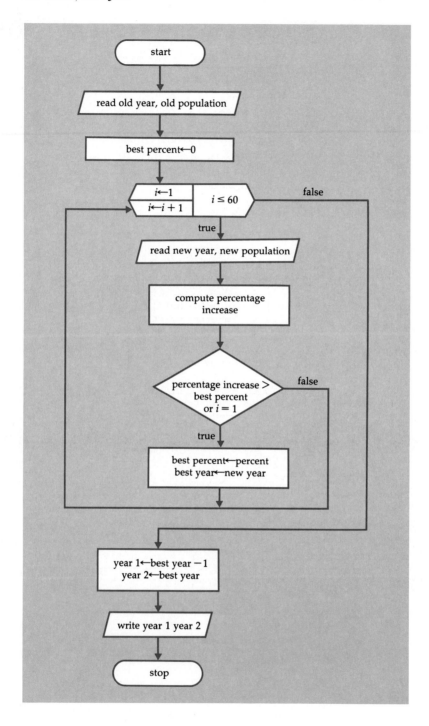

POWER IN FREQUENCY BANDS (Section 11-3)

PROGRAM *area 1*

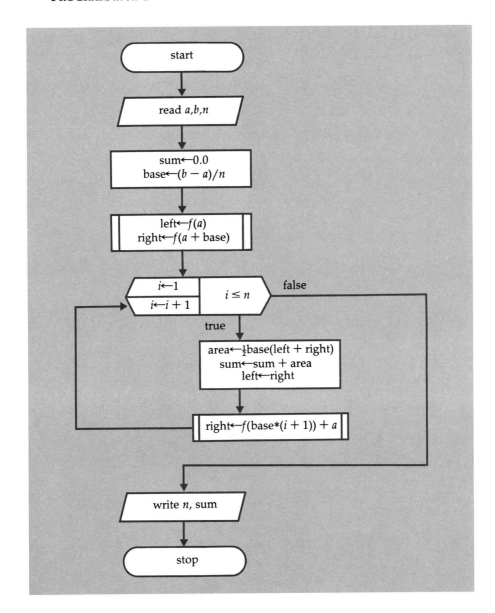

APPENDIX C

ADDITIONAL PASCAL TOPICS

This appendix summarizes several features of Pascal that were not introduced in earlier chapters but that should be included for completeness.

C-1 FORWARD REFERENCES

Procedures and functions are ordered such that they are defined before they are referenced in a Pascal program or module. In some situations it is not possible to include a procedure or function before it is referenced. For example, we may be linking together modules that have already been compiled, and two sets of modules may contain references to modules in the other group; therefore, either order will not solve the forward reference problem. Also, we may need to define modules that will reference each other; that is, module x references module y, and module y references module x. The solution to both of these situations is to include a forward reference that indicates that the module will be defined later. The following statements illustrate this forward reference with a program segment containing modules x and y that reference each other.

```
{----------------------------------------------------------------}
program example (input,output);
    {This program illustrates a forward reference.}
var
    sum, count: integer;
{----------------------------------------------------------------}
procedure  x (var sum:integer); forward;
procedure  y(var count,sum:integer);
begin {y}
    .
    .
    .
    x (sum)
```

```
        .
        .
        .
   end; {y}
   procedure  x;
        .
        .
        .
      y (count,sum)
        .
        .
        .
   end; {x}
   {- - - - - - - - - - - - - - - - - - - - - - - - - - - - - - - - - - - - - - - - - - - - -}
   begin {example}
        .
        .
        .
   end. {example}
   {- - - - - - - - - - - - - - - - - - - - - - - - - - - - - - - - - - - - - - - - - - - - -}
```

Note that the parameter list appears only in the forward reference, and not when the module is actually defined. If the module in the forward reference is a function, the function type is also listed in the forward reference, as shown here:

```
   function sum (x:list; n:integer): real; forward;
```

C-2   PROCEDURES AND FUNCTIONS AS PARAMETERS

Pascal allows us to use user-written procedures and functions as parameters in other procedures and functions that we write. To illustrate this feature, suppose that we want to compute the average of a function that is evaluated for the set of values stored in a one-dimensional array. In a single program, we might have several different functions that we want to use in computing the average, so we would like to compute the average value in a module that has as one of its parameters the function to be evaluated. In the following sample program, we define two different functions that are then used as parameters in the average-computing module.

```
{- - - - - - - - - - - - - - - - - - - - - - - - - - - - - - - - - - - - - - - - - - - - -}
program   example (timedata,output);
   {This program illustrates the use of modules as
   parameters to other modules.}
type
   list = array [1..100] of real;
var
   i: integer;
   timedata: text;
   time: list;
{- - - - - - - - - - - - - - - - - - - - - - - - - - - - - - - - - - - - - - - - - - - - -}
function   sinc (t:real): real;
   {This function evaluates the sinc function which
   is defined to be (sin t)/t. At t=0, the function is
   defined to be 1.0.}
```

```
begin {sinc}
   if  abs(t) < 0.001   then
      sinc := 1.0
   else
      sinc := sin(t)/t
end; {sinc}
{- - - - - - - - - - - - - - - - - - - - - - - - - - - - - - - - - - - - - - - - - - - - -}
function  polynomial (t:real): real;
   {This function evaluates a polynomial.}
begin {polynomial}
   polynomial := 3.0*t*t*t - 2.5*t*t + 5.7
end; {polynomial}
{- - - - - - - - - - - - - - - - - - - - - - - - - - - - - - - - - - - - - - - - - - - - -}
function  average (function f(x:real):real; time:list): real;
   {This function computes the average of a set of
   function values.}
var
   sum: real;
   i: integer;
begin {average}
   sum := 0.0;
   for i := 1 to 100 do
      sum := sum + f(time[i]);
   average := sum/100.0
end; {average}
{- - - - - - - - - - - - - - - - - - - - - - - - - - - - - - - - - - - - - - - - - - - - -}
begin {example}
   reset (timedata);
   for i := 1 to 100 do
      readln (timedata,time[i]);
   writeln ('AVERAGE VALUE OF SINC OVER TIME DATA = ',
            average (sinc,time):8:2);
   writeln ('AVERAGE VALUE OF POLYNOMIAL OVER TIME DATA = ',
            average (polynomial,time):8:2)
end. {example}
{- - - - - - - - - - - - - - - - - - - - - - - - - - - - - - - - - - - - - - - - - - - - -}
```

Note that the formal parameter x in the function f is not used anywhere except in the header for the function *average*.

C-3 GOTO STATEMENT AND LABELS

The *goto* statement is an unconditional branch from one point in a program to another. We did not include this statement in the chapter on control structures because we discourage the use of this statement. Programs with unconditional branches are not structured programs; therefore, they are harder to read and harder to debug. Some of the earlier high-level languages did not have the flexible types of control structures that Pascal has, and thus programs in these earlier languages had to use the *goto* statement to implement some of the control structures needed. FORTRAN 77 is an example of a language that does not have a *while* statement, and thus a *goto* statement is needed to implement a *while* loop. Even in FORTRAN 77, the *goto* statement should be strictly avoided except when used to implement *while* loops. Although we recommend that you thus do not use the *goto* statement in your Pascal statements, we will include a brief discussion for completeness and because you may encounter this statement in programs that you need to use and understand.

The syntax diagram of a *goto* statement is shown here:

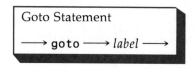

Goto Statement

$\longrightarrow$ goto $\longrightarrow$ *label* $\longrightarrow$

where *label* is a number between 1 and 9999 that has been attached to a Pascal statement elsewhere in the program. Any labels used in a program must also appear before the constant section of the program. The following segments show the use of the *goto* statement to implement a loop in which we compute the sum of the integers from one to twenty.

```
{-----------------------------------------------------------}
program   example (input,output);
    {This program illustrates the goto statement.}
label   10;
var
    count, sum: integer;
begin
    .
    .
    .
    count := 1;
    sum := 0;
10: sum := sum + count;
    count := count + 1;
    if   count <= 20 then
        goto 10;
    writeln ('SUM =',sum:8)
    .
    .
    .
end. {example}
{-----------------------------------------------------------}
```

Note that the label is followed by a colon when it is attached to a statement in the program.

APPENDIX D

TURBO PASCAL

The Turbo Pascal* compiler is a very popular compiler for personal computers. It follows standard Pascal with only minor differences. The following information shows some of the differences between Turbo Pascal and the standard Pascal described in this text.

1. *Assign* statements must be used with all files except for the standard system input and output files.

   Standard Pascal   `program  test (dataxy,output);`

   `.`

   `.`

   `.`

   `reset (dataxy)`

   Turbo Pascal   `program  test (dataxy,output);`

   `.`

   `.`

   `.`

   `assign (dataxy,'dataxy');`
   `reset (dataxy)`

2. The *close* statement must be used with all output files other than the standard output file.

   Standard Pascal   `program  test (input,results,output);`

   `.`

   `.`

   `.`

   `rewrite (results)`

*Turbo Pascal is a registered trademark.

Turbo Pascal

```
program test (input,results,output);
          .
          .
          .
assign (results,'results');
rewrite (results)
          .
          .
          .
close (results)
```

3. Integers in Turbo Pascal can range from $-32,768$ to $32,767$, and thus integers outside this range cannot be used.

4. When reading from the standard input file, the *read* statement executes the same as the *readln* statement. Therefore, all information needed from an input line must be read using a single statement. This also implies that loops cannot be used to read multiple characters from a single line of the standard input file.

5. The standard procedures *get* and *put* are not implemented in Turbo Pascal, but the *read* and *write* procedures have been extended.

6. The standard procedures *pack* and *unpack* are not implemented in Turbo Pascal, but packing occurs automatically whenever possible.

Now that we have summarized a few of the differences between Turbo Pascal and the standard Pascal described in this text, we illustrate these differences with the programs from the special Problem Solving sections in the text. For example, the random-number procedure presented in Section 5-4 used integers outside the range of Turbo Pascal, and hence a built-in Turbo Pascal function was used to generate random numbers in the program from Section 5-4. The program in Section 5-6 used Social Security numbers, which are nine-digit integers and thus too large for Turbo Pascal, so it was modified to represent the Social Security numbers as real numbers. The program from Section 8-5 that computed the average word length of a string entered from the system input file was modified to read the string from a data file. This change was necessary because we cannot use a loop to read characters from the same line from the system input file in Turbo Pascal. The programs from Section 9-4 (Instrument Usage Log) and Section 10-2 (Whooping Crane Migration) were also modified because they used date comparisons that generated integers outside the range of Turbo Pascal.

In each program that follows, color identifies the statements that had to be modified to run with the Turbo Pascal compiler. If a Problem Solving program ran with no changes, it is not listed here; this listing contains only the Problem Solving programs that required changes in order to run on the Turbo Pascal compiler.

Problem Solving—National Park Snowfall (page 163)

```
{----------------------------------------------------------------}
program  snowfall (january,output);
   {This program computes the average snowfall
   for January and counts the number of days
   with above-average snowfall.}
type
   index = 1..31;
   list = array[index] of real;
var
   total, average: real;
   count: integer;
   january: text;
   i: index;
   snow: list;
begin
   assign (january,'january');
   reset (january);
   total := 0.0;
   count := 0;
   for i := 1 to 31 do
      begin
         read (january,snow[i]);
         total := total + snow[i]
      end;
   average := total/31.0;
   writeln ('AVERAGE SNOWFALL IS',average:6:2,' INCHES');
   for i := 1 to 31 do
      if  snow[i] > average  then
         count := count + 1;
   writeln (count:2,' DAYS WITH ABOVE-AVERAGE SNOWFALL')
end.
{----------------------------------------------------------------}
```

Problem Solving—Integrated Circuit Defects (page 168)

```
{----------------------------------------------------------------}
program  quality (defects,output);
   {This program uses data in a defect file to compute
   and write a Quality Analysis Report.}
type
   index = 1..1000;
   list = array[index] of integer;
var
   percdef, percwire, percic, percnonic: real;
   boards, defectbd, wirebd, icbd, nonicbd,
   wiretotal, ictotal, nonictotal, total,
   wire, ic, nonic: integer;
   defects: text;
   i: index;
   id: list;
begin
   defectbd := 0;
   wirebd := 0;
   icbd := 0;
   nonicbd := 0;
   wiretotal := 0;
```

```
          ictotal := 0;
          nonictotal := 0;
          i := 1;
          assign (defects,'defects');
          reset (defects);
          readln (defects,boards);
          readln (defects,id[i],wire,ic,nonic);
          while  id[i] <> 9999  do
              begin
                  defectbd := defectbd + 1;
                  if  wire > 0  then
                      wirebd := wirebd + 1;
                  if  ic > 0  then
                      icbd := icbd + 1;
                  if  nonic > 0  then
                      nonicbd := nonicbd + 1;
                  wiretotal := wiretotal + wire;
                  ictotal := ictotal + ic;
                  nonictotal := nonictotal + nonic;
                  i := i + 1;
                  readln (defects,id[i],wire,ic,nonic)
              end;
          percdef := defectbd/boards*100.0;
          total := wiretotal + ictotal + nonictotal;
          percwire := wiretotal/total*100.0;
          percic := ictotal/total*100.0;
          percnonic := nonictotal/total*100.0;
          writeln ('             MONTHLY QUALITY ANALYSIS REPORT');
          writeln;
          writeln ('TOTAL NUMBER OF BOARDS ASSEMBLED = ',boards:4);
          writeln;
          writeln ('TOTAL BOARDS WITH DEFECTS = ',defectbd:4);
          writeln;
          writeln (wirebd:9,' BOARDS WITH BROKEN WIRES');
          writeln (icbd:9,' BOARDS WITH DEFECTIVE IC COMPONENTS');
          writeln (nonicbd:9,' BOARDS WITH DEFECTIVE NON-IC
                    COMPONENTS');
          writeln;
          writeln ('DEFECT ANALYSIS');
          writeln;
          writeln (percdef:10:1,'% OF BOARDS HAVE DEFECTS');
          writeln (percwire:10:1,'% OF DEFECTS WERE BROKEN WIRES');
          writeln (percic:10:1,'% OF DEFECTS WERE DEFECTIVE IC ',
                    'COMPONENTS');
          writeln (percnonic:10:1,'% OF DEFECTS WERE DEFECTIVE NON-IC ',
                    'COMPONENTS');
          if  percdef > 10.0  then
              begin
                  writeln;
                  writeln;
                  writeln ('IDENTIFICATION NUMBERS FOR DEFECTIVE BOARDS');
                  for i := 1 to defectbd do
                      writeln (id[i])
              end
end.
{--------------------------------------------------------------------}
```

Problem Solving — Earthquake Measurements (page 199)

```
{--------------------------------------------------------------------}
program  seismic (motion,output);
    {This program reads a data file of earthquake data,
    sorts it in ascending order, and prints it.}
```

```
type
    index = 1..200;
    list = array[index] of real;
var
    hold: real;
    id, count, indexmin, first, last: integer;
    motion: text;
    i, k: index;
    quake: list;
begin
    assign (motion,'motion');
    reset (motion);
    readln (motion,id);
    i := 1;
    readln (motion,quake[i]);
    while  quake[i] > 0.0  do
        begin
            i := i + 1;
            readln (motion,quake[i])
        end;
    count := i - 1;
    for i := 1 to count-1 do
        begin
            indexmin := i;
            first := i + 1;
            last := count;
            for k := first to last do
                if  quake[k] < quake[indexmin]  then
                    indexmin := k;
            hold := quake[i];
            quake[i] := quake[indexmin];
            quake[indexmin] := hold
        end;
    writeln ('FIELD LABORATORY ',id:5,' MEASUREMENTS');
    for i := 1 to count do
        writeln (i:3,'.',quake[i]:9:3)
end.
{------------------------------------------------------------}
```

Problem Solving—Oil Well Production (page 228)

```
{------------------------------------------------------------}
program  report (production,output);
    {This program generates a report from the daily
    production information for a set of oil wells.}
var
    oiltotal, average: real;
    month, day, year, pages, wellcount, id: integer;
    production: text;
{------------------------------------------------------------}
                (no changes in procedure printheader)
{------------------------------------------------------------}
                (no changes in procedure compute)
{------------------------------------------------------------}
begin {report}
    assign (production,'production');
    reset (production);
    read (production,month,day,year);
    wellcount := 0;
    oiltotal := 0.0;
    pages := 1;
```

```
        read (production,id);
        while  id <> 9999  do
            begin
                if  wellcount mod 20 = 0   then
                    printheader (month,day,year,pages);
                compute (production,average);
                writeln (id:4,average:17:2);
                wellcount := wellcount + 1;
                oiltotal := oiltotal + average;
                read (production,id)
            end;
        if   wellcount mod 20 = 0   then
            printheader (month,day,year,pages);
        writeln ('OVERALL AVERAGE FOR',wellcount:4,' WELLS IS',
                oiltotal/wellcount:7:2);
        writeln
end. {report}
{-------------------------------------------------------------}
```

Problem Solving — Simulation Data (page 234)

```
{-------------------------------------------------------------}
program  generate (input,output,signal);
    {This program generates a signal composed
    of a sine wave plus random noise.}
const
    pi = 3.141593;
var
    t, f, noise: real;
    signal: text;
{-------------------------------------------------------------}
begin {generate}
    assign (signal,'signal');
    rewrite (signal);
    t := 0.0;
    while  t <= 1.00   do
        begin
            noise := random;
            f := 2.0*sin(2.0*pi*t) + noise;
            writeln (signal,t,f);
            t := t + 0.01
        end;
    close (signal)
end. {generate}
{-------------------------------------------------------------}
```

Problem Solving — Computer Security (page 250)

```
{-------------------------------------------------------------}
program  update (input,access,output,newaccess);
    {This program updates a computer access list.}
const
    arraysize = 500;
    trailer = 999999999.0;
type
    index = 1..500;
    list = array[index] of real;
var
    old, new: real;
    i, code, count: integer;
```

```
        done: boolean;
        access, newaccess: text;
        ssn: list;
{---------------------------------------------------------------}
procedure  insert (arraysize:integer; new:real;
                   var count:integer; var x:list);
    {This procedure inserts an element in an ordered list.}
var
    i, k: integer;
    done: boolean;
begin {insert}
    if  count = arraysize  then
        writeln ('ARRAY IS FULL - LAST VALUE WILL BE LOST');
    done := false;
    i := 1;
    while  (i <= count) and (not done)  do
        if   x[i] < new   then
            i := i + 1
        else
            done := true;
    if  i > count  then
        begin
            if   count < arraysize   then
                begin
                    count := count + 1;
                    x[count] := new
                end
        end
    else
        if  x[i] = new   then
            writeln ('SSN ALREADY IN FILE')
        else
            begin
                if   count < arraysize   then
                    count := count + 1;
                for k := count downto i+1 do
                    x[k] := x[k-1];
                x[i] := new
            end
end; {insert}
{---------------------------------------------------------------}
procedure  delete (old:real; var count: integer; var x:list);
    {This procedure deletes an element from an ordered list.}
var
    i, k: integer;
    done: boolean;
begin {delete}
    done := false;
    i := 1;
    while  (i <= count) and (not done)  do
        if  x[i] < old   then
            i := i + 1
        else
            done := true;
    if  (i > count) or (x[i] > old)  then
        writeln ('VALUE TO DELETE NOT IN THE LIST')
    else
        begin
            count := count - 1;
            for k := i to count do
                x[k] := x[k+1]
        end
```

```
end; {delete}
{-------------------------------------------------------------}
begin {update}
    assign (access,'access');
    assign (newaccess,'newaccess');
    reset (access);
    rewrite (newaccess);
    i := 1;
    done := false;
    while  not done  do
        begin
            readln (access,ssn[i]);
            if  ssn[i] = trailer  then
                done := true
            else
                i := i + 1
        end;
    count := i - 1;
    done := false;
    while  not done  do
        begin
            writeln ('ENTER -1 FOR DELETION, 1 FOR INSERTION, ',
                     '0 TO QUIT');
            readln (code);
            if  code = -1  then
                begin
                    writeln ('ENTER SSN FOR DELETION');
                    readln (old);
                    delete (old,count,ssn)
                end
            else if  code = 1  then
                if  count = arraysize  then
                    writeln ('LIST IS FULL - DO DELETIONS FIRST')
                else
                    begin
                        writeln ('ENTER SSN FOR INSERTION');
                        readln (new);
                        insert (arraysize,new,count,ssn)
                    end
            else
                done := true
        end;
    for i := 1 to count do
        writeln (newaccess,ssn[i]);
    writeln (newaccess,trailer);
    close (newaccess)
end. {update}
{-------------------------------------------------------------}
```

Problem Solving — Traffic Flow (page 288)

```
{-------------------------------------------------------------}
program  analyze (input,output,traffic);
    {This program reads traffic information and computes the
    average number of cars per minute through an intersection.}
var
    id, begintime, endtime, cars,
    totaltime, totalcars, fileid: integer;
    traffic: text;
{-------------------------------------------------------------}
```
                    (no changes in function *minutes*)
```
{-------------------------------------------------------------}
```

```
begin {analyze}
   totaltime := 0;
   totalcars := 0;
   assign (traffic,'traffic');
   reset (traffic);
   writeln ('ENTER INTERSECTION IDENTIFICATION');
   readln (id);
   while  not eof(traffic)  do
      begin
         readln (traffic,fileid,begintime,endtime,cars);
         if  fileid = id  then
            begin
               totaltime := totaltime +
                                 minutes(begintime,endtime);
               totalcars := totalcars + cars
            end
      end;
   if  totaltime = 0  then
      writeln ('NO OBSERVATION FOR INTERSECTION ',id:3)
   else
      begin
         writeln ('INTERSECTION ',id:3);
         writeln ('AVERAGE CARS PER MINUTE = ',
                     totalcars/totaltime:6:2)
      end
end. {analyze}
{------------------------------------------------------------------}
```

Problem Solving — Project Management (page 304)

```
{------------------------------------------------------------------}
program  manage (input,project,output);
   {This program determines the timetable for a project.}
type
   index = 1..100;
   list = array[index] of integer;
var
   i, j, k, maxevent, totaltasks, totaldays,
   mindays, maxdays, weeks, daysleft: integer;
   project: text;
   event, task, days, hold: list;
{------------------------------------------------------------------}
                 (no changes in function minimum)
{------------------------------------------------------------------}
                 (no changes in function maximum)
{------------------------------------------------------------------}
begin {manage}
   i := 0;
   maxevent := 0;
   assign (project,'project');
   reset (project);
   while  not eof(project)  do
      begin
         i := i + 1;
         readln (project,event[i],task[i],days[i]);
         if  event[i] > maxevent  then
            maxevent := event[i]
      end;
   totaltasks := i;
   totaldays := 0;
   writeln ('          PROJECT COMPLETION TIMETABLE');
```

```
      writeln;
      writeln ('EVENT NUMBER     MINUMUM TIME     MAXIMUM TIME');
      for i := 1 to maxevent do
         begin
            k := 0;
            for j := 1 to totaltasks do
               if  event[j] = i   then
                  begin
                     k := k + 1;
                     hold[k] := days[j]
                  end;
            mindays := minimum(hold,k);
            maxdays := maximum(hold,k);
            writeln (i:8,mindays:16,maxdays:16);
            totaldays := totaldays + maxdays
         end;
      weeks := totaldays div 5;
      daysleft := totaldays mod 5;
      writeln;
      writeln;
      writeln ('        TOTAL PROJECT LENGTH = ',totaldays:3,
               ' DAYS');
      writeln ('                          = ',weeks:3,' WEEKS ',
               daysleft:1,' DAYS')
end. {manage}
{------------------------------------------------------------------}
```

Problem Solving—Analysis of Power Plant Data (page 335)

```
{------------------------------------------------------------------}
program  powerplant (plant,output);
   {This program computes and prints a composite
   report covering 8 weeks for a power plant.}
type
   index1 = 1..8;
   index2 = 1..7;
   table = array[index1,index2] of integer;
var
   average: real;
   i, j, minimum, total, count: integer;
   power: table;
   plant: text;
begin
   assign (plant,'plant');
   reset (plant);
   total := 0;
   minimum := maxint;
   for i := 1 to 8 do
      for j := 1 to 7 do
         begin
            read (plant,power[i,j]);
            total := total + power[i,j];
            if  power[i,j] < minimum   then
               minimum := power[i,j]
         end;
   average := total/56;
   count := 0;
   for i := 1 to 8 do
      for j := 1 to 7 do
         if  power[i,j] > average   then
            count := count + 1;
```

```pascal
      writeln ('                        COMPOSITE INFORMATION');
      writeln;
      writeln ('AVERAGE DAILY POWER OUTPUT =',
               average:5:1,' MEGAWATTS');
      writeln ('NUMBER OF DAYS WITH GREATER THAN ',
               'AVERAGE POWER OUTPUT = ',count:2);
      writeln ('DAY(S) WITH MINIMUM POWER OUTPUT:');
      for i := 1 to 8 do
         for j := 1 to 7 do
            if  power[i,j] = minimum  then
               writeln ('               WEEK ',i:2,'   DAY ',j:2)
end.
```
{---}

Problem Solving — Terrain Navigation (page 338)

{---}
```pascal
program  topology (elevation,output);
   {This program reads the elevation data for a set of
   land grids and determines the number of peaks in each.}
type
   index = 1..100;
   grid = array[index,index] of integer;
var
   i, j, id, rows, columns: integer;
   elevation: text;
   map: grid;
```
{---}
                    (no changes in function *peaks*)
{---}
```pascal
begin {topology}
   writeln ('SUMMARY OF LAND GRID ANALYSIS');
   writeln;
   writeln ('IDENTIFICATION   NUMBER OF POINTS   ',
            'NUMBER OF PEAKS');
   assign (elevation,'elevation');
   reset (elevation);
   read (elevation,id);
   while  id <> 9999  do
      begin
         read (elevation,rows,columns);
         for i := 1 to rows do
            for j := 1 to columns do
               read (elevation,map[i,j]);
         writeln (id:7,rows*columns:17,
                  peaks(map,rows,columns):17);
         read (elevation,id)
      end
end. {topology}
```
{---}

Problem Solving — Exam Statistics (page 352)

{---}
```pascal
program  statistics (summer,output);
   {This program computes statistics from exam averages
   in 6 section of a class during an 8-week session.}
type
   index1 = 1..6;
   index2 = 1..8;
```

```pascal
      list = array[index2] of real;
      table = array[index1,index2] of real;
var
    average: real;
    month, day, year, section, week: integer;
    summer: text;
    sums, max, min: list;
    scores: table;
{-----------------------------------------------------------------}
                  (no changes in procedure sumcols)
{-----------------------------------------------------------------}
                (no changes in procedure minmaxcols)
{-----------------------------------------------------------------}
begin {statistics}
    assign (summer,'summer');
    reset (summer);
    read (summer,month,day,year);
    writeln ('SUMMER SESSION - ENDED ',month:2,'-',
             day:2,'-',year:2);
    writeln;
    for section := 1 to 6 do
        for week := 1 to 8 do
            read (summer,scores[section,week]);
    sumcols (scores,6,8,sums);
    minmaxcols (scores,6,8,min,max);
    for week := 1 to 8 do
        begin
            writeln ('WEEK',week:3);
            average := sums[week]/6;
            writeln ('        AVE = ', average:6:2);
            writeln ('        MIN = ', min[week]:6:2);
            for section := 1 to 6 do
                if  scores[section,week] = min[week]  then
                    writeln('              SECTION ', section:2);
            writeln ('        MAX = ', max[week]:6:2);
            for section := 1 to 6 do
                if  scores[section,week] = max[week]  then
                    writeln ('              SECTION ', section:2)
        end
end. {statistics}
{-----------------------------------------------------------------}
```

Problem Solving—Cryptography (page 382)

```pascal
{-----------------------------------------------------------------}
program   decode (secret,output);
    {This program aids in decoding a message by counting
    the number of occurrences of vowels in the message.}
type
    list = array[1..5] of real;
    list50 = array[1..50] of char;
var
    count, i, j, n, total: integer;
    secret: text;
    vowel: list;
    message: list50;
{-----------------------------------------------------------------}
                  (no changes in procedure bargraph)
{-----------------------------------------------------------------}
begin {decode}
    total := 0;
```

```
              for i := 1 to 5 do
                 vowel[i] := 0;
              assign (secret,'secret');
              reset (secret);
              readln (secret,n);
              for i := 1 to n do
                 begin
                    count := 1;
                    while  not eoln(secret)  do
                       begin
                          read (secret,message[count]);
                          count := count + 1
                       end;
                    readln (secret);
                    count := count - 1;
                    total := total + count;
                    for j := 1 to count do
                       if  message[j] = 'A'  then
                          vowel[1] := vowel[1] + 1
                       else if  message[j] = 'E'  then
                          vowel[2] := vowel[2] + 1
                       else if  message[j] = 'I'  then
                          vowel[3] := vowel[3] + 1
                       else if  message[j] = 'O'  then
                          vowel[4] := vowel[4] + 1
                       else if  message[j] = 'U'  then
                          vowel[5] := vowel[5] + 1
                 end;
           writeln ('TOTAL NUMBER OF CHARACTERS = ',total:3);
           writeln;
           writeln ('OCCURRENCES OF VOWELS:');
           writeln (' A: ',vowel[1]:6:0);
           writeln (' E: ',vowel[2]:6:0);
           writeln (' I: ',vowel[3]:6:0);
           writeln (' O: ',vowel[4]:6:0);
           writeln (' U: ',vowel[5]:6:0);
           writeln;
           bargraph (vowel,5,20)
        end. {decode}
{-----------------------------------------------------------------}
```

Problem Solving — Authorship Identification (page 402)

```
{-----------------------------------------------------------------}
program  driver (inputtext,output);
   {This program tests the word average computation function.}
type
   list = array[1..18] of char;
var
   j: integer;
   inputtext: text;
   string1: list;
{-----------------------------------------------------------------}
                   (no changes in function wordaverage)
{-----------------------------------------------------------------}
begin {driver}
   assign (inputtext,'inputtext');
   reset (inputtext);
   for j := 1 to 18 do
      read (inputtext,string1[j]);
   for j := 1 to 18 do
      write (string1[j]);
```

```
   writeln;
   writeln ('WORD AVERAGE IS ',wordaverage(string1,18):6:2)
end. {driver}
{----------------------------------------------------------------}
```

Problem Solving—Population Data Analysis (page 422)


```
{----------------------------------------------------------------}
program  analysis (census,output);
   {This program reads 61 population values and determines
   the years of greatest percentage increase in population.}
type
   censusdata = record
                   year, population: integer;
                end;
var
   percent, bestpercent: real;
   i, year1, year2, bestyear: integer;
   census: text;
   old, new: censusdata;
begin {analysis}
   assign (census,'census');
   reset (census);
   readln (census,old.year,old.population);
   bestpercent := 0.0;
   for i := 1 to 60 do
      begin
         readln (census,new.year,new.population);
         percent := (new.population - old.population)*
                    100.0/old.population;
         if (percent > bestpercent) or (i = 1)  then
            begin
               bestpercent := percent;
               bestyear := new.year
            end;
         old.year := new.year;
         old.population := new.population
      end;
   year1 := bestyear - 1;
   year2 := bestyear;
   writeln ('GREATEST PERCENT INCREASE OCCURRED BETWEEN ',
            year1:4,' AND ',year2:4)
end. {analysis}
{----------------------------------------------------------------}
```

Problem Solving—Instrument Usage Log (page 432)


```
{----------------------------------------------------------------}
program  logs (oldlog,updates,newlog,output);
   {This program merges the instrumentation log data with
   new update information to give a new master file.}
type
   date = record
            mo, da, yr: integer
          end;
   logdata = record
                serial: integer;
                out, indate: date;
                group: integer
             end;
```

```pascal
var
    masterdate, updatedate: real;
    done, masterout: boolean;
    oldlog, updates, newlog: text:
    master, update: logdata;
begin {logs}
    assign (oldlog,'oldlog');
    assign (updates,'updates');
    assign (newlog,'newlog');
    reset (oldlog);
    reset (updates);
    rewrite (newlog);
    with  master  do
        readln (oldlog,serial,out.mo,out.da,out.yr,
                indate.mo,indate.da,indate.yr,group);
    with  update do
        readln (updates,serial,out.mo,out.da,out.yr,
                indate.mo,indate.da,indate.yr,group);
    if  (master.serial = 9999) and (update.serial = 9999)   then
        done := true
    else
        done := false;
    while  not done  do
        begin
            if  update.serial < master.serial   then
                masterout := false;
            if  update.serial > master.serial   then
                masterout := true;
            if  update.serial = master.serial   then
                begin
                    with  master  do
                        masterdate := indate.yr*10000.0 +
                                      indate.mo*100.0 + indate.da;
                    with  update  do
                        updatedate := indate.yr*10000.0 +
                                      indate.mo*100.0 + indate.da;
                    if  masterdate <= updatedate   then
                        masterout := false
                    else
                        masterout := true
                end;
            if  masterout   then
                with  master  do
                    begin
                        writeln (newlog,serial,out.mo,out.da,out.yr,
                                 indate.mo,indate.da,indate.yr,group);
                        readln (oldlog,serial,out.mo,out.da,out.yr,
                                indate.mo,indate.da,indate.yr,group)
                    end
            else
                with  update  do
                    begin
                        writeln (newlog,serial,out.mo,out.da,out.yr,
                                 indate.mo,indate.da,indate.yr,group);
                        readln (updates,serial,out.mo,out.da,out.yr,
                                indate.mo,indate.da,indate.yr,group)
                    end;
            if  (master.serial = 9999) and
                (update.serial = 9999)   then
                done := true
        end;
    with  master  do
```

```
            writeln (newlog,serial,out.mo,out.da,out.yr,
                     indate.mo,indate.da,indate.yr,group);
       close (newlog)
end. {logs}
{---------------------------------------------------------------}
```

Problem Solving—Computer Inventory Update (page 437)

```
{---------------------------------------------------------------}
program  update (update1,inventory,output);
   {This program updates the quantity in an inventory file.}
type
   data = record
               stocknumber, quantity: integer;
               price: real
          end;
   table = array[1..500] of data;
var
   i, count, newstock, newchange: integer;
   done, found: boolean;
   update1, inventory: text;
   item: table;
begin {update}
   assign (inventory,'inventory');
   reset (inventory);
   i := 1;
   done := false;
   while  not done  do
      with  item[i]  do
         begin
            readln (inventory,stocknumber,quantity,price);
            i := i + 1;
            if  stocknumber = 999  then
               done := true
         end;
   count := i - 1;
   assign (update1,'update1');
   reset (update1);
   while  not eof(update1)  do
      begin
         readln (update1,newstock,newchange);
         i := 1;
         done := false;
         found := false;
         while  not done  do
            with  item[i]  do
               begin
                  if  newstock = stocknumber  then
                     begin
                        quantity := quantity + newchange;
                        done := true;
                        found := true
                     end
                  else if  newstock < stocknumber  then
                        done := true
                  else
                     begin
                        i := i + 1;
                        if  i > count  then
                           done := true
                     end
               end;
```

```pascal
            if  not found  then
                writeln ('NO MATCH FOR ',newstock:3)
         end;
      rewrite (inventory);
      for i := 1 to count do
         with  item[i]  do
             writeln (inventory,stocknumber,quantity,price:8:2);
      close (inventory)
end. {update}
```
{--}

Problem Solving—Whooping Crane Migration (page 482)

{--}
```pascal
program  migration (cranes,output);
   {This program reads the migration data for the whooping
   cranes and prints the sightings in ascending order.}
type
   pointer = ^sighting;
   sighting = record
                    mo, da, yr, time, grid1, grid2, birds: integer;
                    link: pointer
              end;
var
   cranes: text;
   first, current: pointer;
```
{--}
```pascal
function  rightspot (current,next:pointer): boolean;
   {This function determines whether or not the current
   data should be inserted before the next data.}
var
   currentdate, nextdate: real;
begin {rightspot}
   if  next = nil  then
      rightspot := true
   else
      begin
         currentdate := current^.yr*10000.0 +
                        current^.mo*100.0 + current^.da;
         nextdate := next^.yr*10000.0 +
                     next^.mo*100.0 + next^.da;
         if  currentdate < nextdate  then
            rightspot := true
         else if  currentdate > nextdate  then
            rightspot := false
         else if  currentdate = nextdate  then
             if  current^.time < next^.time  then
                rightspot := true
             else
                rightspot := false
      end
end; {rightspot}
```
{--}
                    (no changes to procedure *insert*)
{--}
                    (no changes to procedure *printlist*)
{--}
```pascal
begin {migration}
   assign (cranes,'cranes');
   reset (cranes);
   new (first);
```

```
        with  first^  do
            readln (cranes,mo,da,yr,time,grid1,grid2,birds);
        first^.link := nil;
        while  not eof(cranes)  do
            begin
                new (current);
                with  current^  do
                    readln (cranes,mo,da,yr,time,grid1,grid2,birds);
                insert (current,first)
            end;
        printlist (first)
end. {migration}
{------------------------------------------------------------}
```

Problem Solving—Accident Survey (page 504)

```
{------------------------------------------------------------}
program  accident (survey,output);
    {This program uses the data in an accident survey file
    to summarize data regarding accidents with injuries.}
type
    id = set of 1..250;
var
    ave, aveinjury, percinj, percped, percother, perccars: real;
    injothercount, injpedcount, injcount, totalid,
    vehicles, idnum, vehinjury, injcarcount,
    ncars, ntrucks, nother, npedestrian, ninjuries: integer;
    survey: text;
    cars, trucks, other, pedestrians, injuries, onlycars: id;
{------------------------------------------------------------}
                    (no changes to function setcount)
{------------------------------------------------------------}
begin {accident}
    totalid := 0;
    vehicles := 0;
    vehinjury := 0;
    cars := [];
    trucks := [];
    other := [];
    pedestrians := [];
    injuries := [];
    assign (survey,'survey');
    reset (survey);
    while  not eof(survey)  do
        begin
            readln (survey,idnum,ncars,ntrucks,nother,
                    npedestrian,ninjuries);
            totalid := totalid + 1;
            vehicles := vehicles + ncars + ntrucks + nother;
            if  ninjuries > 0  then
                begin
                    vehinjury := vehinjury + ncars + ntrucks + nother;
                    injuries := injuries + [idnum]
                end;
            if  ncars > 0  then
                cars := cars + [idnum];
            if  ntrucks > 0  then
                trucks := trucks + [idnum];
            if  nother > 0  then
                other := other + [idnum];
```

```
                     if    npedestrian > 0  then
                        pedestrians := pedestrians + [idnum]
        end;
  ave := vehicles/totalid;
  injcount := setcount(injuries);
  injpedcount := setcount(injuries*pedestrians);
  injothercount := setcount(injuries*other);
  onlycars := cars - ((trucks+other)+pedestrians);
  injcarcount := setcount(injuries*onlycars);
  aveinjury := vehinjury/injcount;
  percinj := injcount/totalid*100.0;
  percped := injpedcount/totalid*100.0;
  percother := injothercount/totalid*100.0;
  perccars := injcarcount/totalid*100.0;
  writeln ('       SURVEY OF ACCIDENTS WITH INJURIES');
  writeln ;
  writeln ('AVERAGE NUMBER OF VEHICLES PER ACCIDENT = ',
           ave:4:1);
  writeln;
  writeln ('AVERAGE NUMBER OF VEHICLES PER ACCIDENT');
  writeln ('                           WITH INJURIES = ',
           aveinjury:4:1);
  writeln;
  writeln ('PERCENT OF ACCIDENTS WITH INJURIES = ',
           percinj:5:1,' %');
  writeln;
  writeln ('PERCENT OF ACCIDENTS WITH INJURIES');
  writeln ('            INVOLVING PEDESTRIANS = ',
           percped:5:1,' %');
  writeln;
  writeln ('PERCENT OF ACCIDENTS WITH INJURIES');
  writeln ('           INVOLVING VEHICLES OTHER');
  writeln ('             THAN CARS AND TRUCKS = ',
           percother:5:1,' %');
  writeln;
  writeln ('PERCENT OF ACCIDENTS WITH INJURIES');
  writeln ('                 INVOLVING ONLY CARS = ',
           perccars:5:1,' %')
  end. {accident}
{-----------------------------------------------------------------}
```

Problem Solving—Coil Deflection Model (page 523)

```
{-----------------------------------------------------------------}
program  linear (xydata,output);
    {This program computes a linear model for a set of data and
    then computes the residual sum to evaluate the model.}
type
   list500 = array[1..500] of real;
var
   slope, intercept, ynew, residual, sumx, sumy,
   sumxy, sumxx, sumresidual: real;
   i, count: integer;
   xydata: text;
   x, y: list500;
begin {linear}
   sumx := 0;
   sumy := 0;
   sumxy := 0;
   sumxx := 0;
   sumresidual := 0;
```

```pascal
      i := 1;
   assign (xydata,'xydata');
   reset (xydata);
   while  not eof(xydata)  do
      begin
         readln (xydata,x[i],y[i]);
         sumx := sumx + x[i];
         sumy := sumy + y[i];
         sumxy := sumxy + x[i]*y[i];
         sumxx := sumxx + x[i]*x[i];
         i := i + 1
      end;
   count := i - 1;
   slope := (sumx*sumy - count*sumxy)/
            (sumx*sumx - count*sumxx);
   intercept := (sumy - slope*sumx)/count;
   writeln ('THE LINEAR EQUATION IS');
   writeln ('Y = ',slope:6:2,' X + ',intercept:6:2);
   writeln;
   writeln ('ORIGINAL     ORIGINAL     ESTIMATED     RESIDUAL');
   writeln ('    X          Y            Y                    ');
   writeln;
   for i := 1 to count do
      begin
         ynew := slope*x[i] + intercept;
         residual := y[i] - ynew;
         sumresidual := sumresidual + residual*residual;
         writeln (x[i]:6:2,y[i]:12:2,ynew:13:2,residual:13:2)
      end;
   writeln;
   writeln ('RESIDUAL SUM = ',sumresidual:6:2)
end. {linear}
{-----------------------------------------------------------}
```

GLOSSARY OF KEY WORDS

actual parameter A parameter listed in a procedure reference or a function reference; it can be an identifier or an expression.

algorithm A stepwise procedure for solving a problem.

approximation An estimate of a value that is used instead of the actual value.

arithmetic logic unit (ALU) A fundamental computer component that performs all the arithmetic and logic operations.

array A data structure whose components share a common identifier and are specified individually with indices.

array of records A data structure whose components are records.

ascending order An order from lowest to highest.

ASCII code A binary code (American Standard Code for Information Interchange) commonly used by computers to store information.

assembly language A programming language that is unique to an individual computer system.

base type The data type of the elements of a set.

batch processing A method of interacting with the computer in which programs are executed in generally the same order in which they are submitted.

binary A term used to describe something that has two values, such as a binary digit that can be 0 or 1.

binary search An efficient search algorithm for an ordered list that continually divides in half the part of the list that we are searching.

binary string   A string or group of binary values, such as 11011100.

binary tree   A linked data structure that begins with a single element (root) that has a left branch and a right branch. The element at each branch also has a left branch and a right branch.

block   A group of Pascal statements that can contain constant definitions, type definitions, variable declarations, module declarations, and Pascal statements.

Boolean data type   A data type used to define variables or constants whose values are true or false.

Boolean expression   An expression that can be evaluated to be either true or false, and often contains relational operators.

Boolean function   A function whose value is false or true.

Boolean operator   An operator used with Boolean expressions that forms a new Boolean expression; the Boolean operator *not* is used with one Boolean expression, and the Boolean operators *and* and *or* are used with two Boolean expressions.

bubble sort   A sort algorithm that is based on interchanging adjacent values in the array until all the values are in the proper position.

bug   An error in a computer program.

built-in function   An operation that is part of the Pascal language and that can be referenced in other Pascal statements.

central processing unit (CPU)   The combination of the processor unit, the ALU, and the internal memory that forms the basis of a computer.

character data   Data that can contain characters as well as numbers.

character string   A string or group of characters that contains numerical digits, alphabetical letters, or special characters.

circularly linked list   A linked list data structure in which the last element in the linked list points to the first element in the list.

collating sequence   The ascending order of characters specified by a particular code.

column sums   Sums computed by adding the values in columns in a two-dimensional array.

compilation   The process of converting a program written in a high-level language into machine language.

compiler   The program that converts a program written in a high-level language into machine language.

compound Boolean expression   A Boolean expression that contains one or more of the Boolean operators *and*, *or*, and *not*.

compound statement   A group of Pascal statements that start with *begin* and end with *end*, and are handled as if they were a single statement.

computer graphics   A term referring to graphics that have been generated by a computer.

condition   An expression that can be evaluated to be true or false.

connector   The operators *not, and,* and *or* that are used with Boolean expressions.

constant   A specific value used in expressions.

control structure   A structure that controls the order of execution of a series of steps.

conversational computing   A method of interacting with the computer in which the computer seems to converse with the user in an English-like manner.

counting loop   A loop that is repeated a specific number of times.

Cramer's rule   A mathematical technique for computing the solution to a set of simultaneous equations using determinants.

data file   A file used to store information used by a program or generated by a program.

debugging   The process of eliminating bugs or errors from a program.

decomposition   Dividing a problem solution into a series of smaller problems.

deletion   A technique for removing an element from an ordered list.

descending order   An order from highest to lowest.

design phases   A procedure for solving a problem by dividing the solution into a series of phases that begins with the problem description and ends with the problem solution.

determinant   A real number that is computed from a matrix.

dot product   An operation performed between two vectors that computes the sum of the products of values in corresponding positions in the vectors.

doubly linked list   A linked list data structure with two links in each element; one link points to the next element and the other link points to the previous element.

driver   A program written specifically to test a module.

dynamic data structure   A data structure whose memory is not defined during the compilation of the program, but rather during the execution of the program.

dynamic variable   A variable defined in terms of a pointer to a memory location.

EBCDIC code   A binary code (Extended Binary-Coded-Decimal Interchange Code) commonly used by computers to store information.

echo   A debugging aid in which the values of variables are printed immediately after they are read.

editor   A program in a time-sharing system that allows the user to modify programs entered into the system.

element   A specific location in an array.

empty set   A set with no elements.

end-of-file   An indicator that is placed at the end of a data file that can be detected with the *eof* Boolean function.

enumerated data type   A data type that is defined with an ordered set of identifiers; the Boolean data type is an enumerated data type with identifiers false and true.

error condition   Situations that occur during the execution of the program that are generally caused by errors in the input data.

execution   The process of executing the steps specified by a program.

exponential notation   A notation for real values that uses the letter *e* to separate the mantissa and the exponent.

field identifier   The identifier used for an individual item in a record.

file buffer variable   The variable used to reference the file buffer that is associated with a nontext file.

flowchart   A graphical diagram used to describe the steps in an algorithm.

for loop   A counting loop that performs the initialization of a counter, the modification of the counter, and the condition test for the counter with one statement, the *for* statement.

formal parameter   A parameter listed in the procedure header; it can only be an identifier.

function   A module that returns a single value to the program.

function header   A Pascal statement that lists the function, its parameters, and the data type for the value returned by the function.

global parameter   A variable whose scope is the entire program.

hardware   The physical components of a computer.

hierarchical records   A data structure that contains records defined within records.

high-level language   An English-like language that must be converted into machine language before it can be executed.

identifier   A name that is given to items such as variables or constants that we want to reference in our program.

identity matrix   A matrix that has the value one on the main diagonal and zero elsewhere.

if structure   A structure that tests a condition and executes a set of steps if the condition is true.

index   An integer or integer expression used to reference an element in an array.

infinite loop   A loop in which the loop condition is always true, and thus there is no way to exit the loop properly.

input/output (I/O)   The information that a program reads or writes.

insertion   A technique for adding an element to an ordered list.

insertion sort   A sort algorithm that begins at the top of the list, comparing adjacent elements. If an element is out of order, it is continually exchanged with the value above it in the list until it is in its proper place. The sort then continues with the next element out of order.

integer value   A value that contains no fractional portion.

interactive computing   Computing in which the user interacts with the program by answering questions and entering data.

interval halving technique   A technique for approximating roots of a function by determining an interval in which the function crosses the x axis and then halving the interval to find a new smaller interval in which the function crosses the x axis.

invoke   A term used to indicate a reference to a module, such as "to invoke a sort procedure."

iterative technique   A technique that is repeated to give better and better approximations to a value that cannot be computed through direct computation.

levels of recursion   The number of times that a recursive module references itself.

lexicographic order   Dictionary order.

linear model   A linear equation that approximates the relationship between two variables.

linkage editor   A program that finishes preparing a program in machine language (object program) for execution by the computer.

linked list   A data structure that is a group of dynamic variables linked together.

list   Another name often used for the one-dimensional array data structure.

local variable   A variable defined within a module; the scope of the variable is the module in which it is defined.

logic error   An error in the logic used to define an algorithm.

loop   A group of statements that are executed repeatedly.

master file   A file that contains the master information or the most accurate information.

mathematical function   A function whose value is a number.

matrix   A group of values that can be represented by a two-dimensional array.

matrix operation   An operation performed on matrices.

memory   The storage available for the variables and constants needed in a program.

merge   An operation that combines two ordered lists into one ordered list.

method of least squares   A mathematical technique used to determine a linear model from a set of data values.

module   A nearly independent set of statements; in Pascal, modules can be procedures or functions.

multidimensional array   A group of variables that share the same identifier and whose elements are specified by more than one index or subscript.

nested for loops   *For* loops that are completely contained within other *for* loops.

nested if structures   *If* structures that are completely contained within other *if* structures, as illustrated by the *if-else-if* structure.

nested procedure   A procedure that is defined within another procedure.

nil constant   A constant that represents the end of a linked list.

nontext file   A file of components other than character components.

numerical differentiation   Numerical techniques for estimating the derivative (or slope) of a function at a specified point.

numerical integration   Numerical techniques for estimating the integral of a function (or the area under the graph of the function) over a specified interval.

object program   A program in machine-language form.

one-dimensional array   A data structure in which a group of elements share the same identifier and whose elements are specified by one index or subscript.

ordinal data type   A data type whose values are ordered such that each value (except the first) has a unique predecessor and each value (except the last) has a unique successor.

ordinal function   A function whose parameters are ordinal values.

packed array   An array that has been stored so that less memory is required to store the information in the array, but more computer time may be needed to perform calculations with the packed array.

parameter   An identifier that represents input or output to a module.

parameter list   The list of parameters to a module. The parameter list for a procedure contains both input and output parameters; the parameter list for a function contains only input parameters.

Pascal   A structured computer language developed by Niklaus Wirth in 1968 that was named after a French mathematician.

pattern detection A term used to specify an algorithm that searches for a specific pattern or set of values in data.

pointer variable A variable that contains the memory address of a dynamic variable.

pop routine A routine used to remove elements from a stack.

predecessor The value that precedes a given value that is an ordinal data type. The first value in an ordinal data type does not have a predecessor.

printer plot Plot generated by a computer using printed characters as opposed to actually drawing lines.

procedure A Pascal module that is used to define a set of steps that can be referenced by using the procedure reference.

procedure header A Pascal statement that lists the procedure name and the procedure parameters.

processor A fundamental computer component that controls the operation of the other parts of the computer.

pseudocode The English-like statements used to describe the steps in an algorithm.

push routine A routine used to add elements to a stack.

queue A linked data structure in which items can be added at one end and removed from the other.

quicksort A recursive sort algorithm that is based on the steps that separate a list into a group of values larger than a pivot value and a group of values smaller than a pivot value.

random number generator A set of steps that generate numbers in a random order; random number generators commonly generate values between 0.0 and 1.0.

real value A value that may contain a fractional or decimal portion.

record A set of information that contains fields or components.

record structure A data structure that contains fields or components.

recursive function A function that references itself.

recursive procedure A procedure that references itself.

reference by address A reference to a parameter in a procedure or a function that uses the memory address of the actual parameter each time that it is referenced.

reference by value A reference to a parameter in a procedure or a function that uses a copy of the value stored in the memory address of the actual parameter each time that it is referenced.

relational operator An operator used to compare two arithmetic expressions.

repeat until loop A loop that is executed until a condition is true; the condition is tested at the end of the loop instead of at the beginning as in a *while* loop.

repetition structure   A structure in which steps are repeated, such as in a *while* loop or a counting loop.

residual   A value used to determine the quality of a linear model for a set of data.

roots of polynomials   Values that give a functional value of zero when used as the argument or parameter for a specific polynomial.

row sums   Sums computed by adding the values in rows in a two-dimensional array.

scalar data type   A data type in which the set of values is ordered and is composed of elements that cannot be further divided into other elements.

scope   A term used to describe the portion of a program in which it is valid to use a specific identifier; the scope of a global variable is the entire program.

selection sort   A sort algorithm that is based on finding the minimum value and placing it first in the list, finding the next smallest value and placing it second in the list, and so on.

selection structure   A structure that tests a condition to determine which steps are to be performed next.

sentinel signal   A signal at the end of a data file that indicates that no more data follows.

sequence structure   A structure in which steps are performed one after another, or sequentially.

set   A data type composed of a collection of unordered elements of the same ordinal type.

set difference   An operation that removes elements from one set that are also in another set.

set intersection   An operation that determines the set that is composed of elements that are common to two other sets.

set union   An operation that combines elements in two other sets.

side effects   Problems caused by not using the argument list to pass all the input and output information needed by a module.

simultaneous equations   Equations that together describe a situation mathematically.

software   The programs used to specify the operations in a computer.

software tools   Modules that contain techniques commonly used in programs.

source program   A program in a high-level language form.

square matrix   A matrix with the same number of rows as columns.

stack   A linked data structure in which elements are removed from the same end that they are added.

stepwise refinement   A process for converting a general algorithm to one that is detailed enough to be converted into a computer language.

structure chart   A diagram that shows the modules in a program and indicates which modules are contained in other modules.

structured algorithm An algorithm that is described with a set of standard structures, such as sequence, selection, and repetition.

structured program A program with a top-down flow that is easy to follow and modify because of its structure.

subrange data type A data type defined by a subrange of a previously defined ordinal data type, such as a data type representing the integers from 1 to 100.

subscript An integer variable or constant used to specify a unique element in an array.

subset A set a is a subset of the set b if every element of a is also an element of b.

successor The value that follows a given value that is an ordinal data type. The last value in an ordinal data type does not have a successor.

syntax diagram A diagram used to present the general outline of a Pascal statement.

syntax error An error in a Pascal statement.

tag field identifier An identifier used with a variant record to specify which portion of the variant record is to be used.

test data Data generated to test the conditions and paths through an algorithm or program.

text files Files built with an editor or a Pascal program.

text processing Processing of character information.

time-sharing A method of interacting with the computer in which a number of programs are being executed at the same time although the user appears to have the complete attention of the computer.

top-down design Technique for problem solving in which the solution is first decomposed into a set of smaller steps that are then refined individually in more and more detail until the problem is solved.

trailer signal A signal at the end of a data file that indicates that no more data follows.

transaction file A file with information that is used to update a master file of information.

trapezoidal rule A mathematical technique commonly used to estimate the area under a curve.

truncation A technique that approximates a value by dropping its fractional value and using only the integer portion.

two-dimensional array A data structure in which a group of values share the same identifier and whose elements are specified individually by two indices or subscripts.

universal set The set of all elements of the base type of the set.

unpacked array An array that has been stored so that a Pascal statement can reference a specific element of the array without converting the data in memory. This method of storage for an array does not minimize the memory used, but array operations generally require less time than those using packed arrays.

up-arrow   A special character that is used with dynamic variables and with file buffers.

user-friendly   A term used to define a program that is easy to use.

user interface   The part of a program that defines the steps that allow the user to communicate with the program.

value parameter   A parameter that uses a copy of the value of the parameter instead of referencing the memory location of the parameter.

variable   A memory location referenced with an identifier whose value can be changed within a program.

variable parameter   A parameter that uses the memory location of the parameter each time that it is referenced.

variant record   A data structure that has a variable set of information.

Venn diagram   A diagram often used to illustrate set operations using intersecting circles.

while loop   A loop that is executed as long as a specified condition is true.

window   A term used to reference the memory used as the file buffer.

word processing   Processing of character information.

ANSWERS TO SELF-TESTS

Self-test 1-1, page 20

1. valid
2. valid
3. valid
4. valid
5. invalid character (—)
6. invalid character (—)
7. invalid characters (parentheses)
8. invalid (starts with a digit)
9. valid
10. invalid character ($)
11. not equal (2300, 23,000)
12. not equal (0.000007, 7000.0)
13. equal
14. not equal (110.0, 110.1)
15. not equal (−34.7, −34.0)
16. not equal (−0.76, 0.76)

Self-test 1-2, page 28

1. `slope := (y2 - y1)/(x2 - x1)`
2. `factor := 1.0 + b/v + c/sqr(v)`
3. `friction := sqr(v)/(30.0*s)`
4. `center := 38.1972*(r*r*r - s*s*s)*sin(a)/((sqr(r) - sqr(s))*a)`
5. `loss := f*p*l/d*sqr(v)/2.0`

6. `req := 1.0/(1.0/x1 + 1.0/x2 + 1.0/x3 + 1.0/x4)`

7. motion $= \sqrt{vi^2 + 2 \cdot a \cdot x}$

8. freq $= \dfrac{1}{\sqrt{2\pi \cdot \dfrac{1}{x1} \cdot c}}$

9. range $= \dfrac{2\ vi^2\ \sin(b)\ \cos(b)}{8}$

10. length $= li \sqrt{1 - \left(\dfrac{v}{c}\right)^2}$

11. energy $= 1.6747 \times 10^{-24} \cdot (2.99 \times 10^{10})^2$

12. volume $= 2\pi \cdot x^2 \cdot \left(\left(1 - \dfrac{\pi}{4}\right) \cdot y - \left(0.8333 - \dfrac{\pi}{4}\right) \cdot x\right)$

Self-test 2-1, page 57

```
range 1: count ← 0
         read data value
         maximum ← data value
         minimum ← data value
         while  data value is not zero  do
             count ← count + 1
             if  data value > maximum  then
                maximum ← data value
             if  data value < minimum  then
                minimum ← data value
             read data value
         range ← maximum − minimum
         write 'MAXIMUM DATA VALUE = ', maximum
         write 'MINIMUM DATA VALUE = ', minimum
         write 'RANGE OF VALUES = ', range
         write 'NUMBER OF DATA VALUES = ', count
```


Self-test 2-2, page 59

```
median: count ← 0
        positive count ← 0
        negative count ← 0
        read and save data value
        while  data value is not zero  do
            count ← count + 1
            if  data value > 0  then
               positive count ← positive count + 1
            else
```

```
        negative count ← negative count + 1
        read and save data value
    sort the data values
    if  count is odd  then
        median ← middle value in sorted list
    else
        median ← (sum of two middle values)/2
    write 'TOTAL NUMBER OF DATA VALUES = ', count
    write 'MEDIAN VALUE = ', median
    write 'NUMBER OF POSITIVE DATA VALUES = ', positive count
    write 'NUMBER OF NEGATIVE DATA VALUES = ', negative count
```

Self-test 3-1, page 84

1. true
2. true
3. true
4. false
5. true
6. true
7. true
8. false
9. ```
   if  time > 15.0  then
       time := time + 1
   ```
10. ```
    if  sqrt(poly) < 0.5  then
        writeln (poly)
    ```
11. ```
    if  abs(volt2 - volt1) > 10.0  then
        writeln (volt1,volt2)
    ```
12. ```
    if  den < 0.005  then
        writeln ('DENOMINATOR IS TOO SMALL')
    ```
13. ```
    if  log(x) >= 3.0  then
        begin
            time := 0.0;
            count := count + 1
        end
    ```
14. ```
    if  (distance < 50.0) and (time > 10.0)  then
        time := time + 0.05
    else
        time := time + 2.0
    ```

Self-test 3-2, page 108

1. 18
2. 17

3. 9
4. 11
5. 0
6. 367
7. 10
8. 55
9. 0
10. −15
11. 0
12. 100
13. 16
14. 130

Self-test 4-1, page 160

1.

2	3	4	5	6	7	8	9	10	11

2.

?	2	2	2	2	2	2	2	2	2

3.

9.0	8.0	7.0	6.0	5.0	4.0	3.0	2.0

4.

6	5	4	3	2	1

5.

2.5	2.5	2.5	−2.5	−2.5	−2.5	−2.5	−2.5

6.

?	?	?	?	?	4.0	4.0	4.0	4.0	?

Self-test 4-2, page 196

1. Array contents after each switch:

16		9		9		9		9
83		83		16		16		16
91	→	91	→	91	→	25	→	25
25		25		25		91		72
9		16		83		83		83
72		72		72		72		91

2. Array contents after each switch:

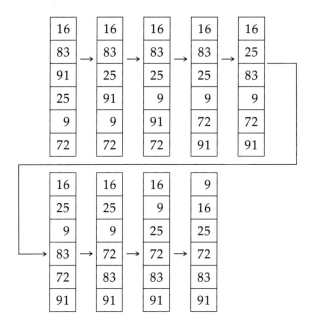

3. Array contents after each switch:

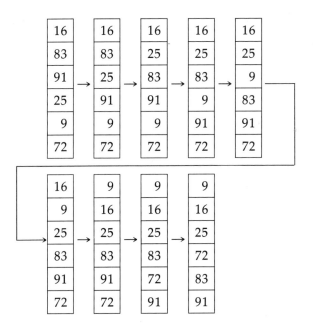

Self-test 5-1, page 223

1. *x, sorted*
2. *x, ordered*

3. *i*   *check, sortcheck*
  ordered *check, sortcheck*
  data *check, sortcheck*
  x   *check*

4. *k*   *sortcheck*
  done *sortcheck*

5. *x*

6. *sorted*

7. Yes, the variable *k* in the procedure is a local variable, so renaming it *i* does not change the program execution.

Self-test 5-2, page 245

```
{-----------------------------------------------------------------}
procedure  normalize (count:integer; var x:list);
   {This procedure normalizes the array x.}
var
   i: integer;
   max: real;
begin {normalize}
   max := x[1];
   for i := 2 to count do
      if  x[i] > max   then
         max := x[i];
   for i := 1 to count do
      x[i] := x[i]/max
end; {normalize}
{-----------------------------------------------------------------}
```

Self-test 6-1, page 274

1. 5

2. 5.0

3. 13

4. 12

5. YES

6. P

7. 4

8. T

Self-test 6-2, page 281

```
{-----------------------------------------------------------------}
function  absolute (x:list): real;
   {This function calculates the sum of the absolute values
    in the array x.}
var
   i: integer;
   sum: real;
```

```
begin {absolute}
   for i := 1 to 50 do
      sum := sum + abs(x[i]);
   absolute := sum
end; {absolute}
{--------------------------------------------------------------}
```

Self-test 7-1, page 330

1.

1	2	3	4
2	4	6	8
3	6	9	12
4	8	12	16
5	10	15	20

2.

1	1	1	1
2	2	2	2
3	3	3	3
4	4	4	4
5	5	5	5

3.

1	2	3	4
1	2	3	4
1	2	3	4
1	2	3	4
1	2	3	4

4.

2	0	1	2
0	1	2	0
1	2	0	1
2	0	1	2
0	1	2	0

5.

0.0	0.1	0.2
0.0	0.1	0.2
0.0	0.1	0.2

6.

-2	-2	-2
2	-2	-2
2	2	-2

Self-test 7-2, page 347

```
{-----------------------------------------------------------------}
function  rowsum (x:table; row,columns:integer): integer;
    {This function computes the sum of a specified row
    of a two-dimensional array.}
var
    j, sum: integer;
begin {rowsum}
    sum := 0;
    for j := 1 to columns do
        sum := sum + x[row,j];
    rowsum := sum
end; {rowsum}
{-----------------------------------------------------------}
procedure  sumrows (x:table; rows,columns:integer;
                        var sums:list);
    {This procedure computes the sums of the rows
    of a two-dimensional array.}
var
    i: integer;
begin {sumrows}
    for i := 1 to rows do
        sums[i] := rowsum(x,i,columns)
end; {sumrows}
{-----------------------------------------------------------}
```

Self-test 8-1, page 375

```
{-----------------------------------------------------------------}
program  hello (input,output);
    {This program asks for the user name and prints a greeting.}
type
    list10 = array[1..10] of char;
var
    i, lastchar: integer;
    first: list10;
begin {hello}
    writeln ('ENTER YOUR FIRST NAME');
    writeln (' ( < 11 CHARACTERS )');
    i := 1;
    while (not eoln) and (i <= 10) do
        begin
            read (first[i]);
            i := i + 1
        end;
    lastchar := i - 1;
    writeln;
    write ('HI ');
    for i:= 1 to lastchar do
        write (first[i])
end. {help}
{-----------------------------------------------------------}
```

Self-test 8-2, page 399

```
{-----------------------------------------------------------------}
program describe (input,output);
```

```
     {This program counts the number blanks at
     the end of a given string to eliminate them
     when printed}
type
     list = array[1..30] of char;
var
     string: list;
     i, length: integer;
     item: text;
begin
     writeln ('ENTER ITEM DESCRIPTION (30 CHARACTERS)')
     for i := 1 to 30 do
         read (item,string[i]);
     i := 30;
     while  string[i] = ' ' do
         i := i - 1;
     length := i;
     for i := 1 to length do
         write (string[i]);
     writeln (' IS THE DESCRIPTION OF THE ITEM ORDERED')
end.
{-------------------------------------------------------------}
```

Self-test 9-1, page 419

```
{-------------------------------------------------------------}
with fiction do
    begin
        for i := 1 to 30 do
            write (title[i]);
        writeln;
        write ('BY ');
        for i := 1 to 15 do
            write (author[i]);
        writeln (year:6,'    $ ',price:6:2)
    end
{-------------------------------------------------------------}
```

Self-test 9-2, page 426

```
{-------------------------------------------------------------}
yearcount := 0;
for i := 1 to 100 do
    begin
        with library[i] do
            if  library[i].year = 1985  then
                yearcount := yearcount + 1
    end;
writeln ('NUMBER OF BOOKS PUBLISHED IN 1985 IS ',yearcount:3)
{-------------------------------------------------------------}
```

Self-test 10-1, page 477

```
{-------------------------------------------------------------}
if  first = nil  then
    writeln ('LIST IS EMPTY')
else
    begin
```

```
        next := first;
        sum := 0.0;
        count := 0;
        while  next <> nil  do
            begin
                sum := sum + next^.x;
                count := count + 1;
                next := next^.ptr
            end;
        average := sum/count;
        writeln ('AVERAGE IS ',average:7:3)
    end
{------------------------------------------------------------}
```

Self-test 10-2, page 499

1. [6, 8]
2. [2]
3. [−2, 0, 1, 2, 3, 4, 6, 8]
4. []
5. [1, 3]

ANSWERS TO SELECTED PROBLEMS

Answers that contain Pascal statements are not usually unique. Although these answers represent good solutions to the problems, they are not necessarily the only valid solutions.

Chapter 1

4.
```
{------------------------------------------------------------}
program   convert (input,output);
    {This program converts dollars to pounds sterling and
    deutsche marks.}
var
    dollars, pounds, marks: real;
begin
    writeln ('ENTER AMOUNT IN DOLLARS');
    readln (dollars);
    pounds := dollars/1.68;
    marks := dollars*1.8;
    writeln (dollars:7:2,' DOLLARS = ',pounds:7:2,' POUNDS',
            ' AND',marks:7:2,' DEUTSCHE MARKS')
end.
{------------------------------------------------------------}
```

6.
```
{------------------------------------------------------------}
program   growth (input,output);
    {This program predicts bacteria growth.}
var
    yold, ynew, time, minutes: real;
begin
    writeln ('ENTER INITIAL POPULATION');
```

```
      readln (yold);
      writeln ('ENTER TIME ELAPSED IN MINUTES');
      readln (minutes);
      time := minutes/60.0;
      ynew := yold*exp(1.386*time);
      writeln ('INITIAL POPULATION = ',yold:9:4);
      writeln ('TIME ELAPSED (HOURS) = ',time:9:4);
      writeln ('TIME ELAPSED (MINUTES) = ',minutes:9:4);
      writeln ('PREDICTED POPULATION = ',ynew:9:4)
end.
{------------------------------------------------------------}
```

12.
```
{------------------------------------------------------------}
program   age (input,output);
    {This program estimates the age of an artifact from the
    proportion of carbon remaining in the artifact.}
var
    carbon, age: real;
    years: integer;
begin
    writeln ('ENTER PROPORTION REMAINING FOR CARBON DATING');
    readln (carbon);
    age := (-ln(carbon))/0.0001216;
    years := round(age);
    writeln ('ESIMATED AGE OF ARTIFACT IS ',years:6,' YEARS')
end.
{------------------------------------------------------------}
```

19.
```
{------------------------------------------------------------}
program   circle (input,output);
    {This program computes the radius, area, and
    circumference of a circle.}
const
    pi = 3.14159;
var
    radius, area, circumference, diameter: real;
begin
    writeln ('ENTER THE DIAMETER OF THE CIRCLE');
    readln (diameter);
    radius := diameter/2.0;
    circumference := 2.0*pi*radius;
    area := pi*sqr(radius);
    writeln ('PROPERTIES OF A CIRCLE WITH DIAMETER ',diameter:8:3);
    writeln ('(1)   RADIUS = ',radius:8:3);
    writeln ('(2)   CIRCUMFERENCE = ',circumference:8:3);
    writeln ('(3)   AREA = ',area:8:3)
end.
{------------------------------------------------------------}
```

Chapter 2

4. COMPUTE: sum ← 0
               count ← 0
               read data value
               while count < 100 do
                   sum ← sum + data value
                   count ← count + 1

```
                    read the next data value
                    average ← sum/100.0
                    write 'AVERAGE = ', average


  7. TABLE: write report heading
            degrees ← 0.0
            count ← 0
            read increment
            while count < 37 do
                radians ← degrees X 0.01745
                write degrees, radians
                degrees ← degrees + increment
                count ← count + 1


11. GPA: total points ← 0
         total hours ← 0
         count ← 0
         read number of courses
         while count < number of courses do
             write message to user to enter course data
             read course hours, letter grade
             if  letter grade = A then
                number grade ← 4.0
             else if  letter grade = B then
                number grade ← 3.0
             else if  letter grade = C then
                number grade ← 2.0
             else if  letter grade = D then
                number grade ← 1.0
             else if  letter grade = F then
                number grade ← 0.0
             else
                write 'ERROR IN LETTER GRADE, ENTER AGAIN'
                number grade ← 0
                course hours ← 0
             if  course hours > 0 then
                total hours ← total hours + course hours
                points ← number grade X course hours
                total points ← total points + points
                count ← count + 1
         grade point average ← total points/total hours
         write 'GRADE POINT AVERAGE', grade point average
         if  grade point average ≥ 3.0 write 'HONOR ROLL'


18. ROCKET: time ← 0
            height ← 60
            read incr1
```

```
            read incr2
            while  height < 0 and time ≤ 100 do
                compute height using equation
                write time, height
                if  height < 50 then
                    time ← time + incr2
                else
                    time ← time + incr1
```

24. PAYMENT: read amount
              monthly payment ← 250
              number of month ← amount div 250
              last payment ← amount − (number of months X 250)
              write 'NUMBER OF MONTHS = ', number of months
              write 'AMOUNT OF LAST PAYMENT = ', last payment

Chapter 3

2.
```
{-------------------------------------------------------------}
program   seals (input,output);
    {This program analyzes data on batches of sutures that have
    not been properly sealed, and then writes a report.}
var
    temperature, pressure, dwell, perct, percp, percd: real;
    batch, count, rejectt, rejectp, rejectd: integer;
begin
    count := 0;
    rejectt := 0;
    rejectp := 0;
    rejectd := 0;
    writeln ('ENTER BATCH NUMBER, TEMPERATURE, PRESSURE, DWELL');
    writeln ('FOR BATCHES THAT HAVE BEEN REJECTED');
    writeln ('(NEGATIVE BATCH NUMBER TO STOP)');
    readln (batch,temperature,pressure,dwell);
    while  batch >= 0 do
        begin
            if  (temperature < 150.0) or (temperature > 170.0) then
                rejectt := rejectt + 1;
            if  (pressure < 60.0) or (pressure > 70.0) then
                rejectp := rejectp + 1;
            if  (dwell < 2.0) or (dwell > 2.5) then
                rejectd := rejectd + 1;
            count := count + 1;
            writeln ('ENTER NEXT SET OF DATA');
            readln (batch,temperature,pressure,dwell)
        end;
    percp := rejectp/count*100.0;
    perct := rejectt/count*100.0;
    percd := rejectd/count*100.0;
    writeln;
    writeln ('SUMMARY OF BATCH REJECT INFORMATION);
    writeln;
    writeln (perct:6:2,' % REJECTED DUE TO TEMPERATURE');
    writeln (percp:6:2,' % REJECTED DUE TO PRESSURE');
    writeln (percd:6:2,' % REJECTED DUE TO DWELL TIME');
```

```
    writeln (rejectt:6,' TOTAL BATCHES REJECTED DUE TO ',
            'TEMPERATURE');
    writeln (rejectp:6,' TOTAL BATCHES REJECTED DUE TO PRESSURE');
    writeln (rejectd:6,' TOTAL BATCHES REJECTED DUE TO DWELL TIME')
end.
{------------------------------------------------------------------}
```

7.
```
{------------------------------------------------------------------}
program  cable (input,output);
    {This program computes the velocity of a cable car
    on a thousand-foot cable with three towers.}
var
    velocity: real;
    tower, distance, nearest, increment: integer;
begin
    writeln ('ENTER DISTANCE INCREMENT');
    readln (increment);
    writeln ('CABLE CAR REPORT');
    writeln;
    writeln ('DISTANCE  NEAREST TOWER  VELOCITY');
    writeln ('  (FT)                   (FT/SEC)');
    distance := 0;
    while distance <= 1000 do
        begin
            if   distance <= 250 then
                begin
                    tower := 1;
                    nearest := distance
                end
            else if  distance <= 750 then
                begin
                    tower := 2;
                    nearest := abs(distance - 500)
                end
            else
                begin
                    tower := 3;
                    nearest := 1000 - distance
                end;
            if  nearest <= 30 then
                velocity := 2.425 + 0.00175*nearest*nearest
            else
                velocity := 0.625 + 0.12*nearest -
                            0.00025*nearest*nearest;
            writeln (distance:5, tower:10, velocity:16:2);
            distance := distance + increment
        end
end.
{------------------------------------------------------------------}
```

11.
```
{------------------------------------------------------------------}
program  timber (input,output);
    {This program computes a reforestation summary
    for an area which has not been completely harvested.}
var
    total, uncut, rate, reforested: real;
    id, year, n: integer;
begin
    writeln ('ENTER LAND IDENTIFICATION (5 DIGITS)');
```

```
      readln (id);
      writeln ('ENTER TOTAL NUMBER OF ACRES');
      readln (total);
      writeln ('ENTER NUMBER OF ACRES UNCUT');
      readln (uncut);
      writeln ('ENTER REFORESTATION RATE');
      readln (rate);
      if  uncut > total then
         writeln ('UNCUT AREA LARGER THAN ENTIRE AREA');
      else
         begin
            writeln;
            writeln ('REFORESTATION SUMMARY');
            writeln;
            writeln ('IDENTIFICATON NUMBER ',id:5);
            writeln ('TOTAL ACRES = ',total:10:2);
            writeln ('REFORESTATION RATE = ',rate:5:3);
            writeln;
            writeln ('YEAR  REFORESTED   TOTAL REFORESTED');
            for year := 1 to n do
               begin
                  reforested := uncut*rate;
                  uncut := uncut + reforested;
                  writeln (year:3,reforested:11:3,uncut:17:3)
               end
      end
end.
{-------------------------------------------------------------}


22.
{-------------------------------------------------------------}
program   classification (input,output);
   {This program prints a student's grade classification.}
var
   studentid, hours: integer;
begin
   writeln ('ENTER STUDENT ID AND HOURS');
   readln (studentid, hours);
   while  studentid <> 9999  do
      begin
         if  hours < 30  then
            writeln ('STUDENT ID ',studentid:4,'  - FRESHMAN')
         else if  (30 <= hours) and (hours < 60)  then
            writeln ('STUDENT ID ',studentid:4,'  - SOPHOMORE')
         else if  (60 <= hours) and (hours < 90)  then
            writeln ('STUDENT ID ',studentid:4,'  - JUNIOR')
         else if  hours > 90  then
            writeln ('STUDENT ID ',studentid:4,'  - SENIOR')
      end
end.
{-------------------------------------------------------------}
```

Chapter 4

1.
```
{-------------------------------------------------------------}
program   snowfall (january,output);
   {This program computes the average snowfall
   for January and counts the number of days
   with above-average snowfall.  It also computes the
   number of days with no snowfall.}
```

```pascal
type
    index = 1..31;
    list = array[index] of real;
var
    total, average: real;
    count, nosnow: integer;
    january: text;
    i: index;
    snow: list;
begin
    reset (january);
    total := 0.0;
    count := 0;
    nosnow := 0;
    for i := 1 to 31 do
        begin
            read (january,snow[i]);
            total := total + snow[i];
            if  snow[i] = 0.0 then
                nosnow := nosnow + 1
        end;
    average := total/31.0;
    writeln ('AVERAGE SNOWFALL IS',average:6:2,' INCHES');
    for i := 1 to 31 do
        if  snow[i] > average  then
            count := count + 1;
    writeln (count:2,' DAYS WITH ABOVE-AVERAGE SNOWFALL');
    writeln (nosnow:2,' DAYS WITH NO SNOW FALL')
end.
{------------------------------------------------------------}


7.
{------------------------------------------------------------}
program  quality (defects,output);
    {This program uses data in a defect file to compute
    and write a Quality Analysis Report.}
type
    index = 1..100;
    list = array[index] of integer;
var
    percdef, percwire, percic, percnonic: real;
    boards, defectbd, wirebd, icbd, nonicbd,
    wiretotal, ictotal, nonictotal, total,
    wire, ic, nonic: integer;
    defects: text;
    i: index;
    id: list;
begin
    defectbd := 0;
    wirebd := 0;
    icbd := 0;
    nonicbd := 0;
    wiretotal := 0;
    ictotal := 0;
    nonictotal := 0;
    i := 1;
    reset (defects);
    readln (defects,boards);
    readln (defects,id[i],wire,ic,nonic);
    while  id[i] <> 99999  do
        begin
            defectbd := defectbd + 1;
```

```
            if  wire > 0  then
                wirebd := wirebd + 1;
            if  ic > 0  then
                icbd := icbd + 1;
            if  nonic > 0  then
                nonicbd := nonicbd + 1;
            wiretotal := wiretotal + wire;
            ictotal := ictotal + ic;
            nonictotal := nonictotal + nonic;
            i := i + 1;
            readln (defects,id[i],wire,ic,nonic)
        end;
    percdef := defectbd/boards*100.0;
    total := wiretotal + ictotal + nonictotal;
    percwire := wiretotal/total*100.0;
    percic := ictotal/total*100.0;
    percnonic := nonictotal/total*100.0;
    writeln ('              MONTHLY QUALITY ANALYSIS REPORT');
    writeln;
    writeln ('TOTAL NUMBER OF BOARDS ASSEMBLED = ',boards:4);
    writeln;
    writeln ('TOTAL BOARDS WITH DEFECTS = ',defectbd:4);
    writeln;
    writeln (wirebd:9,' BOARDS WITH BROKEN WIRES');
    writeln (icbd:9,' BOARDS WITH DEFECTIVE IC COMPONENTS');
    writeln (nonicbd:9,' BOARDS WITH DEFECTIVE NON-IC ',
            'COMPONENTS');
    writeln (total:9,' TOTAL DEFECTS');
    writeln;
    writeln ('DEFECT ANALYSIS');
    writeln;
    writeln (percdef:10:1,'% OF BOARDS WITH DEFECTS');
    writeln (percwire:10:1,'% OF DEFECTS WERE BROKEN WIRES');
    writeln (percic:10:1,'% OF DEFECTS WERE DEFECTIVE IC ',
            'COMPONENTS');
    writeln (pernonic:10:1,'% OF DEFECTS WERE DEFECTIVE NON-IC ',
            'COMPONENTS');
    if  percdef > 10.0  then
        begin
            writeln;
            writeln;
            writeln ('IDENTIFICATION NUMBERS FOR DEFECTIVE BOARDS');
            for i := 1 to defectbd do
                writeln (id[i])
        end
end.
{-----------------------------------------------------------------}


14.
{-----------------------------------------------------------------}
program  seismic (motion,output);
    {This program reads a data file of earthquake data,
    sorts it in ascending order, and prints it.  It also
    computes the median earthquake value.}
type
    index = 1..200;
    list = array[index] of real;
var
    hold, median: real;
    id, count, indexmin, first, last, middle: integer;
    motion: text;
    i, k: index;
```

```pascal
      quake: list;
begin
   reset (motion);
   readln (motion,id);
   i := 1;
   readln (motion,quake[i]);
   while  quake[i] > 0.0  do
      begin
         i := i + 1;
         readln (motion,quake[i])
      end;
   count := i - 1;
   for i := 1 to count-1 do
      begin
         indexmin := i;
         first := i + 1;
         last := count;
         for k := first to last do
            if  quake[k] < quake[indexmin]  then
               indexmin := k;
         hold := quake[i];
         quake[i] := quake[indexmin];
         quake[indexmin] := hold
      end;
   writeln ('FIELD LABORATORY ',id:5,' MEASUREMENTS');
   for i := 1 to count do
      writeln (i:3,'.',quake[i]:9:3);
   middle := count div 2;
   if  middle mod 2 = 0  then
      median := (quake[middle] + quake[middle + 1])/2.0;
      writeln ('MEDIAN EARTHQUAKE VALUE = ', median:9:3)
   else
      writeln ('MEDIAN EARTHQUAKE VALUE = ', quake[middle+1])
end.
{-------------------------------------------------------------}


25.
{-------------------------------------------------------------}
program  reorder (numbers,output);
   {This program reads integers from a file, numbers, and prints
   the data in the reverse order from which it was read.}
type
   index = 1..20;
   list = array[index] of integer;
var
   i, count: index;
   value: list;
   numbers: text;
begin
   reset (numbers);
   count := 1;
   readln (numbers, value[count]);
   while  value[count] <> 9999  do
      begin
         count := count + 1;
         readln (numbers, value[count])
      end
   writeln ('THE DATA IN REVERSE ORDER IS');
   for i := count downto 1 do
      writeln (value[count]:3)
end.
{-------------------------------------------------------------}
```

Chapter 5

2.
```
{--------------------------------------------------------}
program  report (input,production,output);
    {This program generates a report from the daily
    production information for a set of oil wells.}
var
    oiltotal, average: real;
    month, day, year, page,
    wellcount, id: integer;
    production: text;
{------------------------------------------------------}
procedure  printheader (month,day,year: integer;
                             var page: integer);
    {This procedure prints the header for an
    oil well production summary report.}
begin {printheader}
    writeln ('                          PAGE ',page:4);
    if  page = 1  then
        writeln ('     CLAYTON OIL ')
    else
        writeln;
    writeln;
    writeln ('    OIL WELL PRODUCTION');
    writeln ('    WEEK OF ',month:2,'-',day:2,'-',year:2);
    writeln;
    writeln ('WELL ID          AVERAGE PRODUCTION');
    writeln ('                 (IN BARRELS)');
    writeln;
    page := page + 1
    end; {printheader}
{--------------------------------------------------------}
                (no changes in procedure compute)
{--------------------------------------------------------}
begin {report}
    reset (production);
    read (production, month, day, year);
    wellcount := 0;
    oiltotal := 0.0;
    page := 1;
    read (production, id);
    while  id <> 9999  do
        begin
            if  wellcount mod 19 = 0  then
                printheader (month,day,year,page);
            compute (production,average);
            writeln (id:5,average:16:2);
            wellcount := wellcount + 1;
            oiltotal := oiltotal + average;
            read (production, id)
        end;
    if  wellcount mod 19 = 0  then
        printheader (month, day, year, page);
    writeln ('OVERALL AVERAGE FOR',wellcount:4,' WELLS IS',
             oiltotal/wellcount:7:2);
    writeln
end. {report}
{--------------------------------------------------------}
```

7.
```
{----------------------------------------------------------------}
program  generate (input,output,signal);
   {This program generates a signal composed
   of a sine wave plus random noise.}
const
   pi = 3.141593;
var
   t, f, noise, incr: real;
   seed: integer;
   signal: text;
{-------------------------------------------------------------}
              (no changes in procedure random)
{-------------------------------------------------------------}
begin {generate}
   rewrite (signal);
   t := 0.0;
   writeln ('ENTER A POSITIVE INTEGER SEED');
   readln (seed);
   writeln ('ENTER A TIME INCREMENT');
   readln (incr);
   while  t <= 1.00  do
      begin
         random (seed,noise);
         f := 2.0*sin(2.0*pi*t) + noise;
         writeln (signal,t,f);
         t := t + incr
      end;
end. {generate}
{---------------------------------------------------------}


11.
{---------------------------------------------------------}
program  update (input,access,output,newaccess);
   {This program updates a computer access list.}
const
   arraysize = 500;
   trailer = 9999;
type
   index = 1..500;
   list = array[index] of integer;
var
   inser, del, i, code, count, old, new: integer;
   done: boolean;
   access, newaccess: text;
   ssn: list;
{-----------------------------------------------}
procedure  insert (arraysize,new:integer;
                   var count,inser:integer; var x:list);
   {This procedure inserts an element in an ordered list.}
var
   i, k: integer;
   done: boolean;
begin {insert}
   if  count = arraysize  then
      writeln ('ARRAY IS FULL - LAST VALUE WILL BE LOST');
   done := false;
   i := 1;
   while  (i <= count) and (not done)  do
      if  x[i] < new  then
         i := i + 1
```

```
        else
            done := true;
    if  i > count   then
        if  count < arraysize   then
            begin
                inser := inser + 1;
                count := count + 1;
                x[count] := new
            end
    else
        if  x[i] = new   then
            writeln ('SSN ALREADY IN FILE')
        else
            begin
                if  count < arraysize   then
                    begin
                        inser := inser + 1;
                        count := count + 1
                    end;
                for k := count downto i+1 do
                    x[k] := x[k-1];
                x[i] := new
            end
end; {insert}
{-----------------------------------------------------------------}
procedure  delete (old:integer; var count,del:integer;
                    var x:list);
    {This procedure deletes an element from an ordered list.}
var
    i, k: integer;
    done: boolean;
begin {delete}
    done := false;
    i := 1;
    while  (i <= count) and (not done)  do
        if  x[i] < old   then
            i := i + 1
        else
            done := true;
        if  (i > count) or (x[i] > old)   then
            writeln ('VALUE TO DELETE NOT IN THE LIST')
        else
            begin
                del := del + 1;
                count := count - 1;
                for k := i to count do
                    x[k] := x[k+1]
            end
end; {delete}
{-----------------------------------------------------------------}
begin {update}
    inser := 0;
    del := 0;
    reset (access);
    rewrite (newaccess);
    i := 1;
    while  not done  do
        begin
            readln (access,ssn[i]);
            if  ssn[i] = trailer   then
                done := true
            else
                i := i + 1
```

```
            end;
         count := i - 1;
         done := false;
         while  not done  do
             begin
                 write ('ENTER -1 FOR DELETION, 1 FOR INSERTION,');
                 writeln ('0 TO QUIT');
                 readln (code);
                 if  code = -1  then
                     begin
                         writeln ('ENTER SSN FOR DELETION');
                         readln (old);
                         delete (old,count,ssn)
                     end
                 else if  code = 1  then
                     if  count = arraysize  then
                         writeln ('LIST IS FULL - DO DELETIONS FIRST')
                     else
                         begin
                             writeln ('ENTER SSN FOR INSERTION');
                             readln (new);
                             insert (arraysize,new,count,ssn)
                         end
                 else
                     done := true
             end;
         for i := 1 to count do
             writeln (newaccess,ssn[i]);
         writeln (newaccess,trailer);
         writeln ('THERE WERE ',inser:2,' INSERTIONS AND ',del:2,
                   ' DELETIONS MADE FROM THE LIST.')
end. {update}
{-----------------------------------------------------------------}


20.
{-----------------------------------------------------------------}
procedure   absolute (var time:list);
    {This procedure will replace each element of the list
    with its absolute value.}
var
    temp: real;
    i: integer;
begin {absolute}
    for i := 1 to 100 do
        begin
            temp := abs(list[i]);
            list[i] := temp
        end
end; {absolute}
{-----------------------------------------------------------------}
```

Chapter 6

1.
```
{-----------------------------------------------------------------}
program   reliability (input,output);
    {This program computes the reliability of
    instrumentation using a Bernoulli equation.}
var
    n: integer;
```

```
        p, percent: real;
        done: boolean;
{--------------------------------------------------------------}
                    (no changes in function exponentiation)
{--------------------------------------------------------------}
begin {reliability}
    done := false;
    while  not (done)  do
        begin
            writeln;
            writeln ('ENTER RELIABILITY OF SINGLE COMPONENT');
            writeln ('(USE PERCENTAGE BETWEEN 0 AND 100)');
            readln (p);
            writeln ('ENTER NUMBER OF COMPONENTS IN EQUIPMENT');
            readln (n);
            if  n = 0  then
                done := true;
            percent := exponentiation(p/100.0,n)*100.0;
            writeln ('PERCENT OF THE TIME THAT THE EQUIPMENT ');
            writeln ('SHOULD WORK WITHOUT FAILURE IS ',
                    percent:6:2,' %')
        end
end. {reliability}
{--------------------------------------------------------------}
```

6.
```
{--------------------------------------------------------------}
program   analyze (input,output,traffic);
    {This program reads traffic information and computes the
    average number of cars per minute through an intersection.}
var
    id, begintime, endtime, cars, totaltime, totalcars,
    fileid: integer;
    traffic: text;
{--------------------------------------------------------------}
                    (no changes in function minutes)
{--------------------------------------------------------------}
begin {analyze}
    totaltime := 0;
    totalcars := 0;
    reset (traffic);
    writeln ('ENTER INTERSECTION IDENTIFICATION');
    readln (id);
    while  not eof(traffic)  do
        begin
            readln (traffic,fileid,begintime,endtime,cars);
            if  fileid = id  then
                begin
                    totaltime := totaltime +
                                minutes(begintime,endtime);
                    totalcars := totalcars + cars
                end
        end;
    if  totaltime = 0  then
        writeln ('NO OBSERVATION FOR INTERSECTION ',id:3)
    else
        begin
            writeln ('INTERSECTION ',id:3);
            writeln ('THE TOTAL NUMBER OF CARS: ',totalcars);
            writeln ('THE TOTAL NUMBER OF MINUTES: ',totaltime);
            writeln ('AVERAGE CARS PER MINUTE = ',
                    totalcars/totaltime:6:2)
```

```
              end
   end. {analyze}
   {-------------------------------------------------------------}

12.
   {-------------------------------------------------------------}
   program  manage (input,project,output);
       {This program determines the timetable for a project.}
   type
       index = 1..10;
       list = array[index] of integer;
   var
       i, j, k, maxevent, totaltasks, totaldays, tasknum,
       maxtask, mindays, maxdays, weeks, daysleft: integer;
       project: text;
       event, task, days, hold: list;
   {-------------------------------------------------------------}
                     (no changes in function minimum)
   {-------------------------------------------------------------}
                     (no changes in function maximum)
   {-------------------------------------------------------------}
   begin {manage}
       i := 0;
       maxevent := 0;
       reset (project);
       while  not eof(project)  do
           begin
               i := i + 1;
               readln (project, event[i], task[i], days[i]);
               if  event[i] > maxevent  then
                   maxevent := event[i]
           end;
       totaltasks := i;
       totaldays := 0;
       writeln ('        PROJECT COMPLETION TIMETABLE');
       writeln;
       writeln ('EVENT NUMBER    MINUMUM TIME    MAXIMUM TIME');
       for i := 1 to maxevent do
           begin
               k := 0;
               for j := 1 to totaltasks do
                   if  event[j] = i  then
                       begin
                           k := k + 1;
                           hold[k] := days[j]
                       end;
               mindays := minimum(hold,k);
               maxdays := maximum(hold,k);
               writeln (i:8,mindays:16,maxdays:16);
               totaldays := totaldays + maxdays
           end;
       maxtask := days[1];
       tasknum := 1;
       for j := 2 to totaltasks do
           if  maxtask < days[j]  then
               begin
                   maxtask := days[j];
                   tasknum := j
               end;
       weeks := totaldays div 5;
       daysleft := totaldays mod 5;
       writeln;
```

```
      writeln ('TASK NUMBER ',task[tasknum]:3,
               ' REQUIRED THE MOST TIME');
      writeln;
      writeln ('       TOTAL PROJECT LENGTH = ',totaldays:3,
               ' DAYS');
      writeln ('                            = ',weeks:3,' WEEKS ',
               daysleft:1,' DAYS');
end. {manage}
{-----------------------------------------------------------------}
```

25.
```
{-----------------------------------------------------------------}
function  switch (digit:integer): integer;
   {This function returns the 2-digit input in reverse order.}
var
   ones, tens: integer;
begin {switch}
   ones := digit mod 10;
   tens := digit div 10;
   switch := ones*10 + tens
end; {switch}
{-----------------------------------------------------------------}
```

Chapter 7

1.
```
{-----------------------------------------------------------------}
program  powerplant (plant,output);
   {This program computes and prints a composite
   report covering 8 weeks for a power plant.}
type
   index1 = 1..8;
   index2 = 1..7;
   table = array[index1,index2] of integer;
var
   average: real;
   i, j, minimum, total, count: integer;
   power: table;
   plant: text;
begin
   reset (plant);
   total := 0;
   minimum := maxint;
   for i := 1 to 8 do
      for j := 1 to 7 do
         begin
            read (plant,power[i,j]);
            total := total + power[i,j];
            if  power[i,j] < minimum  then
               minimum := power[i,j]
         end;
   average := total/56;
   count := 0;
   for i := 1 to 8 do
      for j := 1 to 7 do
         if  power[i,j] > average  then
            count := count + 1;
   writeln ('             COMPOSITE INFORMATION');
   writeln ('AVERAGE DAILY POWER OUTPUT =',
            average:5:1,' MEGAWATTS');
```

```
        writeln ('NUMBER OF DAYS WITH GREATER THAN ',
                 'AVERAGE POWER OUTPUT = ',count:2);
        writeln ('DAY(S) WITH MINIMUM POWER OUTPUT:');
        for i := 1 to 8 do
           for j := 1 to 7 do
              if  power[i,j] = minimum  then
                 writeln ('               WEEK ',i:2,
                          '    DAY ',j:2);
        writeln ('THE MINIMUM POWER OUTPUT WAS: ',minimum:4)
end.
{- - - - - - - - - - - - - - - - - - - - - - - - - - - - - - - - - - - - - - - - - - - - - - - - - -}


7.
{- - - - - - - - - - - - - - - - - - - - - - - - - - - - - - - - - - - - - - - - - - - - - - - - - -}
program  topology (elevation,output);
   {This program reads the elevation data for a set of
   land grids and determines the number of peaks in each.}
type
   index = 1..100;
   grid = array[index,index] of integer;
var
   count, i, j, id, rows, columns: integer;
   elevation: text;
   map: grid;
{- - - - - - - - - - - - - - - - - - - - - - - - - - - - - - - - - - - - - - - - - - - - - - - -}
function  peaks (map: grid; rows, columns: integer): integer;
   {This function determines the number of peaks in a map.}
var
   i, j, count: integer;
begin {peaks}
   count := 0;
   writeln;
   writeln ('THE LOCATION OF THE PEAKS ARE :');
   for i := 2 to rows-1 do
      for j := 2 to columns-1 do
         if  (map[i,j] > map[i-1,j]) and
             (map[i,j] > map[i+1,j]) and
             (map[i,j] > map[i,j-1]) and
             (map[i,j] > map[i,j+1])   then
            begin
               writeln ('ROW ',i:2,' COLUMN ',j:2);
               count := count + 1
            end;
      peaks := count;
   writeln
end; {peaks}
{- - - - - - - - - - - - - - - - - - - - - - - - - - - - - - - - - - - - - - - - - - - - - - - -}
               (no changes in program topology)
{- - - - - - - - - - - - - - - - - - - - - - - - - - - - - - - - - - - - - - - - - - - - - - - -}


11.
{- - - - - - - - - - - - - - - - - - - - - - - - - - - - - - - - - - - - - - - - - - - - - - - -}
program  statistics (summer,output);
   {This program computes statistics from exam averages
   in 6 sections of a class during an 8-week session.}
type
   index1 = 1..6;
   index2 = 1..8;
   list2 = array[index2] of real;
   table = array[index1,index2] of real;
```

```
var
    total, average: real;
    month, day, year, section, week: integer;
    summer: text;
    sums, max, min: list2;
    scores: table;
{----------------------------------------------------------------}
                    (no changes in procedure sumcols)
{----------------------------------------------------------------}
                    (no changes in procedure minmaxcols)
{----------------------------------------------------------------}
begin {statistics}
    reset (summer);
    read (summer,month,day,year);
    writeln ('SUMMER SESSION - ENDED ',month:2,'-',
             day:2,'-',year:2);
    writeln;
    for section := 1 to 6 do
        for week := 1 to 8 do
            read (summer,scores[section,week]);
    sumcols (scores,6,8,sums);
    minmaxcols (scores,6,8,min,max);
    total := 0;
    for week := 1 to 8 do
        begin
            writeln ('WEEK',week:3);
            total := total + sums[week];
            average := sums[week]/6;
            writeln ('        AVE = ', average:6:2);
            writeln ('        MIN = ', min[week]:6:2);
            for section := 1 to 6 do
                if  scores[section,week] = min[week]   then
                    writeln('            SECTION ', section:2);
            writeln ('        MAX = ', max[week]:6:2);
            for section := 1 to 6 do
                if  scores[section,week] = max[week]   then
                    writeln ('            SECTION ', section:2)
        end;
    writeln ('THE AVERAGE FOR ALL WEEKS IS ',total/48:4:1)
end. {statistics}
{----------------------------------------------------------------}

16.
{----------------------------------------------------------------}
program  rainreport (input,rainfall,output);
    {This program will read data from a rainfall data file and
    write a report.}
type
    index1 = 1..12;
    index2 = 1..5;
    table = array[index1,index2] of real;
var
    rainfall: text;
    rain: table;
    total, maxrain, minrain: real;
    i, j, maxmon, maxyear, minmon, minyear: integer;
begin {rainreport}
    reset (rainfall);
    for i := 1 to 12 do
        for j := 1 to 5 do
            read (rainfall,rain[i,j]);
```

```
        maxmon := 1;
        maxyear := 1;
        minmon := 1;
        minyear := 1;
        maxrain := rain[1,1];
        minrain := rain[1,1];
        writeln ('AVERAGE YEARLY RAINFALL');
        for i := 1 to 5 do
            begin
                write ('198',i-1:1);
                total := 0;
                for j := 1 to 12 do
                    begin
                        if  rain[j,i] < minrain then
                            begin
                                minrain := rain[j,i];
                                minyear := i;
                                minmon := j
                            end
                        else if  rain[j,i] > maxrain   then
                            begin
                                maxrain := rain[j,i];
                                maxyear := i;
                                maxmon := j
                            end;
                        total := total + rain[j,i]
                    end;
                writeln (' - ',total/12:6:2);
            end;
        writeln;
        writeln ('MAXIMUM RAINFALL');
        writeln ('MONTH ',maxmon:2,'  YEAR 198',maxyear-1:1);
        writeln;
        writeln ('MINIMUM RAINFALL');
        writeln ('MONTH ',minmon:2,'  YEAR 198',minyear-1:1);
end. {rainreport}
{----------------------------------------------------------------}
```

Chapter 8

2.
```
{----------------------------------------------------------------}
program  decode (secret,output);
    {This program aids in decoding a message by counting
    the number of occurrences of vowels in the message.}
type
    list5 = array[1..5] of real;
    list50 = array[1..50] of char;
var
    count, i, j, n, total: integer;
    secret: text;
    vowel: list5;
    message: list50;
{----------------------------------------------------------------}
procedure  bargraph (data:list5; n,line:integer);
    {This procedure prints a bar graph using an array of
    positive data values and a maximum line length.}
const
    asterisk = '*';
var
    min, max, scale: real;
```

```
        i, j, k, l: integer;
    begin {bargraph}
        {Find minimum and maximum data values.}
        min := data[1];
        max := data[1];
        for i := 2 to n do
            begin
                if  data[i] < min  then
                    min := data[i];
                if  data[i] > max  then
                    max := data[i]
            end;
            {Check for error conditions.}
            if  (min < 0.0) or (line < 0) or (line > 132)  then
                writeln ('BARGRAPH PARAMETERS NOT VALID')
            else
                {Scale data values and print bars.}
                begin
                    scale := line/max;
                    writeln;
                    for i := 1 to n do
                        begin
                            k := round(data[i]*scale);
                            for l := 1 to 3 do
                                begin
                                    for j := 1 to k do
                                        write (asterisk);
                                    writeln
                                end;
                            writeln
                        end
                end
    end; {bargraph}
    {------------------------------------------------------------}
                    (no changes in program decode)
    {------------------------------------------------------------}


7.
    {------------------------------------------------------------}
    program  graphics (input,output);
        {This program contains a simple set of graphics routines
        for creating and manipulating a 2-dimensional object.}
    type
        list50 = array[1..50] of integer;
    var
        wrow, wcol, n: integer;
        code: char;
        row, col: list50;
    {------------------------------------------------------------}
                    (no changes in procedure create)
    {------------------------------------------------------------}
    procedure  draw (n:integer; row,col:list50; wrow,wcol:integer);
        {This procedure draws an object using
        coordinate arrays row and col.}
    const
        asterisk = '*';
        top = '-';
        side = '|';
    type
        table50x50 = array[1..50,1..50] of char;
    var
        r, slope: real;
```

```
      i, j, m, r1, c1, r2, c2, c, rsub, minr, maxr: integer;
   switch: boolean;
   window: table50x50;
begin {draw}
   for i := 1 to wrow do
      for j := 1 to wcol do
         window[i,j] := ' ';
   {Set first endpoint.}
   r1 := row [1];
   c1 := col[1];
   for m := 2 to n do
      begin
         switch := false;
         {Set second endpoint.}
         r2 := row[m];
         c2 := col[m];
         {Switch endpoints if needed so first point is leftmost.}
         if  c1 > c2  then
            begin
               switch := true;
               r2 := r1;
               c2 := c1;
               r1 := row[m];
               c1 := col[m]
            end;
         {If vertical line, fill points between row values.}
         if  c1 = c2  then
            begin
               if  r1 < r2  then
                  begin
                     minr := r1;
                     maxr := r2
                  end
               else
                  begin
                     minr := r2;
                     maxr := r1
                  end;
               for rsub := minr to maxr do
                  if  (1 <= c1) and (c1 <= wcol) and
                      (1 <= rsub) and (rsub <= wrow)  then
                     window[rsub,c1] := asterisk
            end
         else
            {If not vertical, use slope algorithm to fill.}
            begin
               slope := (r2 - r1)/(c2 - c1);
               r := r1;
               for c := c1 to c2 do
                  begin
                     if  (1 <= c) and (c <= wcol) and
                         (1 <= round(r)) and
                         (round(r) <= wrow) then
                        window[round(r),c] := asterisk;
                     r := r + slope
                  end
            end;
         {Set end of line segment to beginning of next segment.}
         if  not switch  then
            begin
               r1 := r2;
               c1 := c2
            end
```

```
          end;
       {Print the contents of the window array on the screen.}
       for i := 1 to wcol+2 do
          write (top);
       writeln;
       for i := 1 to wrow do
          begin
             write (side);
             for j := 1 to wcol do
                write (window[i,j]);
             write (side);
             writeln
          end;
       for i := 1 to wcol+2 do
          write (top);
       writeln;
       writeln;
       for i := 1 to n do
          writeln ('COORDINATES ',i:2,' ARE',row[i]:2,
                   ',',col[i]:2)
    end; {draw}
    {------------------------------------------------------------}
                   (no changes in procedure translate)
    {------------------------------------------------------------}
                   (no changes in program graphics)
    {------------------------------------------------------------}

11.
{------------------------------------------------------------}
program  driver (input,inputtext,output);
    {This program tests the word average computation function.}
type
    list20 = array[1..20] of char;
var
    j: integer;
    inputtext: text;
    string1: list20;
{------------------------------------------------------------}
function  wordaverage (string1: list20; n: integer): real;
    {This function computes the average word length
    of character information stored in an array.}
const
    blank = ' ';
    period = '.';
    comma = ',';
var
    notletter, first, nextblank, m, words, letters: integer;
    wordend: boolean;
begin {wordaverage}
    words := 0;
    letters := 0;
    first := 1;
    notletter := 0;
    while  first <= n  do
       if  string1[first] <> blank  then
          begin
             m := first;
             wordend := false;
             while  not wordend  do
                begin
                   if  (string1[m] = period) or
                       (string1[m] = comma)  then
```

```
                          notletter := notletter + 1;
                m := m + 1;
                if  m > n then
                    wordend := true
                else
                    if  string1[m] = blank  then
                        wordend := true
            end;
          nextblank := m;
          letters := letters + (nextblank - first);
          words := words + 1;
          first := nextblank + 1
        end
      else
          first := first + 1;
    if  words = 0  then
        wordaverage := 0.0
    else
        wordaverage := (letters - notletter)/words
end; {wordaverage}
{-----------------------------------------------------------------}
                    (no changes in program driver)
{-----------------------------------------------------------------}


17.
{-----------------------------------------------------------------}
program  test (input,testfile,output);
   {This program will test the procedure condense.}
type
   list50 = array[1..50] of char;
var
   testfile: text;
   inarray, outarray: list50;
   i: integer;
{-----------------------------------------------------------------}
procedure  condense (inarray: list50; var outarray: list50);
   {This procedure will receive a character array inarray of 50
   characters and returns a character array outarray, also 50
   characters, which has no adjacent blanks except at the end of
   the string.}
const
   blank = ' ';
var
   i, countout: integer;
begin {condense}
   countout := 1;
   for i := 1 to 50 do
      if  inarray[i] <> blank  then
         begin
            outarray[countout] := inarray[i];
            countout := countout + 1
         end;
      for i := countout to 50 do
         outarray[i] := blank;
end; {condense}
{-----------------------------------------------------------------}
begin {test}
   reset (testfile);
   for i := 1 to 50 do
      read (testfile,inarray[i]);
   condense (inarray,outarray);
   for i := 1 to 50 do
```

```
            write (outarray[i]);
      writeln;
end. {test}
{-------------------------------------------------------------}
```

Chapter 9

3.
```
{-------------------------------------------------------------}
program   analysis (census, output);
    {This program reads 61 population values and determines
    the years of greatest percentage increase in population.
    It also computes the average increase in population per year
    for the total period of time.}
type
    censusdata = record
                    year, population: integer
                 end;
var
    percent, bestpercent, totincrease, average: real;
    year1, year2: integer;
    old, new: censusdata;
    census: text;
begin {analysis}
    reset (census);
    readln (census, old.year, old.population);
    bestpercent := 0.0;
    totincrease := 0.0;
    for i := 1 to 60 do
        begin
            readln (census, new.year, new.population);
            percent := (new.population - old.population)*
                       100.0/old.population;
            totincrease := totincrease +
                           (new.population - oldpopulation);
            if  (percent > bestpercent) or (i = 1)   then
                begin
                    bestpercent := percent;
                    bestyear := new.year
                end;
            old.year := new.year;
            old.population := new.population
        end;
    average := totincrease/60.0;
    year1 := bestyear - 1;
    year2 := bestyear;
    writeln ('GREATEST PERCENT INCREASE OCCURRED BETWEEN ',
             year1:4, ' AND ', year2:4);
    writeln ('AVERAGE INCREASE IN POPULATION = ', average:5:2)
end. {analysis}
{-------------------------------------------------------------}
```

6.
```
{-------------------------------------------------------------}
program   logs (oldlog,updates,newlog,output);
    {This program merges the instrumentation log data with
    new update information to give a new master file.}
type
    date = record
              mo, da, yr: integer
           end;
```

```
        logdata = record
                  serial: integer;
                  borrowed, returned: date;
                  group: integer
              end;
var
   masterdate, updatedate, count, old: integer;
   done, masterout: boolean;
   master, update: logdata;
   oldlog, newlog, updates: text;
begin
   reset (oldlog);
   reset (updates);
   rewrite (newlog);
   with  master  do
      readln (oldlog,serial,borrowed.mo,borrowed.da,borrowed.yr,
              returned.mo,returned.da,returned.yr,group);
   with  update  do
      readln (updates,serial,borrowed.mo,borrowed.da,borrowed.yr,
              returned.mo,returned.da,returned.yr,group);
   if  (master.serial = 9999) and (update.serial = 9999)  then
      done := true
   else
      done := false;
   while  not done  do
      begin
         if  update.serial < master.serial  then
            masterout := false;
         if  update.serial > master.serial  then
            masterout := true;
         if  update.serial = master.serial  then
            begin
               with  master  do
                  masterdate := returned.yr*10000 +
                                returned.mo*100 + returned.da;
               with  update  do
                  updatedate := returned.yr*10000 +
                                returned.mo*100 + returned.da;
               if  masterdate <= updatedate  then
                  masterout := false
               else
                  masterout := true
            end;
         if  masterout  then
            with  master  do
               begin
                  writeln (newlog,serial,borrowed.mo,borrowed.da,
                           borrowed.yr,returned.mo,returned.da,
                           returned.yr,group);
                  readln (oldlog,serial,borrowed.mo,borrowed.da,
                          borrowed.yr,returned.mo,returned.da,
                          returned.yr, group)
               end
         else
            with  update  do
               begin
                  writeln (newlog,serial,borrowed.mo,borrowed.da,
                           borrowed.yr,returned.mo,returned.da,
                           returned.yr,group);
                  readln (updates,serial,borrowed.mo,borrowed.da,
                          borrowed.yr,returned.mo,returned.da,
                          returned.yr,group)
               end;
```

```
                if   (master.serial = 9999) and
                     (update.serial = 9999)   then
                   done := true
         end;
     with   master   do
        writeln (newlog,serial,borrowed.mo,borrowed.da,
                 borrowed.yr,returned.mo,returned.da,
                 returned.yr,group);
     writeln ('SERIAL NUMBER      NUMBER OF TESTS PERFORMED');
     reset (newlog);
     with   master   do
        begin
           readln (newlog,serial,borrowed.mo,borrowed.da,
                   borrowed.yr,returned.mo,returned.da,
                   returned.yr,group);
           old := serial;
           while  serial <> 9999  do
              begin
                 count := 0;
                 while  old = serial   do
                    begin
                       count := count + 1;
                       readln (newlog,serial,borrowed.mo,borrowed.da,
                               borrowed.yr,returned.mo,returned.da,
                               returned.yr, group)
                    end;
                 writeln (old:8, count:20);
                 old := serial
              end
        end
end. {logs}
{----------------------------------------------------------------}


12.
{----------------------------------------------------------------}
program  update (updates,inventory,output);
   {This program updates the quantity in an inventory file.}
type
   data = record
             stocknumber, quantity: integer;
             price: real
          end;
   table = array[1..500] of data;
var
   i, count, newstock, newchange: integer;
   done, found: boolean;
   stock: table;
   updates, inventory: text;
begin {update}
   reset (inventory);
   i := 1;
   done := false;
   while  not done  do
      with  stock[i]  do
         begin
            readln (inventory, stocknumber, quantity, price);
            i := i + 1;
            if  stocknumber = 999  then
                done := true
         end;
   count := i - 1;
   reset (updates);
```

```
          while  not eof(updates)  do
            begin
                readln (updates,newstock,newchange);
                i := 1;
                done := false;
                found := false;
                while  not done  do
                    with  stock[i]  do
                        begin
                            if  newstock = stocknumber  then
                                begin
                                    quantity := quantity + newchange;
                                    done := true;
                                    found := true
                                end
                            else if  newstock < stocknumber  then
                                begin
                                    i := i + 1;
                                    if  i > count  then
                                        done := true
                                end
                        end;
                if  not found  then
                    writeln ('NO MATCH FOR ',newstock:3)
            end;
        rewrite (inventory);
        for i := 1 to count do
            with  stock[i]  do
                writeln (stocknumber,quantity,price);
        writeln (count:5, 'MASTER RECORDS IN MASTER FILE')
    end. {update}
{------------------------------------------------------------------}

19.
{------------------------------------------------------------------}
function  authorcount (library:array[1..100] of book; n:integer;
                        name:array[1..15] of char): integer;
    {This function counts all book titles that have
    name as the author.}
var
    i, count: integer;
begin {authorcount}
    count := 0;
    for i := 1 to n do
        with  library[i]  do
            if  name = author  then
                count := count + 1;
    authorcount := count
end; {authorcount}
{------------------------------------------------------------------}


Chapter 10

1.
{------------------------------------------------------------------}
program  migration (cranes,output);
    {This program reads the migration data for the whooping
    cranes and prints the sightings in ascending order.}
type
    pointer = ^sighting;
```

```
       sighting = record
                   mo, da, yr, time, grid1, grid2, birds: integer;
                   link: pointer
               end;
var
    count: integer;
    cranes: text;
    first, current: pointer;
{----------------------------------------------------------------}
                 (no changes in function rightspot)
{----------------------------------------------------------------}
                 (no changes in procedure insert)
{----------------------------------------------------------------}
                 (no changes in procedure printlist)
{----------------------------------------------------------------}
begin {migration}
    reset (cranes);
    count := 0;
    new (first);
    with  first^ do
       readln (cranes,mo,da,yr,time,grid1,grid2,birds);
    count := count + 1
    first^.link := nil;
    while  not eof(cranes)  do
       begin
          new (current);
          with  current^  do
             readln (cranes,mo,da,yr,time,grid1,grid2,birds);
          count := count + 1;
          insert (current, first)
       end;
    printlist (first);
    writeln (count:5, ' WHOOPING CRANE SIGHTINGS')
end. {migration}
{----------------------------------------------------------------}


7.
{----------------------------------------------------------------}
program  accident (survey,output);
    {This program uses the data in an accident survey file
    to summarize information regarding accidents with injuries.}
type
    id = set of 1..250;
var
    ave, aveinjury, percinj, percped, perother, perccars: real;
    idnum, totalids, vehicles, vehinjury, ncars, ntrucks, nother,
    npedestrian, ninjuries, injcount, injpedcount, injothercount,
    injcarcount: integer;
    survey: text;
    cars, trucks, other, pedestrians, injuries, onlycars: id;
{----------------------------------------------------------------}
                 (no changes in function setcount)
{----------------------------------------------------------------}
begin {accident}
    totalid := 0;
    .vehicles := 0;
    vehinjury := 0;
    cars := [];
    trucks := [];
    other  := [];
    pedestrians := [];
```

```
         injuries := [];
         reset (survey);
         while  not eof(survey)  do
            begin
               readln (survey,id,ncars,ntrucks,nother,
                       npedestrian,ninjuries);
               totalid := totalid + 1;
               vehicles := vehicles + ncars + ntrucks + nother;
               if  ninjuries > 0  then
                  begin
                     vehinjury := vehinjury + ncars + ntrucks + nother;
                     injuries := injuries + [id]
                  end;
               if  ncars > 0  then
                  cars := cars + [id];
               if  ntrucks > 0  then
                  trucks := trucks + [id];
               if  nother > 0  then
                  other := other + [id];
               if  npedestrian > 0  then
                  pedestrian := pedestrian + [id]
            end;
         ave := vehicles/totalid;
         injcount := setcount(injuries);
         injpedcount := setcount(injuries*pedestrian);
         injothercount := setcount(injuries*other);
         onlycars := cars - ((trucks+other)+pedestrians);
         injcarcount := setcount(injuries*onlycars);
         aveinjury := vehinjury/injcount;
         percinj := injcount/totalid*100.0;
         percped := injpedcount/totalid*100.0;
         percother := injothercount/totalid*100.0;
         perccars := injcarcount/totalid*100.0;
         writeln ('     SURVEY OF ACCIDENTS WITH INJURIES');
         writeln;
         writeln ('AVERAGE NUMBER OF VEHICLES PER ACCIDENT = ',
                  ave:4:1);
         writeln;
         writeln ('AVERAGE NUMBER OF VEHICLES PER ACCIDENT');
         writeln ('                        WITH INJURIES = ',
                  aveinjury:4:1);
         writeln (injcount:5, ' ACCIDENTS WITH INJURIES');
         writeln;
         writeln ('PERCENT OF ACCIDENTS WITH INJURIES = ',
                  percinj:5:1, ' %');
         writeln;
         writeln ('PERCENT OF ACCIDENTS WITH INJURIES');
         writeln ('             INVOLVING PEDESTRIANS = ',
                  percped:5:1,' %');
         writeln;
         writeln ('PERCENT OF ACCIDENTS WITH INJURIES');
         writeln ('          INVOLVING VEHICLES OTHER');
         writeln ('             THAN CARS AND TRUCKS = ',
                  perother:5:1,' %');
         writeln;
         writeln ('PERCENT OF ACCIDENTS WITH INJURIES');
         writeln ('             INVOLVING ONLY CARS = ',
                  perccars:5:1, ' %')
   end. {accidents}
   {-----------------------------------------------------------------}
```

27.
```
{--------------------------------------------------------------}
procedure  readcourse (training);
   {This procedure reads information in the file training and
   generates four sets which contain the employee numbers of the
   employees that have taken one of four given courses.}
var
   course: char;
   idnumber: integer;
begin {readcourse}
   reset (training);
   while  not eof (training)  do
      begin
         readln (training,course,idnumber);
         if  course = 'E'   then
            electronics := electronics + [idnumber]
         else if course = 'C'   then
            complit := complit + [idnumber]
         else if course = 'D'   then
            digital := digital + [idnumber]
         else if course = 'M'   then
            micro := micro + [idnumber]
      end
end; {readcourse}
{--------------------------------------------------------------}
```

Chapter 11

1.
```
{--------------------------------------------------------------}
program  linear (xydata,output);
   {This program computes a linear model for a set of data and
   then computes the residual sum to evaluate the model.}
type
   list500 = array[1..500] of real;
var
   slope, intercept, ynew, residual, sumx, sumy,
   sumxy, sumxx, sumresidual, maxresid: real;
   i, count, max: integer;
   xydata: text;
   x, y: list500;
begin {linear}
   sumx := 0;
   sumy := 0;
   sumxy := 0;
   sumxx := 0;
   sumresidual := 0;
   i := 1;
   reset (xydata);
   while  not eof(xydata)  do
      begin
         readln (xydata,x[i],y[i]);
         sumx := sumx + x[i];
         sumy := sumy + y[i];
         sumxy := sumxy + x[i]*y[i];
         sumxx := sumxx + x[i]*x[i];
         i := i + 1;
      end;
   count := i - 1;
   slope := (sumx*sumy - count*sumxy)/
            (sumx*sumx - count*sumxx);
```

```
      intercept := (sumy - slope*sumx)/count;
      writeln ('THE LINEAR EQUATION IS');
      writeln ('Y = ',slope:6:2,' X + ',intercept:6:2);
      writeln;
      maxresid := 0.0;
      writeln ('ORIGINAL    ORIGINAL    ESTIMATED    RESIDUAL');
      writeln ('   X          Y            Y              ');
      writeln;
      for i := 1 to count do
         begin
            ynew := slope*x[i] + intercept;
            residual := y[i] - ynew;
            if  abs(residual) > maxresid  then
               begin
                  maxresid := abs(residual);
                  max := i
               end;
            sumresidual := sumresidual + residual*residual;
            writeln (x[i]:6:2,y[i]:12:2,ynew:12:2,residual:13:2)
         end;
      writeln;
      writeln ('RESIDUAL SUM = ',sumresidual:6:2);
      writeln ('THE LARGEST RESIDUAL IS',x[max]:6:2,y[max]:6:2)
end. {linear}
```
{- -}
14.
{- -}
```
program  roots (input,output);
   {This program determines the roots in the interval [-5,5]
   for a quartic polynomial using interval halving.}
var
   root, left, right, a, b, c, d, e: real;
   iterations, count, i: integer;
```
{- -}
                        (no changes in function *p*)
{- -}
```
procedure  iterate (left,right:real; var root:real;
                    var iterations:integer);
   {This procedure uses interval halving to find a root.}
var
   size, midpoint: real;
   done: boolean;
begin {iterate}
   done := false;
   size := right - left;
   while  (size > 0.01) and (not done)  do
      begin
         iterations := iterations + 1;
         midpoint := (left + right)/2;
         if  p(midpoint) = 0.0  then
            done := true
         else if  p(midpoint)*p(left) < 0.0  then
            right := midpoint
         else
            left := midpoint;
         size := right - left
      end;
   if  size > 0.01  then
      root := midpoint
   else
      root := (left + right)/2
end; {iterate}
```

```
{--------------------------------------------------------------------}
begin {roots}
    writeln ('ENTER COEFFICIENTS A, B, C, D, E');
    readln (a,b,c,d,e);
    while  (a <> 0.0) or (b <> 0.0) or (c <> 0.0) or
           (d <> 0.0) or (e <> 0.0)  do
        begin
            writeln;
            writeln ('POLYNOMIAL:');
            writeln ('          4              3              2');
            writeln (a:7:3,' X  + ',b:7:3,' X  + ',c:7:3,' X  + ',
                     d:7:3,' X + ',e:7:3);
            writeln;
            count := 0;
            left := -5.0;
            right := -4.75;
            iterations := 0;
            for i := 1 to 40 do
                begin
                    if  p(left) = 0.0   then
                        begin
                            writeln ('ROOT = ',left:7:3,'    P(ROOT)',
                                     ' = ', p(left):7:3,' # OF ITERATIONS',
                                     ' = ', iterations:3);
                            count := count + 1;
                        end
                    else if  (p(left)*p(right)) < 0.0   then
                        begin
                            iterate (left,right,root,iterations);
                            writeln ('ROOT = ',root:7:3,'    P(ROOT)',
                                     ' = ',p(root):7:3,' # OF',
                                     ' ITERATIONS = ', iterations:3);
                            count := count + 1;
                        end;
                    left := right;
                    right := left + 0.25;
                    iterations := 0;
                end;
            if  p(left) = 0.0   then
                begin
                    writeln ('ROOT = ',left:7:3,'    P(ROOT) = ',
                             p(left):7:3,' # OF ITERATIONS = ',
                             iterations:3);
                    count := count + 1
                end;
            if  count = 0   then
                writeln ('NO ROOTS IN INTERVAL [-5,5]');
            writeln ('ENTER COEFFICIENTS A, B, C, D, E');
            writeln ('(ALL ZEROS TO QUIT)');
            readln (a,b,c,d,e);
        end
end. {roots}
{--------------------------------------------------------------------}
```

INDEX

C

Case, 121
Central processing unit, 3
Char, 12
Character
  codes, 366
  data type, 367
  functions, 371
  initialization, 367
  I/O, 368
  string, 368
Checkpoint, 123
Chr, 274
Circularly linked list, 485
Collating sequence, 370
Column sums, 340
Comment, 10
Compilation, 4
Compiler, 4
Compound
  Boolean expression, 79
  statement, 81
Computer
  graphics, 386, 396
  languages, 4
  program, 9
Condition, 51
Connector, 79
Const, 11
Constant declaration, 11
Control structure, 78
Conversational computing, 18
Cos, 25, 270
Counter, 52
Counting loop, 52
CPU. *See* Central processing unit
Cramer's rule, 547
Critical path analysis, 299

D

Data
  file, 136
  structure, 136
  type, 12, 147
Debugging, 6
  aids, 35, 72, 123, 201, 262, 310,
    357, 405, 448, 506, 551
Decomposition, 47
Deletion, 180, 236
Descending order, 187
Design phases, 46
Determinant, 547

Diagnostics, 6
Dispose, 460
Div, 27
Divide and conquer, 47
Division by zero, 6
Do, 95
Documentation. *See* Style/technique
    guidelines
Dot product, 543
Doubly linked list, 486
Downto, 95
Driver, 240
Dynamic
  allocation, 456
  data structure, 456
  variable, 456

E

EBCDIC code, 366
Echo, 35
Editor, 7
Element, 150
Else, 82
Empty set, 492
End, 9
End of file, 140
End of line, 273
Enumerated data type, 148
Eof, 272
Eoln, 273
Error
  compiler, 6
  condition, 59
  logic, 6
  run-time, 6
  syntax, 6
Evaluation order
  arithmetic expressions, 23
  combined expressions, 79
  logic expressions, 79
Execution, 6
Exp, 25, 271
Exponential notation, 14
Exponentiation, 278
Expression, 21
  Boolean, 78
  evaluation rules, 23
  parentheses, 22

F

False, 78
Field identifier, 415